S0-AHK-037

# CHEMICAL AND BIOLOGICAL ASPECTS OF PYRIDOXAL CATALYSIS

I.U.B. Symposium Series

Volume 30

## INTERNATIONAL UNION OF BIOCHEMISTRY SYMPOSIUM SERIES

Vol. 1. *The Origin of Life on the Earth*—A. I. OPARIN *et al.* (Editors)
Vol. 2. *Enzyme Chemistry:* Proceedings of the International Symposium in Tokyo–Kyoto

PROCEEDINGS OF THE FOURTH INTERNATIONAL CONGRESS OF BIOCHEMISTRY VIENNA 1958

Vol. 3. (I) *Carbohydrate Chemistry of Substances of Biological Interest*
Vol. 4. (II) *Biochemistry of Wood*
Vol. 5. (III) *Biochemistry of the Central Nervous System*
Vol. 6. (IV) *Biochemistry of Steroids*
Vol. 7. (V) *Biochemistry of Antibiotics*
Vol. 8. (VI) *Biochemistry of Morphogenesis*
Vol. 9. (VII) *Biochemistry of Viruses*
Vol. 10. (VIII) *Proteins*
Vol. 11. (IX) *Physical Chemistry of High Polymers of Biological Interest*
Vol. 12. (X) *Blood Clotting Factors*
Vol. 13. (XI) *Vitamin Metabolism*
Vol. 14. (XII) *Biochemistry of Insects*
Vol. 15. (XIII) *Colloquia*
Vol. 16. (XIV) *Transactions of the Plenary Sessions*
Vol. 17. (XV) *Biochemistry*
Vol. 18. *Biochemistry of Lipids*—G. POPJÁK (Editor)
Vol. 19. *Haematin Enzymes* (Parts 1 and 2)—R. K. MORTON (Editor)
Vol. 20. *Report of the Commission on Enzymes*, 1961 (I.U.B.)

PROCEEDINGS OF THE FIFTH INTERNATIONAL CONGRESS OF BIOCHEMISTRY MOSCOW 1961

Vol. 21. (I) *Biological Structure and Function at the Molecular Level*
Vol. 22. (II) *Functional Biochemistry of Cell Structures*
Vol. 23. (III) *Evolutionary Biochemistry*
Vol. 24. (IV) *Molecular Basis of Enzyme Action and Inhibition*
Vol. 25. (V) *Intracellular Respiration: Phosphorylating and Non-Phosphorylating Oxidation Reactions*
Vol. 26. (VI) *Mechanism of Photosynthesis*
Vol. 27. (VII) *Biosynthesis of Lipids*
Vol. 28. (VIII) *Biochemical Principles of the Food Industry*
Vol. 29. (IX) *Transactions of the Plenary Sessions and Abstracts of Papers Presented*
Vol. 30. *Chemical and Biological Aspects of Pyridoxal Catalysis*—E. E. SNELL, P. M. FASELLA, A. BRAUNSTEIN and A. ROSSI FANELLI (Editors)

# CHEMICAL AND BIOLOGICAL ASPECTS OF PYRIDOXAL CATALYSIS

Proceedings of a symposium of the International Union of Biochemistry, Rome, October 1962

Contributory Support from the Italian National Council of Research and the Accademia Nazionale dei Lincei

*Edited by*

E. E. SNELL
P. M. FASELLA
A. BRAUNSTEIN
A. ROSSI FANELLI

**A Pergamon Press Book**

THE MACMILLAN COMPANY
NEW YORK
1963

THE MACMILLAN COMPANY
60 Fifth Avenue
New York, 11, N.Y.

This book is distributed by
THE MACMILLAN COMPANY · NEW YORK
pursuant to a special arrangement with
PERGAMON PRESS LIMITED
Oxford, England



Library of Congress Card No. 63–21972

*Printed in Great Britain by Bell and Bain, Ltd., Glasgow*

# PREFATORY NOTE

by E. E. Snell

PUBLISHED records of scientific symposia lose much of their value if publication is unduly delayed. In the present instance, we have chosen to proceed with publication at the expense of omitting much of the interesting (and sometimes heated) discussion which occurred during the meeting. Unfortunately, requests for a written clarification of questions and answers were frequently not met by the respondents within the " deadline " period set by the Editors; on occasion extensive elaborations of special viewpoints were submitted which it seemed unfair to present without affording equal opportunity to others whose views were questioned. In general, such comments have been omitted; with minor exceptions the published discussion is an incomplete record of that actually offered during the meeting.

Unfortunately, a manuscript of the interesting paper presented by Dr. Gunsalus ($B_6$-linked Enzymes in Serine and Glycine Transformations) was not submitted. Dr. Velick's valuable contribution (A Kinetic and Equilibrium Analysis of the Glutamate–Oxalacetate Transaminase Mechanism) has already appeared in full elsewhere (S. F. Velick and J. Vavra; *J. Biol. Chem.* **237**, 2109 (1962)).

The Editors take this occasion to thank the participants once more for their contributions to a most interesting and successful meeting.

# CONTENTS

# OPENING ADDRESS

by A. Rossi Fanelli

It is an honour and a privilege for me to welcome you to the Accademia dei Lincei and to the opening session of our Symposium.

I wish, first of all, to express to the Chief of the Italian State our gratitude for having honoured us with his presence. His participation in a strictly scientific gathering such as ours is a source of real joy to me, because it is a further proof of his vast and deep interest in science. Scientists feel now more than before the necessity of leaving, at times, the seclusion of their laboratories to meet the people to whom their research is dedicated and to seek the understanding and support of the representatives of the people. I heartily thank, therefore, the representatives of the Italian Senate, Government, Supreme Court and the other authorities who accepted our invitation.

Most of all I am grateful to my fellow scientists, who suffered the discomforts of long or very long journeys to bring us the precious contributions of their knowledge and experience.

We are gathered here to begin a week's work on one of the most exciting and promising problems of modern enzymology: pyridoxal catalysis. The importance of this vitamin as the key compound in some of the most important reactions of protein metabolism is now universally acknowledged. In recent years, another even more interesting aspect of pyridoxal biochemistry has been investigated: the detailed mechanisms by which pyridoxal catalysis occurs. These researches have opened new perspectives for a more general understanding of enzyme action, a subject of fundamental importance, both theoretical and practical, for all biological sciences.

Later Professor E. E. Snell, to whom we owe so much of what we know about vitamin $B_6$, will give you a synoptic view of the development of studies in this field.

Then Professor Braunstein, the discoverer of biological transamination, will outline the present status and outlook for research on pyridoxal catalysis.

The idea of organizing this Symposium originated last year in Moscow, where we had gathered for the Fifth International Congress of Biochemistry. Recent work on pyridoxal catalysis impressed Professors Braunstein, Snell and myself as being so outstanding in quality and quantity, as to make a high-level meeting dedicated to this subject not only useful but necessary.

Thus, a proposal was made to gather the " wise men of pyridoxal " halfway between Moscow and Berkeley for a thorough discussion of the biological and chemical aspects of $B_6$ catalysis. Rome was suggested as the meeting place because of its geographical location, the traditional majesty of the city and our interest in this field. Though well aware of the difficulties and responsibilities involved, we accepted the proposal, persuaded as we were of its soundness and confident of the support afforded by Professors Braunstein's and Snell's authority and experience.

The International Union of Biochemistry, ready as usual to meet the problems and to facilitate the enterprises of biochemists, willingly accepted the sponsorship of the Symposium. Dr. Stotz, will welcome you here on behalf of the Union.

I personally wish to express to Dr. Stotz our gratitude for the moral support and financial help the Union gave us.

The Italian National Research Council (CNR) contributed equal moral and economic aid to our endeavour and also deserves our gratitude. Professor Califano is here to represent Professor Polvani and to greet you on behalf of the CNR.

The invitations to participate in the Symposium were warmly accepted by most of the researchers in the field.

You may have noticed that the emblem of our Symposium carries the carved image of a Lynx, which for four centuries has been the symbol of the Accademia dei Lincei. This symbol was adopted by our Symposium in gratitude for our host, the Accademia, as a souvenir representing its traditions in the history of science, and also as a source of inspiration for all of us during the works of the Symposium. You came to a city that is almost three thousand years old and you must grant something to the Roman tendency to look at current events in the perspectives of centuries. The Accademia dei Lincei was founded in 1603 by a group of young people, of different nationalities, united by the desire to cultivate science according to the experimental method that had been recently proposed and applied for the first time by Galileo Galilei. The Lynx was chosen as the symbol of the Academy because of its sharpsightedness, a quality that well represents what the mental attitude of a researcher should be.

Since its foundation, it has been a specific purpose of the Academy to encourage the synthesis between experimental approaches and theoretical deductions for a common, deeper interpretation of truth. I am certain that this principle of mutual understanding and collaboration will inspire all participants to this Symposium, despite the difference in backgrounds and interests.

The ideal of international collaboration, that has also been pursued in this Academy since its foundation, derives further strength from your presence here.

To all of you, I express my thanks for what you will teach us in these days, and to all of you I wish a week of fruitful and pleasant work.

# OPENING REMARKS

by E. H. STOTZ

Treasurer of the International Union of Biochemistry

IT IS a pleasure indeed to attend this significant event in the scientific program of the International Union of Biochemistry and of the other sponsoring bodies; and on behalf of the Union to express its gratitude to Professors A. E. Braunstein, E. E. Snell and A. Rossi Fanelli for their parts in organizing the program. It is fitting that this International Symposium on the " Biological and Chemical Aspects of Pyridoxal Catalysis " be held here in Rome in view of the great contributions that Italian biochemists are making in this field and in Biochemistry generally.

It occurs to me that only a limited number of those present may know what the International Union of Biochemistry is, and what its sponsorship of a symposium means. The simplest objective of the International Union of Biochemistry (IUB) is to promote co-operation and exchange of information at the international level. Prior to 1955 there was an informal International Committee of Biochemistry, which organized two International Congresses of Biochemistry. In January 1955 the IUB was formally constituted, and later in the same year was admitted to the International Council of Scientific Unions (ICSU). The latter organization has a number of member Unions, of which IUB is one of the newest. ICSU receives a very modest annual subvention from UNESCO, which it divides among its member Unions. In addition to these funds, IUB receives annual subscriptions from its member countries, of which there are presently twenty-six. Italy is of course a member of IUB, has a National Committee of Biochemistry, and our host, Professor Rossi Fanelli, has been the representative of Italy in the General Assembly and Council of IUB.

Since becoming a Union in 1955, IUB has sponsored three International Congresses of Biochemistry, Brussels in 1955, Vienna in 1958, and Moscow in 1961. The 1964 Congress will be in New York, and the 1967 Congress probably in Tokyo. IUB maintains close relations with the International Union of Pure and Applied Chemistry, the International Union of Physiological Sciences, and the International Union of Biological Sciences to promote co-operation and avoid duplication of effort. IUB is itself a member group in the Council of International Organizations of Medical Sciences (CIOMS), which is part of WHO.

IUB has had a Commission of Enzymes, which has made a first report on enzyme nomenclature and classification, and after collection of comments a final definitive report will be made which it is hoped will greatly clarify understanding and nomenclature throughout the world. A Commission of Editors of Biochemical Journals has also been established, which will deal with recommendations of various nomenclature groups in all phases of biochemistry. Acceptance of a recommendation by this group may be translated into journal use with minimum delay.

Finally, since the large Congress has certain limitations for the intimate exchange of information, IUB has also sponsored symposia. Sponsorship means that the Union accepts the proposal made by an organizing group of biochemists, and may agree to support it financially. Even though such support is severely limited, sponsorship is frequently the condition which permits various agencies in the individual countries to support the travel of their national participants. IUB has thus far sponsored symposia on Enzyme Chemistry in Tokyo, on the Origin of Life in Moscow, on Hematin Enzymes in Canberra, and a joint Symposium with the Union of Biological Sciences on " Biological Structure and Function " in Stockholm.

Now we are gathered for the International Symposium on Biological and Chemical Aspects of Pyridoxal Catalysis. IUB extends its thanks to the organizers and participants in this Symposium and wishes all good success for a profitable exchange of scientific information among biochemists of several nations.

# WELCOMING ADDRESS

by Luigi Califano

Representative of the Italian National Research Council (CNR)

It is a pleasure to extend to you, on behalf of Professor Giovanni Polvani, President of the CNR, a formal welcome to this meeting and to express our gratitude for having honoured us with your presence.

The Italian National Research Council has always encouraged biochemical studies; in recent years new research centers have been created in order to keep pace with the rapid progress of this Science; the center for Enzymology of Rome, which is responsible for the local organization of this Symposium is one of them. Closer contacts between researchers interested in related fields have been promoted by developing inter-departmental programs.

Persuaded as we are of the necessity of direct exchange of ideas and informations among scientists of all nations, we promptly accepted to co-sponsor this Symposium which promises to mark a significant point in our knowledge of a very important field of biochemistry, and to present detailed explanations of the physicochemical mechanisms of various fundamental biological processes.

On behalf of the CNR I wish you all a week of constructive work.

# NON-ENZYMATIC REACTIONS OF PYRIDOXAL AND THEIR SIGNIFICANCE

by ESMOND E. SNELL

Department of Biochemistry, University of California,
Berkeley 4, California

AS AN introduction to the scientific portion of this conference, I should like to review briefly a few historical aspects of the chemistry of vitamin $B_6$ and pyridoxal-containing systems, and their significance for our present understanding of the catalytic effects of pyridoxal.

That pyridoxine (pyridoxol) is an unexpectedly reactive substance became apparent shortly after its synthesis when, in attempts to develop a microbiological assay for this compound, we observed that its growth-promoting activity for lactic acid bacteria was extremely low, and increased greatly as a result of autoclaving it with the medium.[1,2] Such assays also showed that the growth-promoting activity of natural materials for lactic acid bacteria under these conditions could not be accounted for by their pyridoxine content, and that pyridoxine was converted into one or more much more active growth-promoting substances for these bacteria by feeding it to animals. When yeast was used as an assay organism, however, no such changes were apparent.

These observations led us to study systematically the effectiveness of various chemical treatments in increasing the growth-promoting activity of pyridoxine for lactic acid bacteria; the latter investigation lead to the recognition of the existence of two different compounds, an aldehyde and an amine, that had such increased activity[2,3] and to suggestions concerning their structure that led directly to the synthesis and evaluation of the biological activity of pyridoxal and pyridoxamine.[3–8]

During assay of the synthetic compounds, pyridoxal was found to be converted smoothly to pyridoxamine by autoclaving it with the amino acid-containing medium or by heating it with any of a variety of amino acids;[8,9] the reaction was fully reversible.[9,10] This facile chemical transamination reaction led us to suggest[4,9] that these compounds might serve as amino group carriers in enzymatic transamination, and to the subsequent demonstration in our own and other laboratories that pyridoxal phosphate did indeed serve a coenzymatic role in transamination.[11–13]

In view of these striking results, we continued with an investigation of the interaction of pyridoxal with amino acids. It was soon found that the transamination reaction between pyridoxal and amino acids was greatly accelerated by addition of appropriate metal ions ($Fe^{3+}$, $Cu^{2+}$, or $Al^{3+}$),[10] and that pyridoxal plus metal ions also catalyzed racemization of amino acids,[14] dehydration of serine and threonine,[15] the reversible cleavage of serine to

TABLE 1. REACTIONS OF α-AMINO ACIDS CATALYZED BY PYRIDOXAL IN MODEL, NON-ENZYMATIC SYSTEMS

A. Reactions resulting from labilization of an α-hydrogen atom (bond *a*, Fig. 1).
1. Transamination (a general reaction).[9,10]
2. Racemization (a general reaction).[14]
3. Dehydration of α-amino-β-hydroxyacids (e.g. serine → pyruvate, threonine → α-ketobutyrate).[15]
4. Desulfhydration of cysteine (→ $H_2S$ + pyruvate).[18]
5. Synthesis of *tryptophan* from *serine*.[18]
6. Synthesis of *sulphur amino acids* from *serine*.[19]
7. Other α, β-elimination reactions or α, β-addition reactions (e.g. phosphoserine → pyruvate + $PO_4^{3-}$ + $NH_3$).[20]
8. Synthesis of α-amino-β-hydroxyacids and their peptides from glycine or from glycine peptides + an aldehyde.[16]

B. Reactions resulting from labilization of the carboxyl group (bond *b*, Fig. 1).
1. Decarboxylation of α-amino acids to corresponding primary amines (a general reaction).
   (*a*) Histidine.[34]
   (*b*) α-Methylserine,[36] α-methylolserine,[36] phenylglycine.[36]
   (*c*) Aminomalonate.[43,44]
2. Decarboxylation-dependent transamination of α-amino acids bearing an α-substituent.
   (*a*) α-Methylserine, α-methylolserine.[36]
3. Decarboxylation with addition of an aldehyde to position vacated by carboxyl group.
   (*a*) Synthesis of serine from aminomalonate + HCHO.[43]

C. Reactions resulting from labilization of an R group (bond *c*, Fig. 1).
1. Degradation of α-amino-β-hydroxyacids (or α-amino-β-hydroxy-acylpeptides) to aldehydes and glycine (or glycyl peptides) (a general reaction).
   (*a*) Serine.[16] (*c*) α-Methylserine.[31]
   (*b*) Threonine.[16] (*d*) α-Methylolserine.[31]

D. Unclassified reactions (probably belonging to class A).
1. Pyridoxal–$Cu^{2+}$ catalyzed oxidative deamination of amines and amino acids.[45]

yield glycine and formaldehyde[16] and of threonine (or allothreonine) to yield glycine and acetaldehyde,[17] the synthesis of tryptophan from serine and indole[18] and several other related reactions. In short, pyridoxal alone, or pyridoxal plus metal ions, in dilute aqueous solutions at physiological pH values and room temperature or above, catalyzed a whole series of reactions of amino acids which also occur in living organisms and which are catalyzed *in vivo* by pyridoxal phosphate enzymes. A listing of these model reactions is given in Table 1.

Occurrence of the non-enzymatic reactions permitted an investigation of the structural features of pyridoxal prerequisite for the transamination reaction.[18,21] The heterocyclic N, the formyl group, and a free phenolic group in the spatial arrangement provided by pyridoxal or the electronically equivalent compound, 2-formyl-3-hydroxypyridine, were necessary for the reaction. The function served by the heterocyclic nitrogen of the pyridine ring could be simulated by the nitro group of 4-nitrosalicyl-aldehyde, indicating that the strong electronegativity of these groupings was the common feature essential for catalytic activity of the parent compounds.[18]

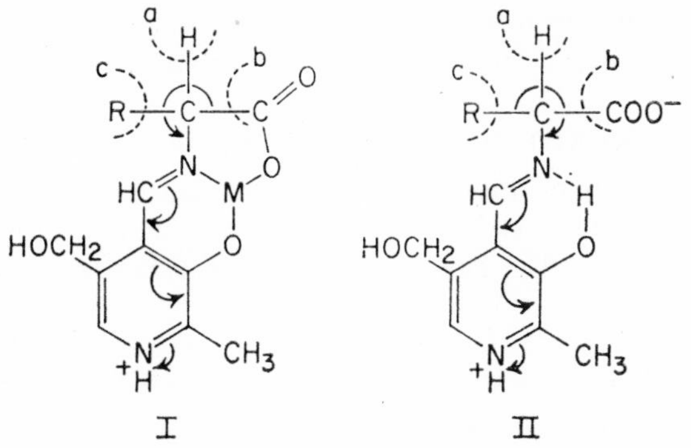

FIG. 1. Structures of aldimines formed between amino acids and pyridoxal, and the nature of the labilization of bonds *a*, *b* and *c* to groupings surrounding the $\alpha$-carbon atom.

These studies thus provided a sound experimental basis for the well-known mechanisms of pyridoxal catalysis presented independently almost 10 years ago by Metzler *et al.*[18] and by Braunstein and Shemyakin[22]. Extensive reviews from these and other laboratories[23–27] have summarized and extended these concepts; they are summarized briefly here merely as a basis for further discussion and development during the conference.

Both proposals envisage formation of a Schiff's base between amino acid and pyridoxal (or a pyridoxal-containing catalyst) with a resultant shift of electrons from bonds surrounding the $\alpha$-carbon atom of the amino acid toward the electrophilic nitrogen of pyridoxal, as shown in Fig. 1. By this primary catalytic act, these bonds to the $\alpha$-carbon atom are weakened, and the amino acid is thus " activated " for any of a large number of subsequent reactions that have been observed in both enzymatic and non-enzymatic systems. Which of these reactions actually occurs is determined by the structure of the amino acid, by the reaction conditions (pH, ionic strength, etc.), and by other catalysts (metal ions, apoenzymes, etc.) present. Even in the non-enzymatic systems it is frequently possible to arrange conditions in such a way that one of several possible reactions of an amino acid will predominate. A careful study of such controlling conditions could well help to clarify the way in which the rigid reaction specificity characteristic of enzymatic reactions is achieved.

While it is clear that a great number of pyridoxal-catalyzed reactions proceed as a consequence of labilization of the α-hydrogen atom of the amino acid (see Table 1), the course of the reactions in which cleavage of the bond to the carboxyl group (bond *b*, Fig. 1) or the R group (bond *c*, Fig. 1) of an amino acid occurs had not until recently been equally clear. Such reactions can be formulated as resulting either by direct labilization of that bond, or as a secondary result of labilization of the α-hydrogen atom. The separate consideration of these two cases is instructive.

## 1. CLEAVAGE OF α-AMINO-β-HYDROXY ACIDS

We have previously mentioned the facile way in which cleavage of serine or threonine occurs in model systems to yield glycine and formaldehyde or acetaldehyde, respectively. The reaction is a general one, as indicated by Eq. (1),

$$\mathrm{RCHOHCHNH_2COOH} \overset{\text{Pyridoxal}}{\rightleftharpoons} \mathrm{RCHO + H_2NCH_2COOH} \qquad (1)$$

and is closely analogous to the enzymatic cleavage of threonine by threonine aldolase[28] which yields the same products, and somewhat less closely analogous to the cleavage of serine by serine hydroxymethylase (Eq. 2) which requires tetrahydrofolate (THF) as a formaldehyde acceptor.[29,30]

$$\text{Serine + THF} \overset{\substack{\text{PLP}\\\text{Enzyme}}}{\rightleftharpoons} \text{Glycine + 5,10-methylene-THF} \qquad (2)$$

Reaction (1) can be formulated either as proceeding by direct weakening of the bond between the α- and β-carbon atoms[18] (Fig. 2, reactions 1, 2′, 3′, 4′) or by labilization of the α-hydrogen followed by a sequence of reactions formally analogous to the base-catalyzed cleavage of acyloins to aldehydes[22] (Fig. 2, reactions 1–5). Non-enzymatic experiments showed[31] that α-methylserine, when heated with pyridoxal and $Cu^{2+}$ or $Al^{3+}$, was degraded to alanine, formaldehyde and other products according to reactions (3) and (4).

$$\mathrm{HOCH_2C(CH_3)(NH_2)COOH} \overset{\text{PL, Cu}^{2+}}{\rightleftharpoons} \mathrm{HCHO + CH_3CHNH_2COOH} \qquad (3)$$

$$\text{Alanine + Pyridoxal} \rightleftharpoons \text{Pyruvate + Pyridoxamine} \qquad (4)$$

Thus, an α-hydrogen is not required, and the non-enzymatic result suggests the mechanism indicated by reactions 1–4′ of Fig. 2. The result does not, however, preclude the possibility that the *enzymatic* degradation of α-amino-β-hydroxy acids according to Eq. (1) might take a different course that requires an α-hydrogen atom.

To obtain evidence on this latter point we turned to a study of the degradation of α-methylserine in living organisms. This amino acid is not metabolized by mammalian tissues,[33] a finding originally interpreted to mean that an α-hydrogen was required for the aldolase reaction. By employing α-methyl-DL-serine as substrate in cultures inoculated with soil, an organism of the genus *Pseudomonas* was isolated that grew with this compound as a sole source of carbon and nitrogen. Only 50 per cent of the substrate was

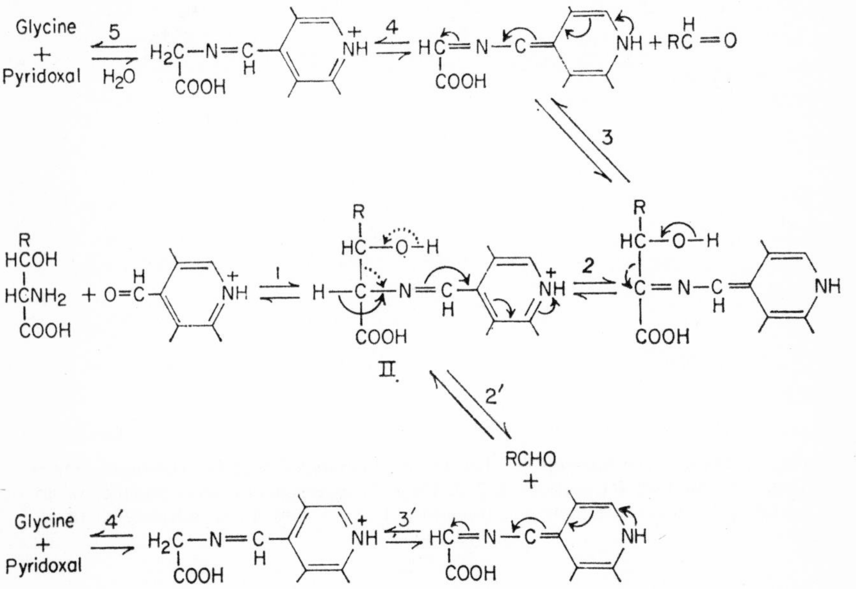

FIG. 2. Possible mechanisms for the pyridoxal-catalyzed cleavage of α-amino-β-hydroxy acids to glycine and aldehydes. Mechanism 1 (reactions 1, 2, 3, 4 and 5) requires an α-hydrogen atom; mechanism 2 (reactions 1, 2′, 3′ and 4′) is independent of an α-hydrogen atom.

utilized; from the spent culture medium (—)-α-methylserine was isolated. Cell-free extracts of the organism attacked α-methylserine in a manner exactly analogous to the serine hydroxymethylase reaction (Eq. 2) to yield D-alanine and 5,10-methylenetetrahydrofolate (Eq. 5).

$$(+)\text{-}\alpha\text{-Methylserine} + \text{THF} \rightleftharpoons \text{D-Alanine} + 5{,}10\text{-CH}_2{=}\text{THF} \qquad (5)$$

Purified preparations of the enzyme required pyridoxal phosphate and also catalyzed the reactions shown in Eqs. (6) and (7).

$$\alpha\text{-Hydroxymethylserine} + \text{THF} \rightleftharpoons \text{D-Serine} + 5{,}10\text{-CH}_2{=}\text{THF} \qquad (6)$$

$$(-)\text{-}\alpha\text{-Ethylserine} + \text{THF} \rightleftharpoons \text{D-}\alpha\text{-Aminobutyrate} + 5{,}10\text{-CH}_2{=}\text{THF} \qquad (7)$$

The reactions are reversible, and have equilibrium constants very similar to that found by Blakley[30] and by Greenberg (cf. Ref. 29) for the corresponding reaction of serine. The enzymatic cleavage of these α-substituted substrates must proceed by direct weakening of the bond between the α-carbon atom and the hydroxymethyl group, as correctly indicated by the non-enzymatic experiments,[31] and an α-hydrogen atom is not required. A unitary hypothesis of enzyme action would demand that the analogous cleavage of serine and threonine take a similar course.

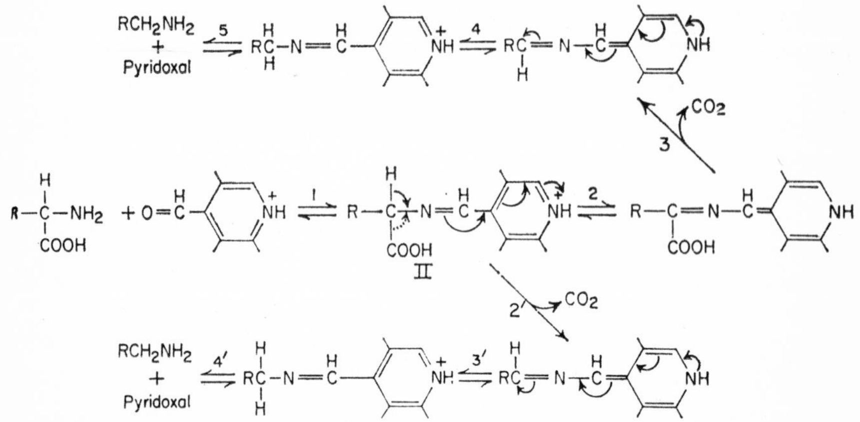

FIG. 3. Possible mechanisms for the pyridoxal-catalyzed decarboxylation of amino acids. Mechanism 1 (reactions 1, 2, 3, 4 and 5) is dependent upon presence of an α-hydrogen atom; mechanism 2 (reactions 1, 2′, 3′ and 4′) is independent of an α-hydrogen atom.

## 2. DECARBOXYLATION OF AMINO ACIDS

Like the aldol cleavage of α-amino-β-hydroxyacids, the decarboxylation of amino acids can be formulated as proceeding independently of an α-hydrogen atom, by direct weakening of the bond to the carboxyl group[18,33] (Fig. 3, reactions 1, 2′, 3′, 4′), or by preliminary labilization of an α-hydrogen atom and subsequent loss of the carboxyl group[22,34] (Fig. 3, reactions 1–5). Mandeles *et al.*[33], on a suggestion of Westheimer, showed that the α-hydrogen atom of tyrosine was not labilized during decarboxylation to tyramine by tyrosine decarboxylase. Belleau and Burba[35] showed further that decarboxylation of tyrosine proceeds with full retention of configuration, i.e. the proton picked up from water during decarboxylation occupies the same stereochemical position as the carboxyl group that is lost. Thus reactions 1–4′, Fig. 3, most closely represent the enzymatic reaction.

The dispensability of the α-hydrogen for decarboxylation reactions can also be demonstrated in model, non-enzymatic reactions. For this purpose we studied the decarboxylation of amino acids such as α-aminoisobutyrate and α-methylserine.[36] Decarboxylation is readily observed and proceeds according to Eq. (8):

$$\alpha\text{-Aminoisobutyrate} \xrightarrow{\text{Pyridoxal}} \text{Isopropylamine} + CO_2 \qquad (8)$$

however, the extent of reaction, as measured by $CO_2$ formation, is inhibited rather than catalyzed by metal ions, and acetone and pyridoxamine are also formed by a decarboxylation-dependent transamination reaction:

$$\alpha\text{-Aminoisobutyrate} + \text{Pyridoxal} \rightarrow \text{Acetone} + \text{Pyridoxamine} + CO_2 \qquad (9)$$

Reaction (10) does not occur under these conditions,

$$\text{Acetone} + \text{Pyridoxamine} \nrightarrow \text{Isopropylamine} + \text{Pyridoxal} \qquad (10)$$

so that reaction (8) is a true decarboxylation reaction, and not the sum of reactions (9) and (10).

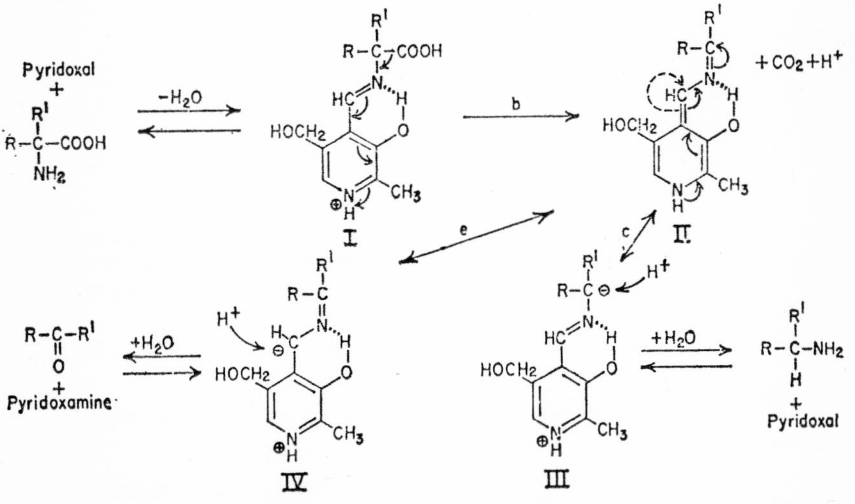

FIG. 4. Suggested mechanism for the non-enzymatic decarboxylation of amino acids in the presence of pyridoxal (I→II→III→products) and for the decarboxylation-dependent transamination reaction between pyridoxal and amino acids (I→II→IV→products). From Kalyankar and Snell.[36]

These observations are readily explained in terms of previously discussed concepts (Fig. 4). Decarboxylation occurs as a result of labilization of the bond to the carboxyl group, as in the enzymatic reaction; it does not require presence of an α-hydrogen atom. Following release of carbon dioxide, the common transition form II, Fig. 4, can stabilize either as III, an imine of pyridoxal and an amine, or as IV, the imine of pyridoxamine and a ketone. Hydrolysis of the former gives reaction (8), and of the latter, reaction (9).

Metal ions inhibit both reactions because they chelate with the carboxyl group, thus impeding the release of $CO_2$.[36]

A third interesting result was obtained when the reactions of α-methylserine in the presence of pyridoxal were compared in the presence and absence of metal ions (Table 2). In the absence of metal ions, decarboxylation of the amino acid predominated, according to Eqs. (11) and (12).

$$\alpha\text{-Methylserine} \xrightarrow{\text{Pyridoxal}} CO_2 + HOCH_2CHNH_2CH_3 \tag{11}$$

$$\alpha\text{-Methylserine} + \text{Pyridoxal} \rightarrow CO_2 + HOCH_2COCH_3 + \text{Pyridoxamine} \tag{12}$$

TABLE 2. THE EFFECT OF $Cu^{2+}$ ON THE COURSE OF THE PYRIDOXAL-CATALYZED CLEAVAGE OF α-METHYLSERINE[36]

Solutions (3 ml) containing 2 μmoles of pyridoxal and 10 μmoles of α-methylserine were heated for 2 hr at 100° with and without added $Cu^{2+}$ (1 μmole). The initial pH at 25° was 6.7 – 6.8.

| | Residual reactants (μmoles) | | Products (μmoles) | | | | | |
|---|---|---|---|---|---|---|---|---|
| | α-Methyl-serine | Pyrid-oxal | Pyridox-amine | Acetol | Pyru-vate | Ala-nine | HCHO | $NH_3$ |
| − $Cu^{2+}$ | 7.6 | 1.60 | 0.30 | 0.28 | 0 | 0 | 0 | 0 |
| + $Cu^{2+}$ | 4.8 | 1.14 | Traces | 0.12 | 1.32 | 0.92 | 2.65 | 0.56 |

In the presence of $Cu^{2+}$, essentially all of the amino acid that disappeared followed the reaction course indicated by Eqs. (3) and (4). In the absence of metal ions, bond *b* was predominantly labilized; in the presence of $Cu^{2+}$, bond *c* (Fig. 1) was predominantly labilized. The result illustrates the pronounced effect of conditions in determining the course of the reaction of a given substrate in the non-enzymatic systems. Enzymatic specificity may result from similar effects made possible by the structure of the catalyst itself, effects which determine which of several possible bond labilizations shall take place and lead to reactions of the substrate.

From consideration of these examples, it is clear that labilization of each of three bonds, *a*, *b* and *c* (Fig. 1) to the α-carbon atom of an amino acid can occur directly, and that labilization of bonds *b* and *c* occurs independently of an α-hydrogen atom. Such weakening appears to be the primary catalytic effect exerted by pyridoxal in both non-enzymatic and enzymatic reactions catalyzed by this compound and its derivatives.

Having emphasized several points which have been established through study of model and enzymatic reactions, it is only proper that I close this introduction by listing a few of the many aspects of pyridoxal catalysis that have not been adequately resolved, but are open to study in both model and enzymatic systems.

First, none of the mechanisms so far presented says anything about the process of formation and hydrolysis of the aldimines (Schiff bases) which are the essential intermediates in these reactions. Recent kinetic measurements[37] indicate that this is a very fast process, and not rate-limiting, in the case of the glutamic–aspartic transaminase; whether this is true of other enzymatic reactions and of the non-enzymatic reactions is not known. Bruice and Topping[38] have emphasized that both the formation of these intermediates and their interconversion should be subject to general acid–base catalysis; we shall hear more of this during these sessions. It is possible that part of the catalytic role of metal ions in the non-enzymatic reactions lies in catalysis of formation of these intermediates; that this is not their exclusive role is shown by the marked effect of $Cu^{2+}$ on the nature of the reactions of α-methylserine with pyridoxal, discussed above.

Secondly, the role of metal ions in many of the individual enzymatic reactions catalyzed by pyridoxal phosphate enzymes is not clear. We have emphasized repeatedly[18,22,23,39] that the functional role played by metal ions in catalysis of the non-enzymatic reactions might well be played by protein alone in the enzymatic systems. Most of the pyridoxal phosphate enzymes so far purified do not, in fact, contain functional metal ions. We have considered, however, that the number of such purified enzymes so far studied is insufficient to exclude the possibility of the direct involvement of metal ions in certain enzymatic reactions.[39] Dr. Yasanobu's report of a pyridoxal-$Cu^{2+}$ enzyme, to be heard later, is of special interest in this connection.

Thirdly, it is now clear that in those pyridoxal phosphate enzymes so far studied the carbonyl group of the coenzyme is not free but is combined either as an aldimine (usually with the ε-amino group of lysine) or in a form that readily gives rise to such an aldimine. Thus formation of the aldimines visualized as enzyme–substrate intermediates must take place by a process of transaldimination[40,41] rather than by elimination of water. The demonstration by Cordes and Jencks[42] in model systems that aldimine formation actually increases the reactivity of pyridoxal and of pyridoxal phosphate toward other carbonyl reagents is of great importance, and indicates one way in which combination with an appropriate apoenzyme serves to enhance the catalytic potentialities of pyridoxal phosphate. These observations, coupled with those of Bruice and Topping[38], have stimulated us to present (Fig. 5) a wholly speculative extension of a previously presented[18] scheme for non-enzymatic transamination which is presented only to illustrate how aldimine formation between PLP and an apotransaminase might enhance the catalytic effects of the coenzyme, both through speeding the process of formation of intermediates (by transaldimination) and by providing immediately adjacent acid–base catalysts which assist in the labilization and relocation of protons. When one adds to such effects (whatever the mechanism by which they are realized may be) the specific affinities of individual enzymes for their substrates, the greatly enhanced rates of the enzymatic reactions,

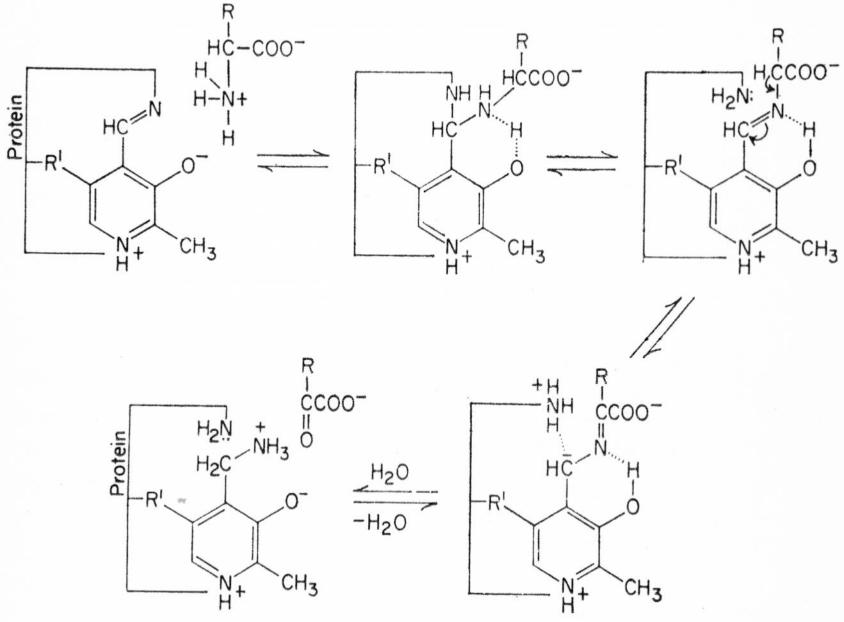

FIG. 5. Speculative mechanism for the transamination reaction catalyzed by enzyme-bound pyridoxal phosphate. Enzyme substrate complexes form by a transaldimination process; interconversion of intermediates is aided by proximal —$NH_2$ and —$NH_3^+$ groupings which serve as base–acid catalysts. The scheme is intended merely to illustrate the catalytic role of appropriately placed, general acid–base catalysts, and is not intended to suggest that the group involved is necessarily the ε-amino group of the lysine residue freed by complex formation with the substrate.

as compared to the non-enzymatic reactions, become more understandable. The nature of subsidiary catalytic groups that increase the catalytic effects inherent in pyridoxal or its phosphate, as well as the requisite spatial relationships between these activating groupings are intriguing and important problems, to the solution of which the further intensive study of model systems may be expected to contribute generously.

## REFERENCES


1. E. E. SNELL; *Proc. Soc. Exptl. Biol. Med.* **51**, 356 (1942).
2. E. E. SNELL, B. M. GUIRARD and R. J. WILLIAMS; *J. Biol. Chem.* **143**, 519 (1942).
3. E. E. SNELL; *J. Am. Chem. Soc.* **66**, 2082 (1944).
4. E. E. SNELL; *J. Biol. Chem.* **154**, 313 (1944).
5. S. A. HARRIS, D. HEYL and K. FOLKERS; *J. Biol. Chem.* **154**, 315 (1944).
6. E. E. SNELL and A. N. RANNEFELD; *J. Biol. Chem.* **157**, 475 (1945).
7. S. A. HARRIS, D. HEYL and K. FOLKERS; *J. Am. Chem. Soc.* **66**, 2088 (1944).
8. E. E. SNELL; *J. Biol. Chem.* **157**, 491 (1945).
9. E. E. SNELL; *J. Am. Chem. Soc.* **67**, 194 (1945).
10. D. E. METZLER and E. E. SNELL; *J. Am. Chem. Soc.* **74**, 979 (1952).
11. F. SCHLENK and E. E. SNELL; *J. Biol. Chem.* **157**, 425 (1945).
12. H. C. LICHSTEIN, I. C. GUNSALUS and W. W. UMBREIT; *J. Biol. Chem.* **161**, 311 (1945).
13. F. SCHLENK and A. FISHER; *Arch. Biochem.* **12**, 69 (1947).
14. J. OLIVARD, D. E. METZLER and E. E. SNELL; *J. Biol. Chem.* **199**, 669 (1952).
15. D. E. METZLER and E. E. SNELL, *J. Biol. Chem.* **198**, 353 (1952).
16. D. E. METZLER, J. B. LONGENECKER and E. E. SNELL; *J. Am. Chem. Soc.* **75**, 2786 (1953); **76**, 639 (1954).
17. A. E. BRAUNSTEIN and G. Y. VILENKINA; *Doklady Akad. Nauk S.S.S.R.* **66**, 243 (1949); M. A. KARESEK and D. M. GREENBERG; *J. Biol. Chem.* **227**, 191 (1957).
18. D. E. METZLER, M. IKAWA and E. E. SNELL; *J. Am. Chem. Soc.* **76**, 648 (1954).
19. P. FROMAGEOT *et al.*; This volume, p. 395.
20. J. B. LONGENECKER and E. E. SNELL; *J. Biol. Chem.* **225**, 409 (1957).
21. M. IKAWA and E. E. SNELL; *J. Am. Chem. Soc.* **76**, 653 (1954); D. E. METZLER, J. OLIVARD and E. E. SNELL; *ibid.* **76**, 644 (1954).
22. A. E. BRAUNSTEIN and M. M. SHEMYAKIN; *Biokhimiya* **18**, 393 (1953).
23. E. E. SNELL; *Special Lecturers in Biochemistry* pp. 1–16, University College, London H. K. Lewis, Distributors (1954–1955).
24. A. E. BRAUNSTEIN; *The Enzymes* (edited by P. D. BOYER, H. LARDY and K. MYRBÄCK), Vol. 2, ch. 6, Academic Press, New York (1960).
25. E. E. SNELL; *Vitamins and Hormones* **16**, 78 (1960).
26. A. M. PERAULT, B. PULLMAN and C. VALDEMORO; *Biochim. et Biophys. Acta* **46**, 555 (1961).
27. F. H. WESTHEIMER; *The Enzymes* (edited by P. D. BOYER, H. LARDY and K. MYRBÄCK), vol. 1, ch. 6, Academic Press, New York (1960).
28. A. E. BRAUNSTEIN and G. YA. VILENKINA; *Doklady Akad. Nauk S.S.S.R.* **80**, 639 (1951); M. A. KARASEK and D. M. GREENBERG, *J. Biol. Chem.* **227**, 191 (1957).
29. F. M. HUENNEKINS and M. J. OSBORN; *Advances in Enzymol.* **21**, 369 (1959).
30. R. L. BLAKLEY; *Biochem. J.* **61**, 315 (1955); **65**, 342 (1957).
31. J. B. LONGENECKER, M. IKAWA and E. E. SNELL; *J. Biol. Chem.* **226**, 663 (1957).
32. E. M. WILSON and E. E. SNELL; *J. Biol. Chem.* **237**, 3171, 3180 (1962).
33. S. MANDELES, R. KOPPELMAN and M. E. HANKE; *J. Biol. Chem.* **209**, 327 (1954).
34. E. WERLE and W. KOCH; *Biochem. Z.* **319**, 305 (1949).
35. B. BELLEAU and J. BURBA; *J. Am. Chem. Soc.* **82**, 5751 (1960).
36. G. D. KALYANKAR and E. E. SNELL; *Biochemistry* **1**, 594 (1962).
37. S. F. VELICK and J. VAVRA; *J. Biol. Chem.* **237**, 2109 (1962).
38. T. C. BRUICE and R. M. TOPPING; *J. Am. Chem. Soc.* **84**, 2448 (1962).
39. D. S. HOARE and E. E. SNELL; *Proc. Int. Symp. Enzyme Chemistry*, Tokyo and Kyoto 1957, pp. 142–148, Maruzen, Tokyo (1958).
40. E. E. SNELL and W. T. JENKINS; *J. Cell. Comp. Physiol.* **54**, suppl. 1, 161 (1959).
41. E. E. SNELL; *Brookhaven Symposia in Biology* **15**, 32 (1962).
42. E. H. CORDES and W. P. JENCKS; *Biochemistry* **1**, 773 (1962).
43. A. NEUBERGER; This volume, pp. 243.
44. J. W. THANASSI and J. S. FRUTON; *Biochemistry* **1**, 975 (1962).
45. M. IKAWA and E. E. SNELL; *J. Am. Chem. Soc.* **76**, 653 (1954).

## DISCUSSION

DR. S. MARDASHEV:

I wish to ask Dr. Snell about the aspartic acid decarboxylation mechanism. There are some difficulties from the point of view of your theory for the understanding of the decarboxylation of aspartic acid and especially hydrogen labilization and some others, because there is a β-decarboxylation. How can you explain this?

DR. SNELL:

The mechanism I discussed deals only with the decarboxylation of α-amino acids. We agree fully with your view and that of Dr. Braunstein that the β-decarboxylation of L-aspartate can best be considered as an α, β-elimination reaction that would require the presence of a hydrogen atom on the α-carbon atom.

DR. J. C. SENEZ:

In the course of experiments on non-enzymic transamination between PLP and amino acids in the presence of metals ($Cu^{2+}$), it was found that the stable form of the intermediary complex is characterized by an absorption band at 360mμ. This maximum of absorption being attributable to conjugated double bonds, it seems that the stable form of the complex in such reactions is the aldimine form.

DR. H. K. KING:

Dr. Snell has mentioned analogies between the chelated metals in Schiff base complexes and the protein holoenzyme in pyridoxal phosphate systems. In most pyridoxal phosphate enzymes the stability constant of the amino acid–PLP imine, in absence of a chelating metal ion is about equal in value to the classical Michaelis constant. There are three decarboxylases, however, for which the Schiff base stabilities are much lower than the appropriate enzyme affinities. If, however, the Schiff base stability is measured in presence of the actively chelated metal ion $Co^{2+}$, its stability is brought up to that of the enzyme–substrate complex. In these systems this would suggest that the protein does indeed stabilize the enzyme–substrate complex in a manner analogous to the action of a metal ion.

DR. W. P. JENCK:

I am not sure that I understand the reason for the agreement between the equilibrium constants for Schiff base formation from free pyridoxal phosphate with enzyme $K_m$ values, in view of the fact that with a number of enzymes the pyridoxal phosphate exists in the enzyme in the form of a Schiff base, rather than as free pyridoxal phosphate.

DR. H. N. CHRISTENSEN:

Dr. Snell has mentioned the observation (Christensen, Aspen and Rice, *J. Biol. Chem.* **220**, 287, 1956) that α-methylserine and α-hydroxymethylserine are not catabolized extensively in the rat. Recently we have had occasion to test the catabolism of α-hydroxymethylserine by a more sensitive procedure. We now observe that about 3 per cent of the $C^{14}$ injected into the rat as $(HOC^{14}H_2)_2C(NH_2)C^{14}OOH$ appears subsequently as $C^{14}O^2$ in the atmosphere around the animal. Therefore a small but appreciable attack of this amino acid does occur in the animal organism (Christensen and Clifford, *Proc. Soc. Exp. Biol., N.Y.* **111**, 140, 1962). This result does not mean that all amino acids with tertiary carbon are attacked, since we cannot observe significant release of $C^{14}O_2$ from injected $(CH_3)_2C(NH_2)C^{14}OOH$.

DR. GUNSALUS:

Is there any data on the rate of amino acid carboxyl–$CO_2$ exchange in the heat and metal catalyses of amino acid pyridoxal phosphate reactions?

DR. SNELL:

We have no data bearing on this question.

DR. GUNSALUS:

Is there any enzymatic data on $CO_2$–carboxyl exchange by amino acid decarboxylases other than the early data of Hanke and colleagues (*J. Biol. Chem.* **220**, 327, 1954)?

DR. SNELL:

If any such data have been published, I am unaware of them.

# SCHIFF BASES OF PYRIDOXAL ANALOGS: MOLECULAR SPECIES IN SOLUTION

by Arthur E. Martell

Department of Chemistry, Illinois Institute of Technology
Chicago, Illinois

The synthesis of 3-hydroxypyridine-2 and 4-aldehydes in our laboratory[1] led to a detailed spectrophotometric investigation[2] of these compounds, and of their O-methyl derivatives, as analogs of pyridoxal. The purpose of this paper is to describe some Schiff bases of these pyridine aldehydes, and the results of a detailed spectrophotometric study of their solution equilibria as a function of added acid or base.

The acid–base equilibria of the pyridoxal analogs III–VI were elucidated through a study of their ultraviolet absorption spectra as a function of pH.[3,4] Assignments of the absorption bands to definite species in solution were made by studying the solvent effects of the absorption bands. The resulting acid–base dissociation constants obtained for these and similar compounds are summarized in Table 1. It is seen that all of the pyridine aldehydes listed have two dissociation constants, the second of which is relatively very small if no aromatic hydroxyl group is present, and results from the dissociation of a proton from the hydrated carbonyl group. For the model hydroxyaldehydes, the equilibria may be expressed as follows:

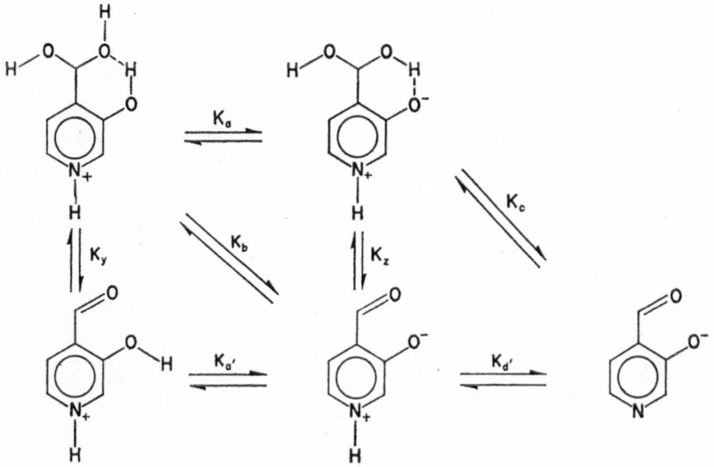

$K_a$ $K_b$ $K_c$ $K_y$ $K_z$ $K_{a'}$ $K_{d'}$

TABLE 1. ACID DISSOCIATION CONSTANTS OF PYRIDOXAL ANALOGS

| | Thermodynamic constants | | Microscopic dissociation constants | | | | |
|---|---|---|---|---|---|---|---|
| Pyridine derivative | $pK_1$ | $pK_2$ | $pK_a$ | $pK_b$ | $pK_c$ | $pK_d$ | $K_z$ |
| 2-Aldehyde | 3.80 | 12.80 | 4.2 | 4.0 | 12.6 | 12.6 | 0.6 |
| 3-Methoxy-2-aldehyde | 3.89 | 12.95 | 4.4 | 4.0 | 12.4 | 12.8 | 0.4 |
| 3-Hydroxy-2-aldehyde | 3.40 | 6.95 | 3.6 | 3.8 | 6.7 | 6.6 | 1.3 |
| 4-Aldehyde | 4.77 | 12.20 | 5.2 | 5.0 | 11.8 | 12.0 | 0.6 |
| 3-Methoxy-4-aldehyde | 4.45 | 11.7 | 4.8 | 4.7 | 11.3 | 11.5 | 0.8 |
| 3-Hydroxy-4-aldehyde | 4.05 | 6.77 | 4.4 | 4.2 | 6.4 | 6.6 | 0.6 |
| 5-Desoxypyridoxal | 4.17 | 8.14 | 4.5 | 4.3 | 7.8 | 8.0 | 0.6 |
| Pyridoxal | 4.20 | 8.66 | 4.3 | 5.3 | 8.6 | 7.6 | 11.5 |

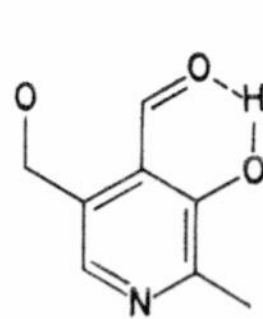

I Pyridoxal

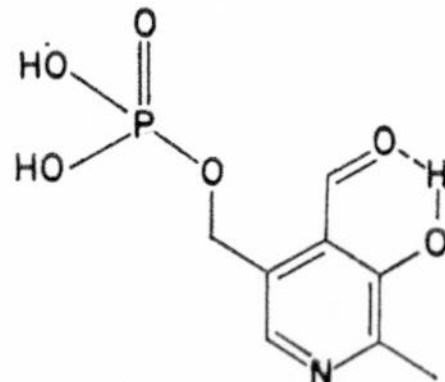

II Pyridoxal phosphate

III 3-hydroxypyridine-4-carboxaldehyde

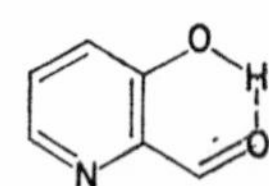

IV 3-hydroxypyridine-2-carboxaldehyde

V 3-methoxypyridine-4-carboxaldehyde

VI 3-methoxypyridine-2-carboxaldehyde

Pyridoxal phosphate equilibria has similar absorption characteristics and follows the same pattern as do the model compounds. It is apparent from the dissociation constants and spectra, however, that pyridoxal is remarkably different.[4] The almost complete lack of the free or "anhydrous" aldehyde form in aqueous equilibria indicates that the hemiacetal form is the predominant structure. Thus if one neglects the small proportion of hydrated species that is probably present, the aqueous equilibria of pyridoxal may be expressed by the following scheme:

AQUEOUS EQUILIBRIA OF PYRIDOXAL

$K_a$ $K_c$ $K_b$ $K_z$ $K_d$ $K_{d'}$

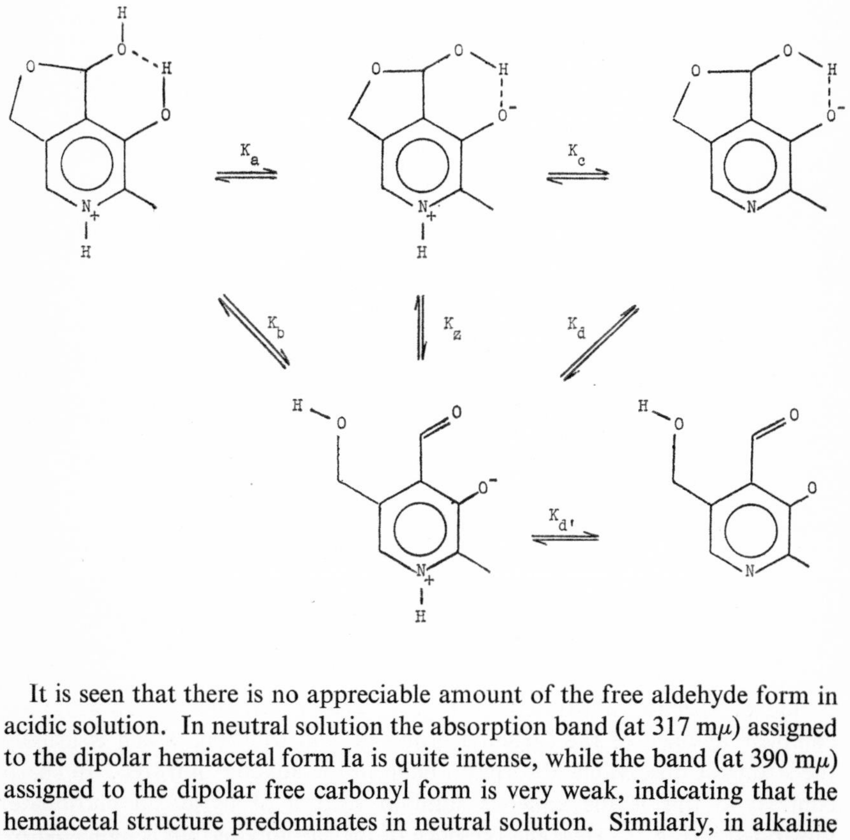

It is seen that there is no appreciable amount of the free aldehyde form in acidic solution. In neutral solution the absorption band (at 317 mμ) assigned to the dipolar hemiacetal form Ia is quite intense, while the band (at 390 mμ) assigned to the dipolar free carbonyl form is very weak, indicating that the hemiacetal structure predominates in neutral solution. Similarly, in alkaline solution the hemiacetal form was found to predominate over the free aldehyde, although the proportion of free aldehyde increases at high pH.

The spectral evidence for these molecular species in aqueous solution, though indirect, is in accord with the observed dissociation equilibria, and the known sluggish behavior of pyridoxal in Schiff base formation, as compared to desoxypyridoxal, pyridoxal phosphate, and the other analogs listed in Table 1. Further confirmation of these assignments of aqueous species has recently been found[5] in these laboratories by infrared measurements of aqueous pyridoxal and pyridoxal phosphate solutions. Aqueous

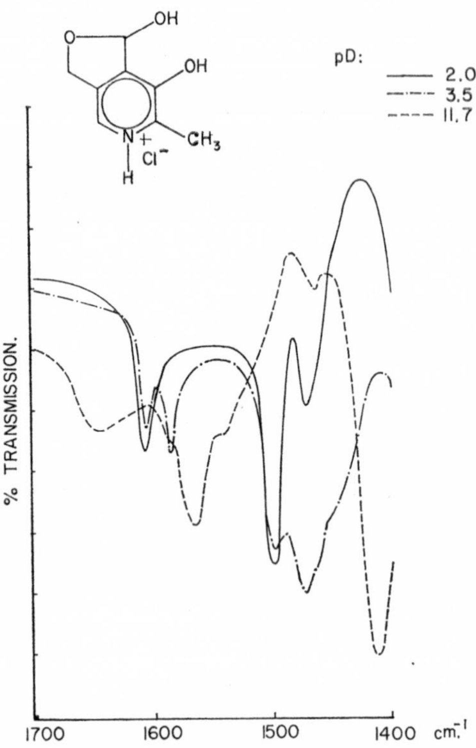


FIG. 1. Infrared spectra of pyridoxal phosphate in deuterium oxide as a function of pD.

pyridoxal spectra, illustrated in Fig. 1, are remarkable in showing the complete absence of the carbonyl group in acid solution, which is usually the strongest observable absorption band in the aqueous infrared. In sharp contrast to this is the aqueous solution spectra of pyridoxal phosphate, illustrated in Fig. 2. Here the presence of the carbonyl group is indicated by the strong bands near 1660 $cm^{-1}$. The variation of the absorption frequencies and intensities as a function of pH make it possible to distinguish between successive steps in the dissociation of the compound. In Fig. 2 it is seen that dissociation of the pyridoxal phosphate is accompanied by increases in intensity and shifts to lower frequencies for the carbonyl absorptions near 1660 cm$^{-1}$, and for the C=N and C=C ring vibrations occurring in the ranges 1537–1565 cm$^{-1}$ and 1450–1490 cm$^{-1}$, respectively.

General formulas VII, VIII and IX represent the structures of three series of Schiff bases prepared from compounds II–VI, and from benzenoid analogs.[6] The infrared spectra of these compounds differ considerably

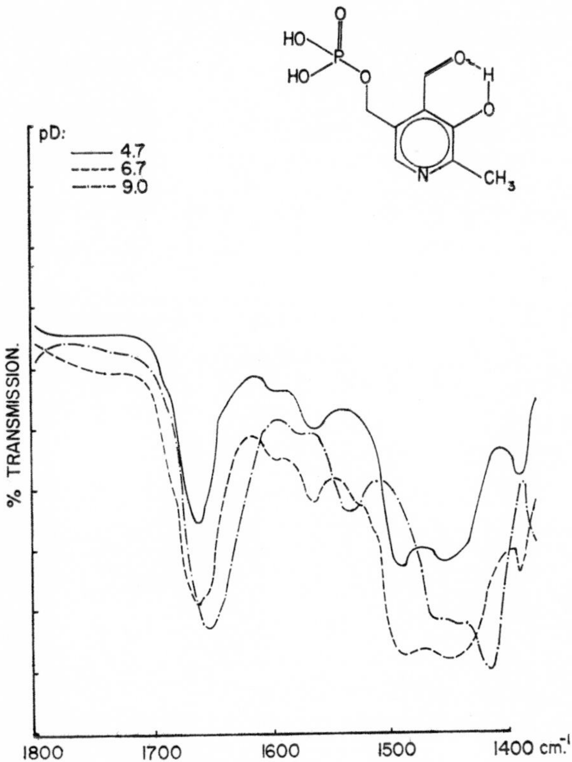


FIG. 2. Infrared spectra of pyridoxal in deuterium oxide as a function of pD.

from those of the parent pyridinealdehydes. From Table 2, it is seen that the formation of a Schiff base from 2-pyridinecarboxaldehyde results in the replacement of the carbonyl stretching frequency (1700–1715 cm$^{-1}$) by a specific imine absorption band (1630–1640 cm$^{-1}$), which frequently appears as a shoulder on a new broad and intense band, considered to be a superimposing of the absorptions of the ring C=C and C=N vibrations, and of the asymmetric carboxylate absorptions (resolved in several Schiff bases into two bands at 1596 and 1586 cm$^{-1}$, respectively). The other frequencies observed in the aldehydes are found at about the same position in the Schiff base spectra. Thus the only remaining new band in the Schiff bases, found

TABLE 2. INFRARED SPECTRA OF SCHIFF BASES*

| Compound | C=O, st. aldehyde | C=O, st. II | C=N, st. imine | C=O, st. amide I | COO⁻ st. asymm. | C=C/C=N ring st. | C=C/C=N ring st. | C=C, conj. amide, st. | C=C/C=N ring st. | $CH_2$ + $CH_3$ symm. def. | C=C/C=N ring st. | COO⁻ st. symm. | $CH_3$, def. symm., or C—C st. conj. |
|---|---|---|---|---|---|---|---|---|---|---|---|---|---|
| 4-Pyridinecarboxaldehyde | 1712s | 1671m | — | — | — | 1595w | 1563s | — | 1491w | — | 1414m | — | 1390m |
| N-(4-Pyridylmethylene)-valine | — | — | 1640s | — | 1588vs | — | 1564ssh | — | 1469msh | 1461m | 1409ssh | 1370s | 1395s |
| 3-Methoxy-4-pyridine-carboxaldehyde | 1703s | — | — | — | — | 1595m | 1564m | — | 1489m | 1463m | 1418s | — | 1391w |
| N-(3-Methoxy-4-pyridyl-methylene)-valine | — | — | 1632s | — | 1596vs | — | 1563msh | — | 1493s | 1466m | 1413s | 1368m | 1391m |
| 3-Hydroxy-4-pyridinecarbox-aldehyde | 1687ssh | 1674s | — | — | — | 1602m | 1583m | — | 1498w | — | 1413s | — | 1357m |
| N-(3-Hydroxy-4-pyridyl-methylene)-valine | — | — | — | 1632ssh | 1600vs | — | 1567msh | 1512m | 1463msh | 1442m | — | 1367s | 1340msh |
| 2-Pyridinecarboxaldehyde | 1713s | 1665w | — | — | — | 1588s | 1573w | — | 1472m | — | 1439m | — | 1367m |
| N-(2-Pyridylmethylene)-valine | — | — | 1632s | — | 1596vs | 1588vs | — | — | 1466m | 1435w | — | 1391s | 1367s |
| 3-Methoxy-2-pyridine-carboxaldehyde | 1708s | 1640vw | — | — | — | 1576s | 1562msh | — | 1469s | 1460ssh | 1430s | — | 1395m |
| N-(3-Methoxy-2-pyridyl-methylene)-valine | — | — | 1639ssh | — | 1588vs | — | 1562msh | — | 1464m | 1451m | 1431m | 1364s | 1390m |
| 3-Hydroxy-2-pyridine carboxaldehyde | 1688ssh | 1677s | — | — | — | 1580s | 1564msh | — | 1468s | — | 1408w | — | 1352m |
| N-(3-Hydroxy-2-pyridyl-methylene)-valine | — | — | — | 1643ssh | 1631vs l | — | — | 1509s | 1463m | 1433m | — | 1395m | 1360s |

*Potassium salts used in KBr media; vs = very strong; s = strong; m = medium; w = weak; sh = shoulder.

between 1365 and 1400 cm$^{-1}$, is assigned to the symmetric stretching frequency of the carboxylate group.

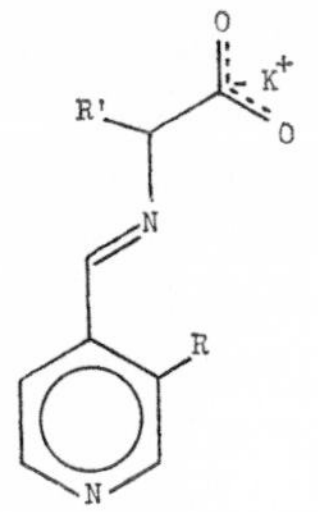

VII 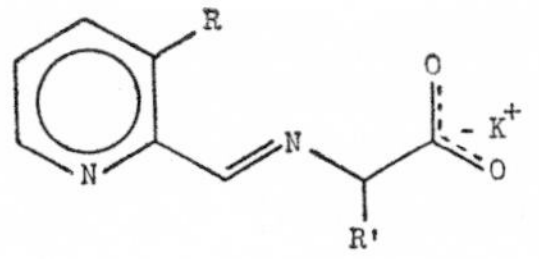 VIII

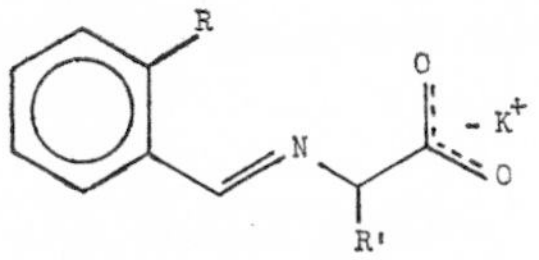

IX

R = H, OH, $OCH_3$

R' = H, $CH_3$, $CH(CH_3)_2$, $CH_2C_6H_5$, $CH_2CH_2COOK$

The spectra of the Schiff bases of the orthohydroxyaldehydes, on the other hand, differ markedly from those of the simple aldehydes. The hydrogen-bonded (chelated) carbonyl stretching frequency of the *o*-hydroxyaldehyde at 1677–1688 cm$^{-1}$ is replaced by two new bands at 1613 and 1641 cm$^{-1}$. The 1613 cm$^{-1}$ band was first assigned to a relatively intense imine absorption frequency. The other band is assigned to the superimposing of two bands, resulting from the C=N/C=C ring vibrations, and from the asymmetric carboxylate stretching frequency. The symmetric carboxylate stretching frequency appears at 1402 cm$^{-1}$, and the other vibrations in Table 2 are also found at the same location as for the parent aldehydes. This analysis leaves one absorption unassigned: the relatively strong band near 1510 cm$^{-1}$, which appears in all of the *o*-hydroxyaldehyde Schiff bases, and is absent from the spectra of all Schiff bases which do not have the *o*-hydroxy group. This anomalous absorption near 1510 cm$^{-1}$, and the unusual intensity of the "imine" frequency at 1625–1650 cm$^{-1}$, led to a re-examination of the relation of spectra to bonding in this type of Schiff base, and of analogous compounds. Through a comparison with many model compounds, it was concluded that the most probable explanation for the origin of these new bands is in the carbonyl stretching frequency of the amide (amide I band) for the 1625–1650 cm$^{-1}$ absorption, and the C=C stretching frequency found in vinilogous amides for the 1510 $cm^{-1}$ band. Thus for *o*-hydroxyaldehyde Schiff bases we have structures of the type indicated by X and XI. Of these, XI is expected to predominate, with the dipolar form XIa contributing to a greater extent in polar media. On the other hand it is impossible to rule out completely the hydroxyaldimine structure X. In the solid hydroxyaldehyde Schiff bases, which are soluble in solvents of low polarity and are indicated by infrared studies not to have strong intermolecular hydrogen bonding, the proton is probably strongly bonded by a three-way (bifurcated) hydrogen bond as indicated in formula XI. According to this representation, the proton is surrounded by donor groups very much as a metal ion would be co-ordinated by the same groups.

The interpretation of the electronic absorption spectra[7] of the *o*-hydroxypyridinealdimines is complicated by the fact that a number of species may be present: three different tautomeric forms (X–XII) and two hydrated

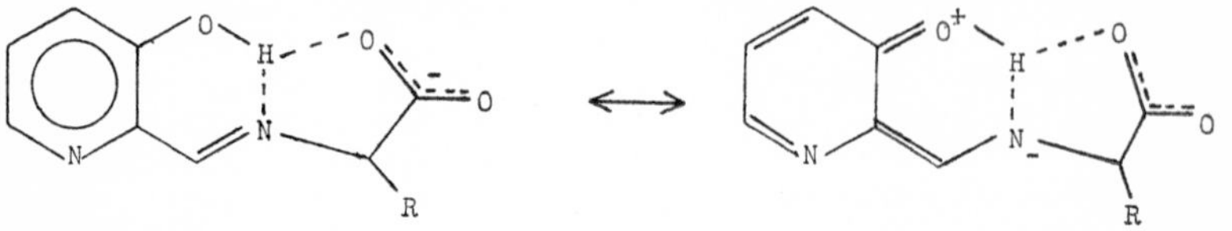

Xa Xb

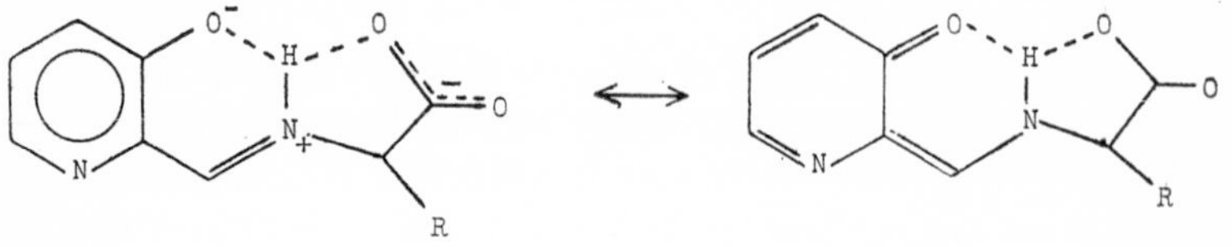

XIa XIb

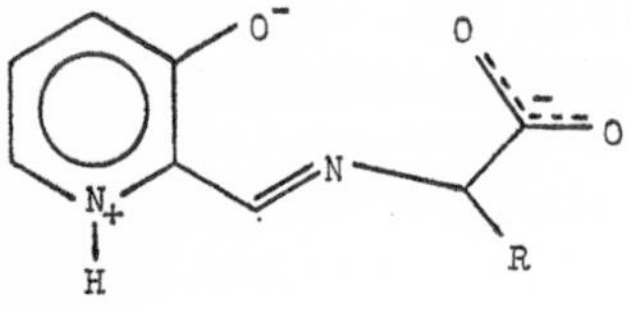

XII 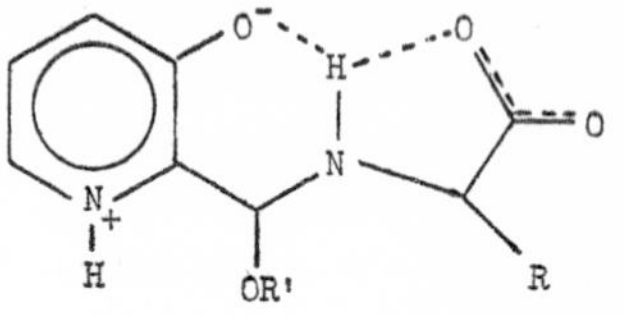 XIII

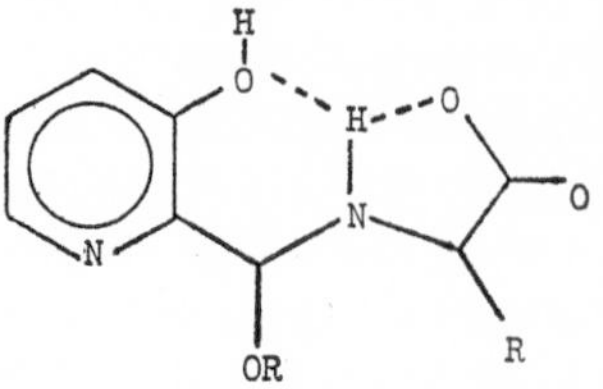

XIV

forms (or hemiacetal, XIII and XIV) must be considered in aqueous or alcohol solutions. A further complication is extensive hydrolysis of the Schiff base in aqueous solution, leading to the formation of additional hydroxyaldehyde species. Since aqueous Schiff base formation may not be complete even in the presence of a large excess of amino acid, interpretation of electronic absorption spectra was carried out by a study of non-aqueous solutions and of the crystalline compounds.

The absorption maxima of *o*-hydroxypyridinealdehyde Schiff bases of valine are listed in Table 3. Since it has been shown[4] that pyridine compounds of this type are characterized by two absorption bands (designated as $\pi_1$ and $\pi_2$ bands), the occurrence of four absorption bands in dioxane solution

TABLE 3. ELECTRONIC ABSORPTION SPECTRA OF VALINE SCHIFF BASES[a]

| Compound | Medium | Transition[b] | | | | $K_x$[c] |
|---|---|---|---|---|---|---|
| | | $\pi-\pi_2{}^*$ | $\pi-\pi_2{}^*$ | $\pi-\pi_1{}^*$ | $\pi-\pi_1{}^*$ | |
| N-(3-hydroxy-2-pyridylmethylene) valine | Dioxane | 253(0.71) | 265(0.62) | 319(0.28) | 404(0.94) | 2.74 |
| | MeOH | 245(0.65) | 264(0.37) | 318(0.55) | 395(0.52) | |
| | KBr | 250(1.61) | — | 316(0.65) | 399(1.25) | |
| N-(3-hydroxy-4-pyridylmethylene) valine | Dioxane | 252(0.70) | 270(0.62) | 323(0.25) | 425(0.39) | 1.14 |
| | MeOH | 250(0197) | — | 310(0163) | 414(0.21) | |
| | KBr | 252(2.15) | — | 313(1.38) | — | |

[a]Wavelength in m$\mu$. [b]Absorbency $\times 10^4$ = molecular extinction coefficient.

$$^{c}K_x = \frac{\text{(enamine)}}{\text{(enol)}}.$$

indicated the presence of two species. All of the parent aldehydes, as well as the Schiff bases of the O-methyl derivatives, have only two absorption bands, corresponding to a single species, in dioxane solution. These absorption maxima occurring in the ranges 305–330 and 230–255 m$\mu$ coincide with one pair of absorption bands of the hydroxypyridinemethylene Schiff bases, and are therefore assigned to the uncharged (not dipolar) species X. From this correlation it is seen that replacement of the carbonyl oxygen of the parent hydrocarbons by a substituted nitrogen atom does not produce a marked change in the absorption spectrum.

The remaining absorption bands found in the ranges 404–425 and 265–280 m$\mu$ are assigned to the keto-enimine form XI. The large red shift that occurs from X to XI is due to the strong " amide " type of resonance possible in the latter structure. The amide vinylog structure XIb is related to the intensely colored *o*-hydroxyazoaromatic compounds and to the merocyanine dyes. Equilibrium constants for the two forms present in dioxane solution were estimated by assuming the extinction coefficient of the neutral form to be the same as that of the methoxy derivative (no effect of substitution of $CH_3$ for H).

In methanol solution, the extinctions of the 320 m$\mu$ bands increase, and those of the 400 m$\mu$ bands decrease, as the result of the partial conversion of the equilibrium between the species X and XI into a dipolar form XII, and to the dipolar hemiacetal XIII. Thus the 400 m$\mu$ band is assigned to the $\pi_1$ band of XI (present in lower concentrations), together with a small contribution from the $\pi_1$ absorption of species XII. The 320 $\pi\mu$ band is assigned to a combination of the $\pi_1$ band of X, present in reduced concentration, and the $\pi_1$ band of the dipolar hemiacetal structure XIII.

For the solid state (KBr media) the positions of the $\pi_1$-absorption bands are nearly identical to the spectra of the corresponding dioxane solution. It is therefore concluded that the Schiff bases exist in both tautomeric forms in the solid state, with the keto-enamine structure predominating.

## EQUILIBRIUM CONSTANTS

The equilibria resulting from acidification of N-(3-hydroxy-4-pyridylmethylene)-valine in dioxane are illustrated in the following diagram.

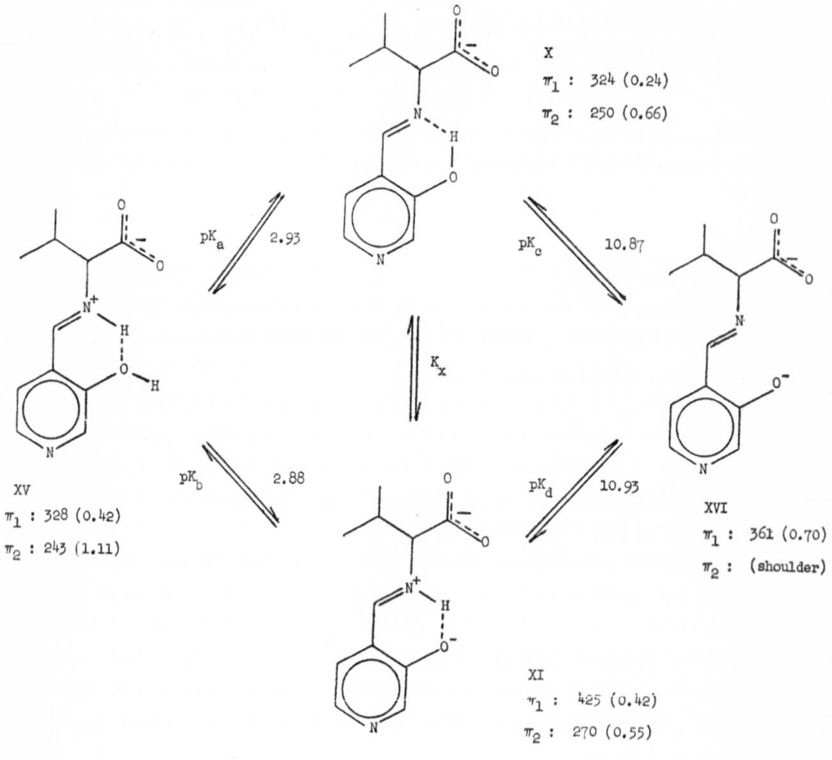

X
$\pi_1$ : 324 (0.24)
$\pi_2$ : 250 (0.66)

$pK_a$ 2.93

$pK_c$ 10.87

$K_x$

$pK_b$ 2.88

$pK_d$ 10.93

XV
$\pi_1$ : 328 (0.42)
$\pi_2$ : 243 (1.11)

XVI
$\pi_1$ : 361 (0.70)
$\pi_2$ : (shoulder)

XI
$\pi_1$ : 425 (0.42)
$\pi_2$ : 270 (0.55)

Acidification of the neutral solution results in the disappearance of the keto-enamine species XI, as indicated by a decrease in the intensities of its absorption bands, while the absorption bands attributed to X increase in intensity and shift slightly in position. These changes are interpreted as being due to the formation of a single acid species XV, in view of the fact that protonation of the pyridine nitrogen or the imine group of X would not be expected to result in more than a slight shift in the frequency of the absorption maximum.[3,4] Similar results were obtained with the corresponding Schiff base of salicylaldehyde.

Although the Schiff bases were converted to insoluble salts in dioxane on the addition of an alkali hydroxide, measurements in alkaline media were found to be quite feasible in methanol. Addition of potassium hydroxide to a neutral methanol solution of the X–XI mixture resulted in a solution having only one strong absorption band in the 361–377 mμ range, assigned to XVI. Another absorption at about 250 mμ was assigned to the $\pi_2$-transition of this compound. The intensities of the specific bands as a function of acid or base concentration were employed to determine the equilibrium constants for the conversion of the neutral form to acidic and basic species. These constants, together with the $K_x$ values given above, were used to determine the microscopic dissociation constants for the interconversion of the various species indicated in the diagram on p. 22. The relationships used are

$$K_x = \frac{[\mathrm{XI}]}{[\mathrm{X}]} = \frac{K_b}{K_a} = \frac{K_c}{K_d}$$

$$K_I = K_a + K_b$$

$$K_{II} = \frac{1}{K_c} + \frac{1}{K_d}$$

The results obtained are:

$K_I = 10^{-2.60}$ $\qquad K_{II} = 10^{-11.2}$

$K_a = 10^{-2.93}$ $\qquad K_b = 10^{-2.88}$

$K_c = 10^{-10.87}$ $\qquad K_c = 10^{-10.93}$

It should be noted that because of a change in solvent, the $K_c$ and $K_d$ values are not accurate. The values given are included here as examples of the relationships that can generally be obtained for such systems. For dioxane solutions in the presence of a soluble base, these constants would be shifted to lower values, but the ratios between them would be the same.

## EQUILIBRIA IN ACIDIC METHANOL

The addition of a strong acid to a methanol solution of the X–XI mixture produces a much different result from that observed for dioxane. Both of the neutral species disappear on the addition of acid, and a new compound, absorbing at 289 and 222 m$\mu$, is formed. Since the highest absorption of this completely protonated species occurs at a shorter wavelength than the acidic form in dioxane solution (XV), these transitions are assigned to the hemiacetal XVII. These conclusions, combined with the results obtained in alkaline methanol, indicate that the acid–base equilibria in this system may be formulated as indicated in the following diagram.

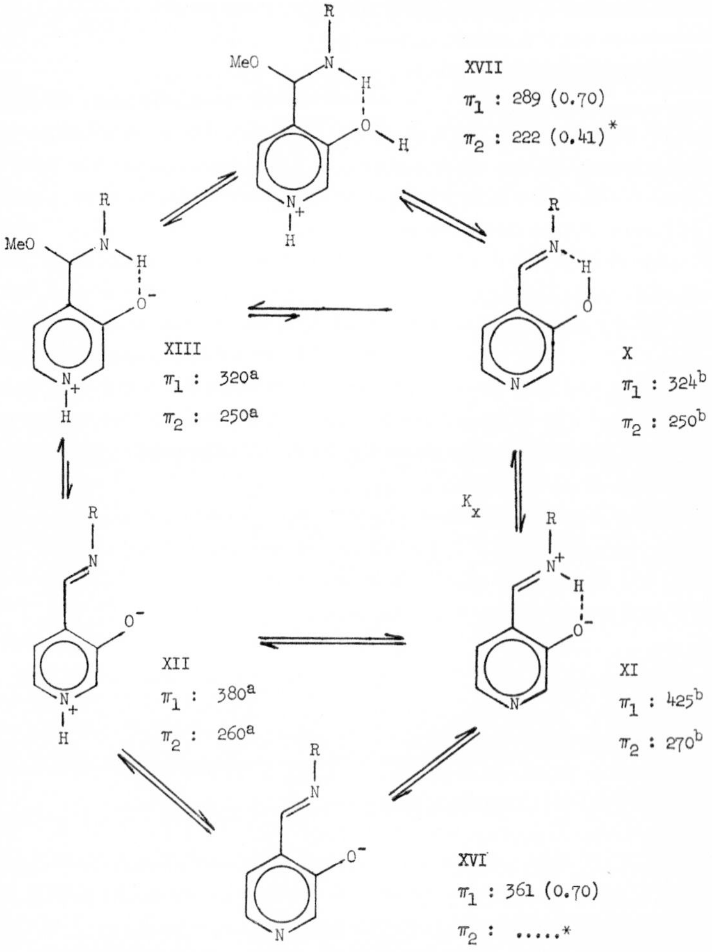

XVII
$\pi_1$ : 289 (0.70)
$\pi_2$ : 222 (0.41)*

XIII
$\pi_1$ : 320[a]
$\pi_2$ : 250[a]

X
$\pi_1$ : 324[b]
$\pi_2$ : 250[b]

$K_x$

XII
$\pi_1$ : 380[a]
$\pi_2$ : 260[a]

XI
$\pi_1$ : 425[b]
$\pi_2$ : 270[b]

XVI
$\pi_1$ : 361 (0.70)
$\pi_2$ : .....*

[a] estimated, [b] approximated from dioxane data, * shoulder.

## IMPLICATIONS FOR THE SOLUTION EQUILIBRIA OF PYRIDOXAL

It is of interest to reconsider the information available on pyridoxylideneamino acids in view of the spectral assignments of the pyridoxal analogs described above. Although the possibility of the formation of tautomeric forms of pyridoxal Schiff bases has been recognized,[8] no direct experimental evidence has been obtained thus far. On the other hand, comparison of the spectra of N-(3-hydroxy-4-pyridylmethylene)-valine obtained in this research, with those of pyridoxal amino acid Schiff bases described by Matsuo[9], show that they are very similar under similar experimental conditions. Thus tentative assignments of equilibrium solution species of pyridoxal may now be made on the basis of the results reported in this paper.

It has been the practice for workers in this field to use the absorption intensity in the 330 m$\mu$ region as a measure of the ketimine concentration. The results of this investigation, however, indicate the danger inherent in this practice, since species similar to XIII derived from the addition of methanol (or water) to the aldimine (X, XI, XII) would also absorb in the same region of the ultraviolet spectrum, as would one of the perhaps less important forms of the aldimine itself, the neutral (non-dipolar) *o*-hydroxy-aldimine analogs of X.

Assignment of the absorption bands of pyridoxal Schiff bases found at 330 m$\mu$ to the dipolar species similar to XII[10] seem inconsistent with the results described in this paper. Other possible species that would have absorption bands in this region are unreacted pyridoxal[8] and the dipolar hemiacetal of the Schiff base[8] (similar to XIII). On the other hand, the occurrence of significant amounts of the neutral non-polar form analogous to X would appear to be unlikely.

The results of this investigation suggest that appreciable quantities of the keto-enamine structure (see XI) are present in solutions containing pyridoxal Schiff bases. If this is the case, there would be a strong electron acceptor on the nitrogen atom adjacent to the two carbon atoms involved in proton exchange during transamination and racemization. Thus it is seen that the presence of a proton at the imine nitrogen would facilitate the rate-determining loss of a proton from the adjacent saturated carbon atom to form the transition state illustrated in the following diagram.

This mechanism would also apply to transamination reactions in ethanol solution, described by Matsuo[9], since significant amounts of the enamine form would also be expected in this solvent.

The presence of a proton on the enamine nitrogen atom would seem to favor the formation of the transition state without the necessity of a positive pyridinium nitrogen as a requirement for the reaction. On the other hand, the inductive effect of the pyridine nitrogen atom would certainly assist in the formation of the transition state, whatever the structure and environment of the aldimine group, so that pyridinoid derivatives would be expected to undergo more rapid racemization and transamination than would the corresponding benzenoid analogs.

The large difference in the dissociation constants (in methanol) of the imine hydrogens of the pyridinoid and benzenoid Schiff bases is probably

RCOCOOH

$M^{n+}$ $H^+$

Transition State

Transition State

$M^{n+}$ $H^+$

$H_3\overset{+}{N}CHRCOO^-$

significant in view of their known differences in catalytic activity in the presence of metal ions. The fact that the dissociation constant of the pyridine derivative is about one hundred times greater than that of salicylidenevaline would favor the formation of a metal chelate compound in which the enamine proton is displaced. Thus the formation of the metal chelate in the manner shown below would take place to a much larger extent in the pyridinium compound.

Therefore there are two alternative mechanisms for pyridoxal and pyridoxal phosphate catalyzed reactions, as indicated in the diagram on p. 26, whereby the electronic influence of a proton or a metal ion attached to the imine hydrogen facilitates the formation of one of two transition states. The electronic influence of the proton on the adjacent nitrogen atom would be expected to be greater than that of the metal ion. On the other hand certain metal ions such as those of Fe(III) would be expected to favor the formation of a planar transition state by the stabilization of the planar resonating structure through $\pi$-bonding. In this manner, metal ions would be expected to exert a steric influence on the reaction that would not be found in proton catalysis. Further, the simultaneous binding of all three co-ordinating groups by a planar set of octahedral co-ordinate bonds of the metal ion would materially aid the elimination of the proton. The planar arrangement of the metal chelate rings thus formed would provide the most favorable structure for the delocalization of an electron pair between the two carbon atoms adjacent to the enamine nitrogen.

## REFERENCES


1. D. Heinert and A. E. Martell; *Tetrahedron* **3**, 49 (1958).
2. D. Heinert and A. E. Martell; *J. Am. Chem. Soc.* **81**, 3933 (1959).
3. K. Nakamoto and A. E. Martell; *J. Am. Chem. Soc.* **81**, 5857 (1959).
4. K. Nakamoto and A. E. Martell; *J. Am. Chem. Soc.* **81**, 5863 (1959).
5. F. J. Anderson and A. E. Martell; To be published.
6. D. Heinert and A. E. Martell; *J. Am. Chem. Soc.* **84**, 3257 (1962).
7. D. Heinert and A. E. Martell; *J. Am. Chem. Soc.* In press.
8. D. E. Metzler; *J. Am. Chem. Soc.* **79**, 485 (1957).
9. Y. Matsuo; *J. Am. Chem. Soc.* **79**, 2016 (1957).
10. H. N. Christensen; *J. Am. Chem. Soc.* **80**, 99 (1958).


## DISCUSSION

Dr. F. H. Westheimer:

Would you care to elaborate on your statement that a proton causes a greater electronic displacement than a metal ion does?

Dr. A. E. Martell:

Evidence of the relative electron interactions of protons and metal ions may be found in the spectral shifts observed for multidentate ligands containing nitrogen and oxygen donors. Thus the frequencies of the absorption maxima of chelating agents containing phenolic, conjugated carbonyl, *o*-hydroxyazo, or similar groups, are much lower for the anion than for the corresponding structures in which a proton is attached to one of the oxygen or nitrogen donor groups. When the proton is replaced by a metal ion, the frequencies of the absorption maxima vary between the extremes of the protonated and dissociated ligands in such a manner that the frequencies increase with the stabilities of the metal chelates. Thus far, I have not seen any cases where the frequency of the metal chelate absorption maximum is higher than that of the corresponding proton complex.

This kind of behavior is what one might expect from first principles, since the binding of an electron pair (from the donor) through the 1*s* orbital of hydrogen would be expected to be much stronger than the binding of the electron pair through hybridized 3*p*–4*s*–4*d* orbitals of the first row transition metals, or through the appropriate orbitals of other metal ions.

DR. W. T. JENKINS:

Enzyme substrate complexes with maxima at about 490 mμ have been observed with glutamic–aspartic and glutamic–alanine aminoferases by us and by Schirch and Mason with serine hydroxymethylase. Could you suggest a possible structure for such derivatives?

DR. A. E. MARTELL:

No.

# THE IMIDAZOLE–IMIDAZOLIUM ION CONCERTED GENERAL ACID, GENERAL BASE CATALYSIS OF THE TRANSAMINATION OF PYRIDOXAL BY α-AMINOPHENYLACETIC ACID

by THOMAS C. BRUICE and RICHARD M. TOPPING

Cornell University, Department of Chemistry,
Ithaca, New York, U.S.A.

## INTRODUCTION

INTEREST in the process of biochemical transamination led Herbst and Engell[1] and Nakada and Weinhouse[2] to investigate the direct transamination of amino acids with α-keto acids. The general course of reaction was noted to be decarboxylation accompanied by transamination. However, in the case of glyoxylic acid, a simple transamination occurred to yield glycine and the keto acid corresponding to the amino acid employed (1).

Enzymatic transamination reactions were shown by Braunstein[3] and Cohen[4] to require pyridoxal phosphate as a cofactor and more recently Snell[5] has described enzymes requiring pyridoxal itself as a cofactor. The non-enzymatic transamination of pyridoxal by an α-amino acid was first shown by Snell in 1945.[6] The important studies of Snell and Metzler and co-workers on model transamination reactions involving pyridoxal is now an eminently well-known chapter in bio-organic chemistry.[7–10] The transamination reaction in model systems has been correctly pictured by Metzler *et al.*[10] in the United States and independently by Braunstein[29] in Russia to involve the same reactions as noted by Nakada and Weinhouse[2] in the transamination of glyoxylic acid by α-amino acids (1).

In the experiments of Snell, which were followed by both chemical and biological assay procedures, autoclave temperatures and a large excess of pyridoxal were employed. The order of reactivity of various amino acids with pyridoxal was found to be that previously noted with glyoxylic acid, and as in the latter case, the transamination occurred without decarboxylation. On the basis that the addition of chelating agents, as citrate and EDTA, slowed down the reaction, the influence of metal ions on the transamination reactions of pyridoxal and amino acids was investigated.[7] These studies were generally carried out at 100° in water and the most effective metal ions for promoting the transamination of amino acids by pyridoxal were found to be $Cu^{2+}$, $Fe^{3+}$ and $Al^{3+}$. The transamination of glyoxylic acid by $\alpha$-amino acids was also shown to be metal ion promoted. The mechanism of the transamination reactions involving pyridoxal and metal ion have been suggested by Snell and Metzler to be as shown in (2).[10]

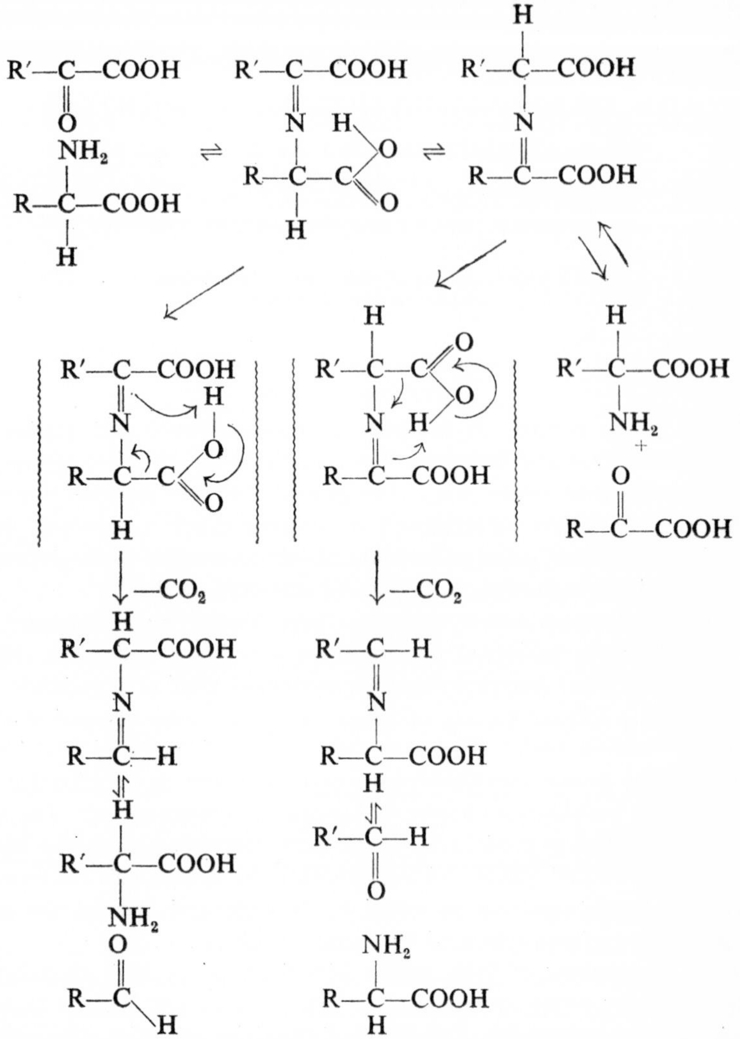

The metal ion, in forming a chelate with the imine, was suggested to facilitate the reaction by: (*a*) stabilization of the imine formed from pyridoxal and amino acid; (*b*) providing a planar conjugated system; and (*c*) increasing the inductive withdrawal of electrons away from the $\alpha$-carbon and thereby increasing its acidity. The metal ion promotion of the transamination of pyridoxal by α-amino acids may or may not be of biochemical significance. It would appear as though a number of highly or partially purified pyridoxal phosphate-requiring enzymes do not require addition of metal ions for full activity[11–14] and in at least one instance a highly purified, fully active transaminase has been shown to be devoid of metal ions.[14a]

(2)

With the single exception of the investigation of Banks *et al.*[15] attention has not been directed to the means of catalysis of what is undoubtedly the rate-determining step in the transamination of pyridoxal—the prototropic shift resulting in the conversion of the imine of pyridoxal to the imine of pyridoxamine. In the enzymatic reaction the abstraction of the proton is presumably carried out by the weakly basic groups available to the protein.

At pH values near neutrality, the most effective functional group available to the protein would be the imidazolyl group of histidine. Physical organic studies of the catalysis of the interconversion of simple azomethines in aqueous solution have not been made. One may write three hypothetical mechanisms for the catalysis of the prototropic shift by a weak base (B) leading to the interconversion of isomeric azomethines:

$$\mathrm{B{:}} + \mathrm{H{-}\overset{R}{\underset{R}{C}}{-}N{=}CR'_2} \underset{}{\overset{K_e}{\rightleftharpoons}} \overset{\oplus}{\mathrm{BH}} + \left[\mathrm{R_2C{\cdots}N{\cdots}CR'_2}\right]^{\ominus} \quad \text{(a)} \tag{3}$$

$$\left[\mathrm{R_2C{\cdots}N{\cdots}CR'_2}\right]^{\ominus} + \overset{\oplus}{\mathrm{BH}} \overset{K_f}{\rightleftharpoons} \mathrm{R_2C{=}N{-}\overset{R'}{\underset{R'}{C}}{-}H} + \mathrm{B{:}} \quad \text{(b)}$$

$$\mathrm{H{-}\overset{R}{\underset{R}{C}}{-}N{=}CR'_2} + \mathrm{H_3\overset{\oplus}{O}} \overset{K_a}{\rightleftharpoons} \mathrm{H{-}\overset{R}{\underset{R}{C}}{-}\overset{\oplus}{N}H{=}CR'_2} + \mathrm{H_2O} \quad \text{(a)} \tag{4}$$

$$\mathrm{B{:}} + \mathrm{H{-}\overset{R}{\underset{R}{C}}{-}\overset{\oplus}{N}H{=}CR'_2} \underset{k_{-r}}{\overset{k_r}{\rightleftharpoons}} \overset{\oplus}{\mathrm{BH}} + \mathrm{R_2C{=}N{-}\overset{R'}{\underset{R'}{C}}{-}H} \quad \text{(b)}$$

$$\mathrm{B{:}} + \mathrm{H{-}\overset{R}{\underset{R}{C}}{-}N{=}CR'_2} + \overset{\oplus}{\mathrm{HB}} \rightarrow \left[\overset{+\delta}{\mathrm{B}}\cdots\mathrm{H}\cdots\overset{R}{\underset{R}{\mathrm{C}}}{\cdots}\mathrm{N}{\cdots}\overset{R'}{\underset{R'}{\mathrm{C}}}\cdots\mathrm{H}\cdots\overset{+\delta}{\mathrm{B}}\right] \quad \text{(a)} \tag{5}$$

$$\overset{\oplus}{\mathrm{BH}} + \mathrm{R_2C{=}N{-}\overset{R'}{\underset{R'}{C}}{-}H} + \mathrm{B} \quad \text{(b)}$$

Mechanism (3) involves the abstraction of a proton from the azomethine to yield a resonantly stabilized anion which could then be protonated to yield an equilibrium mixture of azomethine *a* and *b*. This mechanism may be disregarded on the basis that the $\mathrm{p}K_a'$ of the C—H bond is so great that the concentration of the intermediate anion would only be controlled by the pH of the medium and not by the concentration of feebly basic species present. It might be noted that the mechanism of (3) was that originally favored by Ingold[16] but was disregarded on the basis that the rate of racemization of an optically active azomethine was found to be identical with the rate of isomerization as measured by other means. These studies were carried out in methanol employing $MeO^-$ as base.[16,17] Mechanisms (4) and (5) do not involve the formation of an intermediate anionic species. Mechanism (4) refers to a specific acid general base catalysis and mechanism (5) to a concerted general acid general base catalysis. These latter processes are those anticipated, *a priori*, to be involved in the enzymatic catalysis and are those which we searched for in model systems.

## ESTABLISHMENT OF THE CATALYSIS OF THE TRANSAMINATION OF PYRIDOXAL BY BUFFER IONS

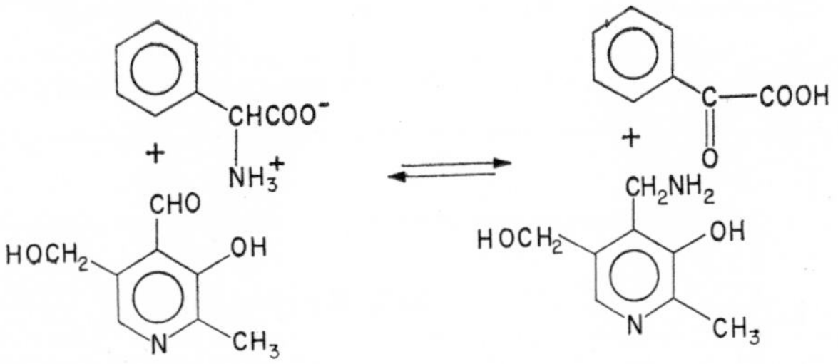

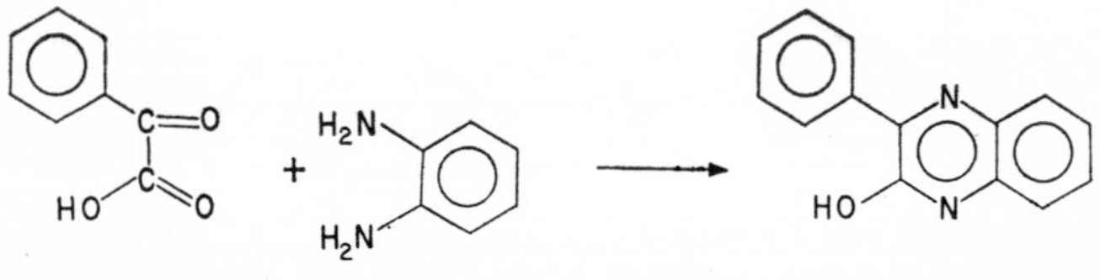

The studies which we shall describe involve the transamination of pyridoxal by α-aminophenylacetic acid to yield phenylglyoxylic acid and pyridoxamine (6). All reactions were carried out at 30° and at constant ionic strength. Reaction (6) can be conveniently followed by conversion of the phenylglyoxylic acid to its 2-hydro-3-phenylquinoxaline derivative by reaction with *o*-phenylenediamine (7).[18] In the analytical procedure employed the yield of quinoxaline could be shown to account quantitatively for the phenylglyoxylic acid produced. When reaction (6) was investigated in buffer solutions the results of Table 1 were obtained. In borate buffer no reaction occurred and the α-aminophenylacetic acid remained, in the main, as a precipitate affording a heterogeneous reaction mixture. In morpholine and carbonate buffered solution the insoluble amino acid gradually dissolved to afford a homogeneous solution which after about 7 days afforded 43 per cent and 34 per cent yields respectively of phenylglyoxylic acid. When imidazole was employed as buffer the amino acid quickly dissolved to provide a clear yellow solution from which the keto acid could be isolated as its quinoxaline derivative. The homogeneity of the reaction solution when

TABLE 1. PREPARATIVE EXPERIMENTS

$PCHO_0 = 1.0$ mmole; $A = 1.0$ mmole
$T = 30°$; pH = 8.62; $\mu = 1.0$ M
Vol. = 20 ml $H_2O$

| Catalyst | mmoles | Ketoacid at equilibrium (%) | Reaction mixture |
|---|---|---|---|
| Imidazole | 51 | 43 | Homogenous |
| Carbonate | 6 | 34 | Heterogenous |
| Morpholine | 2 | 43 | Heterogenous |
| Borate | 8 | No reaction | Heterogenous |

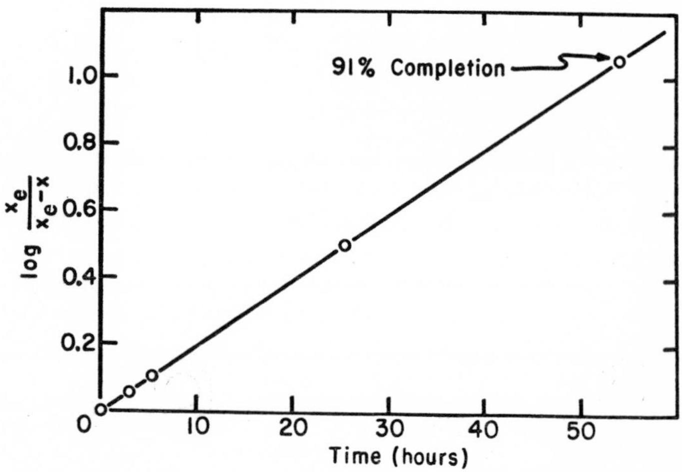


FIG. 1. First-order plot for the formation of phenylglyoxylic acid (isolated as the 3-phenyl-2-oxyquinoxaline derivative) in the reaction of pyridoxal with $\alpha$-aminophenylacetic acid in imidazole buffer (pH 8.61; 30°).

imidazole buffer was employed permitted the time course of the reaction to be followed. In practice the reaction mixture was distributed into ampules, the air displaced by nitrogen, and the ampules capped and shaken in the dark at 30°. In Fig. 1 there is presented a conventional first-order plot of the formation of keto acid. It may be noted that the reaction has followed first-order kinetics to 91 per cent completion of reaction but that at $t_\infty$ only 43 per cent of the amino acid had been converted into keto acid. This result points out the fact that we are following the reaction to completion of equilibrium and that the approach to equilibrium is first order. Our results also show that imidazole is not unique as a catalyst in this system and that other bases will also catalyze the transamination reaction. The only unique feature of imidazole, in these experiments, is that it solubilizes the amino acid. This

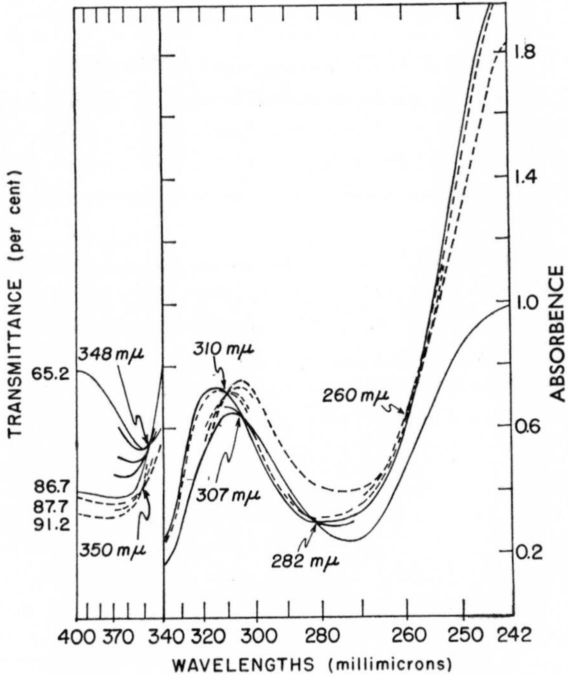


FIG. 2. Spectral–time study for the reaction of pyridoxal ($10^{-4}$ M) with α-amino-phenylacetic acid ($2 \times 10^{-4}$ M) in the presence of imidazole (1.8 M) in water at pH 8.61 and a temperature of 30°. The tracing shows the shape of the absorbence curves and isosbestic points for the first (———) and second (– – – – –) phases of the reaction.

observation, as we shall see, is an important one. On the grounds that the catalytic inactivity of borate buffer might arise as a result of the possible formation of a complex with the inactive internal hemiacetal form of pyridoxal (8), the effect of borate buffer on the imidazole-catalyzed reaction was investigated. For these experiments the spectrophotometric procedure described below was employed. It was determined that the catalytic rate and the final equilibrium position of the reaction was insignificantly influenced by addition of borate (at least to 0.1 M). Thus, it would appear as though borate is simply an inert reagent toward the transamination reaction.

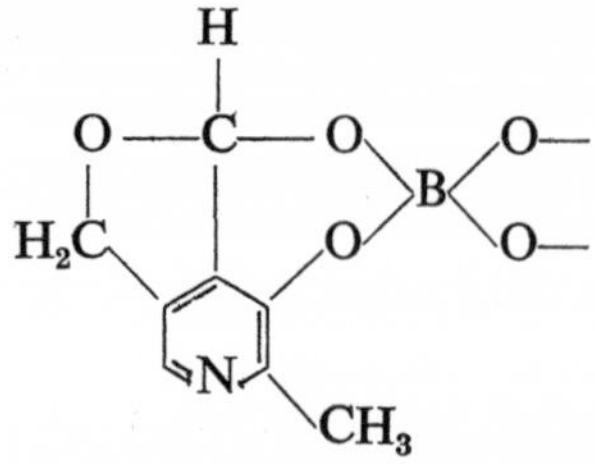

(8)

SPECTROPHOTOMETRIC STUDIES

The remainder of this paper describes a detailed kinetic investigation of the imidazole catalyzed transamination reaction in aqueous solution under restricted condition of temperature (30°) and ionic strength (calc. $\mu = 1.0$ M with KCl). These investigations were carried out spectrophotometrically by observing the decrease in absorbence of pyridoxal and the increase in absorbence of intermediates and products. In the initial experiments to be described, pyridoxal and α-aminophenylacetic acid were at equal initial concentrations of $1 \times 10^{-4}$ M. The results of a typical spectral–time study are presented in Fig. 2. Inspection of Fig. 2 reveals that the overall reaction may be divided conveniently into two phases. In the initial phase the reactants are converted into a product (S″) without the accumulation of an intermediate (intermediates would have to be present at a low steady state concentration) (9).

$$\text{(A)}\quad C_6H_5\text{–CH(NH}_2\text{)–COOH} + \text{PCHO} \overset{K_1}{\rightleftharpoons} C_6H_5\text{–CH(COOH)–N=CH–P}\ \text{(S}'\text{)} \overset{K_2}{\rightleftharpoons}$$

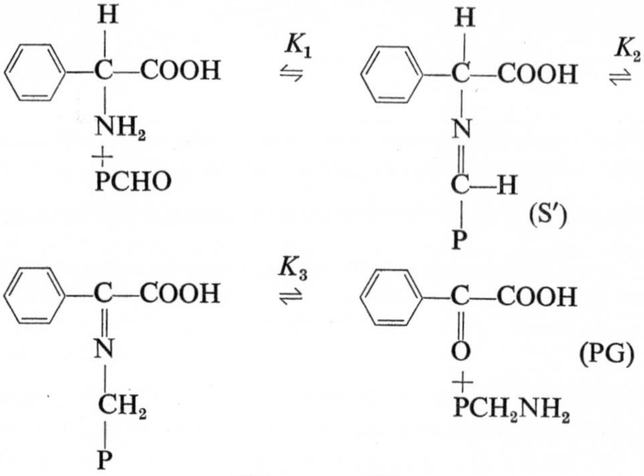

$$\text{(S}''\text{)}\quad C_6H_5\text{–C(COOH)=N–CH}_2\text{–P} \overset{K_3}{\rightleftharpoons} C_6H_5\text{–CO–COOH}\ \text{(PG)} + \text{PCH}_2\text{NH}_2 \qquad (9)$$

When P = [3-hydroxy-2-methyl-5-(hydroxymethyl)pyridin-4-yl: ring bearing HO, $CH_3$, N, $CH_2OH$]

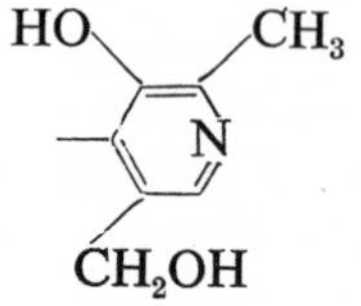

This conclusion is reached from the observation of true isosbestic points at 348 mμ, 307 mμ and 282 mμ. Furthermore, a linear relationship exists between the decrease in absorbence at 395 mμ and the increase in absorbence at 246 mμ (Fig. 3). The decrease in absorbence at 395 mμ may be related to the disappearance of pyridoxal or conceivably to the disappearance of the imine of pyridoxal and α-aminophenylacetic acid (S′), while the increase in absorbence at 246 mμ may be related to the formation of the imine of pyridoxamine and phenylglyoxylic acid (S″) and/or phenylglyoxylic acid (PG) plus pyridoxamine ($PCH_2NH_2$) (9). That the product whose absorbence is

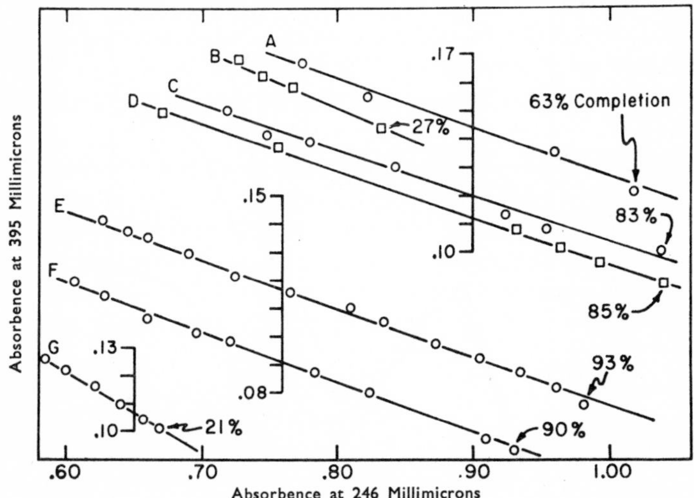


FIG. 3. Linear relationship between the decrease in absorbence at 395 mμ and increase in absorbence at 246 mμ for phase 1 in the reaction of pyridoxal with α-aminophenylacetic acid.

increasing at 246 mμ is not a mixture of $PCH_2NH_2$ and PG is shown by the fact that there are no common isosbestic points between the combined spectra of $PCH_2NH_2$ + PG and the combined spectra of PCHO + A (Fig. 4). Inspection of Fig. 4 shows that PG does show absorbence at 246 mμ. It would then be expected that S″ would also exhibit absorbence at 246 mμ and that the product of the first phase is S″ (Fig. 5). The rate of disappearance of PCHO measured at 395 mμ is necessarily identical to the rate of production of S″ as measured at 246 mμ (see below). The reaction of amino acids with PCHO in water to form aldimines has been studied by Metzler[24] and found to be a rapid process. The equilibrium constant ($K_1$) for aldimine formation (10) has been determined[24] to be in the range of from 1 to 100 for a number of $\alpha$-amino acids. Therefore, one would anticipate that the

$$K_1 = \frac{S'}{PCHO.A} \qquad K_2 = \frac{S''}{S'}$$

$$K_1K_2 = \frac{S''}{PCHO.A} \tag{10}$$

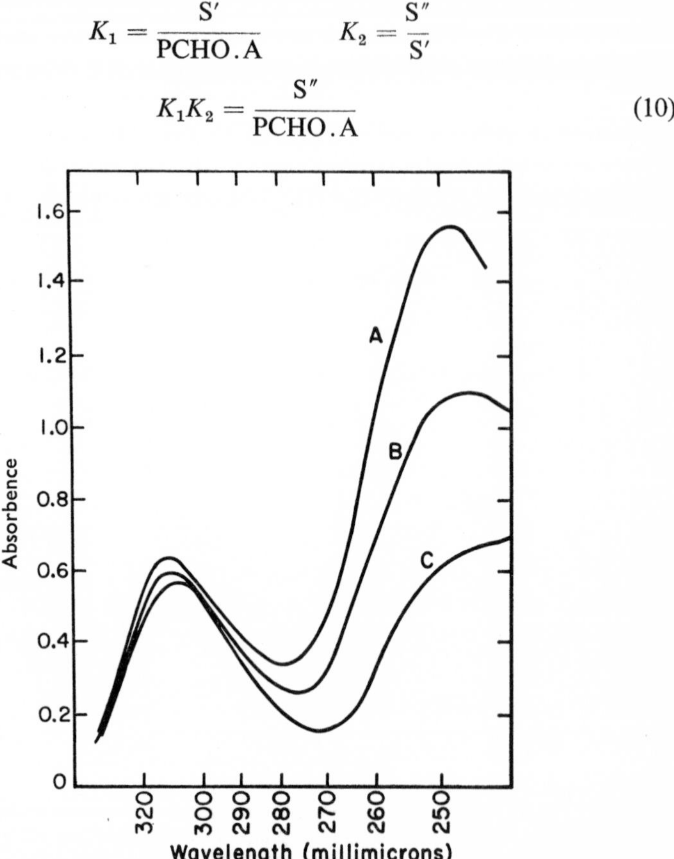


FIG. 4. Combined spectra of: A, phenylglyoxylic acid and pyridoxamine both at $10^{-4}$ M; B, phenylglyoxylic acid, pyridoxamine, pyridoxal and $\alpha$-aminophenylacetic acid all at $0.5 \times 10^{-4}$ M; C, pyridoxal and $\alpha$-aminophenylacetic acid both at $10^{-4}$ M. Curves A, B and C show that there would be no isosbestic points for the direct conversion of pyridoxal plus $\alpha$-aminophenylacetic acid to phenylglyoxylic acid plus pyridoxamine. Spectra taken at pH 8.61, 30° in aqueous solution, 1.8 M in imidazole buffer.

concentration of S′ (where S′ denotes total aldimine, both free and as any complex with the catalyst) would be from $10^{-6}$ M to $10^{-8}$ M, in our experiments in which PCHO = A = $10^{-4}$ M at $t_0$. These results are all in agreement with our supposition that the first phase of the reaction, which is characterized by three isosbestic points at 282 m$\mu$, 307 m$\mu$ and 348 m$\mu$, can be related to the conversion of PCHO + A through S′ to S″ with S′ at a low steady state concentration.

In the second phase of the reaction absorbence at 395 m$\mu$ continues to decrease. This clearly, then, represents a reaction in which PCHO is still consumed. Isosbestic points are no longer encountered at 282 m$\mu$, 307 m$\mu$

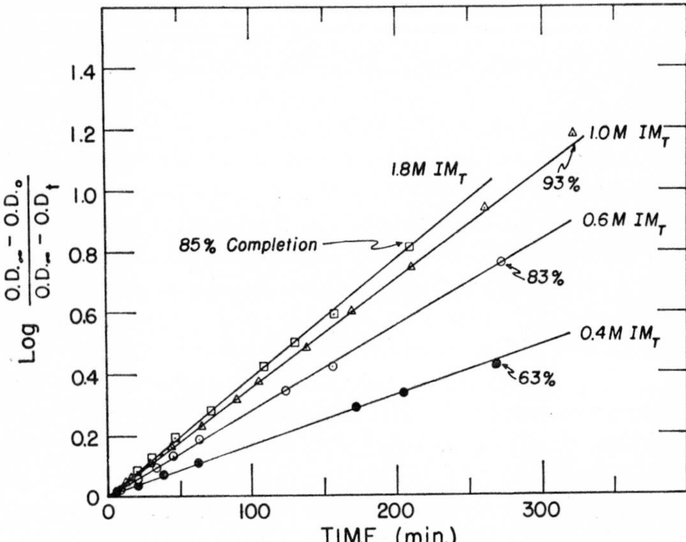


FIG. 5(A). First-order plots for the appearance of S″ (as determined at 246 m$\mu$) in the presence of varying concentrations of imidazole. (Pyridoxal and $\alpha$-aminophenylacetic acid initially at $10^{-4}$ M; pH 8.61; $\mu = 0.05$ M; 30°.)

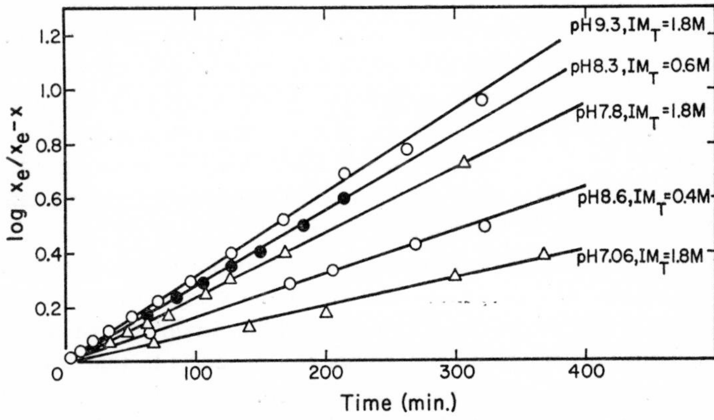


FIG. 5(B). First-order plots for the appearance of S″ at various pH values. (Pyridoxal and $\alpha$-aminophenylacetic acid initially at $10^{-4}$ M; 30°.)

and 348 m$\mu$, where absorbence continually increases, but are now present at 260 m$\mu$, 310 m$\mu$ and 350 m$\mu$ (Fig. 2). This second phase, a slower reaction, represents conversion of S″ to PG and $PCH_2NH_2$. This reaction does not go to completion as can be shown by the fact that the spectra at $t_\infty$ do not superimpose upon the combined spectra of $10^{-4}$ M PG and $10^{-4}$ M $PCH_2NH_2$ (Fig. 4). Also at $t_\infty$ considerable PCHO remains, as can be seen by the residual absorbence at 395 mμ. The second phase of the reaction then represents the attainment of equilibrium between all components [i.e. PCHO + A ⇌ S′ (steady state) ⇌ S″ ⇌ PG + $PCH_2NH_2$].

In the first phase of the reaction, the appearance of S″ as measured at 246 mμ and the disappearance of PCHO as measured at 395 mμ, have been found to follow apparent first-order kinetics at all concentrations of PCHO and A investigated. Examples of the first-order plots for the appearance of S″ are provided in Fig. 5. Inspection of Fig. 5 reveals the reaction to be first-order to as much as 85–95 per cent of attainment of equilibrium, and inspection of Fig. 3 reveals that the same rate law pertains to the disappearance of PCHO. In practice, the value of the experimentally obtained first-order rate constant ($k_{obs}$) was initially obtained by the method of Guggenheim. From the value of $k_{obs}$ so determined, the absorbence at 246 mμ at $t_\infty$ could be calculated and was found to be that obtained at the end of the first phase of reaction (within 3.0 per cent). Employing the value of the absorbence at $t_\infty$ so calculated, the value of $k_{obs}$ was then recalculated employing the usual integrated expression of the first-order rate law (Fig. 5). The values obtained by the Guggenheim and log $x_e/(x_e - x)$ plots were found to agree within a few per cent. Thus, the rate of attainment of the equilibrium $K_1K_2$ (10) is strictly first-order.

The use of absolute alcohol instead of water as the reaction medium renders the separate identification of the two phases of the reaction difficult at low imidazole buffer concentrations (e.g. IM = 0.25 M, $IMH^{\oplus}$ = 0.005 M) owing to the absence of definitive isosbestic points. This appears to result from a greater rate of cleavage of ketimine in the alcohol system than in the water system. Only at high imidazole buffer concentrations (e.g. IM = 1.25 M, $IMH^{\oplus}$ = 0.025 M) are isosbestic points again discernible as in the water system, indicating that a high catalyst concentration has greatly enhanced the rate of formation of ketimine with relatively little effect on its cleavage. As in the water system the reaction, as measured by the increasing absorbence at 246 mμ, adheres strictly to first-order kinetics. Examination of the spectrum from 400 mμ to 235 mμ of the above system after attainment of equilibrium reveals a similar distribution of reactants and products to that found in the water system. Thus, a residual absorption at *ca.* 395 mμ indicates unchanged PCHO in agreement with the less than 100 per cent conversion to PG and $PCH_2NH_2$ revealed by the absorption at 246 mμ. In contrast, however, the reaction may be driven to 100 per cent completion by replacing the imidazole buffer by imidazole free base. Thus, when a mixture of PCHO.HCl ($10^{-4}$ M), A ($10^{-4}$ M), and imidazole (0.5 M) in absolute alcohol is allowed to attain equilibrium (5 days), the ultraviolet spectrum of a sample (diluted to 50 per cent aqueous alcohol) revealed *no* absorption in the 395 mμ region indicating complete removal of PCHO from the system (full line, Fig. 6). Furthermore, the spectrum was found to conform closely to that of a mixture of PG ($10^{-4}$ M), $PCH_2NH_2$ ($10^{-4}$ M) and imidazole (0.5 M) in absolute alcohol after similar dilution to 50 per cent aqueous alcohol (broken line, Fig. 6). These results suggest 100 per cent conversion

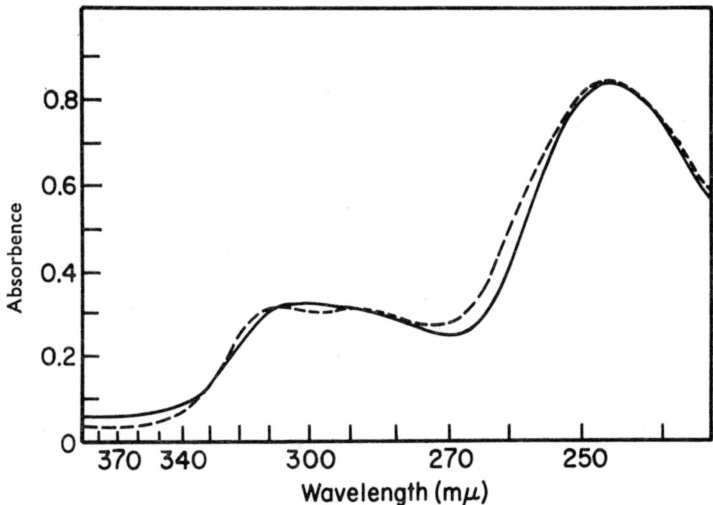


FIG. 6. A comparison of the spectra of (a) a mixture of pyridoxal ($10^{-4}$ M), α-aminophenylacetic acid ($10^{-4}$ M), and imidazole (0.5 M) in absolute alcohol at equilibrium (diluted to 50 per cent aq. alcohol) (full line) and (b) a mixture of phenylglyoxylic acid ($10^{-4}$ M), pyridoxamine ($10^{-4}$ M) and imidazole (0.5 M) in absolute alcohol (diluted to 50 per cent aq. alcohol) (broken line).

of reactants to products. This result provides striking confirmation of the stoichiometry of the system under investigation and provides further support for the proposal that interference from side reactions under the conditions used in the study is negligible.

Employing the knowledge that the attainment of equilibrium in S″ is first-order, we may now calculate the numerical values for equilibrium constants (10). The low steady state in S′ prevents its spectroscopic measurement. Although this condition is ideal for the application of the steady state approximations, as will be seen later, it prevents the separate determination of the constants $K_1$ and $K_2$. The product $K_1K_2$, however, may be evaluated as follows. From the Guggenheim method for determining the *pseudo* first-order rate of the approach to equilibrium in S″ we may determine the optical density corresponding to the maximum value of S″ *prior* to its cleavage to PG + $PCH_2NH_2$. By suitable extrapolation of this value on the linear plot of $O.D._{395}$ vs. $O.D._{246}$ (Fig. 3), the corresponding decrease in absorbence at 395 m$\mu$ is found. As the maximum absorbence at 395 m$\mu$ is an index of the known initial concentration of PCHO (after a small correction for the absorption of other species at this wavelength) it is possible to compute the PCHO remaining after establishment of the equilibrium $K_1K_2$. The essential conditions of Beer's law are followed by PCHO at 395 m$\mu$. Since stoichiometrically equivalent amounts of PCHO and A are consumed, the concentration of the latter at equilibrium is also obtained. Subtraction of the determined concentration of PCHO at equilibrium from the known initial concentration provides the equilibrium molar concentration of S″ before its cleavage to PG + $PCH_2NH_2$. Also obtained is the extinction

TABLE 2. THE DETERMINED RATE CONSTANTS FOR THE IMIDAZOLE-CATALYZED TRANSAMINATION OF PYRIDOXAL ($10^{-4}$ M) BY $\alpha$-AMINOPHENYLACETIC ACID ($10^{-4}$ M). (pH 8.6, $T = 30°$, $\mu = 0.05$ M)

| Run | $IM_T$ (M) | $k_{obs} \times 10^3$ (min$^{-1}$) | $k_{obs} \times 1.15/c$ (l. mole$^{-1}$ min$^{-1}$) | $k_2K_1$ |
|---|---|---|---|---|
| (60 | 0.000* | negligible | — | — |
| (4) | 0.102 | 0.05 | 0.9 | 0.7 |
| (3) | 0.204 | 0.49 | 8.9 | 6.2 |
| (55) | 0.306 | 1.12 | 20.2 | 14.1 |
| (54) | 0.408 | 3.84 | 69.1 | 51.8 |
| (53) | 0.612 | 6.47 | 116.3 | 94.7 |
| (1) | 1.02 | 8.20 | 147.6 | 131.3 |
| (2) | 1.275 | 8.54 | 153.6 | 136.3 |
| (56) | 1.836 | 8.79 | 158.2 | 186.3 |

*pH 8.6 maintained by 0.4 M borate buffer.

coefficient of S″ at 246 m$\mu$ ($\epsilon = 13{,}600$; pH 8.61). The concentrations of PCHO, A and S″ now known, the value of the product $K_1K_2$ is obtained (10). Having determined $K_1K_2$ it is possible to trace the course of the second phase. The second phase is sufficiently slow that it is permissible to assume the first phase maintains equilibrium. Thus, at any time subsequent to departure from the isosbestic points, signifying establishment of equilibrium in the first phase, it is possible to determine the absorbence at 395 m$\mu$ and hence evaluate the concentration of PCHO and A in the system at that time. The use of (10) then permits the determination of the concentration of S″ and from a material balance PG and $PCH_2NH_2$. The relative slowness of phase 2, however, prevents the precise determination of final equilibrium owing to complicating side reactions. The validity of the above method of calculation (for phase 2) as a semiquantitative tool and justification for the premises on which it is based is provided by the close agreement between the calculated and experimental values for the distribution of products at any given stage of phase 2. Two examples, the first at low and the second at high buffer concentration, follow. In run Sp-53 (Table 2) the product distribution after 19 hr was estimated to be: PCHO ($0.39 \times 10^{-4}$ M); A ($0.39 \times 10^{-4}$ M); S″ ($0.32 \times 10^{-4}$ M); $PCH_2NH_2$ ($0.29 \times 10^{-4}$ M); and PG ($0.29 \times 10^{-4}$ M). Knowing the extinction coefficients of each component at 246 mμ a value of 1.126 for the absorbance of a mixture of the above composition at 246 mμ was obtained, in good agreement with the experimental value of 1.155. In a run in which the initial concentrations were $IM_T = 2.5$ M, PCHO = A = $10^{-4}$ M, the product distribution after 2 days resulted in a calculated value of $O.D._{246m\mu}$ of 1.121 and an experimental value of 1.170.

The expected side reaction between PCHO and the $PCH_2NH_2$ produced in phase 2 is only of possible significance in the slowest reactions studied (below 0.3 M imidazole buffer concentration). This conclusion is based upon a separate determination of the rate constant for the reaction

$$\mathrm{PCHO} + \mathrm{PCH_2NH_2} \rightarrow \mathrm{PCH{=}N{-}CH_2P}.$$

Thus at initial concentrations of reactants of $10^{-3}$ M (i.e. ten times greater than the initial PCHO concentration in the kinetic runs and many hundred times the concentration of $PCH_2NH_2$ before the completion of phase 1) in the presence of 1.0 M imidazole buffer (pH 8.6, $T = 30°$, $\mu = 0.05$ M), the observed *pseudo* first-order rate constant for approach to equilibrium was only $1.78 \times 10^{-3}$ min$^{-1}$.

The question arises as to whether the approach to the equilibrium conditions given by $K_1K_2$ in phase 1 should follow first-order kinetics.

$$\mathrm{PCHO} + \mathrm{A} \underset{k_{-1}}{\overset{k_1}{\rightleftharpoons}} \mathrm{S'} \underset{k_{-2}}{\overset{k_2}{\rightleftharpoons}} \mathrm{S''} \tag{11}$$

At $t_0$, PCHO $= a$, A $= b$, and at any time ($t$), S″ $= x$ and PCHO $= a - x$, A $= b - x$, since S′ is at a low steady state.

Then

$$\frac{\mathrm{d}S''}{\mathrm{d}t} = \frac{\mathrm{d}x}{\mathrm{d}t} = k_2\mathrm{S'} - k_{-2}\mathrm{S''} \tag{12}$$

Since we suppose a rapid establishment of steady state in aldimine

$$\mathrm{S'} = K_1 \,.\, \mathrm{PCHO} \,.\, \mathrm{A} \tag{13}$$

$$\frac{\mathrm{d}x}{\mathrm{d}t} = k_2K_1 \,.\, \mathrm{PCHO} \,.\, \mathrm{A} - k_{-2}\mathrm{S''} \tag{14}$$

and from (10)

$$\frac{\mathrm{d}x}{\mathrm{d}t} = k_2K_1 \,.\, \mathrm{PCHO} \,.\, \mathrm{A} - \frac{k_2}{K_2}\mathrm{S''} \tag{15}$$

$$= k_2K_1\left[(a-x)(b-x) - \frac{x}{K_1K_2}\right]$$

Integration of (15) provides (16)

$$k_2K_1t = \frac{1}{2c}\ln\left(\frac{c-\mu}{c+\mu}\right) + \mathrm{B} \tag{16}$$

where
$$c = \left[\frac{a^2 + b^2 + 2\left(\dfrac{(a+b)}{K_1K_2} - ab\right) + \dfrac{1}{(K_1K_2)^2}}{4}\right]^{\frac{1}{2}} \tag{17}$$

$$\mu = x - \left[\frac{a + b + 1/(K_1K_2)}{2}\right]$$

$$\mathrm{B} = \frac{-1}{2c}\ln\left(\frac{c-\mu+x}{c+\mu-x}\right)$$

In (17), $c - \mu$ changes by only ~20 per cent while $c + \mu$ goes to zero at $t_\infty$ so that the term $\ln (c - \mu)/(c + \mu)$ approaches very closely the general form $\ln (ya - x)/(a - x)$ where $ya \gg x$ resulting in a close approximation to first-order kinetics. The observed first-order rate constant for attainment of equilibrium is then

$$k_{\mathrm{obs}} \cong \frac{k_2K_12c}{2.303} = \frac{1}{t}\log\left(\frac{c-\mu}{c+\mu}\right) + \mathrm{B} \tag{18}$$

and the second-order rate constant ($k_{\mathrm{II}}$) for the reaction of PCHO and A to equilibrium in S″ is

$$k_{\mathrm{II}} \cong k_2K_1 = \frac{1.15}{ct}\log\left(\frac{c-\mu}{c+\mu}\right) + \mathrm{B} \tag{19}$$

The value of $k_{\mathrm{II}}$ is then obtained from plots of $\log [(c - \mu)/(c + \mu)]$ vs. $t$ (Fig. 7). Inspection of Fig. 7 reveals that the derived equation is as satisfactory in correlating the experimental data as is the conventional first-order rate equation (Fig. 5). It should be noted (Table 2) that $1.15k_{\mathrm{obs}}/c$ and $k_2K_1$ are quite comparable. For the evaluation of $c$ and $\mu$ the product $K_1K_2$ had to be known with certainty. The calculated values of $K_1K_2$ from runs in which the initial concentration of PCHO and A were equal, were found to be independent of the total imidazole concentration. However, when the initial concentrations of PCHO and A are other than equal (e.g. 0.5 : 1, 2 : 1, 3 : 1, etc.) then the reactant at lower concentration may be all but consumed at equilibrium, rendering the computed value of $K_1K_2$ unduly sensitive to the experimental error in assessing equilibrium concentrations. As a result the value of $K_1K_2$ used in Eqs. (16) to (19) to evaluate $k_{\mathrm{II}}$ was an average, calculated from runs in which the initial concentrations of reactants were equal.

An interesting confirmation of Eqs. (16) to (19) is provided by a study of the influence of the variation of initial concentration of reactants upon the observed first-order rate constant. It may be seen from Table 3 that at a constant concentration of $\mathrm{IM}_T$ of 1.8 M, the value of $k_{\mathrm{obs}}$ increases by only

40 per cent on doubling the initial concentration of either PCHO or A while halving the initial concentration of A has little effect on the rate constant (Table 3). This influence of initial concentration on $k_{obs}$ is predicted by

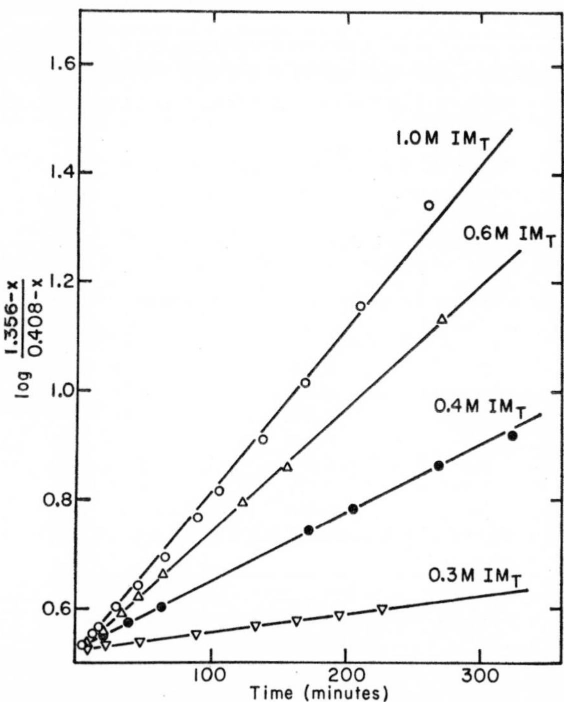


FIG. 7. Plots of the experimentally determined rates of formation of S″ (determined at 246 mμ) employing the derived theoretical rate expression for approach to equilibrium in phase 1 (16).

TABLE 3. THE INFLUENCE OF VARIATION OF REACTANT CONCENTRATION UPON THE DETERMINED RATE CONSTANTS FOR THE IMIDAZOLE-CATALYZED TRANSAMINATION OF PYRIDOXAL BY α-AMINOPHENYLACETIC ACID ($IM_T = 1.8$ M, pH 8.6, $T = 30°$, $\mu = 0.05$ M)

| Run | Pyridoxal (M × $10^4$) | α-Amino-phenyl-acetic acid (M × $10^4$) | $k_{obs} \times 10^3$ (min$^{-1}$) | $c$ (M) | $k_{obs} \times 1.15/c$ (l. mole$^{-1}$ min$^{-1}$) |
|---|---|---|---|---|---|
| (56) | 1 | 1 | 8.79 | $0.64 \times 10^{-4}$ | 158.2 |
| (59) | 2 | 1 | 12.09 | $0.92 \times 10^{-4}$ | 151.3 |
| (57) | 1 | 2 | 12.17 | $0.92 \times 10^{-4}$ | 152.2 |
| (58) | 1 | 0.5 | 8.92 | $0.62 \times 10^{-4}$ | 165.6 |

Eq. (16). Upon converting the first-order constants to the corresponding second-order constants by dividing by the appropriate value of $0.87c$ (see Eq. 19), the same second-order constant of $156.8 \pm 5.1$ l. mole$^{-1}$ min$^{-1}$ is obtained. Since in phase 1 we are following the rate of attainment of equilibrium, a change in the observed rate constant may reflect either a change in the equilibrium position of the reaction or an actual catalysis of the rate determining step. The data of Table 4 is proof that the concentration of imidazole employed does not influence the concentration of S″ at $t_\infty$ for phase 1 (as measured at 246 m$\mu$) but does have a definite effect on the observed rate constant. The results of Table 4 then confirm that imidazole is behaving as a true catalyst.

TABLE 4. INFLUENCE OF IMIDAZOLE ON RATE OF ATTAINMENT OF EQUILIBRIUM ($k_{obs}$) AND POSITION OF EQUILIBRIUM AT $t_\infty$
(pH 9.3; $\mu = 1.0$ M; $H_2O$; $T = 30°$)

| $IM_T$ (M) | O.D. $_{246m\mu}$ | $k_{obs} \times 10^3$ (min$^{-1}$) |
|---|---|---|
| 0.6 | 0.400 | 0.58 |
| 1.0 | 0.386 | 4.51 |
| 1.3 | 0.420 | 5.66 |
| 1.8 | 0.400 | 7.00 |
| 2.1 | 0.482 | 8.37 |
| 2.5 | 0.477 | 9.00 |
| 3.0 | 0.440 | 8.44 |
| | Av. 0.430 ± 0.030 | |

TABLE 5. VALUES OF $K_m$ AND $V_m$ CALCULATED FROM EQ. (20) AND THE FINAL EQUILIBRIUM CONCENTRATIONS OF S″ AT $t_\infty$ FOR THE IMIDAZOLE CATALYSIS OF PHASE 1*

| pH | Buffer | IM (mole fraction) | $IMH^{\oplus}$ (mole fraction) | $V_m$ $10^3$ min$^{-1}$ | $K_m$ (mole$^2$ l$^{-2}$) | S″ at $t_\infty$ (M) |
|---|---|---|---|---|---|---|
| 7.06 | Imidazole | 0.466 | 0.534 | 2.46 | — | — |
| 7.80 | Imidazole | 0.827 | 0.173 | 5.5 | $7.15 \times 10^{-3}$ | $5.2 \times 10^{-5}$ |
| 8.30 | Imidazole | 0.938 | 0.062 | 8.0 | $7.0 \times 10^{-3}$ | $5.3 \times 10^{-5}$ |
| 8.60 | Imidazole | 0.968 | 0.032 | 9.5 | $6.2 \times 10^{-3}$ | $5.6 \times 10^{-5}$ |
| 9.30 | Carbonate | 0.993 | 0.0066 | 10.5 | $8.5 \times 10^{-3}$ | $5.3 \times 10^{-5}$ |
| 10.20 | Carbonate | | | > 11 | — | $4.8 \times 10^{-5}$ |

*Initial concentration of pyridoxal and amino acid was $10^{-4}$ M, temperature 30°, ionic strength 1.0 M, and solvent water.

In Fig. 8 are presented plots of the observed first-order rate constants for the approach to equilibrium in phase 1 at several pH's vs. the product of the concentrations of free imidazole (IM) and the conjugate acid of imidazole ($IMH^{\oplus}$). The points represent experimental values and the lines are theoretical having been calculated from Eq. (20):

$$k_{obs} = \frac{V_m(IM)(IMH^{\oplus})}{K_m + (IM)(IMH^{\oplus})} \tag{20}$$

In Table 5 are recorded the values of $V_m$ and $K_m$ so determined for each pH.

Also recorded in Table 5 are the equilibrium concentrations of S″ at $t_\infty$ for phase 1. Equation (20) is of the Michaelis–Menten form and the values of $V_m$ and $K_m$ possess their usual significance (i.e. $V_m$ is the first-order rate of

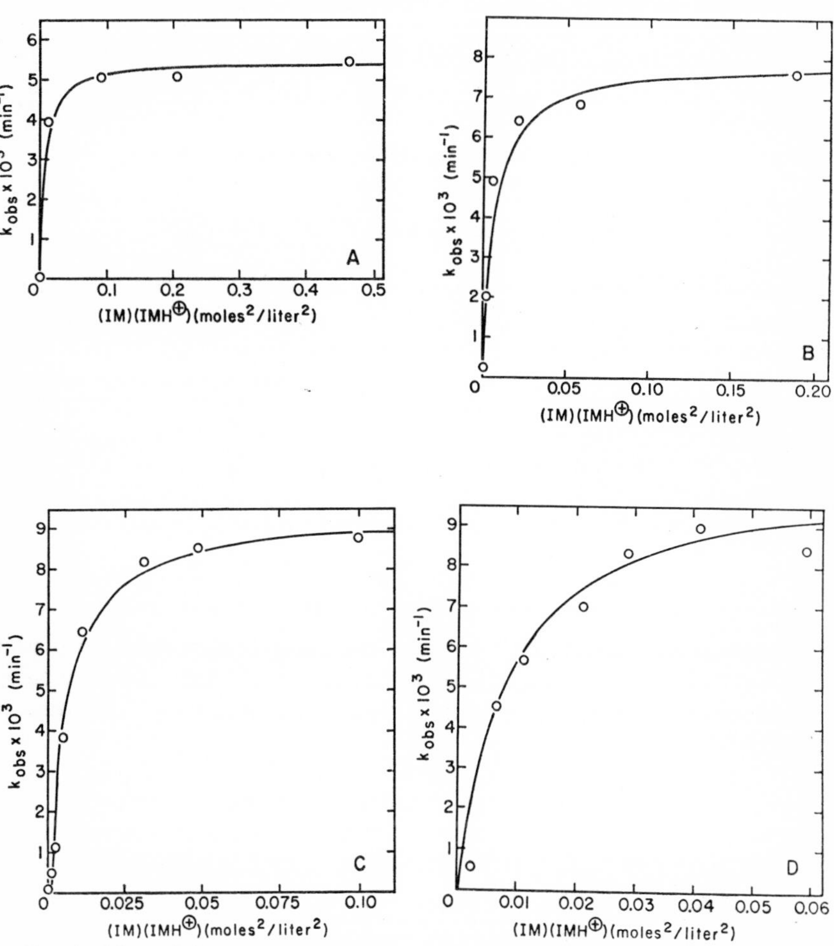


FIG. 8. Plots of the observed first-order rate constants ($k_{obs}$) for the appearance of S″ vs. the product of the concentrations of imidazole and imidazolium ion. The points are experimental and the curves are those obtained from equation (20) employing the constants provided in Table 5.

approach to equilibrium at saturation by IM and IMH$^\oplus$ and $K_m$ the dissociation constant of a complex of IM and IMH$^\oplus$ with a reactant or intermediate).

Three mechanisms may be invoked to explain the Michaelis–Menten type kinetics, but only the first, as will be shown, is tenable. The first mechanism requires saturation of S′ by an imidazole molecule and an imidazolium ion followed by a rate-determining intracomplex general base and/or general acid conversion of S′ to S″ as depicted in (21):

$$C_6H_5\text{—}CH(NH_2)\text{—}CO_2H + \text{PCHO} \underset{k_{-1}}{\overset{k_1}{\rightleftharpoons}} S' \tag{21}$$

$$S' + \text{IM} + \text{IMH}^{\oplus} \underset{\text{fast}}{\overset{\text{fast}}{\rightleftharpoons}} \text{complex } S'$$

$$\text{complex } S' \underset{k_{-2}}{\overset{k_2}{\rightleftharpoons}} \text{complex } S'' \underset{\text{fast}}{\overset{\text{fast}}{\rightleftharpoons}} S'' + \text{IM} + \text{IMH}^{\oplus}$$

The second mechanism (22) involves the catalysis of a rate-determining formation of S′ by the two imidazole species. At high imidazole buffer concentrations this step would no longer be rate-controlling:

$$\text{PCHO} + C_6H_5\text{—}CH(NH_2)\text{—}CO_2H \underset{k_{-1}\ (\text{IM}+\text{IMH}^{\oplus})}{\overset{(\text{IM}+\text{IMH}^{\oplus})\ k_1}{\rightleftharpoons}} S' \tag{22}$$

$$S' \underset{k_{-2}}{\overset{k_2}{\rightleftharpoons}} S''$$

The third mechanism (23) involves a rate-controlling complex formation between PCHO and the two imidazole species which at high imidazole buffer concentrations becomes zero-order in imidazole as a result of saturation of the PCHO:

$$\text{PCHO} + \text{IM} + \text{IMH}^{\oplus} \underset{\text{slow}}{\overset{\text{slow}}{\leftrightarrows}} \text{complex}$$

$$\text{complex} + C_6H_5\text{—}CH(NH_2)\text{—}CO_2H \overset{\text{fast}}{\rightleftharpoons} \text{aldimine} \overset{\text{fast}}{\rightleftharpoons} \text{ketimine} \tag{23}$$

Thus, imidazole buffer is acting as a catalyst for the prototropic shift in (21) and for the formation of Schiff base in (22) and (23). Although these mechanisms explain the observed rate dependence on imidazole buffer concentration (20) equally well, compelling evidence points to mechanism (21) as being the correct one. Thus, if mechanism (23) were operative then the observed overall rate should be independent of amino acid concentration. The observed rate, however, is found to show exactly the same dependence upon amino acid concentration as it does upon PCHO concentration.

Furthermore, all previous work on this reaction suggests that imine formation is much more rapid than prototropy. Convincing evidence that (22) does not represent the reaction path is obtained from experiments in which the morpholine imine (S) of PCHO is used in place of PCHO. Thus the catalytic rate constants for the imidazole-catalyzed formation of ketimine (S″) from S (24) are similar to those for the reaction involving PCHO.

$$\text{(S)} + C_6H_5\text{—}CH(NH_2)\text{—}CO_2H \underset{\text{fast}}{\overset{\text{fast}}{\rightleftharpoons}} S' + \text{morpholine} \underset{k_{-2}}{\overset{k_2}{\rightleftharpoons}} S'' \quad (24)$$

(S)

This result would not be predicted on the basis of (24) since it is well established that imines react at a greater rate with general reagents of type R—$NH_2$ than do the corresponding aldehydes or ketones.[19–22] Recently, Cordes and Jencks[23] have shown that S reacts with semicarbazide at a greater rate than does PCHO.

It may be noted that morpholine, which is a stronger base than imidazole, does not alone catalyze the transamination reaction between PCHO and α-aminophenylacetic acid under conditions (e.g. $10^{-4}$ M reactants) which provide a facile transamination using imidazole buffers. This observation lends support to the suggestion that the catalytic activity of imidazole buffer arises from its ability to form a complex with a reactant.

The catalysis would, therefore, appear to be best expressed by the path of (21) in which a complex of S′ with imidazole and its conjugate acid is followed by a rate-controlling intracomplex catalysis of the prototropic shift converting S′ to S″. Only (21) is compatible with the determined kinetic scheme (12–19). Thus, the kinetic treatment is based upon the assumption of a rate-determining prototropic shift following a rapidly established low steady state in S′, and is found not only to provide a rate equation which accommodates the rate data to 80–90 per cent completion but also predicts the somewhat unusual rate variation caused by variation of the initial reactant concentrations (see Table 3).

Returning now to plausible interpretations of the mechanistic significance of the data of Table 5 in the frame of the necessity to invoke a mechanism as (21). The constancy of the values of $K_m$ calculated on the basis of the involvement of one neutral and one acidic species of imidazole is convincing evidence that the complexes of S′ and S″ which partake in the prototropic shift have one of the compositions of (25):

$$\underset{(a)}{\text{Imine, IM, IMH}^{\oplus}} \quad \text{or} \quad \underset{(b)}{\text{Imine, IMH}^{\oplus}\text{, IMH}^{\oplus}\text{, OH}^{\ominus}}$$

$$\text{or} \quad \underset{(c)}{\text{Imine, IM, IM, H}^{\oplus}} \tag{25}$$

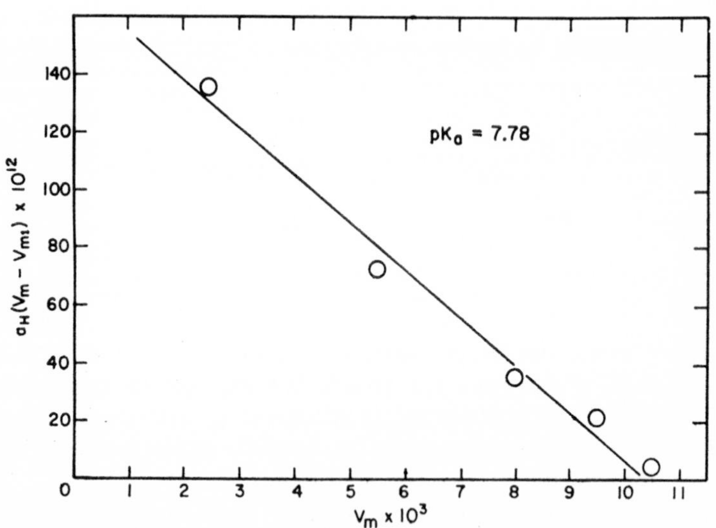


FIG. 9. Plot of equation (27). The slope provides the value of $-K_a'$ and the intercept at $(\mathrm{H}^{\oplus})\,(V_m - V_{m1}) = 0$ is $V_{m2}$.

It is, of course, not possible to differentiate between (*a*), (*b*) and (*e*). The catalytic complex, as represented by (25*a*), would appear to be the most likely, however, only three species, rather than four, being involved.

Inspection of Table 5 shows that $V_m$ increases with increasing pH. The values of $V_m$ have been shown to follow Eq. (26),

$$V_m = \frac{V_{m1}(\mathrm{H}^{\oplus}) + V_{m2}K_a'}{K_a' + (\mathrm{H}^{\oplus})} \tag{26}$$

where $V_{m1}$ and $V_{m2}$ are rate constants for attainment of equilibrium in phase 1 at saturation by imidazole and imidazolium ion and $K_a'$ is a kinetically apparent dissociation constant. Rearrangement of (26) provides (27):

$$(\mathrm{H}^{\oplus})(V_m - V_{m1}) = K_a'(V_{m2} - V_m) \tag{27}$$

The value of $V_{m1}$ was determined to be $0.9 \times 10^{-3}\ \mathrm{min}^{-1}$ by the fitting of a theoretical dissociation curve to a plot of $V_m$ vs. pH. In Fig. 9 is plotted $(\mathrm{H}^{\oplus})(V_m - V_{m1})$ vs. $V_m$ and from the slope of the line the value of $-K_a'$ was determined (p$K_a'$ = 7.78) while from the intercept at $(\mathrm{H}^{\oplus})(V_m - V_{m1}) = 0$

the value of $V_{m2}$ was determined to be $10.2 \times 10^{-3}\ \text{min}^{-1}$. Inspection of Table 5 reveals that the final equilibrium position of phase 1 is not pH-dependent and that, therefore, $V_{m1}$ and $V_{m2}$ must refer to rate constants for the prototropic shift for unionized and ionized complexes respectively.

One other piece of information must be fitted into the story before we are in a position to write a credible mechanistic scheme which will account for the catalysis at all pH values investigated. In the previous discussion it was established that S′ must be at a steady state concentration. However, if S′ becomes complexed by imidazole and imidazolium ion then it would be anticipated that at saturation by these species all pyridoxal and amino acid

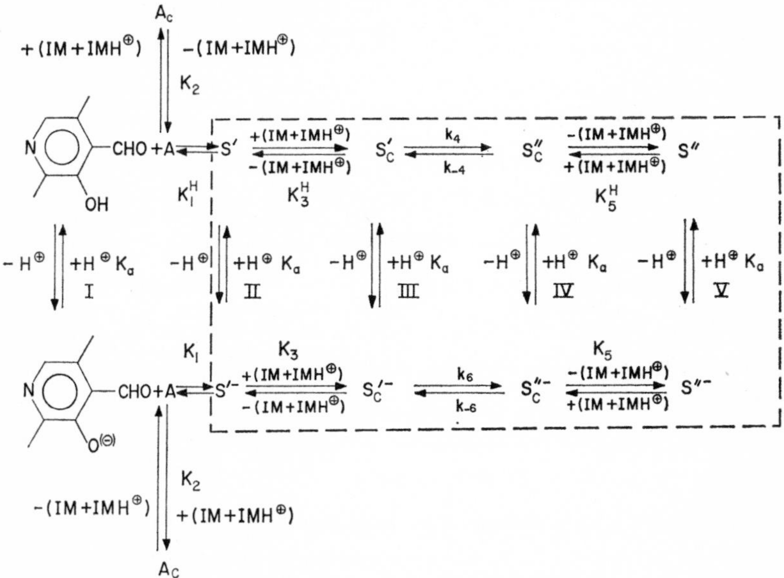


FIG. 10. Reaction scheme for phase 1. ($K_a$ values are dissociation constants. All other equilibrium constants are formation constants.)

would be converted to the complexed S′ species and, therefore, this species could not remain at steady state. The only means by which steady state could be maintained would be to have either reactant (i.e. pyridoxal or amino acid) also complexed by imidazole and imidazolium ion. Phase solubility studies carried out at pH 8.6 and pH 7.06 have shown that α-aminophenylacetic acid is complexed by imidazole buffer and that the complex is composed of one IM and one $IMH^{\oplus}$ species. In addition it was found that the formation constant for the amino acid complex was approximately that determined kinetically as $K_m$.

We are now in a position to expand the reaction scheme described by

Eq. (21) in order to accommodate the above considerations. In the reaction scheme of Fig. 10, if we assume, as an approximation, that

$$K_a^{\mathrm{I}} \cong K_a^{\mathrm{II}} \cong K_a^{\mathrm{III}} \cong K_a^{\mathrm{IV}} \cong K_a^{\mathrm{V}} \cong K_{\mathrm{app}}' \tag{28}$$

and that

$$K_1^{\mathrm{H}} \cong K_2^{\mathrm{H}} \cong K_3^{\mathrm{H}} \cong K_5^{\mathrm{H}} \cong K_1 \cong K_2 \cong K_3 \cong K_5 \tag{29}$$

then the rate of approach to equilibrium in phase 1 is provided by the expression of (30).

$$v = \left[\frac{k_6K_1K_3K_a' + k_4K_1K_3(\mathrm{H}^\oplus)}{(K_a' + (\mathrm{H}^\oplus))}\right]\left[\frac{(\mathrm{PCHO}_T)(\mathrm{A}_T)(\mathrm{IM})(\mathrm{IMH}^\oplus)}{[K_2(\mathrm{IM})(\mathrm{IMH}^\oplus) + 1]} - \frac{K_5(\mathrm{IM})(\mathrm{IMH}^\oplus)(\mathrm{S}_T'')}{[K_1K_3K_4(K_5(\mathrm{IM})(\mathrm{IMH}^\oplus) + 1)]}\right] \tag{30}$$

where

$$\mathrm{PCHO}_T = \mathrm{PCHO} + \mathrm{PCHO}^\ominus + \mathrm{S}' + \mathrm{S}'^\ominus + \mathrm{S}_c' + \mathrm{S}_c'^\ominus$$
$$\mathrm{A}_T = \mathrm{A} + \mathrm{A}_c$$
$$\mathrm{S}'' = \mathrm{S}_c'' + \mathrm{S}_c''^\ominus + \mathrm{S}'' + \mathrm{S}''^\ominus$$

At saturation in imidazole and imidazolium ion (30) reduces to (31)

$$v = \frac{k_6K_1K_3K_a' + k_4K_1K_3(\mathrm{H}^\oplus)}{(K_a' + (\mathrm{H}^\oplus))K_2}\left[(\mathrm{PCHO}_T)(\mathrm{A}_T) - \frac{K_2(\mathrm{S}_T'')}{K_1K_3K_4}\right] \tag{31}$$

which provides, for the equilibrium position at $t_\infty$, for phase 1, the following expression:

$$K_\infty = \frac{(\mathrm{S}''_{T\infty})}{(\mathrm{PCHO}_{T\infty})(\mathrm{A}_{T\infty})} = K_1K_4 = K_1K_6 \tag{32}$$

The assumption (28) is certainly an oversimplification so that the value of $K_a'$ must be considered to be merely a kinetically apparent value. The value of p$K_a'$ (Fig. 9) approaches closely the recorded value of 8.3 for pyridoxal.[24] The approximations of (29) are reasonably based on experimental data. Comparison of the expressions of (26) and (31) reveals the following identity

$$V_{m1} = k_4K_1c/1.15 \text{ and } V_{m2} = k_6K_1c/1.15 \tag{33}$$

so that the two maximum velocity constants refer to the rate of the prototropic shift in the interconversion of the protonated and unprotonated complexes of the intermediate azomethines.

## THE NATURE OF THE CATALYTIC MECHANISM

The unique feature of this study has been the demonstration that in dilute aqueous solution the transamination of pyridoxal by an α-amino acid occurs via pre-equilibrium formation of a complex of the pyridoxal-amino acid mine with imidazole and imidazolium ion. The establishment that the formation of the complex of catalyst and substrate is of real kinetic significance (bases as morpholine and carbonate which cannot form complexes do not catalyze the reaction in dilute solution) is also of great interest with reference to the mechanism of the enzymatic reaction. It is reasonable to propose that the imidazole catalyzed intracomplex protropic shift represents a case of general acid general base catalysis (Fig. 11) in which a proton is abstracted from the α-carbon by the general base species and a proton is donated to the

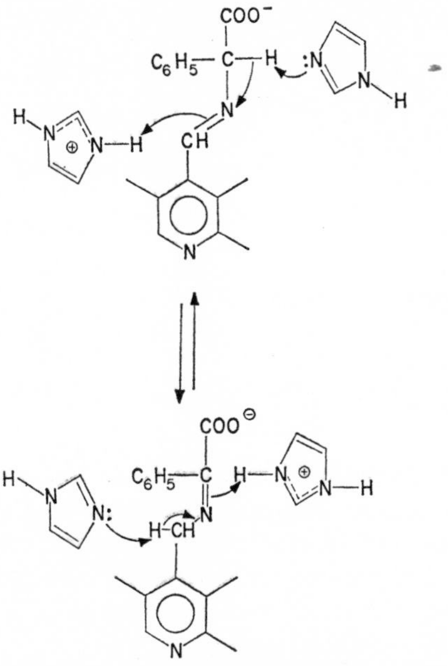

FIG. 11. Proposed mechanism for the imidazole catalysis of the transamination of pyridoxal by α-aminophenylacetic acid.

azomethine bond by the general acid species of imidazole. The position of the critical transition state along the reaction co-ordinate cannot be specified though it may be noted that Banks *et al.*[15] have reported a feeble general acid catalysis in the transamination of pyridoxamine by pyruvic acid. The complete symmetry of the mechanism of Fig. 11 is compelling and it may be noted that the mechanism is formally of the "push–pull" type as reported by Swain and Brown[25] for the catalysis of the mutarotation of tetramethyl glucose by carboxylic acids and α-pyridone in benzene solution. Like the latter reaction the imidazole catalysis of the transamination of α-aminophenylacetic acid by pyridoxal also involves a pre-equilibrium complex formation. Unlike the catalysis of Swain and Brown, however, the imidazole catalysis of the transamination reaction takes place in aqueous solution. From the expressions of (33) and the $c$ constant of Table 3 we can estimate the values of the rate constant for the catalyzed prototropic shift ($k_6$) to be between 4 $\text{min}^{-1}$ and 200 $\text{min}^{-1}$.

In the enzymatic catalysis of the transamination of pyridoxal phosphate by amino acids the pyridoxal phosphate is present on the enzyme surface in combination with the $\epsilon$-amino group of a lysine residue as an imine.[26–28] The formation of the imine of substrate and enzyme-bound cofactor then

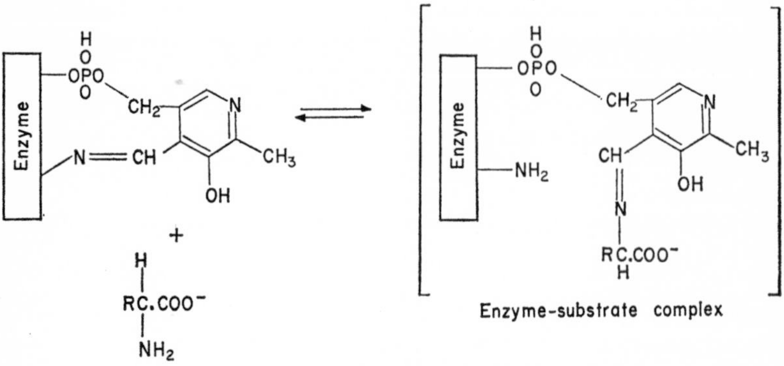

Enzyme-substrate complex

FIG. 12. The " transimination " step.

occurs via a " transimination " reaction (Fig. 12). From studies of semicarbazone formation from pyridoxal phosphate in the presence of excess morpholine, Cordes and Jencks[23] have concluded that the most reactive species of pyridoxal phosphate imines toward transimination is protonated (34*a*) and that the morpholine imine (34*b*) serves as a useful model of the protonated imine of a primary amine.

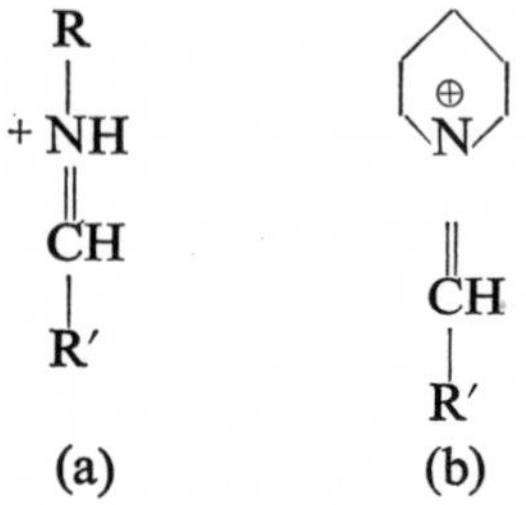

(a) (b) (34)

On this basis, the influence of morpholine upon the rate and final equilibrium position of the imidazole-catalyzed transamination of pyridoxal by $\alpha$-aminophenylacetic acid was investigated. Observation of the absorbance at 395 m$\mu$ indicates the degree of conversion of pyridoxal to the morpholine imine and it is found that even when free pyridoxal is no longer detectable the kinetic scheme as characterized by location of isosbestic points, close adherence to first-order kinetics, magnitude of rate constants, etc., remains essentially unchanged. Morpholine does not catalyze the prototropic shift but merely lowers the steady state concentration of the aldimine, which is reflected by a reduction in the rate of appearance of ketimine and an exactly parallel reduction in the equilibrium concentration of ketimine. These observations, therefore, suggest that the enzymatic transamination reaction would proceed at least as readily with the pyridoxal phosphate moiety attached to the enzyme surface via the aldehyde group and an amino group on the enzyme as with the pyridoxal coenzyme attached to the protein residue only through the phosphate.

The present studies will be published in complete form in the *Journal of the American Chemical Society.*

*Acknowledgment*:—This work was supported by the United States Government through grants in aid from the National Institutes of Health and the National Science Foundation.

## REFERENCES


1. R. M. Herbst and L. I. Engell; *J. Biol. Chem.* **107**, 505 (1934); *J. Am. Chem. Soc.* **58**, 2239 (1963).
2. H. I. Nakada and S. Weinhouse; *J. Biol. Chem.* **204**, 831 (1953).
3. A. E. Braunstein; *Enzymologica* **7**, 25 (1934).
4. P. P. Cohen; *Biochem. J.* **33**, 1478 (1939).
5. H. Wada and E. E. Snell; *J. Biol. Chem.* **237**, 127 and 133 (1926).
6. E. E. Snell; *J. Am. Chem. Soc.* **67**, 194 (1945).
7. D. E. Metzler and E. E. Snell; *J. Am. Chem. Soc.* **74**, 979 (1952).
8. D. E. Metzler, J. Olivard and E. E. Snell; *J. Am. Chem. Soc.* **76**, 644 (1954).
9. J. B. Longenecker and E. E. Snell; *J. Am. Chem. Soc.* **79**, 142 (1957).
10. D. E. Metzler, M. Ikawa and E. E. Snell; *J. Am. Chem. Soc.* **76**, 648 (1954).
11. W. T. Jenkins and I. W. Sizer; *J. Am. Chem. Soc.* **79**, 2655 (1957); *J. Biol. Chem.* **234**, 51 and 1179 (1959); *ibid.* **235**, 620 (1960).
12. Y. Matsuo and D. M. Greenberg; *J. Biol. Chem.* **230**, 545, 561 (1958).
13. N. Alexander and D. M. Greenberg; *J. Biol. Chem.* **220**, 775 (1956).
14. M. A. Karasek and D. M. Greenberg; *J. Biol. Chem.* **227**, 191 (1957).

14a. B. Vallee; Private communication.

15. B. E. C. Banks, A. A. Diamantis and C. A. Vernon; *J. Chem. Soc.* 4235 (1961).
16. C. K. Ingold; *J. Chem. Soc.* 1477 (1926).
17. C. K. Ingold; *J. Chem. Soc.* 1778 (1935).
18. J. Buraczweski and L. Marchlewski; *Ber. deut. chem. ges.* **34**, 4009 (1901).
19. E. H. Cordes and W. P. Jencks; *J. Am. Chem. Soc.* **84**, 826 (1962).
20. Mme Bruzau; *Ann. Chem. Liebigs* (11), **1**, 332 (1934).
21. E. A. Brodhag and C. R. Hauser; *J. Am. Chem. Soc.* **77**, 3024 (1955).
22. C. R. Hauser and D. S. Hoffenberg; *J. Am. Chem. Soc.* **77**, 4885 (1955).
23. E. H. Cordes and W. P. Jencks; *Biochemistry* **1**, (1962).
24. D. E. Metzler; *J. Am. Chem. Soc.* **79**, 485 (1957).
25. C. G. Swain and J. F. Brown; *J. Am. Chem. Soc.* **74**, 2534, 2538 (1952).
26. E. H. Fischer, A. B. Kent, E. P. Snyder and E. G. Krebs; *J. Am. Chem. Soc.* **80**, 2906 (1958).
27. E. H. Fischer and E. G. Krebs; Abstr. 136th Mtg. Am. Chem. Soc., 24c.
28. W. T. Jenkins; *Federation Proc.* **20**, 978 (1961).
29. A. E. Braunstein and M. M. Shemyakin; *Doklady Akad. Nauk. S.S.S.R.* **85**, 1115, (1952); *Biokhimiya* **18**, 393 (1953).

## DISCUSSION

DR. F. H. WESTHEIMER:

Can you suggest a reason for the complexing between imidazole, imidazolium ion and the amino acid?

DR. BRUICE:

We are not certain, at present, just what type of complex is formed. It may turn out to involve the phenyl group of the amino acid and intermediate imines. The formation of complexes between aromatic lyophobic compounds and heterocyclic nitrogen bases in water is a well established, if perhaps not well understood phenomenon, though catalysis proceeding through such complexes in aqueous solution has not been previously observed (see T. Higuchi and D. A. Zuck, *J. Am. Pharm. Assoc.* (*Sci. ed.*) **42**, 132 (1953); T. Higuchi and J. L. Lach, *ibid.* **43**, 349 (1954); E. H. Gans and T. Higuchi, *ibid.* **46**, 458 (1957); T. Higuchi and S. Bolton, *ibid.* **48**, 557 (1959); J. W. Poole and T. Higuchi, *ibid.* **48**, 592 (1959)).

# TRANSALDIMINATION REACTIONS OF PYRIDOXAL AND RELATED COMPOUNDS*

by WILLIAM P. JENCKS and EUGENE CORDES

Graduate Department of Biochemistry,
Brandeis University, Waltham, Massachusetts, U.S.A.

Two mechanisms of catalysis which have been thoroughly studied in non-enzymatic systems and for which there is evidence in certain enzymatic reactions are general acid–base catalysis, in which the function of the catalyst is to aid proton transfer, and covalent catalysis, in which the catalyst forms a covalent bond with the substrate. Enzymatic and non-enzymatic transamination reactions catalyzed by pyridoxal derivatives are examples of covalent (electrophilic–nucleophilic) catalysis. It has recently been shown by Vernon and co-workers[1] that the slow step of the non-enzymatic transamination reaction is the tautomerization step and that this step is subject to classical general acid–base catalysis. Velick has concluded, from a detailed kinetic study, that the tautomerization step is also rate-determining in the reaction catalyzed by glutamic–aspartic transaminase.[2] This communication deals with an earlier step, the formation of the Schiff base between the pyridoxal derivative and the amino acid substrate, which must precede the tautomerization step.

Condensation reactions between aldehydes and nitrogen bases, such as simple amines or semicarbazide, have long been known to be subject to classical general acid catalysis. Although the precise mechanism of this catalysis is not clear, it must certainly involve facilitation of a proton transfer reaction by a general acid or base in the reaction medium and, in the case of the addition step of semicarbazone formation, probably involves polarization of the carbonyl group by a molecule of catalyzing acid (Eq. 1).[3–5]

$$\rangle N\cdots \rangle C \cdots O \cdots H \cdots A \qquad (1)$$

Primary amines, however, are extremely effective catalysts of such reactions

*Publication 221 of the Graduate Department of Biochemistry. Supported by grants from the National Cancer Institute of the National Institutes of Health (C-3975) and the National Science Foundation. This investigation was carried out (by E.C.) during the tenure of a Predoctoral Fellowship from the National Heart Institute, United States Public Health Service.

with a reactivity which is several orders of magnitude greater than would be expected from the acidity of their conjugate acids. A detailed study of the mechanism of this catalysis has demonstrated that the reason for this high reactivity is that primary amines may function as nucleophilic catalysts and that the amine-catalyzed reaction proceeds through the intermediate formation of a Schiff base between the substrate and the catalyst, followed by a reaction of this Schiff base with the final carbonyl group acceptor (Eqs. 2 and 3).[6]

$$>C{=}O + H_2NR \rightleftharpoons >C{=}NR + H_2O \qquad (2)$$

$$>C{=}NR + H_2NNH\overset{\overset{\displaystyle O}{\|}}{C}NH_2 \rightarrow >C{=}NNH\overset{\overset{\displaystyle O}{\|}}{C}NH_2 + H_2NR \qquad (3)$$

Pyridoxal phosphate (PLP) is bound to several pyridoxal-phosphate dependent enzymes in the form of a Schiff base or potential Schiff base.[7–10] It is, therefore, of interest to determine whether a PLP-Schiff base is more reactive than free PLP, so as to determine whether it is advantageous to the enzyme to have the coenzyme initially bound in this form, and to examine the mechanism of the carbonyl group transfer reactions which must occur in the enzymatic and non-enzymatic reactions. The reaction with semicarbazide is a particularly convenient one for study, because it proceeds to completion at a readily measurable rate and the spectral changes which take place upon semicarbazone formation facilitate measurement of the course of the reaction. Although the properties of semicarbazide are somewhat different from those of more basic amines, it may reasonably be inferred that mechanistic principles which are demonstrated for semicarbazone formation apply also to the reaction of other amines.

The reaction of PLP with isonicotinic acid hydrazide has been studied by Bonavita and Scardi and was shown to proceed by both pH-independent and acid-catalyzed reaction paths.[11] Wiegand studied the reactions of PLP with a number of hydrazides, including semicarbazide, at pH 7.4 and found that the reaction rates increase with increasing basicity of the attacking nitrogen base. Pyridoxal (PL) was found to react some 100-fold less rapidly than PLP.[12]

The rate of semicarbazone formation from PL and semicarbazide increases as the concentration of phosphate buffer is increased, at constant pH and ionic strength[13] (Fig. 1). Both the catalyzed reaction, from the slope of the lines, and the uncatalyzed reaction, from the intercepts, increase with increasing acidity and the rate of the catalyzed reaction is proportional to the concentration of the $H_2PO_4^-$ ion, with a catalytic rate constant of 13 $M^{-2}\,min^{-1}$. Thus, this reaction is subject to hydrogen ion catalysis and to classical general acid catalysis by phosphate buffer, as has been demonstrated for similar reactions of many other aldehydes.[3-5]

Under the same conditions, catalysis of the reaction by aniline is very much more effective than by phosphate (Fig. 2—note the difference in the concentration scales for Figs. 1 and 2). Aniline cannot be acting as a general

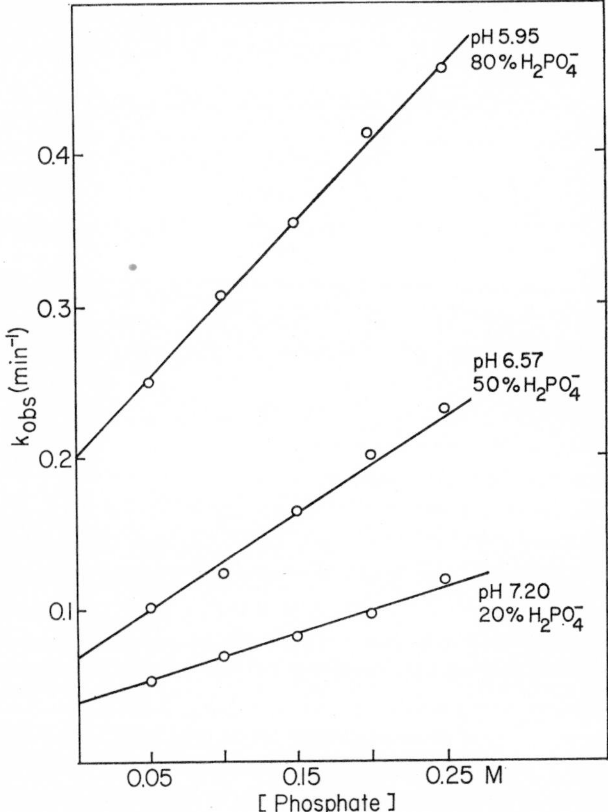


FIG. 1. First-order rate constants for pyridoxal semicarbazone formation as a function of phosphate concentration at several pH values at 25°. Semicarbazide 0.10 M, ionic strength 0.60, pyridoxal $7 \times 10^{-5}$ M, 370 m$\mu$.

acid catalyst in this reaction, because the concentration of anilinium ion is very small near neutrality. The high efficiency of this catalysis indicates that it is an example of nucleophilic catalysis, similar to that observed with other aromatic aldehydes (Eqs. 2 and 3). The catalyzed reaction displays both a neutral and an acid-catalyzed component. Although a detailed kinetic investigation has not been carried out, it is probable that this reaction is similar to aniline-catalyzed reactions of benzaldehydes and proceeds with a rate-determining formation of Schiff base, followed by a fast reaction of Schiff base with semicarbazide.[13]

With more basic amines, catalysis is also observed, but follows a somewhat different kinetic behavior. With glycine ethyl ester, which may be regarded as a model for an α-amino group of an enzyme, an efficient catalysis is observed which occurs at a rate proportional to the concentration of the amine as the free base, with a catalytic rate constant of 75 $\text{M}^{-2}\ \text{min}^{-1}$ (Fig. 3). Again, this behavior is similar to that found in the catalysis of the reaction of

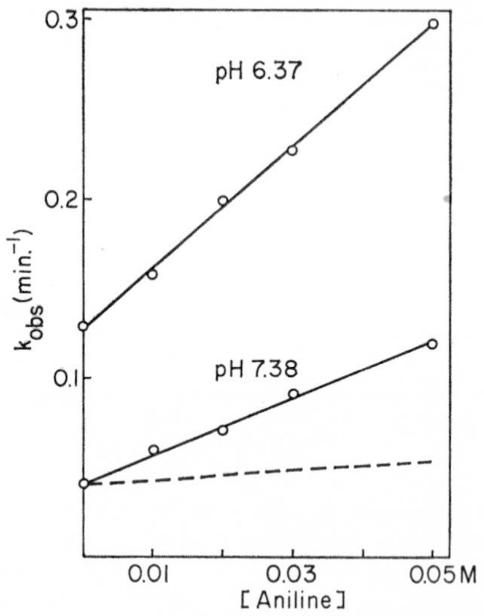


FIG. 2. First-order rate constants for pyridoxal semicarbazone formation as a function of the concentration of aniline at pH 6.37 and pH 7.38. Semicarbazide 0.10 M, ionic strength 0.50, 0.50 M phosphate buffer, pyridoxal $7 \times 10^{-5}$ M, 370 mμ. The dashed line shows the amount of catalysis caused by comparable concentrations of phosphate buffer, pH 7.2 (Fig. 1).

benzaldehyde with methoxyamine catalyzed by glycine.[6] With still more basic amines and amino acids the reaction involves a rapid formation of yellow Schiff base, followed by a slower reaction with semicarbazide (Table 1). Similar results are obtained if the reaction is carried out with the isolated Schiff base, instead of the aldehyde, as the starting material. At neutral pH the rate of semicarbazone formation from the valine and ethylamine Schiff bases is 40 to 50 times faster than from free pyridoxal. Semicarbazone formation from PLP shows a similar catalysis at pH 10.8. At lower pH values, the catalysis is less marked, principally because of an increase in the rate of the uncatalyzed reaction. The higher reaction rate of PLP, compared to PL, is a result of the fact that PL exists in aqueous solution principally as the unreactive internal hemiacetal.

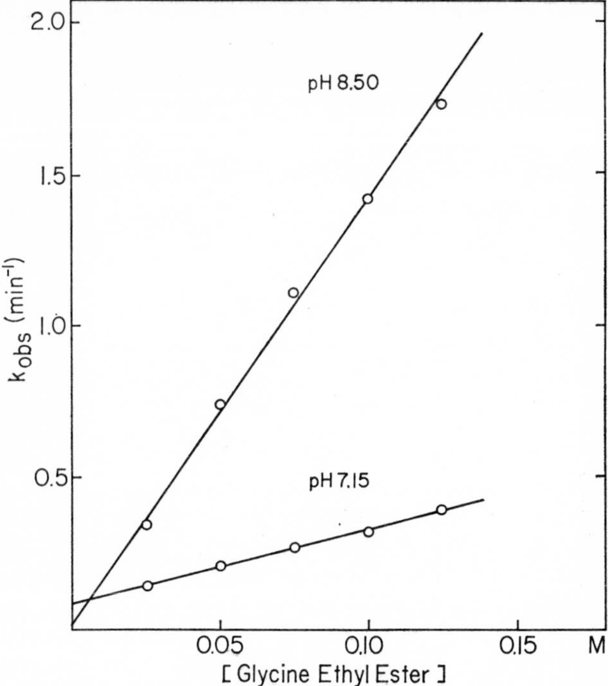


FIG. 3. First-order rate constants for pyridoxal semicarbazone formation as a function of the concentration of glycine ethyl ester at pH 7.15 and pH 8.50. Semicarbazide 0.2 M, ionic strength 0.50, pyridoxal 7 × $10^{-5}$ M, 370 mμ.

TABLE 1. SEMICARBAZONE FORMATION FROM PYRIDOXAL DERIVATIVES AT 25°[13]

| Substrate | Amine (M) | pH | Semicarbazide (M) | $k_{obs}$* (min$^{-1}$) |
|---|---|---|---|---|
| PL | | 6.8 | 0.07 | 0.073 |
| PL | Valine (0.51) | 6.8 | 0.07 | 3.70 |
| PL-ethylamine | Schiff base | 6.8 | 0.07 | 2.87 |
| PLP | | 10.8 | 0.007 | 0.014 |
| PLP | Methylamine (0.20) | 10.8 | 0.007 | 0.432 |
| PLP | | 8.6 | 0.005 | 0.053 |
| PLP | Glycine (0.05) | 8.7 | 0.005 | 0.415 |
| PLP | Lysine (0.04) | 8.7 | 0.005 | 0.166 |
| PLP | Ornithine (0.06) | 8.7 | 0.005 | 0.244 |
| PLP | Methylamine (0.05) | 8.7 | 0.005 | 0.231 |

*Followed at 370 mμ in phosphate, triethylenediamine and carbonate buffers; ionic strength maintained at 0.50 with KCl.

Far more effective catalysis of PLP semicarbazone formation is found with the secondary amine, morpholine (Fig. 4). In contrast to the reactions described above, catalysis by morpholine increases with decreasing pH. Catalysis by triethylenediamine, a tertiary amine of similar basicity, is

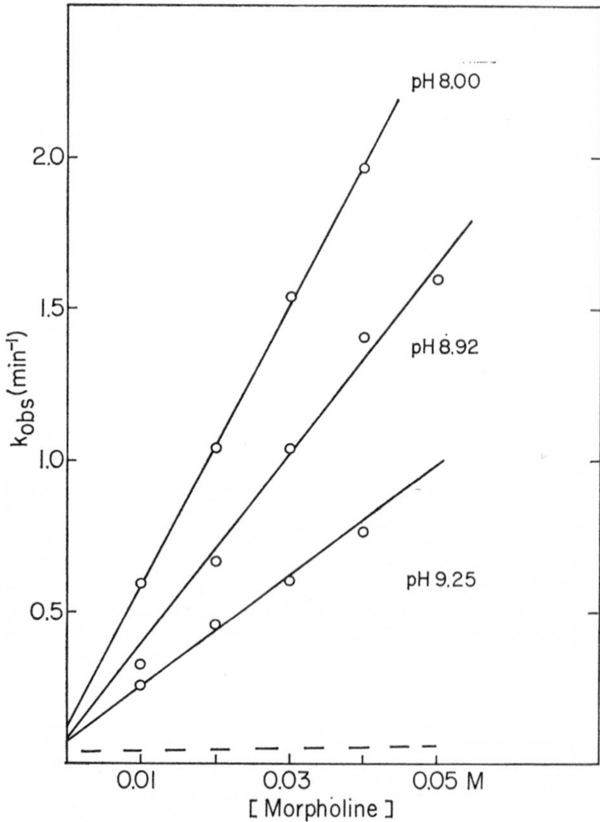


FIG. 4. First-order rate constants for pyridoxal phosphate semicarbazone formation as a function of the concentration of morpholine at several pH values. Semicarbezide 0.005 M, ionic strength 0.50, pyridoxal phosphate $1 \times 10^{-4}$ M, 370 m$\mu$. The dashed line shows the amount of catalysis by triethylenediamine buffer at pH 8.92.

very much less effective than that by morpholine (dashed line, Fig. 4). The rate of the morpholine-catalyzed reaction is dependent on the concentration of semicarbazide, although there is a tendency toward a leveling off of this dependence as the semicarbazide concentration is increased (Fig. 5). Proline is also an effective catalyst, although somewhat less effective than morpholine.[13]

This catalysis by secondary amines cannot involve the formation of a free Schiff base, because the formation of uncharged Schiff bases is impossible with secondary amines. It must, therefore, proceed through the formation of a highly reactive, cationic Schiff base, which is structurally analogous to a protonated Schiff base (Eq. 4).

$$\begin{matrix} R \\ H \end{matrix}\!\!>\!C{=}O + HN\!< + H^+ \rightleftharpoons \begin{matrix} R \\ H \end{matrix}\!\!>\!\underset{\textstyle\mathrm{I}}{C{=}N^+\!<} + H_2O \tag{4}$$

$$\begin{matrix} R \\ H \end{matrix}\!\!>\!C{=}N^+\!< + H_2NR' \rightarrow \begin{matrix} R \\ H \end{matrix}\!\!>\!C{=}NR' + HN\!< + H^+ \tag{5}$$

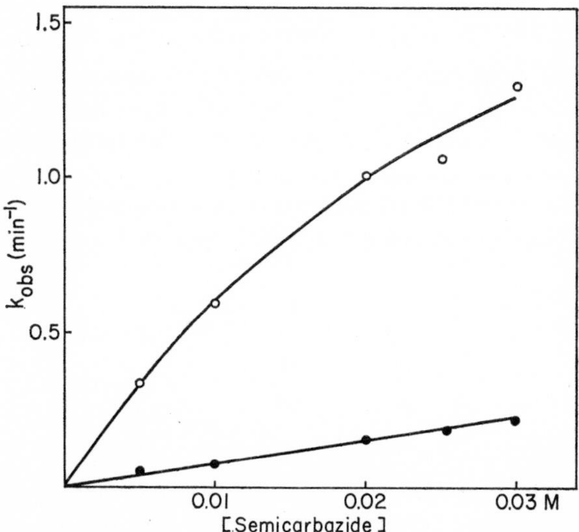


FIG. 5. Dependence of the rate of morpholine-catalyzed semicarbazone formation from PLP on the concentration of semicarbazide at 25°. Triethylenediamine buffer, 0.05 M, pH 8.83, ionic strength 0.5. Upper line: 0.01 M morpholine; lower line: control.

Since the rate of the reaction is dependent on the concentration of semicarbazide, semicarbazide must be involved in the rate-determining step and reaction (4) cannot be rate determining (the leveling off of the rate dependence on semicarbazide concentration as the semicarbazide concentration is increased suggests that at high semicarbazide concentration the first step may become rate determining). The reaction, therefore, must involve the formation of a low, steady state concentration of the cationic Schiff base intermediate (I), followed by a reaction of this intermediate with semicarbazide in a second step (Eq. 5). The increase in the equilibrium concentration of (I) with increasing acidity accounts for the increased rate of the reaction as the pH is lowered.

Imidazole is also a secondary amine and has recently been reported to catalyze a non-enzymatic transamination reaction.[14] Imidazole is, however, inactive as a catalyst for semicarbazone formation at pH 7.4 (0.1 M imidazole, 0.05 M phosphate buffer, 0.005 M semicarbazide) and pH 8.4 (0.2 M imidazole, 0.05 M triethylenediamine buffer, 0.04 M semicarbazide). This inactivity is not surprising, because the formation of a cationic Schiff base intermediate from imidazole would involve loss of resonance stabilization of the aromatic imidazole ring (II).

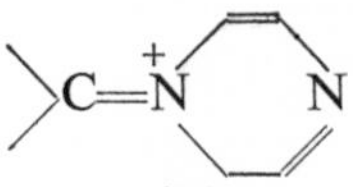

(II)

These results demonstrate the occurrence of nucleophilic catalysis of semicarbazone formation from PL and PLP and suggest that it is advantageous for PLP enzymes to have the coenzyme bound in the form of the Schiff base. A more detailed consideration of the mechanisms of these reactions requires a consideration of the relative reactivities of a free Schiff base (III), a free aldehyde (IV), a hydrogen-bonded Schiff base (V)* and a cationic Schiff base (I).

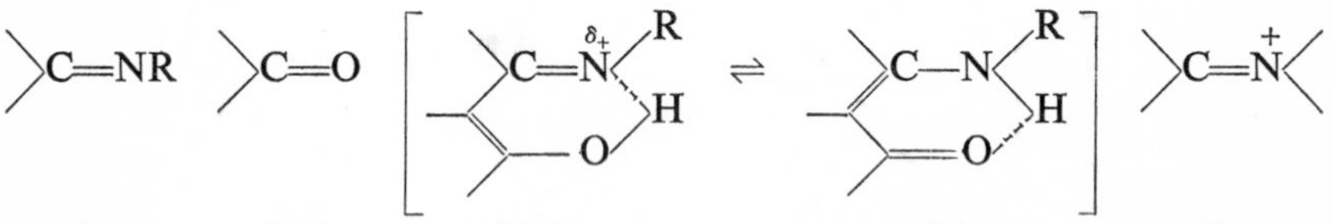

(III) (IV) (Va) (Vb) (I)

Because of the low electronegativity of nitrogen compared to oxygen, the uncatalyzed reactivity of Schiff bases is lower than that of carbonyl compounds and reactions of Schiff bases generally occur largely or entirely through acid-catalyzed pathways. A hydrogen-bonded Schiff base (V), as in pyridoxal derivatives, differs from a free Schiff base in two respects: (a) the hydrogen bond facilitates attack at the carbon atom by intramolecular general acid catalysis. It may also facilitate amine expulsion, the second step of transaldimination, by a similar mechanism. This accounts for the reactivity of PLP Schiff bases over a wide range of pH. (b) The intramolecular hydrogen bond tends to prevent complete protonation of the Schiff base, because it ties up the free electron pair of the nitrogen atom. The reactivity of a fully protonated Schiff base and, as a consequence, the rapid acid-catalyzed reaction path available to most Schiff bases, is restricted in the case of a hydrogen-bonded Schiff base. This accounts for the fact

*The Schiff base may exist wholly or in part as the tautomeric quinoid structures,[15] (Vb), although this form does not predominate in the case of the analogous Schiff base, salicylalbenzylamine.[16] This does not alter the following discussion, except that the reactivity of the PLP Schiff base may be a function, in part, of the reactivity of such a quinoid form, as well as that of the hydrogen bonded species (Va).

that nucleophilic catalysis of semicarbazone formation by primary amines is less striking in the case of pyridoxal compounds than for benzaldehydes. Thus, hydrogen bonding causes a moderate increase in reactivity, but prevents the still greater reactivity found with the fully protonated species.

Catalysis by secondary amines proceeds through unstable cationic intermediates (I). These intermediates are not subject to hydrogen bonding and are highly reactive. The formation of such cationic intermediates accounts for the high catalytic effectiveness of morpholine and proline. If this type of catalysis is utilized in enzymatic reactions, the intermediate (I) could be achieved either by reaction with a secondary amine in the active center of the enzyme or by an enzyme-promoted addition of a proton to the Schiff base.

The transaldimination step (Eq. 3) must itself proceed through two steps, the formation (Eq. 3a) and the decomposition (Eq. 3b) of a tetrahedral addition intermediate. In semicarbazone formation from aldehydes the

$$>C{=}NR + H_2NR' \rightleftharpoons >C\begin{matrix} \diagup NHR \\ \diagdown NHR' \end{matrix} \qquad (3a)$$

$$>C\begin{matrix} \diagup NHR \\ \diagdown NHR' \end{matrix} \rightleftharpoons >C{=}NR' + H_2NR \qquad (3b)$$

addition of the nitrogen base to the aldehyde is rate-determining at acid pH values and the decomposition of the addition intermediate is rate determining at neutral and alkaline pH values; the change in rate-determining step with pH accounts for the pH-rate maxima observed with these reactions.[17,18] It is not known whether the addition or the decomposition step is rate determining in the transaldimination reaction. In the reaction on the active site of the enzyme, it would be expected that the two steps would proceed at rather similar rates because of the symmetry of the reaction: the amino acid groups which are forming and breaking bonds (the $\epsilon$-amino group of a lysine residue and the amino group of the substrate) are chemically similar and would be expected to have similar attacking and leaving abilities.

Although the slow step of enzyme-catalyzed transamination is probably the tautomerization step, as in the non-enzymatic reaction,[1] it appears that the initial reaction of enzyme-bound PLP with an amino acid to give the amino acid–PLP Schiff base must also be catalyzed by the enzyme.[13] The turnover number of glutamic–aspartic transaminase is 380 $\mu$moles of aspartate/min per mg of enzyme.[19] From this value, the molecular weight of the enzyme (110,000) and the $K_m$ for aspartate (0.0039 M),[20] it follows that the rate of Schiff base formation at pH 8.5 must be equal to or greater than $7.7 \times 10^6$ M$^{-1}$ min$^{-1}$. In contrast, the non-enzymatic rate of reaction of PLP with aspartate is approximately 30 M$^{-1}$ min$^{-1}$. Although this rate would be somewhat greater for the PLP Schiff base, it clearly will not approach the observed rate unless the enzyme exerts a strong catalytic influence. One way in which the enzyme might exert such a catalysis would be through an intramolecular formation of a cationic Schiff base (IV).

## REFERENCES


1. B. E. C. BANKS, A. A. DIAMANTIS and C. A. VERNON; *J. Chem. Soc.* 4235 (1961).
2. S. F. VELICK and J. VAVRA; *J. Biol. Chem.* **237**, 2109 (1962).
3. J. B. CONANT and P. D. BARTLETT; *J. Am. Chem. Soc.* **54**, 2881 (1932).
4. E. H. CORDES and W. P. JENCKS; *J. Am. Chem. Soc.* **84**, 832 (1962).
5. E. H. CORDES and W. P. JENCKS; *J. Am. Chem. Soc.* **84**, 4319 (1962).
6. E. H. CORDES and W. P. JENCKS; *J. Am. Chem. Soc.* **84**, 826 (1962).
7. E. H. FISCHER, A. B. KENT, E. R. SNYDER and E. G. KREBS; *J. Am. Chem. Soc.* **80**, 2906 (1958).
8. E. H. FISCHER and E. G. KREBS; Abstract 136th Mtg. Am. Chem. Soc. 24C (1959).
9. C. TURANO, P. FASELLA, P. VECCHINI and A. GIARTOSIO; *Atti. accad. nazl. Lincei, Rend. Classe Sci. fis. mat. e nat.* **30**, 532 (1961).
10. R. C. HUGHES, W. T. JENKINS and E. H. FISCHER; *Proc. Natl. Acad. Sci. U.S.* **48**, 1615 (1962).
11. V. BONAVITA and V. SCARDI; *Arch. Biochem. Biophys.* **82**, 300 (1959).
12. R. G. WIEGAND; *J. Am. Chem. Soc.* **78**, 5307 (1956).
13. E. H. CORDES and W. P. JENCKS; *Biochemistry* **1**, 773 (1962).
14. T. C. BRUICE and R. M. TOPPING; *J. Am. Chem. Soc.* **84**, 2448 (1962).
15. D. HEINERT and A. E. MARTELL; *J. Am. Chem. Soc.* **84**, 3257 (1962).
16. G. O. DUDEK and R. H. HOLM; *J. Am. Chem. Soc.* **83**, 3914 (1961).
17. W. P. JENCKS; *J. Am. Chem. Soc.* **81**, 475 (1959).
18. B. M. ANDERSON and W. P. JENCKS; *J. Am. Chem. Soc.* **82**, 1773 (1960).
19. W. T. JENKINS and I. W. SIZER; *J. Am. Chem. Soc.* **79**, 2655 (1957).
20. W. T. JENKINS, D. A. YPHANTIS and I. W. SIZER; *J. Biol. Chem.* **234**, 51 (1959).


## DISCUSSION

DR. JENKINS:

Dr. Sizer and I will report on the reactivity of glutamic–aspartic transaminase with thiosemicarbazide. We found that both the acidic and the basic form of the derivative could react but that the acidic form was much more reactive. This observation might well be related to the relative efficiencies of morpholine and primary amines in Dr. Jencks' model systems.

DR. JENCKS:

If one ignores, for the moment, any special effects contributed by the enzyme, one would expect that the free base of a nucleophilic reagent should react with the cationic, protonated form of the enzyme-bound Schiff base. The pH dependence of the reaction of a weak base, such as semicarbazide, should therefore follow the titration curve for protonation of the Schiff base. With a stronger base which is protonated at physiological pH, such as an amino acid, the requirement that the free base form should react introduces another term proportional to $1/[H^+]$ into the rate law, and the rate of such a reaction will appear to be proportional to the free base form of the Schiff base, (Eq. 1), although

$$\text{rate} = k[\text{RNH}_3^+]\,[\rangle\text{C}=\text{N}-] \tag{1}$$

actually it represents a reaction of free amine with the protonated form (Eq. 2).

$$\text{rate} = k'[\text{RNH}_2]\,[\rangle\text{C}=\overset{\text{H}^+}{\text{N}}-] \tag{2}$$

DR. BRAUNSTEIN:

(1) Can it be inferred from your data that a suitably positioned amino group could markedly promote the cleavage (e.g. by substitution) of the hydrazone derivatives of PLP? For instance, can such an interaction between the $\epsilon$-$NH_2$ group of lysine in pyridoxal phosphate apoenzymes, which is normally participating in the intramolecular PLP aldimine bond, efficiently displace CO-reagents from PLP hydrazones, etc., otherwise with dissociable difficulty? Such an effect would account for the coenzyme activity of the stable PLP-hydrazones reported by Gonnard and other authors.

(2) Is the term " trans-Schiffization " acceptable to English-speaking chemists? I have raised strong objections when some organic chemists working in our laboratory have independently tried to introduce this jargon term in Russian.

DR. JENCKS:

In regard to the first question, I would answer yes, at least to the extent that results obtained in model systems may be extrapolated to enzymatic reactions. In answer to your second question, I am glad to hear that the term " trans-Schiffization " has not been accepted in Russia. The term " transimination " or " transaldimination " not only sounds more impressive, but is probably preferred usage and should be generally adopted.

# REACTIONS OF PYRIDOXAL-N-METHOCHLORIDE WITH AMINO ACIDS*

by CLARE C. JOHNSTON, HOUSTON G. BROOKS, JERRY D. ALBERT and DAVID E. METZLER

Department of Biochemistry and Biophysics, Iowa State University, Ames, Iowa

THE phosphate ester of vitamin $B_6$ aldehyde (pyridoxal phosphate) in its coenzymic roles, doubtless functions through formation of imines (Schiff bases) with the substrate amino acids.[1,2] These imines can then undergo a variety of reactions depending upon the structure of the amino acids and the nature of the enzyme protein. Studies of non-enzymic reactions of pyridoxal have, in the past, helped to clarify the chemical basis for these catalytic activities. We now wish to report studies of imine formation and other non-enzymic reactions of pyridoxal-N-methochloride† (I), which may contribute in a small way to our understanding of pyridoxal phosphate catalysis.

## ABSORPTION SPECTRUM AND p$K_a$

Pyridoxal methochloride (Ia) can dissociate to form the dipolar ion (Ib) in the same way as does the pyridoxal cation,[3] and as with pyridoxal, the free aldehyde form (Ic) should be present in small amounts in equilibrium with the hemiacetal form.

Figure 1 shows the absorption spectrum of pyridoxal methochloride at low pH (cation) and high pH (dipolar ion).†† The corresponding spectra of pyridoxal (dashed lines) are included for comparison purposes. As with other

---

*Journal Paper No. J-4472 of the Iowa Agricultural and Home Economics Experiment Station, Ames, Iowa, Project No. 1259. This investigation was supported by a research grant (A-1549) from the United States Public Health Service.

†Pyridoxal methochloride (I) was prepared from pyridoxal hydrochloride by the method of Heyl *et al.*[4,5] Anal: Calculated for $C_9H_{12}ClNO_3$: C, 49.7; H, 5.56; N, 6.44. Found C, 50.4, 50.5; H, 5.71, 5.80; N, 6.24, 6.24.

††Beckman model DU and Cary model 14 spectrophotometers and a Beckman model G pH-meter with a general purpose glass electrode were used for all of the experiments described here.

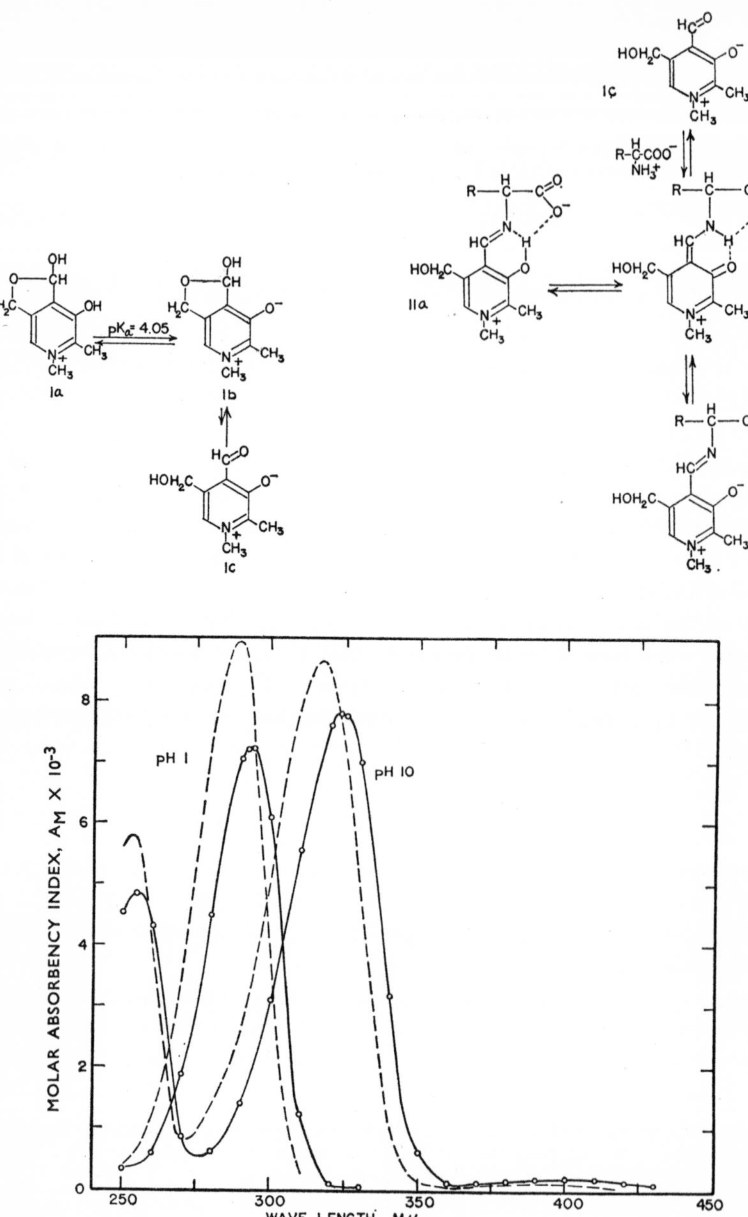


FIG. 1. Absorption spectrum of pyridoxal-N-methochloride. The solutions were $9 \times 10^{-5}$ M in pyridoxal methochloride at pH 1 (HCl solution) and pH 10 (carbonate buffer), 0.5 ionic strength, 25°.

(———) Pyridoxal-N-methochloride.

(- - - - -) Pyridoxal cation and dipolar ion[2].

3-hydroxypyridine compounds,[3] N-methylation of pyridoxal results in a shift of the absorption peak to longer wavelengths, by 5–6 mμ for the high wavelength band. The absorption spectrum of pyridoxal methochloride at pH values near 4 represents a mixture of the two forms, (Ia) and (Ib), and measurements of the absorbencies at 293.5 and 323 mμ at several pH values near 4 permitted a precise evaluation of the apparent $pK_a$ value of $4.05 \pm 0.03$ for dissociation of the phenolic group. This compares with a value of 4.2 for pyridoxal.[3]

Like that of pyridoxal, the spectrum of its N-methochloride displays a weak, broad absorption band centering around 390–400 mμ and apparently representing the free aldehyde form (Ic). It is of interest that this band is about 1.7 times as high in the methylated compound than in pyridoxal itself suggesting that a somewhat higher fraction of the free aldehyde is present in the former compound.

## SCHIFF BASE FORMATION

The reaction of pyridoxal-N-methochloride with amino acids yields imines (II), of which the neutral form (IIa) can be expected to form at low pH. Recent studies of Heinert and Martell[6] suggest that this exists primarily in the form (IIa) in which the bridge hydrogen is closer to the imine nitrogen than to the phenolic oxygen. At higher pH values dissociation to the dipolar anionic form (IIb) can be expected.

The corresponding anion of the imines formed from pyridoxal itself is not known, however, because the imine (IIIa), derived from pyridoxal, dissociates to the hydrogen bonded form (IIIb) instead.

IIIa $\underset{pK \approx 5.9}{\overset{-H^+}{\rightleftharpoons}}$ IIIb $\underset{pK = 10.5}{\overset{-H^+}{\rightleftharpoons}}$ IIIc

At a pH of 11 in aqueous 0.5 valine, pyridoxal methochloride displays a strong absorption peak at 378 mμ (Fig. 2*) which we interpret as representing

*Solutions for spectral measurements were prepared by mixing suitable portions of freshly prepared stock solutions of pyridoxal-N-methochloride valine, buffer and sodium chloride sufficient to bring the ionic strength to a value of 0.5. Spectra were read after ½ hr of standing in the dark at 25°. Only insignificant changes occurred thereafter over a 6-hr period in the dark. However, if placed in a quartz cuvette 2 ft from a 75W incandescent lamp, a solution of pyridoxal methochloride at pH 6 underwent a decrease of absorbency at 323 mμ of about 1.8 per cent per hr.

the dipolar anion of the imine (IIb). The presence of a small shoulder at 320–330 m$\mu$ on the side of the main absorption peak suggests that a small amount of unreacted starting compound remains. We thought it desirable to correct for this, and did so, but by a procedure which some may regard as guess-work rather than science. We arbitrarily assumed that some amount, say 5 per cent, of unreacted starting material remained at equilibrium. We then subtracted from the observed molar absorbency index at every wave-length the absorption expected from this 5 per cent of material. Division of

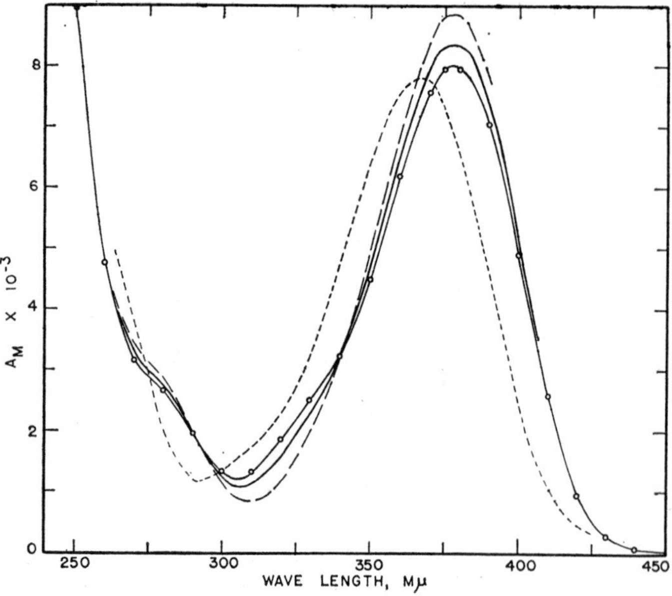


FIG. 2. Spectrum of pyridoxal-N-methochloride in 0.5 M valine, pH 11.

(—o—) Experimental curve.

(———) Spectrum of imine anion (IIb), assuming 5 per cent of unreacted pyridoxal methochloride.

(— — — —) Spectrum of imine anion, assuming 10 per cent unreacted pyridoxal methochloride.

(- - - - -) Spectrum of the pyridoxal valine Schiff base di-anion (IIIc)[2].

the resultant absorbency by the assumed fraction of imine (in this case 0.95) gave the molar absorbency of the imine (IIb). This is shown in Fig. 2 by the plain solid line for the 5 per cent assumption and by a dashed line for the assumption of 10 per cent unreacted methochloride. At least we can now look at these curves and choose one which best fits our taste and preconceived notions. In this case we chose the " 5 per cent curve ", for in it the shoulder at 320–330 m$\mu$ is nearly gone and in the " 10 per cent curve " the main absorption peak is more symmetrical than might be expected from a comparison with the spectra of pyridoxal Schiff bases and other related compounds. We could doubtless have determined the fraction of imine more certainly by extrapolation from measurements of the absorbencies of a series of solutions of various valine concentrations, but the present estimate seems adequate.

Figure 2 also shows the spectrum of the pyridoxal-valine imine at pH 12.[2] This is the spectrum of the dianion (IIIc) differing from the pyridoxal

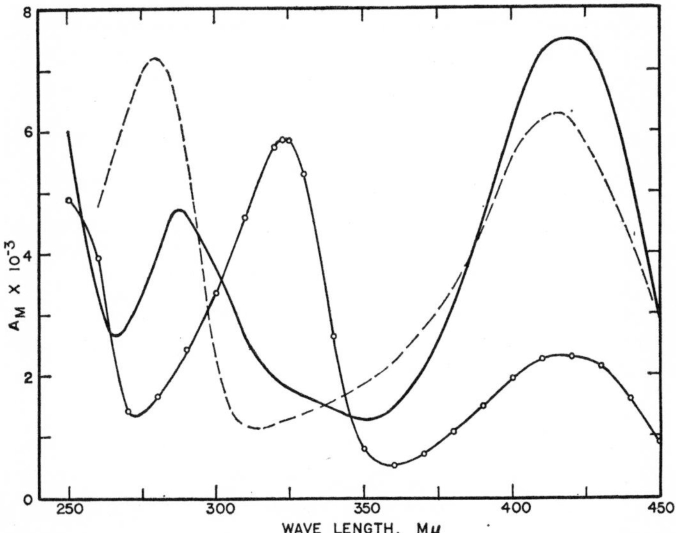


FIG. 3. Spectrum of pyridoxal-N-methochloride in 0.5 M valine, pH 6 phosphate buffer.

(—o—) Experimental curve.

(———) Spectrum of imine dipolar ion (IIa), assuming 70 per cent unreacted pyridoxal methochloride (30 per cent conversion to the Schiff base).

(- - - -) Spectrum of the pyridoxal-valine dipolar anion (IIIb).

methochloride imine in lacking the methyl group and the positive charge on the nitrogen. The effect of this methylation is to shift the absorption peak from 367 to 377 mμ. This is in the same direction but of a different magnitude than the 15 mμ shift of the absorption band of the free pyridoxal anion upon protonation to form the dipolar ion.[3]

At a pH of 6, 0.5 M valine, pyridoxal methochloride is partially converted to a form absorbing at 419 mμ (Fig. 3, —o—) presumably the hydrogen-bonded imine (IIa). The extent of imine formation is apparently low, for a substantial peak remains at 323 mμ, and doubtless represents unreacted pyridoxal methochloride. If we assumed a 30 per cent conversion, and subtracted out the absorption of the 70 per cent of unreacted starting material, a smooth curve showing virtually no 323 mμ peak resulted (Fig. 4). (See also note (1) added in proof.) On the other hand, if 25 or 36 per cent conversion was assumed, the resultant curves showed either a depression or a shoulder in the 323 mμ region. In order to give some idea of the accuracy with which we know the spectrum of this form of the Schiff base, these latter curves are also shown in Fig. 4. We have assumed the spectrum based on 30 per cent reaction to be the correct one, and it is also given as a solid line in Fig. 3. The dashed line in Fig. 3 is the spectrum of the hydrogen-bonded pyridoxal-valine

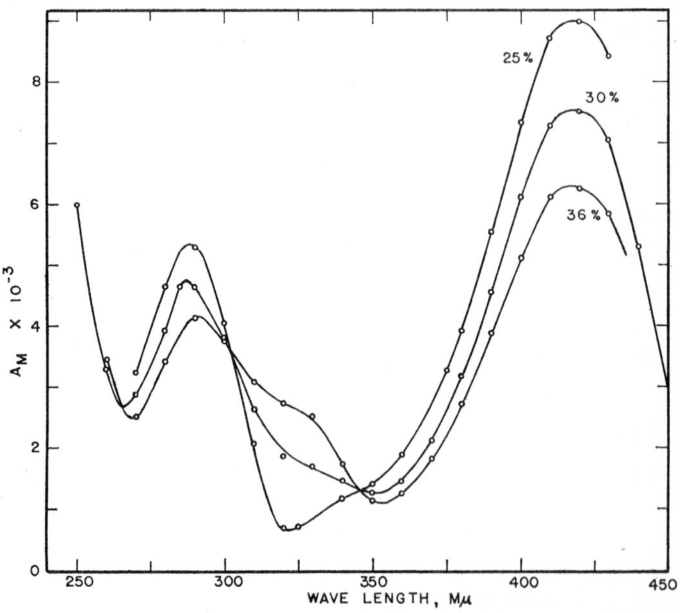


FIG. 4. Spectrum of pyridoxal-N-methochloride valine Schiff base (IIa) at pH 6, assuming various extents of conversion to the Schiff base. These curves were calculated from the experimental curve of Fig. 3 assuming respectively 25, 30 and 36 per cent conversion to the Schiff base.

Schiff base at pH 8.4.[2] A certain similarity between the spectra of the two imines is apparent, and again a 5 mμ peak position shift is observed, but it should be remembered that the pyridoxal Schiff base at pH 8.4 is not protonated on the ring nitrogen. The complete spectrum of the N-protonated pyridoxal imine has not been measured, but we do know that the 414 mμ absorption band has the same general shape and peak position in the N-protonated form as in the mono anion (pH 8.4) form.[2] It is probable, that as in the copper and zinc chelates of pyridoxylidene valine[7] N-protonation increases the intensity of the long wavelength band while decreasing that of the shorter wavelength band.

Data on peak positions and absorbency indices of the various Schiff base forms are presented in Table 1.

TABLE 1. COMPARISON OF ABSORPTION SPECTRA OF PYRIDOXAL-N-METHOCHLORIDE, PYRIDOXAL AND THEIR SCHIFF BASES

| | Pyridoxal N-methochloride | | Pyridoxal | | |
|---|---|---|---|---|---|
| | $\lambda_{max}$ (m$\mu$) | $a_M \times 10^{-3}$ | $\lambda_{max}$ (m$\mu$) | $a_M \times 10^{-3}$ | $\Delta\lambda_{max}$* (m$\mu$) |
| Free cation (Ia) | 293 | 7.2 | 288 | 9.0 | + 5 |
| Dipolar ion (Ib) | 323 | 7.8 | 317 | 8.9 | + 6 |
| | 255 | 4.8 | 252 | 5.8 | + 3 |
| Imine dipolar ion (IIa), (IIIa) | 419 | ~ 7.5 | 414 | (?) | + 5 |
| | 288 | ~ 4.7 | | | |
| Imine dipolar anion (IIb) | 378 | 8.4 | | | |
| Imine anion (IIIb) | | | 367 | 7.9 | |
| Zinc chelate (IV) | 383 | ~ 7.4 | 379 | 8.7 | + 4 |
| | 280 | ~ 5.1 | 277 | 4.8 | + 3 |

*Shift of position of maximum between N-protonated and N-methylated compound.

## SCHIFF BASE FORMATION CONSTANTS

The apparent molar absorbency index for any solution containing valine and pyridoxal methochloride in the pH range 6–11 can be expressed as the sum:

$$a_M \text{ (observed)} = a_{M,1} f_1 + a_{M,2} f_2 + a_{M,3} f_3$$

Where the subscript numbers 1, 2, 3 refer to the three components, the free pyridoxal methochloride dipolar ion (Ib), the imine dipolar ion (IIa) and the imine anion (IIb), and the $f$'s refer to the fraction of the total pyridoxal methochloride in each of the three forms. By measuring $a_M$ at the three wavelengths, 320, 380 and 430 m$\mu$, we were able to solve by a successive approximation method for $f_1$, $f_2$ and $f_3$. The $a_M$ values for the individual forms are given in Table 2 and the results of such calculations on three pairs of duplicate solutions are shown in Table 3. In Table 3 the fit of the data to Eq. (1) has been illustrated by using the values of $f_1$, $f_2$ and $f_3$ and Eq. (1) to calculate the expected absorbencies at three wavelengths. These calculated values are compared with experimentally observed values in Table 3.

From the $f$-values of Table 3 the p$K_a$ for conversion of (IIa) to (IIb) and the formation constants for the imines were calculated. These are given in Table 4. (The value for pH 6.01 was computed from the *assumed* 30 per cent conversion.) It should be noted that all equilibrium constants are apparent constants expressed in terms of molar concentrations, except that apparent hydrogen ion activities (from pH-meter readings) were used instead of hydrogen ion concentrations. Although the results are completely consistent

TABLE 2. MOLAR ABSORBENCY INDICES USED IN CALCULATIONS
Values are for $a_m \times 10^{-3}$

| Compound | Wavelength (mμ) | | | |
|---|---|---|---|---|
| | 280 | 320 | 380 | 430 |
| Pyridoxal methochloride, dipolar ion | 0.85 | 7.52 | 0.16 | 0.09 |
| Pyridoxal methochloride-valine Schiff base | | | | |
| dipolar ion (low pH) | | 1.87 | 3.17 | 7.04 |
| anion (high pH) | | 1.58 | 8.37 | 0.29 |
| zinc chelate | 5.05 | 0.97 | 7.35 | 0.50 |

TABLE 3. ANALYSIS OF ABSORPTION SPECTRA OF SOLUTIONS OF PYRIDOXAL METHOCHLORIDE IN 0.5 M VALINE
Ionic strength 0.5

| pH | Apparent molar absorbency indices | | |
|---|---|---|---|
| | 320 mμ | 380 mμ | 430 mμ |
| 7.82 | | | |
| Experimentally observed | 5.30, 5.12 | 2.32, 2.20 | 1.90, 1.79 |
| Calculated | 5.21 | 2.26 | 1.85 |
| 8.01, 8.04 | | | |
| Experimentally observed | 4.92, 4.92 | 2.78, 2.79 | 1.70, 1.72 |
| Calculated | 4.85 | 2.73 | 1.67 |
| 8.49, 8.50 | | | |
| Experimentally observed | 3.71, 3.79 | 4.67, 4.70 | 1.30, 1.31 |
| Calculated | 3.77 | 4.61 | 1.26 |
| **pH** | **Fraction of total pyridoxal methochloride** | | |
| | Free dipolar ion | Imine dipolar Ion | Imine Anion |
| 7.82 | 0.59 | 0.25 | 0.16 |
| 8.01, 8.04 | 0.55 | 0.22 | 0.23 |
| 8.49, 8.50 | 0.36 | 0.16 | 0.48 |

among themselves, some uncertainty exists in the equilibrium constants because of the uncertainty in our estimate of the imine dipolar ion spectrum. Thus, if we had taken the 25 per cent reaction curve of Fig. 4 rather than the 30 per cent curve the value of log $K_i'$ would be $-0.18$ rather than $-0.10$ and p$K_{2pv}$ would be 7.93 rather than 8.0.

TABLE 4. EQUILIBRIUM CONSTANTS CALCULATED FROM SPECTRA OF PYRIDOXAL-N-METHOCHLORIDE VALINE SOLUTIONS

| pH | log $K_i'$[a] | p$K_{2pv}$(Imine) | log $K_i''$[b] |
|---|---|---|---|
| 6.01 | $-0.07$ | | |
| 7.82 | $-0.07$ | 8.00 | |
| 8.02 | $-0.09$ | 8.01 | |
| 8.50 | $-0.16$ | 8.00 | |
| Average | $-0.10$ | 8.0 | 1.52 |
| For pyridoxal | $-0.27$[2] | | 3.47 |

[a] $K_i' = \dfrac{(\text{Imine}^{\pm})}{(\text{P}^{\pm})(\text{V}^{\pm})}$. [b] $K_i'' = \dfrac{(\text{Imine}^{-})}{(\text{P}^{\pm})(\text{V}^{-})} = K_i' \dfrac{K_{2pv}}{K_{2p}}$

For pyridoxal case we also have $K_i'' = K_i \dfrac{K_{2p}}{K_{3pv}}$

The formation constant of the dipolar ionic imine is represented by

$$K_i' = \frac{[\text{Imine}^{\pm}]}{[\text{P}^{\pm}]\,[\text{V}^{\pm}]}$$

where $[\text{P}^{\pm}]$ is the concentration of pyridoxal or pyridoxal methochloride dipolar ion and $[\text{V}^{\pm}]$ that of valine. The pyridoxal methochloride imine (log $K_i' = -0.10$) is just slightly more stable than the corresponding pyridoxal imine (log $K_i' = -0.27$). The value of $K_i'$ for pyridoxal was calculated from the published formation constant, $K_i$, of the imine di-anion (IIIc) and the dissociation constants of the imine. A diagram of the interrelationships of these various equilibrium constants is shown in Fig. 5.

We also computed the constants

$$K_i'' = \frac{[\text{Imine}^{-}]}{[\text{P}^{\pm}]\,[\text{V}^{-}]}$$

for the formation of (IIb) or (IIIb).* From the values of these constants (Table 4) we see that the hydrogen-bonded anionic imine from pyridoxal is approximately 100 times more stable than the non-hydrogen bonded form from pyridoxal-N-methochloride.

*Use of this constant predicts that in the pH 11 solution of Fig. 2, 6 per cent of free unreacted pyridoxal methochloride would be present, in good agreement with the previously assumed 5 per cent.

We can also look at the hydrogen bond in the following way. Let us suppose that the p$K$ for dissociation of the bridge hydrogen from the pyridoxal imine (IIIa) is very similar to that of the methylated analog, i.e. about 8. Then, as seen from Fig. 6, the equilibrium constant for transfer of a proton from the ring nitrogen to the hydrogen-bonded position is about 125. Yet

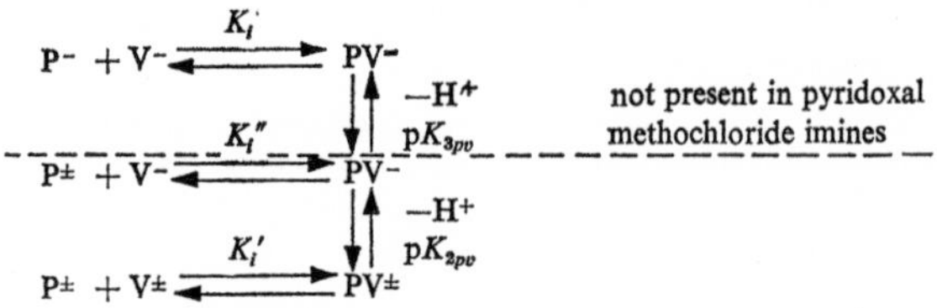

$$P^- + V^- \underset{}{\overset{K_i}{\rightleftharpoons}} PV^-$$

$$\downarrow\uparrow \; -H^+, \; pK_{3pv} \qquad \text{not present in pyridoxal methochloride imines}$$

$$P^\pm + V^- \overset{K_i''}{\rightleftharpoons} PV^-$$

$$\downarrow\uparrow \; -H^+, \; pK_{2pv}$$

$$P^\pm + V^\pm \overset{K_i'}{\rightleftharpoons} PV^\pm$$

$$K_i' = K_i \frac{K_{2p}\,K_{2v}}{K_{2pv}\,K_{3pv}} = K_i'' \frac{K_{2v}}{K_{2pv}}$$

$$K_i'' = K_i \frac{K_{2p}}{K_{3pv}}$$

FIG. 5. Equilibria in pyridoxal valine or pyridoxal-N-methochloride valine solutions.[2]

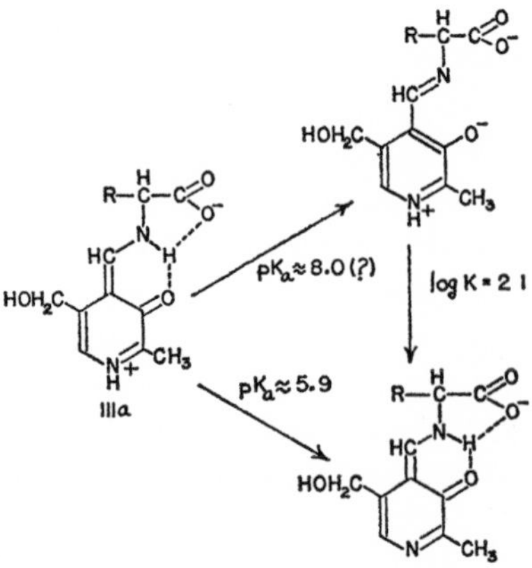

IIIa

$pK_a \approx 8.0\,(?)$

$\log K = 2.1$

$pK_a \approx 5.9$

FIG. 6. Scheme showing method of estimation of equilibrium constant for transfer of proton from ring nitrogen to hydrogen-bonded position.

we know that in pyridoxine itself the tendency is for the proton to stay on the ring nitrogen, with $K = 0.14$ for transfer of the proton to the phenolate anion position.

## COMPARISON WITH ENZYME SPECTRA

Several pyridoxal phosphate dependent enzymes at relatively low pH display an absorption bond near 414 m$\mu$ which is probably caused by a Schiff base formed with the $\epsilon$-amino group of lysine.[9–12] At higher pH the behavior of these enzymes is less obvious. In the case of phosphorylase, the absorption band shifts back to 333 mμ suggesting loss of the —C=N— double bond of the imine. In glutamic–aspartic transaminase the peak shifts to 362 mμ and it has been suggested[9,13] that in this enzyme the dipolar anion form of a lysine Schiff base analogous to (IIb) may be present. The absorption peak of (IIb) is at 377 mμ and that of the corresponding pyridoxal imine would doubtless be about 372 mμ and that of a pyridoxal phosphate imine would probably be nearly the same.[14] Thus a significant difference exists. The protonated form of the enzyme also absorbs maximally at 435 mμ[9] as compared with about 414 mμ for the pyridoxal valine imine. The p$K$ for loss of a proton from the enzyme is 6.2, which can be compared with the value 8.0 for the imine of pyridoxal-N-methochloride. These very substantial differences suggest that if the enzyme-bound coenzyme exists as a dipolar anion, its spectral behavior must be profoundly affected by groups in the protein.

## ZINC CHELATE

The pyridoxal-N-methochloride-valine Schiff base forms a zinc chelate just as does the pyridoxal-valine imine. By choosing conditions carefully, a high conversion to the chelate could be obtained with only 1–2 per cent of imine present. For example a solution of pH 4.85, 0.1 M valine and 0.02 M in zinc perchlorate (and containing potassium perchlorate to bring the ionic strength to 0.5) gave the spectrum shown in Fig. 7. Assuming 16 per cent unreacted pyridoxal methochloride, the spectrum of the chelate (solid line, Fig. 7) was obtained. This is closely similar to that of the corresponding protonated pyridoxal imine chelate[7,8] (dashed line). An equilibrium constant for formation of the chelate was estimated from measurements on several solutions of lower zinc content at pH values between 6 and 7. A formation constant,

$$K_c' = \frac{[\mathrm{MPV}^+]}{[\mathrm{V}^-]\,[\mathrm{P}^\pm]\,[\mathrm{Zn}^{2+}]}$$

was used in order to obtain a constant which was not affected by the presence or absence of hydrogen bonding in the imine. Log $K_c' = 7.2 \pm 0.2$, which can be compared with a value log $K_c' = 7.4$* for the pyridoxal chelate.

## TRANSAMINATION AND DEAMINATION REACTIONS

It is quite likely that in pyridoxal-dependent enzymes, the protein may be attached to the coenzyme in some way, e.g. through hydrogen bonding, at the ring nitrogen atom. Such attachment might have a profound effect on the reactivity of the imines which are presumed to exist as intermediates in the catalytic process. In order to clarify this possibility it would be of interest to

---

* $K_c' = \dfrac{K_C K_I K_{2p}}{K_{mpv}}$ (Ref. 7).

observe the effect of N-methylation, by which a permanent positive charge is placed at the ring nitrogen, on the reactivity of the imines in non-enzymic reactions. At present we can only report a brief study of two reactions, non-enzymic transamination of leucine and deamination of serine. These reactions were conducted at 100° according to the procedures of Metzler and Snell at pH 4.8 (acetate buffer) and 6.6 (phosphate buffer, pH values

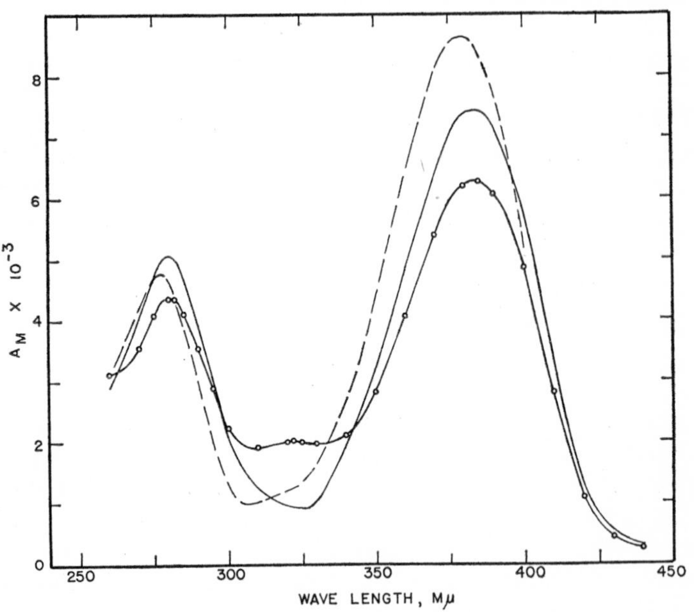


FIG. 7. Spectrum of zinc–pyridoxal-N-methochloride valine chelate.

(—○—) Experimental curve. Pyridoxal-N-methochloride, $9 \times 10^{-5}$ M, Valine, 0.1 M, and zinc perchlorate, 0.02 M. Ionic strength adjusted to 0.5 with potassium perchlorate.

(———) Chelate spectrum assuming 16 per cent unreacted pyridoxal methochloride.

(------) Corresponding pyridoxal chelate (N-protonated form[7,8]). Note that a discrepancy exists between this and the figure in Ref. 8. In the latter figure, through a drafting error the curves for low and high pH were switched throughout the lower wavelength band.

measured at 25°). In both reactions pyridoxal-N-methochloride was a very slightly better catalyst than pyridoxal at pH 4.8, and at pH 6.6 it was markedly better, producing about twice the extent of reaction in 10 min as does pyridoxal.* This result is at least qualitatively in harmony with the idea that

*Solutions of pyridoxal-N-methochloride were heated for 30 min at pH 4.7 and 6.6. Aliquots were then acidified to pH 0 and the optical densities at 288 and 293 mμ read. A maximum of 3 per cent loss in absorption was observed and the ratio of absorbencies at 292 to 288 mμ remained constant within 1 per cent. Thus no demethylation to pyridoxal occurs under the test conditions.

the N-protonated (or N-methylated) form of the metal chelate is the reactive form. More detailed experiments are now in progress by which the relative reactivities of pyridoxal, pyridoxal-N-methochloride, 5-deoxypyridoxal, pyridoxal phosphate and various 5-substituted pyridoxal derivatives will be compared at 25°. Under these conditions where equilibrium constants for Schiff base and metal chelate formation are known it should be possible to measure and compare precise reaction rate constants.

## REFERENCES


1. A. E. BRAUNSTEIN; in *The Enzymes* (edited by P. D. BOYER, H. LARDY and K. MYRBÄCK), 2nd ed., vol. II, p. 113, Academic Press, New York (1960).
2. D. E. METZLER; *J. Am. Chem. Soc.* **79**, 485 (1957).
3. D. E. METZLER and E. E. SNELL; *J. Am. Chem. Soc.* **77**, 2431 (1955).
4. D. HEYL, E. LUZ, S. A. HARRIS and K. FOLKERS; *J. Am. Chem. Soc.* **73**, 3436 (1951).
5. H. G. BROOKS; Ph.D. Thesis, Iowa State University (1960).
6. D. HEINERT and A. E. MARTELL; *J. Am. Chem. Soc.* **84**, 3257 (1962).
7. L. DAVIS, F. RODDY and D. E. METZLER; *J. Am. Chem. Soc.* **82**, 127 (1961).
8. D. E. METZLER; *Federation Proc.* **20**, suppl. **10**, 234 (1961).
9. W. T. JENKINS and I. W. SIZER; *J. Am. Chem. Soc.* **79**, 2655 (1957); W. T. JENKINS, D. A. YPHANTIS and I. W. SIZER; *J. Biol. Chem.* 234, 51 (1959).
10. A. B. KENT, E. B. KREBS and E. H. FISCHER; *J. Biol. Chem.* **232**, 549 (1958).
11. R. SHUKUYA and G. W. SCHWERT; *J. Biol. Chem.* **235**, 1649 (1960).
12. Y. MATSUO and D. M. GREENBERG; *J. Biol. Chem.* **234**, 5–7 (1959).
13. E. E. SNELL and W. T. JENKINS; *J. Cell. Comp. Physiol.* **54**, suppl. 1, 161 (1959).
14. Y. MATSUO; *J. Am. Chem. Soc.* **79**, 2011 (1957).
15. D. E. METZLER and E. E. SNELL; *J. Am. Chem. Soc.* **74**, 979 (1952).
16. J. OLIVARD, D. E. METZLER and E. E. SNELL; *J. Biol. Chem.* **199**, 669 (1952).


## NOTE

Because of the uncertainty in the extent of imine formation at pH 6, we have measured the spectrum of pyridoxal methochloride at pH 6.0 in solutions of varying valine concentration from 0.08 to 0.5 M and have plotted the reciprocal of the apparent molar absorbency index at 319 m$\mu$ (minus that observed in the absence of valine) versus the reciprocal of valine concentration. Although the extrapolation is not highly accurate, the resulting linear plot permits an independent estimate of $a_M$ for the imine dipolar ion, IIa as $9.6 \times 10^3$; cf. Table 1, and $\log K' = -0.20$, cf. Table 4.

# INTERMEDIATE COMPOUNDS OF NON-ENZYMIC TRANSAMINATIONS

by CARLO CENNAMO

Department of Human Physiology,
University of Modena, Italy

WHEN heated with PL* and a suitable metal ion, amino acids undergo various reactions (e.g. reversible transamination to PM and keto acids) which can be considered as models of the corresponding reactions catalyzed by pyridoxal phosphate-containing enzymes.[1,2] According to the mechanism proposed by Metzler *et al.*[1], these non-enzymic reactions take place via the formation of chelate complexes of metal ions with the imines (Schiff bases, pyridoxylidene amino acids) of PL and amino acids. Such complexes have been isolated in some cases[3-5] and studied spectrophotometrically[6] and by chromatography and electrophoresis.[7] A thorough spectrophotometric investigation was accomplished recently by Davis *et al.*[8] Free imines, which are present in solutions containing PL and amino acids, in the absence of metal ions,[9] do not allow non-enzymic reactions to occur rapidly. However, we have observed a rapid non-enzymic transamination, in the absence of metal ions, when the carboxyl group of some amino acids was masked by esterification.[10]

In a previous paper,[11] we studied the formation of aluminum chelates of pyridoxylidene amino acids spectrophotometrically at 25° and pH 5; reactants were present in the concentrations which have been used[12,13] to study non-enzymic transamination at 100°. Notable concentrations of aluminum chelates were found in solutions containing initially PL and amino acids or PM and keto acids. In both cases the chelates exhibited similar absorption spectra between 350 mμ and 450 mμ, with a peak at 370 mμ, and appeared to contain the aldimine form of the Schiff base. Moreover, we observed that solutions containing PL, PM and alum showed a similar behavior and we proposed that an imine chelate was formed also in this case.

This paper deals mainly with an attempt to correlate the chelate formation and the rate of transamination at 25°, 40° and 55°C, in the two systems:

$$\text{PL} + \text{alanine} + Al^{3+} \qquad \text{(a)}$$

$$\text{PM} + \text{pyruvate} + Al^{3+} \qquad \text{(b)}$$

*Abbreviations: PL = pyridoxal; PM = pyridoxamine.

## EXPERIMENTAL

### *Apparatus and Chemicals*

A Beckman Model DU spectrophotometer with thermostatted cell compartment was employed. Selected pairs of 1-cm silica cells and 9-mm silica cell spacers were used in order to obtain an optical path of 1 mm.

Pyridoxal hydrochloride was obtained from Nutritional Biochemicals Co.; pyridoxamine dihydrochloride and L-alanine were supplied by Hoffman–La Roche. Sodium pyruvate and L-alanine ethylester hydrochloride were commercial products, purified by recrystallization.

The reaction mixtures were heated at 25°, 40° and 55° in a thermostatted bath.

### *Transamination*

Our reaction mixtures contained: 0.01 M PL (or PM), 0.01 M alanine (or pyruvate), 0.001 M $KAl(SO_4)_2 \cdot 12H_2O$ and 0.2 M acetate buffer at pH 5. Samples heated for short times were kept in stoppered test tubes and the reaction was stopped at the times fixed by adding versene at 0.0015 M final concentration. Samples heated for long times were kept in sealed test tubes and quickly chilled and diluted. Transamination was measured by determining the decrease of PL concentration in the system (a) and its increase in the system (b). PL was determined according to Metzler and Snell[12]: to 2-ml aliquots of properly diluted mixtures, 2 ml of 50 per cent ethanolamine were added and absorption at 360 mμ was measured with the spectrophotometer. We have observed that this method gives the concentration of total PL (free plus chelate PL). The measurements were more accurate for the reaction (b), than for the reaction (a), since transamination between alanine and PL was slow and it was difficult to measure little decreases of PL concentration.

### *Spectrophotometric Investigations*

Mixtures had the same composition described above. The reaction was started by adding alanine (or pyruvate) to the mixture of the other components, which was kept at the proper temperature in the bath. An aliquot was then transferred quickly into the silica cell, which had already been brought together with its spacer to the same temperature in the cell compartment of the spectrophotometer, and the cell was sealed with parafilm. The increase of optical density with time was followed at 370 mμ. From the values of O.D., corrected for the PL or PM present, chelate concentration was evaluated as described below. Absorption spectra between 350 and 450 mμ were measured rapidly when the reaction was slowed down enough, by correcting the values of O.D. for PL or PM present. The spectra were very similar in both the reaction systems.

*Evaluation of Chelate Concentration*

The concentrations of the reactants in our reaction mixtures were so high that it was not possible to observe the modifications of the whole spectra of PL and PM. Nevertheless, it was possible to study chelate formation, since these complexes absorb above 350 mμ, where the absorption of PL or PM is low.

In order to evaluate the concentration of chelate formed in these conditions, we have determined the molar absorbency indices as follows. Mixtures containing PL at low concentrations ($10^{-3}$ M or $2 \times 10^{-3}$ M), alanine ($10^{-1}$ M and $5 \times 10^{-2}$ M respectively), $10^{-3}$ M or $5 \times 10^{-4}$ M alum and 0.2 M acetate buffer at pH 5, were prepared at 25°. The decrease of O.D. at 317 mμ (absorption maximum of PL) was followed, at the beginning, together with its increase at 370 mμ (absorption maximum of chelate). The observed values of the molar absorbency index of PL at 317 mμ were, respectively: 7200, 7000 and 6700, at the temperatures of 25°, 40° and 55°. The corresponding values of chelate molar absorbency index resulted: 8640, 8400 and 8040. Consistent values were obtained with all the above described mixtures; the value at 25° is very similar to that reported by Davis *et al.*[8] for the zinc chelate containing one pyridoxylidene valine group. We have assumed that the determined molar absorbency indices could be applied for our experimental mixtures, which contained higher concentrations of PL than of alum, but it is known that metal chelates of pyridoxylidene amino acids can contain one or two imine groups according to the concentration conditions.[6,8] Chelates containing one imine group appear to predominate in solution.[8] Davis *et al.*[8] have observed that the zinc chelate with two imine groups exhibits a molar absorbency index for each PL group present, which is lower than that for the simpler chelate. If that holds true also for aluminum chelates, the presence of some chelate with two imine groups in our experimental mixtures might result in " chelate PL " concentrations higher than those calculated, in the case of the alanine reaction system.

*Dilute Mixtures*

In some experiments, the modifications of the whole spectra of PL and PM were followed at 25° in mixtures containing $2 \times 10^{-3}$ M PL (or PM), $5 \times 10^{-2}$ M alanine (or pyruvate), $10^{-3}$ M alum and 0.2 M acetate buffer at pH 5. Spectra were measured after some hours through an optical path of 1 mm. Then the mixtures were diluted tenfold, maintaining the concentration of the buffer constant, and some hours later, spectra were measured again through an optical path of 1 cm. Spectra of alanine or pyruvate were subtracted in every case.

## RESULTS

The results reported in Fig. 1 show that in both the reaction systems studied, already at 25°, chelate complexes were formed in concentrations which were high if compared to that of the alum present. The chelate appeared more rapidly in the pyruvate system (b) than in the alanine system

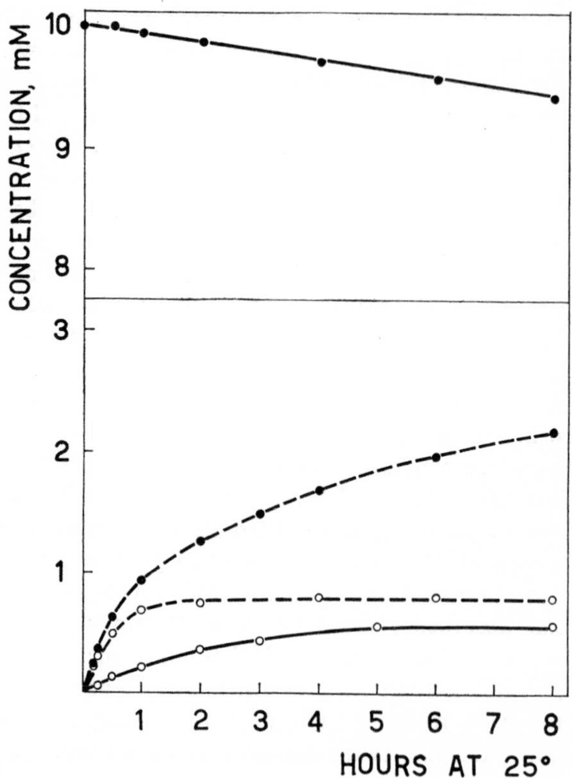


FIG. 1. PL (●) and chelate (○) concentrations vs. time, during reactions at pH 5 and at 25°: ———, in the alanine system; – – – in the pyruvate system.

(a), but in both cases increased to reach a constant concentration. In the system (a), the appearance of the chelate preceded the beginning of an appreciable transamination, whereas in the system (b) the concentration of the total PL formed was higher than that of the chelate, since the first minutes. This behavior suggests that in both cases the aldimine chelate was formed. Correspondingly, transamination was much more rapid in the system (b). At 40° (Fig. 2), the rate of chelate formation and transamination were enhanced in both systems, but much more markedly in the alanine system. At 55° (not shown), the two systems behaved more similarly, too.

The formation of the chelate of the aldimine form in both the systems studied was shown also by the similarity of the spectra between 350 and 450 mμ (see Experimental). In experiments at 25° with more dilute mixtures (Figs. 3 and 4), the modifications of the whole spectra of PL and PM were

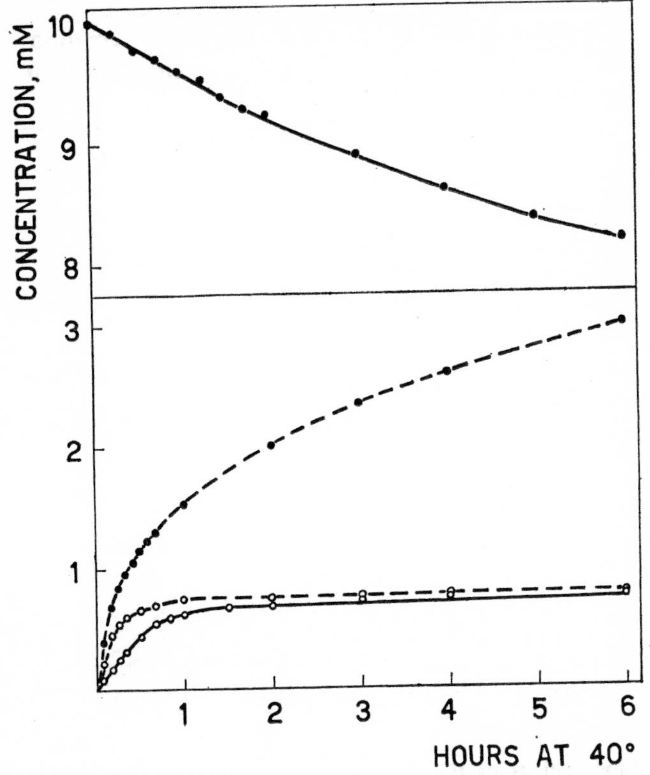


FIG. 2. PL (●) and chelate (○) concentrations vs. time, during reactions at pH 5 and at 40°: ———, in the alanine system; – – –, in the pyruvate system.

followed. The chelate formed exhibited, besides the peak at 370 mμ, an enhanced absorption at about 275 mμ. Peaks near these wavelengths have been observed for other metal chelates of pyridoxylidene amino acids.[8] Therefore, the spectral changes reported in the Figs. 3 and 4 can be explained by the formation of the chelate of the aldimine form and by the progressive appearance of the reaction product (PM in the system (a) and PL in the system (b)).

Aluminum does not form chelates absorbing at 370 mμ with PL and alanine ethylester.

We have also observed that at pH 5 the concentrations of the free imines, in solutions containing 0.01 M PL and 0.01 M alanine or alanine ethylester, but no alum, appeared to be equally low, at 25°, 40° and 55°, as shown by the absorption at 415 mμ (cf. Ref. 9).

## DISCUSSION

In the experiments reported, we have measured the chelate formation and the extent of transamination, in the same experimental conditions, in the course of the aluminum catalyzed reversible reaction between PL and

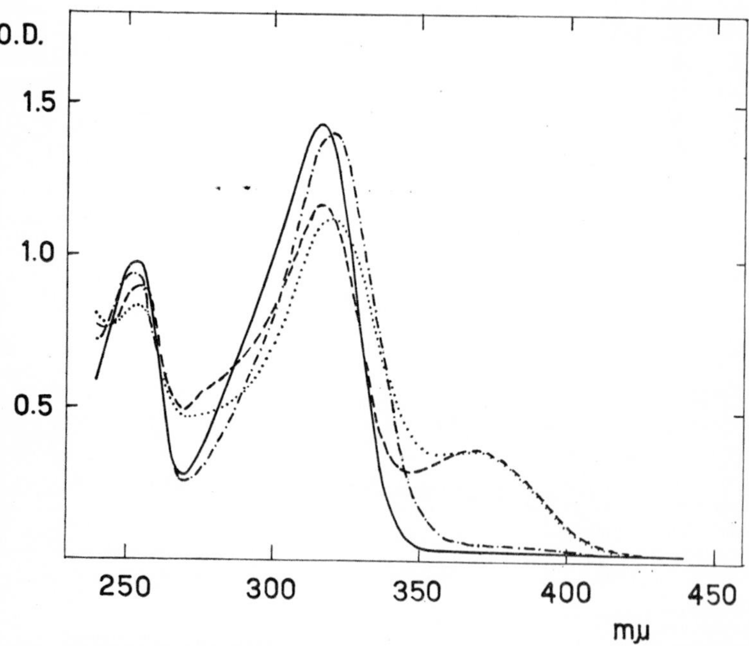


FIG. 3. Modifications of the spectrum of $2 \times 10^{-3}$ M PL, by reaction with $5 \times 10^{-2}$ M alanine and $10^{-3}$ M alum, at pH 5 and 25°: ———, PL alone; — — — —, complete mixture after 2 hr 30 min; ......, the same after 24 hr; —·—·—, the last one, 24 hr after tenfold dilution (see Experimental).

alanine. Our results show that there is a relationship between chelate formation and transamination, in the alanine as well as in the pyruvate system, and if the effects of temperature are considered. Therefore, the results afford some direct experimental evidence for the participation of chelate complexes in the mechanism of non-enzymic transamination. According to Metzler *et al.*[1], this reaction can be represented, in our case, as follows:

$$\text{PL} + \text{alanine} + Al^{3+} \rightleftharpoons C_1 \rightleftharpoons C_2 \rightleftharpoons \text{PM} + \text{pyruvate} + Al^{3+}$$

where $C_1$ and $C_2$ indicate the chelates containing the aldimine or the ketimine form, respectively.

We obtained no evidence for the formation of $C_2$ in an appreciable concentration; the higher stability of $C_1$ was also noticed by Eichhorn and Dawes[6]. $C_2$ appears to be transformed readily to $C_1$ in our conditions, so that transamination is notable in the case of the pyruvate reaction with PM, also at 25°. Fasella *et al.*[7] reported the isolation of both $C_1$ and $C_2$ by chromatography and electrophoresis. However, we proposed[11] that PL,

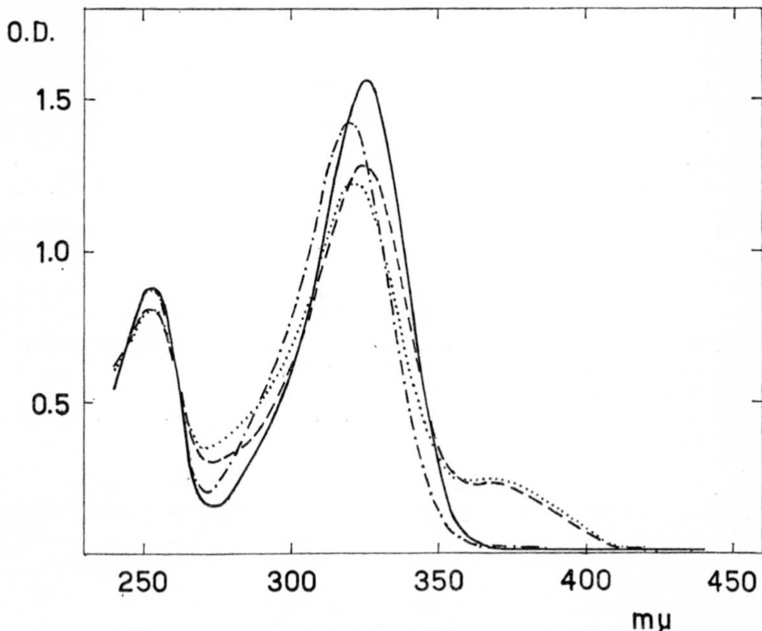


FIG. 4. Modifications of the spectrum of $2 \times 10^{-3}$ M PM, by reaction with $5 \times 10^{-2}$ M pyruvate and $10^{-3}$ M alum, at pH 5 and 25°: ———, PM alone; — — — —, complete mixture after 1 hr; ......, the same after 3 hr; —·—·—·—, the last one, 14 hr after tenfold dilution (see Experimental).

PM and aluminum ion can form an imine chelate, and it is likely that such a complex appears during a transamination reaction. This complex might have been present in the $C_2$ chelate, which was isolated by the above-mentioned authors and was found to hydrolyse to $C_1$, PL and PM.

Our results are in essential agreement with those obtained by Cattanéo *et al.*[14] in the case of non-enzymic reactions with PL-phosphate and PM-phosphate.

The observation that aluminum does not form chelate complexes with PL and alanine ethylester indicates that the carboxyl group of amino acids is involved in aluminum chelation.

At pH 5, free imines of PL and alanine or alanine ethylester are present in equally low concentrations, at 25°, 40° and 55°. Since the imine of the ester was supposed to be the intermediate compound of the metal ion independent non-enzymic transamination between PL and amino acid esters,[10] it might be suggested that the imine of the ester is more active than the chelate in the non-enzymic reaction.

## SUMMARY

Chelate formation and transamination have been measured in the course of the aluminum catalyzed reversible reaction between PL and alanine, at pH 5 and at 25°, 40° and 55°. A relationship between the two processes has been observed. The chelate formed appeared to contain the aldimine form of the Schiff base.

Aluminum does not form chelates with alanine ethylester and PL.

At pH 5, free imines of PL and alanine or alanine ethylester are present in equally low concentrations.

## REFERENCES

1. D. E. Metzler, M. Ikawa and E. E. Snell; *J. Am. Chem. Soc.* **76**, 648 (1954).
2. E. E. Snell; *Vitamins and Hormones* **16**, 77 (1958).
3. G. Baddiley; *Nature* **170**, 711 (1952).
4. D. E. Metzler, J. B. Longenecker and E. E. Snell; *J. Am. Chem. Soc.* **76**, 639 (1954).
5. H. N. Christensen; *J. Am. Chem. Soc.* **79**, 4073 (1957).
6. G. L. Eichhorn and J. W. Dawes; *J. Am. Chem. Soc.* **76**, 5663 (1954).
7. P. Fasella, H. Lis, N. Siliprandi and C. Baglioni; *Biochim. et Biophys. Acta* **23**, 417 (1957).
8. L. Davis, F. Roddy and D. E. Metzler; *J. Am. Chem. Soc.* **83**, 127 (1961).
9. D. E. Metzler; *J. Am. Chem. Soc.* **79**, 485 (1957).
10. C. Cennamo; *Boll. soc. ital. biol. sper.* **37**, 183 (1961).
11. C. Cenammo; *Boll. soc. ital. biol. sper.* **38**, 1037 (1962).
12. D. E. Metzler and E. E. Snell; *J. Am. Chem. Soc.* **74**, 979 (1952).
13. C. Cennamo, B. Carafoli and E. P. Bonetti; *J. Am. Chem. Soc.* **78**, 3523 (1956).
14. J. Cattanéo, J. C. Senez and P. Beaumont; *Biochim. et Biophys. Acta* **44**, 543 (1960).

# NON-ENZYMIC TRANSAMINATION OF $\gamma$-AMINOBUTYRIC ACID*

by F. Olivo, C. S. Rossi and N. Siliprandi

Institute of Biochemistry,
University of Padua, Italy

Many reactions catalyzed by pyridoxal-5'-phosphate enzymes have been easily duplicated non-enzymatically with $\alpha$-amino acids and either PLP or PL.†

Polyvalent metal ions have been found to favor the non-enzymic transamination and to inhibit decarboxylation.[1]

The theory of the mechanism of enzymic and non-enzymic reactions was elaborated by Snell[2] and Braunstein[3]. The interaction between the formyl group of PL or PLP and the $\alpha$-amino group of amino acids should result in the Schiff base (imine) formation. After the imine formation an electron displacement from the $\alpha$-carbon atom of the amino acid weakens the bonds around this carbon atom. In the transamination reaction this weakening of bonds determines the loss of the proton from the $\alpha$-carbon atom and a consecutive rearrangement of the imine in a second intermediate compound.

$\gamma$-Aminobutyric acid also undergoes a non-enzymic transamination with either PL or PLP,[4] but this reaction occurs only to a limited extent even at 90°–100°C, in contrast to the more marked reactivity of the $\alpha$-amino acids.

The reason for the different behaviour of $\alpha$- and $\gamma$-amino acids in the non-enzymic transamination reaction has not been clarified.

In a previous paper[4] evidence was given for the non-enzymic transamination between GABA and PL or PLP, through the imine formation. From the reaction mixture GABA, PL, PM and one very unstable intermediate compound have been isolated by paper chromatography. Absorption spectra of the intermediate compound in acid and alkaline solutions were consistent with a hydrogen-bonded imine structure.

In the present paper measurements were carried out of the extent of the imine formation between PL and GABA, or alternatively PLP and GABA,

*This work was supported by grants from the Rockefeller Foundation and from Consiglio Nazionale delle Ricerche.

†Abbreviations used: PLP, pyridoxal phosphate; PL, pyridoxal; PM, pyridoxamine; GABA, $\gamma$-aminobutyric acid.

at various pH's and temperatures, in order to determine the apparent equilibrium constant for imine formation.

Both PL and PLP have been considered with respect to their different effects on the imine formation reaction rate. In the case of PL the limiting factor in the kinetics of the reaction is the unfavorable equilibrium between the hemiacetal and the open form of the molecule; this equilibrium also affects the final concentration of the imine. On the contrary, PLP and GABA react rapidly to yield the imine almost immediately.

In addition, the influence of metal ions on the imine formation and structure was reinvestigated in order to determine their effects on the transamination between PL or PLP and GABA.

## MATERIALS AND METHODS

PL, PLP and GABA were commercial products from Hoffman–La Roche (Basel). The stock solutions, stored at 0°C and protected from light, were replaced after 4 days.

Buffers used were: pH 6.3 and 7.4, 0.1 M Na-phosphate.

Reactions between PL or PLP and GABA for the determination of the apparent equilibrium constant were performed at different temperatures (from 20°C to 42°C). The concentration of PL or PLP was $1 \times 10^{-4}$ M or $2 \times 10^{-4}$ M and that of GABA in each series of determinations was increased from $3.3 \times 10^{-3}$ M to 0.5 M. In every case the GABA concentration was almost thirty times that of PL or PLP.

The temperature was measured directly in the spectrophotometer cell by a Philips's resistor. The pH of all reaction mixtures was measured after the spectra were taken.

In experiments in which the metal ions $Cu^{2+}$, $Ni^{2+}$, $Co^{2+}$, $Mg^{2+}$ and $Al^{3+}$ were added (in concentrations between $1 \times 10^{-5}$ M and $1 \times 10^{-1}$ M) in order to study the imine chelation, precipitates were formed in buffer systems. To prevent the hydrolysis of metal salts and the precipitate formation, solutions were prepared with distilled water. The pH was that of the GABA solutions. Added metal ions do not alter the absorption spectra of PL or PLP.

Zeiss model M4, Beckman model DU and Beckman DB recorder spectrophotometers, with thermostatted cell holders, were employed.

### *Apparent Equilibrium Constant $K_a$ and Molar Absorbency Indexes Determination*

The apparent equilibrium constant ($K_a$) for the imine formation was determined by spectrophotometric measurements.

$$K_a = \frac{[\text{Imine}]}{[\text{PL}] \cdot [\text{GABA}]}$$

where the concentrations in brackets represents the sum of all the ionic species of each compound.

Molar absorbency indexes and $K_a$ were obtained by the graphic methods of Ketelaar *et al.*[5-6] and Isenberg and Szent-Gyorgyi[7]. These methods are suitable for $K_a$ and $\epsilon$ determination of molecular complexes, in which each component participates with only one molecule, provided that all reactants and reaction products obey Beer's law.

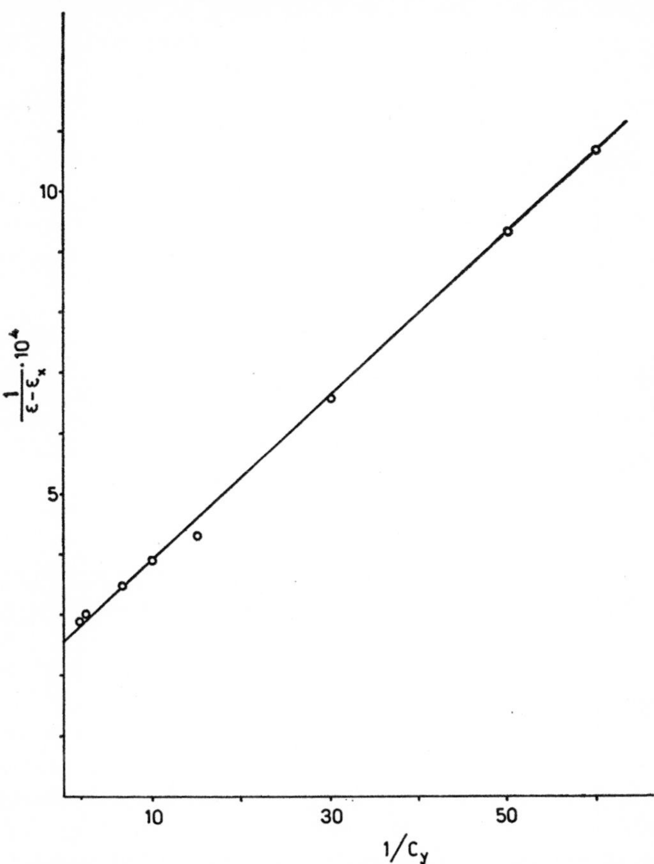


FIG. 1. Determination of the apparent equilibrium constant, $K_a$, and molar absorbency index at 410 m$\mu$ for the GABA–PLP system at pH 6.3 at 43.5°C, according to Eq. (1).

All spectrophotometric data were corrected for the absorbence of GABA. Owing to the high concentration of the amino acid with respect to that of the imine at equilibrium, the small decrease of GABA concentration was neglected in applying the correction. Molar absorbency indexes of PL and PLP were determined at the desired wavelength, pH and temperature, because the contribution of the various ionic forms of these compounds to the total absorbence changes with experimental conditions.

The values thus obtained could be introduced into Katelaar's equation:

$$\frac{1}{(\epsilon - \epsilon_x)} = \frac{1}{K_a\ (\epsilon_i - \epsilon_x)} \cdot \frac{1}{C_y} + \frac{1}{(\epsilon_i - \epsilon_x)} \qquad (1)$$

where $\epsilon$ is the apparent molar absorbency index of the reaction mixture (i.e. ratio between spectrophotometer reading to the molar concentration of

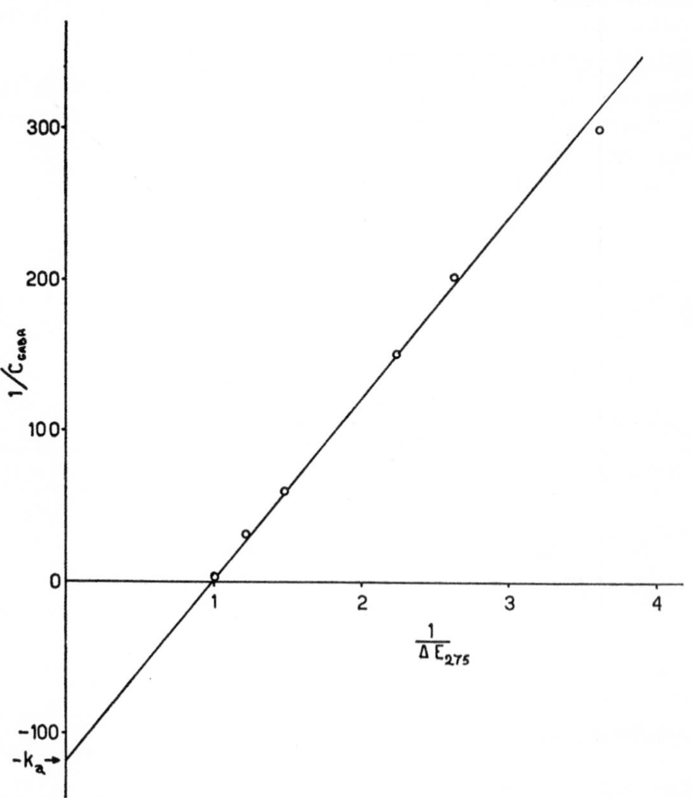


FIG. 2. Determination of the apparent equilibrium constant, $K_a$, and molar absorbency index at 275 mμ for the GABA–PLP system at pH 7.4 at 20.5°C, according to Eq. (2).

PL or PLP); $\epsilon_x$ and $\epsilon_i$, molar absorbency indexes of PL or PLP and imine, respectively; $C_y$, molar concentration of GABA.

By plotting $1/(\epsilon - \epsilon_x)$ against $1/C_y$, a straight line is obtained, where $1/K_a \cdot (\epsilon_i - \epsilon_x)$ is the slope and $1/(\epsilon_i - \epsilon_x)$ the intercept of the plot on the ordinate. Figure 1 illustrates this procedure.

Differential spectra of the reaction mixtures were read against PL or PLP blanks.[7] The reciprocals of the GABA concentrations were plotted against the reciprocal of $\Delta E$ this obtained, according to the Isenberg's equation:

$$\frac{1}{C_y} = K_a \cdot (\epsilon_i - \epsilon_x) \cdot C_x \cdot \frac{1}{\Delta E} - K_a \tag{2}$$

where $C_x$ and $C_y$ are the molar concentrations of GABA and PL or PLP; $\epsilon_i$ and $\epsilon_x$, molar absorbency indexes of imine and PL or PLP, respectively; $\Delta E$, differential spectrophotometer readings of the reaction mixture. The plot results in a straight line with the slope equal to $K_a \cdot (\epsilon_i - \epsilon_x)$ and the ordinate intercept yielding $-K_a$. Figure 2 illustrates this procedure.

The slope and the intercept on the ordinate for both Isenberg's and Ketelaar's equations were algebraically calculated from experimental points of the plots by the least squares method.

TABLE 1. APPARENT EQUILIBRIUM CONSTANT AND MOLAR ABSORBENCY INDEX FOR GABA–PL IMINE FORMATION AT VARIOUS TEMPERATURES IN 0.1 M NA–PHOSPHATE BUFFER pH 7.4, CALCULATED ACCORDING TO ISENBERG

| Temperature (°C) | $Ka$ = moles$^{-1}$ | ln $Ka$ | $E_i \times 10^{-3}$ |
|---|---|---|---|
| 20.00 | 2.94 | 1.077 | 5.45 |
| 25.15 | 3.36 | 1.209 | 5.24 |
| 25.25 | 3.39 | 1.221 | 5.44 |
| 30.00 | 4.12 | 1.416 | 5.20 |
| 30.15 | 4.10 | 1.411 | 5.45 |
| 34.00 | 4.81 | 1.568 | 5.43 |
| 34.50 | 4.82 | 1.572 | 5.25 |
| 38.50 | 5.49 | 1.703 | 5.58 |
| 38.60 | 5.78 | 1.753 | 5.15 |
| 42.00 | 6.31 | 1.842 | 5.17 |

Calculating $K_a$ for each temperature at different wavelengths yielded concordant results. The constancy of the values may be regarded as a further evidence for the correctness of the assumption that the observed spectral changes represent imine formation. Furthermore, it indicates a proper application of Ketelaar's and Isenberg's methods for measures of $K_a$ and $\epsilon$ to our complexes.

## RESULTS

### *Apparent Equilibrium Constant for GABA–PL Imine Formation*

Table 1 summarizes the results of $K_a$ determination at pH 7.4 in 0.1 M Na-phosphate buffer for PL–GABA system at temperatures from 20° to 42°C. $K_a$ rapidly increases with increasing temperature. Almost identical values of $K_a$ were obtained using both Ketelaar's and Isenberg's methods. This is clearcut evidence for the assumption that $K_a$ for GABA–PL system may be calculated from the observed spectral changes.

The molar absorbency index of the GABA–PL imine was independent of temperature over the range 20°–42°C.

The results obtained from some determinations of $K_a$ for valine–PL imine at pH 6.4 at 25°C are in good agreement with the findings of Metzler[8].

The stability of the Schiff base between GABA and PL below pH 7 is

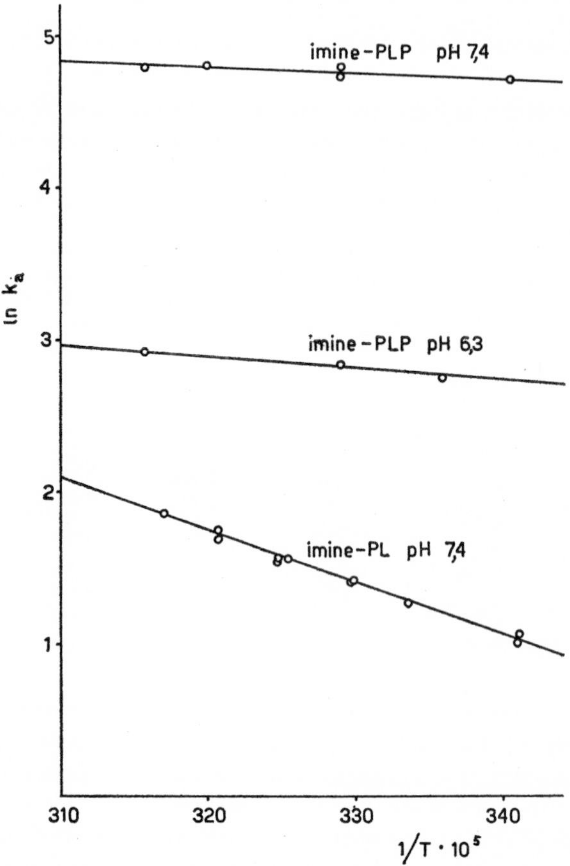


FIG. 3. Relation between ln $K_a$ for GABA–PL and GABA–PLP imines and the reciprocal of $T$ at different pH's.

much weaker than that between valine and PL. At pH 6.3 at 25°C $K_a$ is about 0.3 (moles$^{-1}$).

By plotting ln $K_a$ against $1/T$ ($T$, absolute temperature) (Fig. 3), a straight line was obtained, whose slope was $-\Delta H/R$.

*Apparent equilibrium constant for GABA–PLP imine formation*

The results of a series of measurements of $K_a$ at pH 6.3 and 7.4 in

Na-phosphate buffer at increasing temperatures from 20° to 44°C for GABA–PL–PLP system are summarized in Table 2.

$K_a$ values are always much higher than those of GABA–PL imine at the same temperature (twenty-five times higher). $K_a$ increases when the temperature rises, although relatively less than GABA–PL imine. A straight line is obtained when ln $K_a$ is plotted against the reciprocal of $T$ (Fig. 3). The slope of the plot is the same both at pH 6.3 and 7.4 but differs from that of GABA–PL system at pH 7.4

TABLE 2. APPARENT EQUILIBRIUM CONSTANT FOR GABA–PLP IMINE FORMATION AT VARIOUS TEMPERATURES AND pH'S. NA–PHOSPHATE BUFFERS

| pH | Temperature (°C) | $K_a$ = moles$^{-1}$ | ln $K_a$ |
|---|---|---|---|
| 6.3 | 24.50 | 15.43 | 2.736 |
| | 30.75 | 16.95 | 2.830 |
| | 43 50 | 18.31 | 2.907 |
| 7.4 | 20.50 | 110.96 | 4.709 |
| | 30.75 | 114.81 | 4.742 |
| | 30.75 | 119.88 | 4.780 |
| | 39.25 | 121.93 | 4.805 |
| | 43.50 | 121.74 | 4.790 |

*Kinetics of the GABA–PL reaction*

The increase in the absorbence at 410 mμ with time was recorded at different GABA concentrations (PL $1 \times 10^{-4}$ M) pH 7.4, 30°C. The molar concentration of the imine was calculated from the known molar absorbency indexes of imine and PL (Fig. 4). Assuming the following scheme for GABA–PL reaction in water:

$$\text{PL} + \text{GABA} \underset{k_2}{\overset{k_1}{\rightleftharpoons}} \text{Imine}$$

if the GABA concentration is very much greater than that of PL, the apparent rate constant $k_1$ for the direct reaction may be calculated according to the following equation:

$$k_1 = \frac{C_{i.e}}{C_{\text{PL}} \cdot C_{\text{GABA}}} \cdot \frac{1}{t} \cdot \ln \frac{C_{i.e}}{C_{i.e} - C_i} \qquad (3)$$

where $C_{\text{PL}}$ and $C_{\text{GABA}}$ are the molar stoichiometric concentrations of PL and GABA; $C_{i.e}$, the molar concentration of imine at equilibrium; $C_i$, molar concentration of imine at time $t$; $t$, the time.

The experimental value of $k_1$ (the mean of four determinations at different GABA concentrations) was 0.915 moles$^{-1}$ × min$^{-1}$.

By a similar procedure the pseudo first-order constant $k_2$ for imine dissociation in water was 0.194 min$^{-1}$. The ratio $k_1/k_2 = K_a$ was 4.69 moles$^{-1}$, in good agreement with that calculated according to Isenberg or Ketelaar.

From the following equation the imine concentration, as a function of time, may be calculated, using the value of $k_1$ previously determined:

$$C_i = C_{i.e} \cdot \left[1 - \exp(-k_1 \frac{C_{PL} \cdot C_{GABA}}{C_{i.e}} \cdot t)\right] \tag{4}$$

Figure 4 shows the good agreement between the experimental results and the corresponding data calculated from Eq. (4).

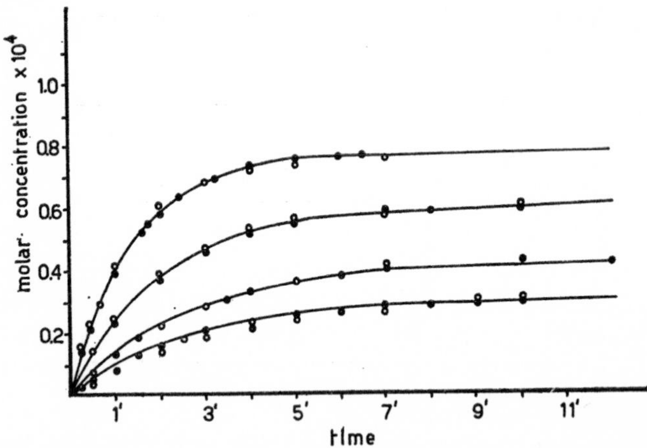


FIG. 4. GABA–PL imine formation as function of time at pH 7.4 at 30°C. Solid line: experimental determinations. White circles: the data calculated according to Eq. (4).

*Effect of Metal Ions on the Imine Formation and Structure*

Measurements were performed in water, always excluding those solutions in which hydrolysis or precipitate formation of metal salts were evident.

$Na^+$ and $Mg^{2+}$ had no effect on either the spectra or the extent of imine formation.

$Co^{2+}$, $Ni^{2+}$ and $Cu^{2+}$ enhance imine formation and cause a shift of the absorption maximum from 410 m$\mu$ to 374 m$\mu$ (Fig. 5). The chelating effect decreases in the following order: $Cu^{2+} > Ni^{2+} > Co^{2+}$.

$Al^{3+}$ shows a chelating effect, but the hydrolysis is so extensive as to make it impossible to determine its chelating activity.

With $1 \times 10^{-5}$ M $Cu^{2+}$, 0.066 M GABA and $2 \times 10^{-4}$ M PL, the position of the maximum of absorbence was intermediate between 410 m$\mu$ and 374 m$\mu$. This indicates the simultaneous formation of both chelated and non-chelated imines.

## DISCUSSION

The Schiff bases formed from PL or PLP and GABA interactions at physiological pH's and temperatures are stable for a very long time. On the contrary those formed from α-amino acids and PL or PLP, as can be deduced

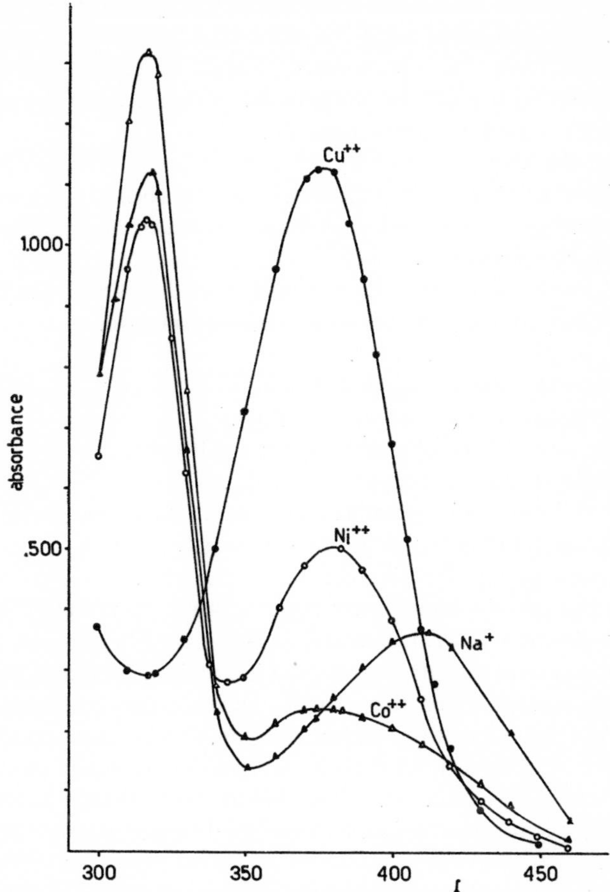


Fig. 5. Absorption spectra of the GABA–PL chelated and non-chelated imines.
▲, NaCl, 0.1 M; GABA, 0.1 M; PL, $2 \times 10^{-4}$ M.
●, ○, △, Metal ions, 0.1 M; GABA, 0.066 M; PL, $2 \times 10^{-4}$ M.

by the decrease of the absorbence at 410 mμ, are slowly split into PM and α-keto acids.

The increase of the apparent equilibrium constant for imine formation reaction with increasing temperature is in agreement with the general observation that the complete non-enzymic reactions proceed more easily at higher temperatures.

The apparent lower stability of PL imines, indicated by the very small values of $K_a$ for GABA–PL system, is due to the presence of the hemiacetal ring in the PL molecule. The effective concentration of the free aldehydic species is much less than the PL concentration used in the $K_a$ calculation.

Straight lines obtained by plotting ln $K_a$ against $1/T$ (Fig. 3) show the formation of a single compound from the interaction between GABA and PL or PLP.

$K_a$ calculated from the same reaction mixture, after different times at a constant temperature, gives the same value. This indicates the stability of the imine with regard to transamination.

The molar absorbency index of GABA–PL imine, at 410 m$\mu$ (pH 7.4), is also constant at a series of temperatures. The absorbence is not affected by temperature and gives further evidence for the formation of a single compound from GABA–PL interaction.

However, these observations do not unequivocally exclude the formation of traces of other compounds followed by transamination.

Variation of pH from 6.3 to 7.4 affects only the stability of the imine. This appears from the identical slopes in plots of ln $K_a$ against $1/T$ for GABA–PLP imine at the different pH values.

The higher slope of the plot of ln $K_a$ for GABA–PL system is partly due to the presence of the hemiacetal ring of PL.

The reactive form of PL for imine formation requires the formyl group to be free.[2] The availability of this group is extremely low in aqueous solutions because it takes part in forming the hemiacetal ring. For this reason the scheme for the pseudo bimolecular reaction must be modified to include consecutive reactions: PL-hemiacetal $\rightleftharpoons$ PL + GABA $\rightleftharpoons$ Imine, provided that GABA is present in a large excess and its concentration may be regarded as a constant and provided that the PL concentration is always very low because of the high rate of the second reaction. Under these conditions the concentration of imine as a function of the time is graphically similar to that calculated according to Eq. (4). However, the factor which determines the rate of reaction is the equilibrium between the hemiacetal ring and the open form of PL.

It is universally accepted that the loss of the proton from the $\alpha$-carbon of the $\alpha$-amino acid in the Schiff base is necessary for the transamination reaction to proceed.

The proton removal is determined, according to Snell[2], by the electron displacement from the $\alpha$-carbon by the combined effects of the conjugated system of double bonds and of the electronegative heterocyclic nitrogen. Of fundamental importance is also the inductive effect of the carboxy group on the $\alpha$-carbon.

In the GABA–PL or GABA–PLP imine there is lacking the inductive effect of the carboxy group on the $\gamma$-carbon atom. This causes an inadequate activation of the two protons bound to the $\gamma$-carbon and the loss of either of these protons is extremely improbable. This fact makes very difficult the formation of the transitional intermediate compound which is necessary for the tautomerization of the imine by protonation of the formyl carbon atom.

This is in agreement with the limited extent of the transamination between PL or PLP and GABA. Our observation of the formation of only one intermediate compound from GABA–PL or GABA–PLP interaction both by chromatographic and spectrophotometric analysis, differs from the results of Fasella *et al.*[9], for $\alpha$-amino acid imines.

Metal ions chelate with the GABA imines, but do not assist transamination. The interpretation of this fact is very difficult because the true mechanism of their action is not too well understood.

This paper shows that the first stage of the non-enzymic reaction (in which imine is in equilibrium with its hydrolysis products) is independent of the later stages which may lead to transamination. The essential stage of the transamination reaction is the labilization of the $\alpha$-proton in the $\alpha$-amino acids or $\gamma$- in the GABA, which seems to be the rate-limiting step in the non-enzymic transamination.

## REFERENCES

1. G. D. Kalyankar and E. E. Snell; *Biochemistry* **1**, 594 (1962).
2. E. E. Snell; *Vitamins and Hormones* **16**, 77 (1958).
3. A. E. Braunstein; *The Enzymes* (edited by P. D. Boyer, H. Lardy and K. Myrbäck), vol. II. p. 113, Academic Press, New York (1960).
4. C. S. Rossi, F. Olivo, A. Rabassini and N. Siliprandi; *Arch. Biochem. Biophys.* **96**, 650 (1962).
5. J. A. A. Ketelaar, C. van de Stolpe, Goudsmit and Dzcubas; *Rec. trav. chim.* **71**, 498 (1951).
6. J. A. A. Ketelaar, C. van de Stolpe, Goudsmit and Dzcubas; *Rec. trav. chim.* **71**, 1104 (1952).
7. I. Isenberg and A. Szent-Gyorgyi; *Proc. Natl. Acad. Sci.* **44**, 857 (1958).
8. D. E. Metzler; *J. Am. Chem. Soc.* **79**, 485 (1958).
9. P. Fasella, H. Lis, N. Siliprandi and C. Baglioni; *Biochim. et Biophys. Acta* **23**, 417 (1957).

## DISCUSSION

Dr. Snell:

The failure of metal ions to catalyze the nonenzymatic transamination reaction between pyridoxal or its phosphates and $\gamma$-aminobutyric acid is readily understandable. We have attributed part of the catalytic effect of such ions for reactions with $\alpha$-amino acids to their formation of a chelate ring involving not only the phenolic group and the azomethine nitrogen but also the carboxyl group of the complex. This chelation of the carboxyl group promotes labilization of the $\alpha$-hydrogen quite independently of the effect of pyridoxal on this same grouping. This effect is not possible in $\beta$- or $\gamma$-amino acids; the chelate ring is too large to form readily and the carboxyl group is too removed from the hydrogen atom that requires labilization to exert its effect in any case. Thus, only the catalytic effect due to complex formation with pyridoxal is evident with the $\gamma$-amino acids, and catalysis by the metal ion, if present at all, should not be expected to be as great as with the $\alpha$-amino acids.

# A QUANTUM-MECHANICAL INVESTIGATION OF PYRIDOXAL-DEPENDENT REACTIONS

by Bernard Pullman

Université de Paris, Institut de Biologie Physico-Chimique,
Paris 5e

The quantum-mechanical investigation of the electronic aspects of pyridoxal-dependent reactions was greatly facilitated by the existence of a detailed theory accounting on the molecular level for the mechanism of these reactions. This is the Braunstein–Snell theory (for general reviews see Refs. 1–6) which postulates the formation of a Schiff base between pyridoxal and the substrate and describes the subsequent transformations and reactions of this complex. Some more recent studies[6–10] seem to indicate that, in fact, the coenzyme may already be linked to the apoenzyme in the form of a Schiff base, in which case the interaction of the coenzyme with the substrate involves a displacement or transaldimination reaction. These new findings do not involve, however, any important modification of the previous theory.[6]

Although we have adopted the chemical representation of the Braunstein–Snell theory as the starting point of our own investigation, we have been induced to doubt some of the postulates of the theory concerned with the fundamental factors responsible for the catalytic influence of pyridoxal. Thus following the essential proposition of Braunstein and Snell, this catalytic influence is due to the fact that in the imine (I), which represents the Schiff base formed between pyridoxal and an α-amino acid, there is " a conjugated system of double bonds extending from the α-carbon of the amino acid to the electronegative group which results in reduced electron density about the α-carbon atom, thus weakening each of the bonds *a*, *b* and *c*. . . . It is this electron displacement, with its consequent weakening of bonds *a*, *b* and *c* that constitutes ' activation ' of the amino acid by the pyridoxal metal ion systems or by pyridoxal phosphate proteins ".[1]

It is this essential proposition which, in the first place, does not seem entirely satisfactory. In the primary Schiff base, (I), the α-carbon does not belong to the conjugated system of the base. The system only extends to the amino nitrogen atom. The α-carbon is a saturated carbon atom, outside the system and its electronic cloud cannot therefore be involved in displacements due to conjugation effects. The α-carbon only becomes incorporated into the conjugated system in a later stage of the catalytic process, namely when the original Schiff base is transformed into *transitional* forms (II), (III) or (IV) through the labilization of different bonds *a*, *b* or *c* of the amino acid. In these transitional Schiff bases the electronic charge of the α-carbon is, however, as will be seen shortly, not decreased but greatly *increased.*

I would like to stress that although this is a kind of a fundamental objection (" objection de principe ") against this particular point of the Braunstein–Snell theory, it seems nevertheless quite possible that the formation of the

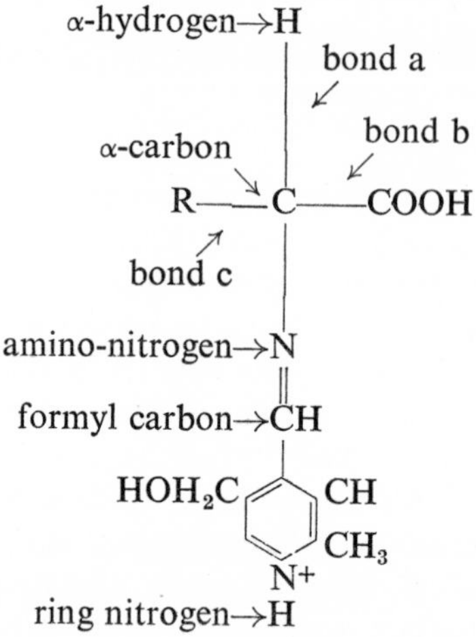

α-hydrogen→H
bond a
bond b
α-carbon
R—C—COOH
bond c
amino-nitrogen→N
formyl carbon→CH
$HOH_2C$ CH
$CH_3$
N+
ring nitrogen→H
(I)

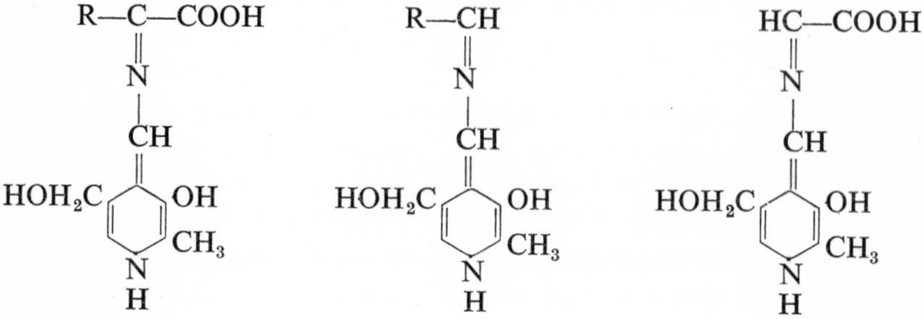

R—C—COOH
N
CH
$HOH_2C$ OH
$CH_3$
N
H
(II)

R—CH
N
CH
$HOH_2C$ OH
$CH_3$
N
H
(III)

HC—COOH
N
CH
$HOH_2C$ OH
$CH_3$
N
H
(IV)

Schiff base (I) results actually in a decrease of the electronic density at the α-carbon. Such a decrease would not, however, be connected with any conjugation effect, but could be due to the inductive effect of the amino nitrogen. Actually, this nitrogen is in the amino acid in a state of hybridization close to $sp^3$. In the Schiff base, its hybridization moves towards $sp^2$, with a resultant increase of its electronegativity. This transformation could bring about a decrease of the electronic charge around the α-carbon, although it is difficult to estimate the order of magnitude of this effect. Complementary effects render such an estimation still more difficult. Thus, the amino nitrogen carries in the Schiff base a net negative charge, the presence of which will tend to diminish its electronegativity. On the other hand, the chelation with the metal cation, which is frequently considered to represent the effect of the apoenzyme, will tend to have the opposite effect. It is not easy to ascertain the result of all these different influences, but it does not seem likely that these essentially inductive effects would really be sufficient to account for the observed " activation " of the amino acids. If this were the case, one would not understand the utility, obviously essential, of the conjugated system of pyridoxal for the success of the catalysis. Supplementary effects must therefore be looked for.

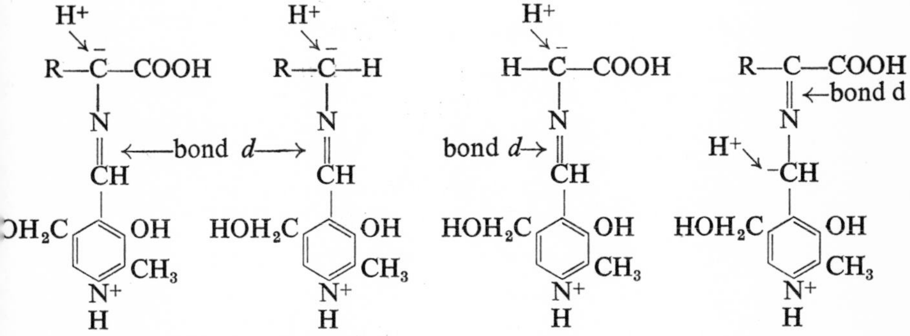

H+ R—C—COOH, N ‖ CH ←bond d→; $HOH_2C$, OH, $CH_3$, N+ H (V)

H+ R—C—H, N ‖ CH; $HOH_2C$, OH, $CH_3$, N+ H (VI)

H+ H—C—COOH, N, bond d→ ‖ CH; $HOH_2C$, OH, $CH_3$, N+ H (VII)

R—C—COOH ‖ ←bond d N, H+ CH; $HOH_2C$, OH, $CH_3$, N+ H (VIII)

Moreover, the interpretation at the electronic level of the transformations leading from the transitional Schiff bases to the final products may also be usefully elaborated. In the Braunstein–Snell mechanism, the authors consider the " localization of the extra electron pair of the transitional form " (i.e. the electrons of the lone pair of the ring nitrogen) either on the $\alpha$-carbon or on the formyl carbon following the reaction: on the $\alpha$-carbon for the racemization (V) and decarboxylation (VI) reactions and also for the reactions due to the labilization of the R-group (VII) and on the formyl carbon for the transamination reaction (VIII). This localization is followed by the corresponding protonations.

In the last stage of the reactions, the C—N bonds indicated as *d* bonds on the formulae (V)–(VIII) are hydrolysed and give the final products.

Now, although the hypothesis about the different electronic localizations in the transitional forms of the Schiff bases agrees with the nature of the final products, it lacks, at this stage, a theoretical justification. In fact, the structures adopted as the reactive forms of the transitional Schiff bases represent only some of the mesomeric formulae of these bases, and their particular importance is not evident *a priori.* It may even seem at first sight surprising to assume high localization of electronic charges on the α- or the formyl carbons, these carbons being *ortho* to an electronegative nitrogen and susceptible, in principle, also to the electron-withdrawing effect of the carboxy group. Moreover, the fact that the protonation of the transitional Schiff base resulting from the labilization of the α-hydrogen may occur either at the α-carbon or at the formyl one, according to the reaction being considered, points also to the necessity of a deeper investigation of the electronic aspects of the reactions involved.

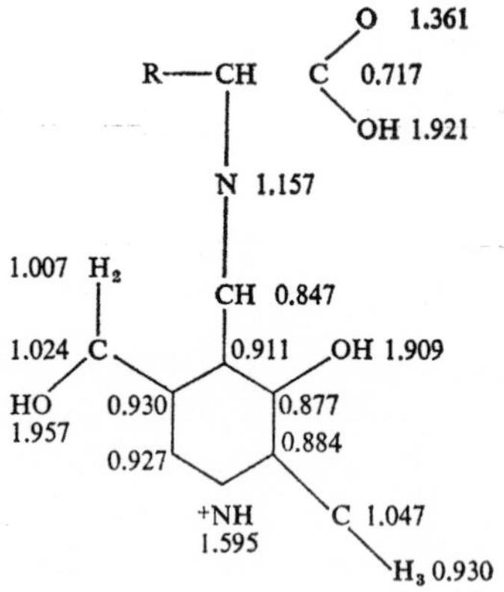

O 1.361
R—CH C 0.717
OH 1.921
N 1.157
1.007 $H_2$
CH 0.847
1.024 C 0.911 OH 1.909
HO 1.957 0.930 0.877
0.884
0.927
+NH 1.595
C 1.047
$H_3$ 0.930

FIG. 1. Distribution of π-electrons in Schiff base (I).

It is in fact the structure and properties of the Schiff bases in their transitional forms which especially need a deeper elucidation.

In view of this elucidation, we have applied the quantum-mechanical method of molecular orbitals to the study of the electronic constitution of these compounds. Details on the procedure may be found in Refs. 4 and 5.

The first result to consider is the electronic distribution in the original form of the Schiff base formed between pyridoxal and an α-amino acid. It is, of course, the distribution of the mobile or π-electrons that we are interested in. This is presented in Fig. 1. The system is composed of two conjugated fragments separated by the α-carbon atom. In agreement with the inferences drawn from p$K_a$ values, the pyridine nitrogen is protonated.[11] It will remain so in most of the compounds and forms considered in this paper.

Although the charge distribution of Fig. 1 is by itself sufficiently illustrative and does not require detailed interpretation, we may nevertheless stress, for future consideration, that the formyl carbon is slightly positive in this base: it bears less than the one $\pi$-electron which it has contributed to the pool of the $\pi$-electrons of the system. Its net positive charge (deficiency of electrons) is consequently $(1 - 0.847)e = 0.153e$. The amino nitrogen bears on the contrary a net negative charge (excess of electrons) of $0.157e$. The resonance energy of the base (considered as the sum of the resonance energies of its two conjugated fragments) equals $3.38\beta$, $\beta$ being the usual resonance integral of the molecular orbital method, whose approximate value is 20 kcal/mole.

Let us now consider the structure, properties and reactions of the transitional forms deriving from this original Schiff base through the labilization of one of the groups attached to the $\alpha$-carbon. In fact, we may centre our attention essentially on the form and reactions resulting from the labilization of the $\alpha$-hydrogen, because the interpretation of the reactions resulting from the labilization of the other $\alpha$-carbon is quite similar.

It was just recalled that the labilization of the $\alpha$-proton was attributed by Snell *et al.* to the decrease in the electron density around the $\alpha$-carbon atom during the formation of the Schiff base. As we have also seen, this argument is not entirely persuasive. A supplementary and, probably, essential driving force responsible for this labilization may reside in a different factor, namely, *the appreciable gain in resonance energy which is associated with the ionization.* The departure of the proton results in the unification of the isolated conjugated fragments of the initial base into one large resonating system. This transformation is accompanied by an increase of resonance energy of the order of $0.5\beta$, which represents approximately 10 kcal/mole. As we shall see later a similar increase in resonance energy is associated with the rupture of any of the *a*, *b* or *c* bonds situated around the $\alpha$-carbon in the initial Schiff base. *It is this gain in resonance energy which we consider as the fundamental factor responsible for the transformation of the initial Schiff base into the transitional forms and therefore for the " activation " of the $\alpha$-amino acids in pyridoxal phosphate catalyzed reactions.*

Moreover, the examination of the electronic distribution in the transitional Schiff base resulting from the departure of the proton yields information which is exceedingly useful for the interpretation of the further steps of the reaction. This distribution is represented in Fig. 2.

The most striking feature of this figure is the unusual charge distribution associated with the extracyclic $C_{formyl}$–$N_{amino}$–$C_\alpha$ chain. All these three atoms carry an excess of $\pi$-electron charges, so that we have a chain of three adjacent atoms all bearing net negative charges. Moreover, in spite of the fact that the greater intrinsic electronegativity of the nitrogen atom has been accounted for *ab initio* by the use of suitable parameters, the net negative charges on the formyl or $\alpha$-carbons are greater than the net negative charge of the amino nitrogen. These two carbons appear thus as the essential centers for possible electrophilic attacks on the molecule and therefore as the essential centers for future protonations. Because of their high net negative charges they are also very reactive centers. The protonation of (II) at the α-carbon leads to racemization, the protonation at the formyl carbon to transamination.

A more complete distinction between the relative reactivities of these two similar centers necessitates the evaluation of the corresponding *localization energies* which represent the essential varying parts of the associated *activation energies*. In the absence of these data, tentative information may be obtained from the values of the corresponding free valencies whose magnitudes are

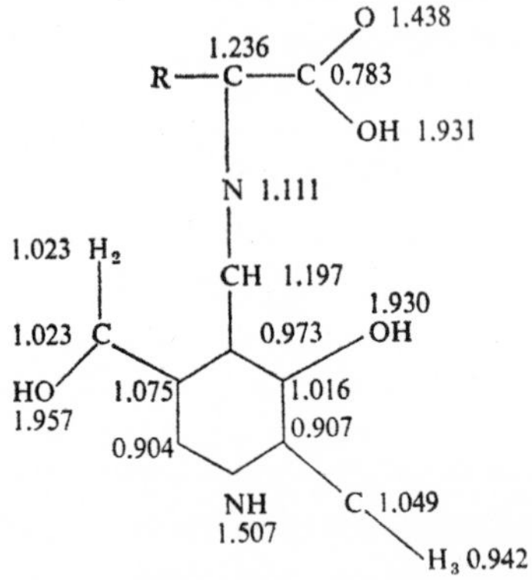

FIG. 2. Distribution of π-electrons in the transitional Schiff base (II).

generally proportional to the polarizabilities of atoms towards external agents.

These complementary indices have been evaluated and thoroughly used in the discussion of the mechanism of pyridoxal-dependent reactions in Refs. 4 and 5. For the sake of simplicity and because of the limits of time imposed upon this lecture, we shall not introduce them here.

Inasmuch as the possible inductive effects due to the R group of the α-amino acid are not taken into account explicitly, the electronic structure of the transitional Schiff base (IV), resulting from the labilization of R is practically identical with that of the transitional Schiff base (II), obtained through the labilization of the α-proton. The interpretation of the catalytic effect of pyridoxal in reactions resulting from the labilization of the R group is thus quite similar to the preceeding one.

In reactions resulting from the labilization of the α-carboxy group, the transitional Schiff base (III) represents a shorter conjugated system than (II) or (IV), but all the fundamental characteristics of the catalytic mechanism are concerned. The resonance energy of (III) exceeds the resonance energy f (I) by about $0.1\beta$. The electronic distribution of III (Fig. 3) indicates the xistence of the same reactive centres for electrophilic attack, the $\alpha$- and the ormyl carbons, carrying appreciable net negative charges.

On the contrary, more complex, larger transitional Schiff bases occur in wo types of reaction resulting from the labilization of the $\alpha$-proton: the –$\beta$ and the $\gamma$-eliminations. The $\alpha$–$\beta$ eliminations occur, as is well known,

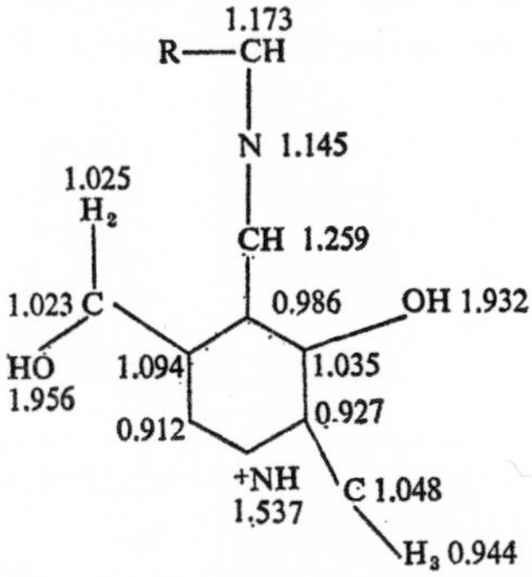

FIG. 3. Distribution of $\pi$-electrons in the transitional Schiff base (III).

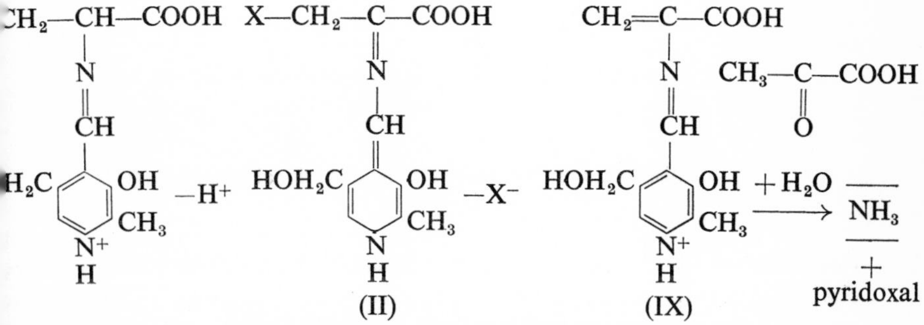

FIG. 4. The course of the $\alpha$–$\beta$ eliminations.

with the $\alpha$-amino acids which possess a strong electrophilic group X (OH, SH, etc.) at the $\beta$-carbon. The mechanism of the reaction may be visualized as shown (Fig. 4).

The first two steps of the reaction (the formation of the Schiff base between the amino acid and pyridoxal phosphate, not indicated at Fig. 4 and the release of the proton from the $\alpha$-carbon of the base) are identical with the initial transformations in the transamination reaction. The new step is represented by the consequent labilization of the $X^-$ ion resulting in the *formation of a new type of a transitional Schiff base* (IX).

The factors responsible for the development of the reaction towards the formation of (IX) are quite similar to those responsible for the formation of the first transitional form (II). Thus, besides an inductive effect of the α-carbon, the primary driving force for the release of $X^-$ resides in the appreciable gain in resonance energy of the order of $0.3\beta$ ($\approx 6$ kcal/mole) associated with the transformation of (II) into (IX).

New features appear also in the distribution of electrical charges in the transitional Schiff base (IX), illustrated in Fig. 5. The most striking results are the noticeable difference in the electronic distribution in (IX) with respect to (II), the high reactivity which this distribution enables to predict for the β-carbon of the transitional base (IX) and the type of this reactivity. Thus,

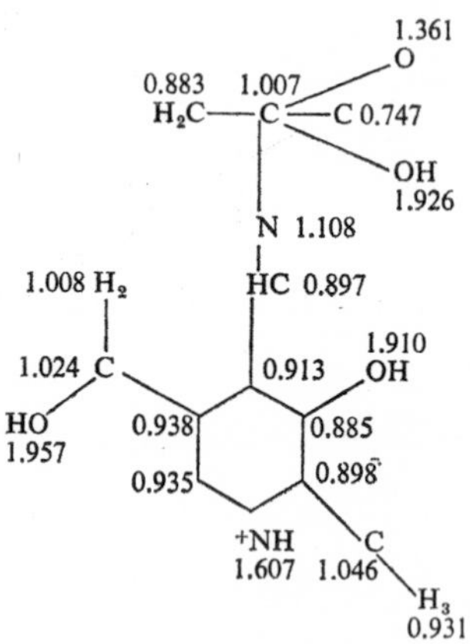


FIG. 5. Distribution of π-electrons in the transitional Schiff base (IX).

this β-carbon is highly deficient in π-electrons and carries a net positive charge of 0.117*e*, greater than that of any other discharged carbon of the molecule. It will consequently represent a particularly reactive center for attacks by nucleophilic agents. As is well known an important consequence of this situation is the possibility of using the base (IX) for the synthesis of higher amino acids. Tryptophan, for example, may be prepared in this way from serine or in the presence of indole. This synthesis requires the condensation of the indole ring with the Schiff base (IX), the reaction taking place between $C_3$ of indole and the β-carbon of (IX) (Fig. 6). Figure 7, which represents the charge distribution in indole, indicates that it is its $C_3$ which effectively carries the greatest net negative charge and which will consequently be the proper center to interact with the β-carbon of (IX).*

*As it also is the essential center for the protonation of indole (R. L. Hinman and F. B. Whipple; *J. Am. Chem. Soc.* **84**, 2534, 1962).

As to the $\gamma$-eliminations, an important example of a reaction of this type is represented in Fig. 8.

The principal stages of the reaction are : (1) the formation of a Schiff base between the pyridoxal phosphate enzyme and P-homoserine (not

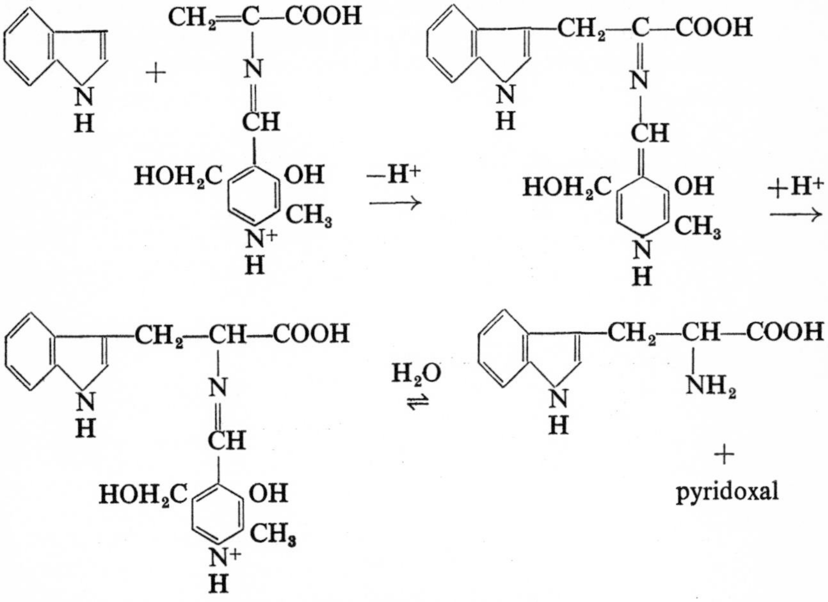

FIG. 6. The synthesis of tryptophan.

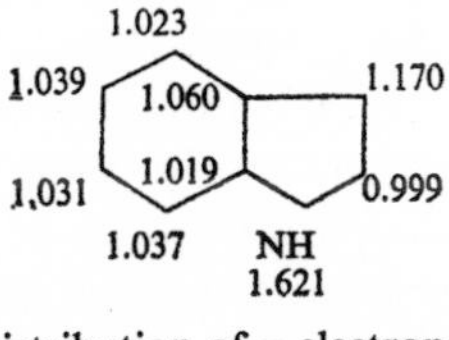

FIG. 7. Distribution of $\pi$-electrons in indole.

indicated in Fig. 8); (2) the transformation of this initial base, through the elimination of the phosphate and two protons, into *a new type of a transitional Schiff base* (*X*); (3) the protonation of this form on the $\gamma$-carbon with the consequent formation of compound (XI) which is a methylated derivative of the transitional Schiff base (IX) (involved in the $\alpha$–$\beta$ eliminations); (4) the hydroxylation of this form on carbon $\beta$ yields compound (XII), which is a derivative of the transitional base (II); (5) the protonation of this last form on the $\alpha$-carbon and subsequent hydrolysis regenerate pyridoxal and produce threonine.

The new structural unit introduced in this type of reaction is thus the transitional Schiff base (X). The essential electronic feature accounting for its formation is again its relatively great resonance energy, the formation of (X) from the initial Schiff base representing a gain of resonance energy of about $1\beta$. The distribution of electronic charges in (X) (Fig. 9) then indicates a great concentration of these charges on its $\gamma$-carbon. The free valence of this carbon being also particularly high (equal to 0.885 against 0.273 for the $\alpha$-carbon and 0.528 for the formyl carbon), there is no doubt

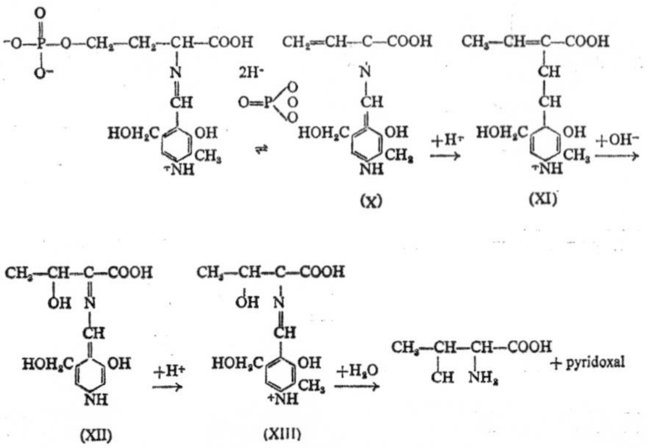

FIG. 8. The synthesis of threonine through the elimination of phosphate from O-phosphohomoserine.

that this carbon must constitute the essential and very reactive center of the molecule towards electrophilic attacks. We can, consequently, understand the fixation of a proton on this carbon. The interpretation of the series of transformations presented in Fig. 9 is now straightforward. In the first place there will be fixation of a proton (an electrophilic attack) on the $\gamma$-carbon. The resultant transitional base (XI) must have, on the contrary, like (IX), a particularly reactive center towards nucleophilic attacks at the $\beta$-carbon, a situation which accounts for the fixation of $OH^-$ on that carbon. In the resulting compound (XII), a center of electrophilic reactivity reappears again, but this time, as in (II), at the $\alpha$-carbon, which consequently undergoes protonation. Hydrolysis yields finally the desired products.

Thus, the three transitional bases, (II), (IX) and (X), all appear in the reaction described in Fig. 10. They represent an interesting example of related forms in which, however, the variations in the dimensions of the conjugated system bring about drastic modifications in their reactional abilities.

Thus, generally speaking, what appears most striking in the mechanism of catalysis by pyridoxal is the extreme variety of the reactions and, at the same time, *the relative simplicity and similarity of the underlying electronic transformations.* The basic features which appear to govern these transformations and to represent the driving force for the catalytic processes are: (1) the strong resonance stabilization of the transitional intermediates, resulting from the transformation of the initial coenzyme-substrate compound, and (2) the appearance of strong reaction centers in these transitional forms, responsible for the subsequent development of the reaction. The production

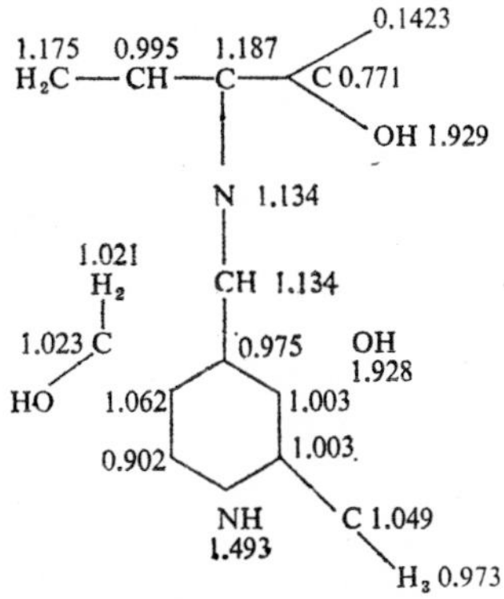

FIG. 9. Distribution of $\pi$-electrons in the transitional Schiff base (XI).

of the transitional intermediates is thus associated with low activation energies, but so is also their subsequent transformation into further reaction products. The situation has an obvious bearing on the high catalytic efficiency of the coenzyme.

It may be particularly significant to indicate at this point that these factors are in no way specific for the reactions catalyzed by pyridoxal enzymes but seem also to be responsible for the catalytic activity of other group-transfer coenzymes. The most outstanding example of this situation is thiamine pyrophosphate (XIV). This is not the place, of course, to describe in detail

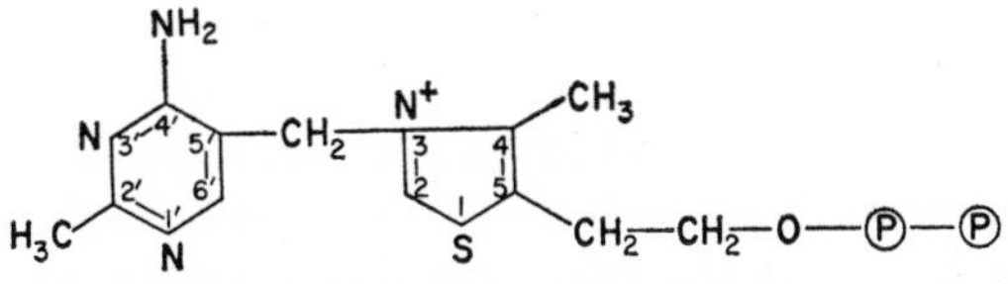

XIV Thiamine pyrophosphate

the thiamine catalyzed reactions. (For general reviews, see Refs. 5, 12–14.) We shall limit ourselves to indicating a typical example. Such an example (benzoin condensation) is shown in Fig. 10.

Following a theory developed by Breslow[13,15] and which has recently received important experimental confirmations, the mechanism of action of

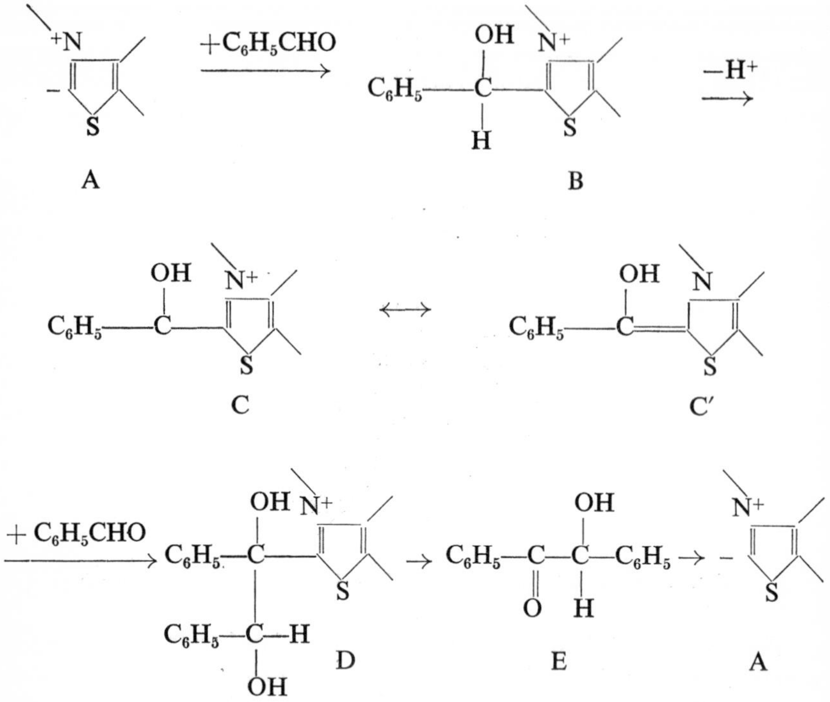

FIG. 10. The mechanism of thiamine-catalyzed benzoin condensation.

thiamine involves the ionization of the thiazolium ring, through the loss of a proton from $C_2$, with the consecutive formation of a zwiterrion:

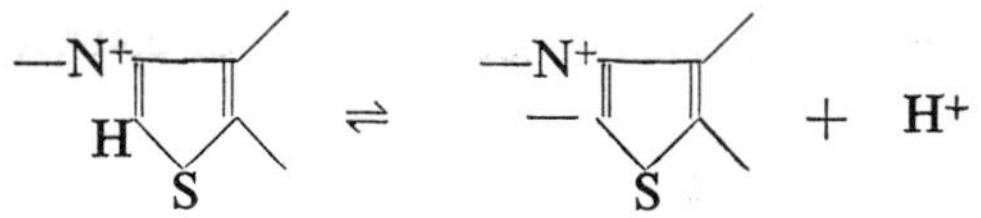

It is this ionized $C_2$ position which is the reactive site of the coenzyme towards interactions with the molecules to be transformed. In our example (interaction with benzaldehyde) this interaction yields the primary compound B of Fig. 10. Now, the next step in the reaction is the release of a proton from the extracyclic aldehyde carbon with formation of the transitional but essential intermediate C the so-called "active aldehyde". An important factor contributing towards this transformation must be the stabilization by resonance of this intermediate (which may also be represented by the other important canonical structure C′). The important point is that the release of a proton creates a unique conjugated system extending over the whole of the molecular periphery. The gain in resonance energy corresponding to this ionization is about 0.2$\beta$, i.e. approximately 4 kcal/mole.[14] Moreover, as indicated in Fig. 11, the " active benzaldehyde " possesses then in its aldehyde carbon an extremely reactive atom. This carbon carries a very great excess of electronic charge: its net negative charge is 0.335*e*.[14] Consequently, it will combine very easily with an electron deficient center, such as the aldehyde carbon atom of a second $C_6H_5CHO$ molecule (compound D of Fig. 10). The splitting of this adduct, which leads to benzoin and regenerates the thiazolium salt, is again accompanied by a gain in resonance energy, due to the

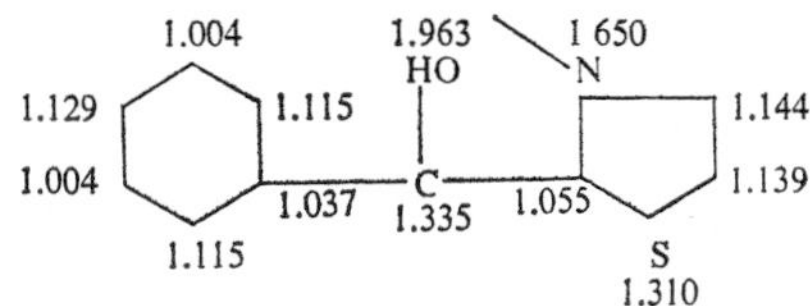


FIG. 11. Electronic charges in " active benzaldehyde ".

establishment of resonance between the phenyl and the C=O group of benzoin and to the increase in resonance energy in the thiazole ring.

Quite similar considerations apply to the other types of thiamine-catalyzed reactions. In particular, the structure of " active acetaldehyde " is similar to that of " active benzaldehyde ".

I do not think that there is any need to insist upon the most striking analogy which appears, in this quantum mechanical treatment, between the electronic factors responsible for the catalytic activity of thiamine and pyridoxal coenzymes.

To some extent a similar mechanism may also be distinguished in the mode of action of folic acid-dependent enzymes.[5,16] The problem is a little more complex and, unfortunately, the lack of time does not allow me to discuss it in detail here. We may, nevertheless, indicate that the mechanism of transfer of one-carbon metabolic units by the coenzyme tetrahydrofolic acid (XV), involves again frequently the transformation of the initial fixation product (XVI), resulting from the acceptance of the one-carbon unit, into a more stable transitional form (XVII), which is at the same time better adapted to be the one-carbon unit donor.

In conclusion, it may thus be said that the quantum mechanical analysis presented here not only throws complementary light on the mechanism of pyridoxal-dependent reactions but that it enables us also to establish the existence of common electronic features responsible for the catalytic activity of a variety of group transfer coenzymes. These features are related to the resonance stabilization and the electronic activation of the transitional intermediates of the catalyzed reactions. This result enables us then to understand what I believe to be a very significant phenomenon, namely, that *most coenzymes are conjugated organic molecules.* This situation is in no way accidental but arises from the fact that such molecules appear to be

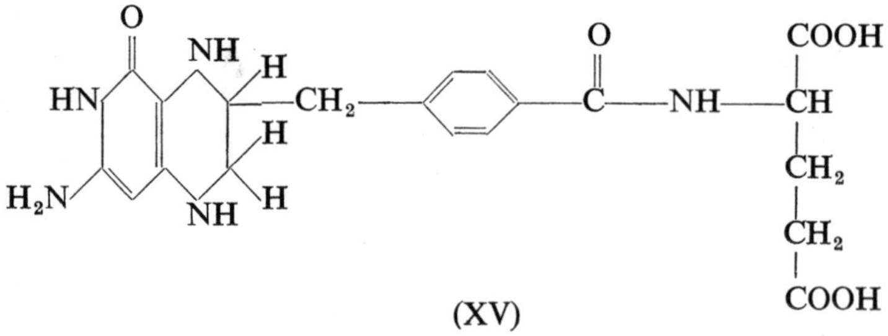

(XV)

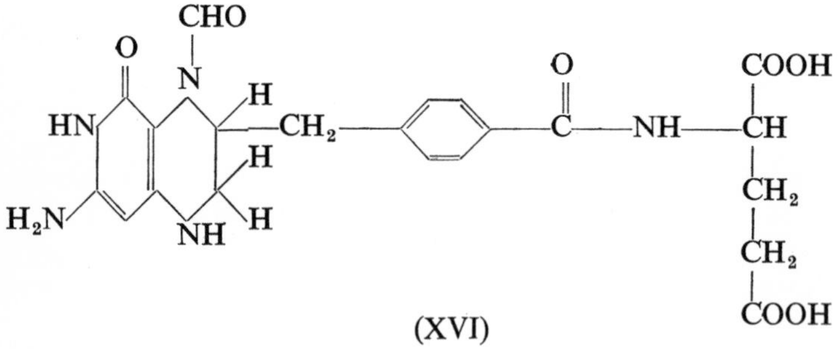

(XVI)

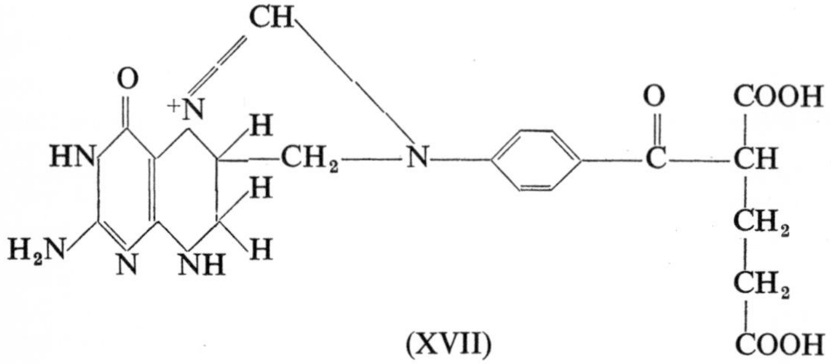

(XVII)

particularly well suited to play the role of reaction sites, as it is in this type of compound that the simultaneous effects of energy stabilization and electronic activation of the transition forms may be obtained with particular ease. Their choice by nature is thus one of the manifestations of quantum effects in biochemical evolution.[17,18]

*Acknowledgment*:—This work was sponsored by grant CY3073 of the United States Public Health Service.

## REFERENCES

1. E. E. SNELL; *Vitamins and Hormones* **16**, 77 (1958).
2. E. E. SNELL and W. T. JENKINS; *J. Cell. Comp. Physiol.* **54**, 161 (1959).
3. A. E. BRAUNSTEIN; *The Enzymes* (edited by P. D. BOYER, H. LARDY and K. MYRBÄCK), vol. III, p. 113. Academic Press, New York (1960).
4. A.-M. PERAULT, B. PULLMAN and C. VALDEMORO; *Biochim. et Biophys. Acta* **46**, 555 (1961).
5. A. PULLMAN and B. PULLMAN; *Quantum Biochemistry*, Wiley's Interscience Division, New York (1963).
6. E. E. SNELL; *The Mechanism of Action of Water-Soluble Vitamins*, p. 18, Ciba Foundation Study Group No. 11, Churchill, London (1961).
7. W. T. JENKINS; *Fed. Proc.* **20**, 978 (1961).
8. D. E. METZLER; *J. Am. Chem. Soc.* **79**, 485 (1957).
9. V. BONAVITA and V. SCARDI; *Experienta* **14**, 7 (1958).
10. E. G. KREBS, E. H. FISCHER and A. B. KENT; *J. Am. Chem. Soc.* **80**, 2906 (1958).
11. D. E. METZLER and E. E. SNELL; *J. Am. Chem. Soc.* **77**, 2431 (1955).
12. D. E. METZLER; *The Enzymes* (edited by P. D. BOYER, H. LARDY and K. MYRBÄCK), vol. II, p. 295, Academic Press, New York (1960).
13. R. BRESLOW; *The Mechanism of Action of Water-Soluble Vitamins*, Ciba Foundation Study Group No. 11, Churchill, London (1961) p. 18; *Ann. N.Y. Acad. Sci.* **98**, 445 (1962).
14. B. PULLMAN and C. SPANJAARD; *Biochim. et Biophys. Acta* **46**, 576 (1961).
15. R. BRESLOW; *Chem. & Ind.* 893 (1957); *J. Am. Chem. Soc.* **79**, 1762 (1957); **80**, 3719 (1958); R. BRESLOW and E. MCNELIS; *J. Am. Chem. Soc.* **81**, 3080 (1959).
16. A.-M. PERAULT and B. PULLMAN; *Biochim. et Biophys. Acta* **44**, 251 (1960).
17. B. PULLMAN and A. PULLMAN; *Nature* **196**, 1137 (1962).
18. B. PULLMAN; *La Biochimie Electronique*, Collection " Que sais-je ", Presses Universitaires de France, Paris (1963).

## DISCUSSION*

DR. JENKINS:

Much of the current interest in the mechanism of pyridoxal phosphate catalysis appears to center on the role of the acidic and basic groups in the Schiff base intermediates. For your derivation of these very precise numerical values, it appears that you made many unjustifiable assumptions such as considering only the undissociated state of the amino acid carboxyl and phenolic hydroxyl groups. Could you give your major assumptions in detail and suggest the order of magnitude of the effect on your numerical values of alternative structures?

DR. PULLMAN:

All the major assumptions concerning our calculations on pyridoxal have been presented in detail in our paper (with Perault and Valdemoro in *Biochim. et Biophys. Acta* **46**, 555, 1961). This includes the parameters adopted for the different heteroatoms and precisions about the simplifications adopted in the calculations. We have not taken into account the ionization of the amino acid carbonyl and phenolic hydroxyl groups because: (1) calculations on ionized groups are less reliable than those on neutral groups, (2) approximate calculations carried out in our laboratory have shown that the introduction of these effects would not change significantly the general aspect of our results. Qualitative considerations based on the resonance theory lead to the same conclusion, too. The effects due to ionized carbonyl or phenolic groups would be more pronounced than those due to the unionized groups. The ionization of COOH would increase the inductive effect

*Answers to the Discussion were submitted by mail subsequent to the Symposium.

of this group on the $\alpha$-carbon of the primary Schiff base. The ionization of the OH group would increase its resonance effect inside the pyridoxal skeleton. None of these ionizations would change the fundamental fact that in this primary Schiff base there are no conjugation effects involving the $\alpha$-carbon. On the other hand, the introduction of these ionizations cannot change greatly the *difference* in energy between the primary and the transitional Schiff bases, because the ionization would have to be considered in both. And it is obviously this difference which is essential.

DR. JENCKS:

I would like to defend the original formulation of the Braunstein–Snell theory in terms of a " bond-weakening " around the $\alpha$-carbon atom. In speaking of reaction mechanisms we are concerned with rates, i.e. the difference in energy between the ground state and an activated complex. From this point of view, a " weak bond " can be due to stabilization of the activated complex through electron-withdrawal by resonance and inductive effects, as well as through a destabilization of the ground state. Thus, the catalytic effects of pyridoxal compounds can be reasonably ascribed to the " electron-sink " properties of the coenzyme which cause a bond-weakening; this is a form of " electrophilic catalysis ".

DR. PULLMAN:

The general remark of Dr. Jencks about the possible reasons of a " bond-weakening " are, of course, exact. However, as he says there are a number of possible reasons for the catalytic effects. In the case of pyridoxal phosphate the Braunstein–Snell theory considered that the weakening of the bonds around the $\alpha$-carbon of the amino acid is due essentially to resonance effects in the ground state of the primary Schiff base. We object to this conception which is based on a small but important error: the idea that in this *primary base* the conjugated system extends till the $\alpha$-carbon atom. You may notice that we have even quite willingly admitted that there may be in this primary base a weakening of the bonds around the $\alpha$-carbon. Following our opinion this weakening can, however, be due only to inductive effects. On the other hand we insist on the role of the *resonance effects in the transitional bases*, and in particular on their increased resonance energy, which these authors did not consider explicitly.

DR. WESTHEIMER:

Dr. Pullman has added to our knowledge and understanding of catalysis by pyridoxal by giving us a quantitative measure of the magnitude of the resonance energies involved in its reactions. However, the qualitative theory which he has presented seems quite similar to that in general use.

The language of modern organic chemistry has reached a stage where many statements serve as almost short-hand communication. I believe that most of us here have understood qualitatively the general nature of pyridoxal catalysis, based on the discussions in the original papers of Braunstein and of Snell, even if these ideas were expressed in slightly different language from that used in the last paper. Perhaps Dr. Pullman has somewhat underestimated the degree of scientific sophistication of those whom he describes as " ordinary chemists ".

Further, Dr. Pullman has here discussed the resonance energy for the conversion of pyridoxal and an amino acid to an intermediate which he calls the " transitional " Schiff base. This is an unfortunate term, which might possibly be confused with " transition state " (i.e. activated complex). It is of course the resonance energy for the formation of the transition state which is required in order to discuss the rate of pyridoxal catalyzed reactions, and the catalytic role of pyridoxal. Although Dr. Pullman did not discuss the transition state, and therefore did not discuss catalysis, one may perhaps assume that the transition state is a resonance hybrid of reactants and the intermediate (" transitional ") Schiff base. Then the resonance energies which Dr. Pullman calculated represent an upper limit to the contribution of resonance to the lowering of activation energy. The discussion by Snell *et al.*, concerning the weakening of the bonds of the $\alpha$-carbon atom of an amino acid in a pyridoxal–amino acid Schiff base, constituted a crude short-hand expression for the transition state, and one which most physical organic chemists readily interpret. From a qualitative point of view, therefore, the original theory properly considered reaction rates and catalysis. The term " transitional " Schiff base should probably be avoided, as one which may bring confusion into the field.

DR. PULLMAN:

The problem does not reside at all in the fact that Braunstein and Snell have used a slightly different language from ours. The fact is that, following our opinion, the qualitative theory which they present is to some extent erroneous. In fact, it contains a small error, but it so happens that this error concerns an important point in the presentation of the theory. This error concerns the *role of resonance in the primary Schiff base for producing the weakening of the bonds around the α-carbon.* I must stress that we question neither the *chemical mechanism* proposed by Braunstein–Snell for pyridoxal reactions nor the fact that these authors consider resonance as an essential factor in this catalysis. The point is that we disagree with the way in which they take this resonance into account. Thus, following these authors, the activation of the amino acid is due to the fact that in the primary Schiff base formed between the pyridoxal and the amino acid there is a " conjugated system of double bonds extending from the α-carbon of the amino acid to the electronegative group which results in reduced electron density about the α-carbon atom, thus weakening each of the bonds *a, b, c* " (the quotation is from Snell in *Vitamins and Hormones*). We disagree with this statement: the α-carbon is not a part of the conjugated system of the Schiff base. It is a saturated carbon outside this system. This is not theory, this is a fact. If you refer to our paper you could see that we even admit that in fact the α-carbon may be discharged in the Schiff base, but that this, however, could be due only to inductive effects and not to the effects of resonance. Consequently, if resonance is playing a role in pyridoxal catalysis, as it obviously does, it has to do it in a different way from that postulated by Snell. Our theory proposes such a different way.

Most authors just repeated the ideas of Snell and Braunstein without paying attention to this particular point and did not notice this difficulty. The fact that there is a difference between our theory and the earlier representation of Snell and Braunstein is substantiated by a very authoritative opinion. It is that of Snell himself. I am quoting Snell from a recent publication (*Ciba Foundation Symposium on the Mechanism of Action of Water-Soluble Vitamins*, 1961, p. 20), where, after having described his own ideas, he says: " Perault, Pullman and Valdemoro (1961) have recently probed deeper into the electronic aspects of this bond labilization. They point out that, strictly speaking, the postulated decrease in electron density around the α-carbon cannot be immediately produced by withdrawal of electrons through the conjugated system of pyridoxal, since in the first-formed Schiff base this conjugation does not extend to the α-carbon. By applying quantum mechanics and molecular orbital theory they have calculated the electronic distribution about each of the atoms of the initially-formed Schiff base and the proposed transitional (*sic!*) forms, and they conclude that the essential driving force responsible for the labilization of the bonds about the α-carbon lies in the very appreciable gain (up to 10 kcal per mole) in the resonance energy that occurs when the initial Schiff base loses one of the groupings about the α-carbon and extends the conjugate system of bonds. However this may be, this change in interpretation of the nature of the forces involved in the initial labilization of the amino acid requires no change in formulation of the mechanism of the reactions." This quotation describes the situation perfectly. The last phrase in it may perhaps be stressed in connection with some of your allegations. *We have never claimed that we change the chemical formulation of the mechanism of the reaction. On the contrary we explicitely adopted this formulation as the basis of our discussion.* We only differ from Snell and Braunstein in the way in which we conceive the role of the resonance factors, but here we definitely differ.

On the other hand you stress the utility of calculations which would be directly related to the activation energies of the transformations. You do not ignore, I am sure, the difficulties connected with such calculations. Intermediates have been chosen because they are much simpler to deal with and because the chemical theory of pyridoxal catalysis is so good that their transient existence is nearly sure. You surely do not mean that the existence of low-energy intermediates is irrelevant to the mechanism of the reactions.

In your own review in the *Enzymes* you yourself only refer to intermediates, too. On the other hand, if you look carefully into our paper in *BBA* you will find, moreover, also elements for the discussion of the associated activation energies. In fact these are introduced there in a way very similar to the one that you are referring to: they concern the deformation of the structure of the intermediates under the effect of the approaching, polarizing reactants. I do not see at all what is wrong with the name of " transitional Schiff bases " given to the intermediates. I do not think that anybody in the field may confuse these with " transition states ". The denomination is used by biochemists themselves. I did not invent it.

DR. METZLER:

Evidence was presented by Metzler, Ikawa and Snell (*J. Am. Chem. Soc.* **76**, 648, 1954) that in the model system transamination occurs more rapidly than does racemization. This suggested that the free anionic " transitional Schiff base " may actually not be formed during the transamination reaction, but that a synchronous addition of a proton at one site and loss of a proton at another may be involved. I want to ask whether you have made calculations for the type of transition state required for such a synchronous reaction?

DR. PULLMAN:

No, we did not consider this reaction mechanism.

F. H. WESTHEIMER (answer to Dr. Pullman, communicated July 9, 1963):

Braunstein and Shemyakin (*Biokhimiya* **18**, 393, 1953) and Metzler, Ikawa and Snell (*J. Am. Chem. Soc.* **76**, 648, 1954) used structural formulas with curved arrows to indicate the electronic mechanism of reactions of pyridoxal phosphate, e.g.

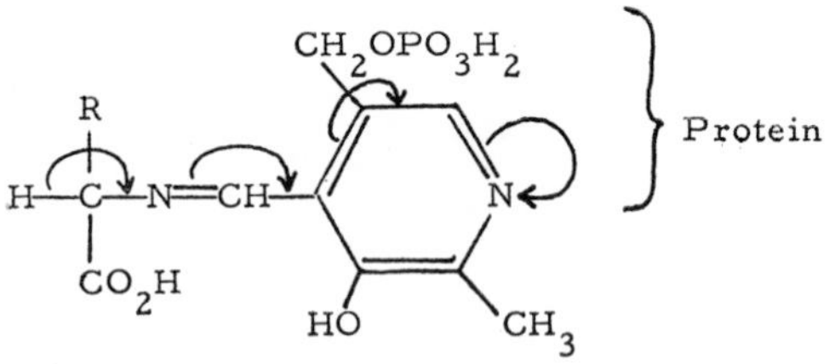

$CH_2OPO_3H_2$
R
H—C—N=CH— (pyridine ring) N
$CO_2H$
HO $CH_3$
Protein

Organic chemists generally interpret such formulas as implying resonance in the transition state, rather than in the stable starting material. Consequently, Professor Pullman's criticism of the qualitative theory, as earlier formulated by Braunstein and Snell, appears unfounded.

DR. BRAUNSTEIN:

This afternoon's session has shown that the physical organic chemists are manifesting increasing interest in the basic catalytic mechanism involved in pyridoxal-dependent reactions; this is to the benefit of the biochemists and enzymologists, although they probably will have to learn a good deal of physical chemistry and even of quantum chemistry so as to keep pace.

To those interested in the theory of PLP-catalyzed reactions, the elaboration of quantum mechanical aspects of these reactions by Professor Pullman and his associates was a source of much satisfaction, in so far as the inferences drawn from those exacting quantitative interpretations, resting on the molecular orbital method, are in essential agreement with the experimentally observed phenomena previously explained or predicted on the basis of qualitative propositions developed by Snell's group and by myself and Shemyakin. Yet it seems probable that the discrepancies mentioned by Dr. Pullman might be even smaller if he had not explicitly disregarded, for the sake of simplification or on other considerations, certain supplementary factors (he named some of them today), e.g. dynamic inductive effects of external electroactive groups (Professor Shemyakin and I have been careful to mention this factor in our paper, and in this session its significance has been demonstrated by Drs. Jencks and Bruice); chelation or hydrogen bonding of the imino nitrogen;

ionization of the $\alpha$-carboxyl of the substrate; the essential significance of the *ortho*-phenolic hydroxyl, etc.; all these factors appear to play a very significant part in the catalytic mechanism of PLP enzymes and should be taken into account in evaluating the electronic aspects of such mechanisms.

Dr. Pullman:

The introduction of the supplementary factors which I have mentioned myself and which Dr. Braunstein has enumerated again while of obvious general importance is to a large extent inessential to the principal point of the discussion which occurred here. The discrepancy between our conceptions concerns the respective roles of the inductive effects and the resonance effects in the catalysis of pyridoxal reactions. We agree, I see, that the role of inductive effects is absolutely predominant in the primary Schiff base and that it produces most probably the weakening of the bonds around the $\alpha$-carbon. What I object to is the role attributed by you and Snell in this respect to resonance effects in the primary Schiff base. These last effects concern the $\alpha$-carbon only in the transitional Schiff bases. The introduction of the supplementary factors enumerated would not change this essential point. I wish to add that these refinements which we believe to have introduced in the definition of the electronic factors involved in pyridoxal catalysis do not change at all the fundamental importance which we attach to the Snell–Braunstein formulation of the reactions involved. This formulation is as I have said and repeated all the time the basis of our own work.

Dr. Holzer:

To the analogy of thiamine pyrophosphate catalyzed reactions with pyridoxal phosphate dependent reactions I should like to add the following: the first intermediate in the phosphoketolase reaction is 1,2-dihydroxy-thiamine pyrophosphate (active glycolaldehyde); this intermediate very probably forms, in the next step (a dehydrase reaction), 1-hydroxy-vinyl-thiamine pyrophosphate. This step is completely analogous to the pyridoxal phosphate catalyzed $\alpha$–$\beta$ eliminations (Holzer and Schroter, *Biochim. et Biophys. Acta*, in press).

# THE REACTIVITY OF THE PYRIDOXAL PHOSPHATE GROUP OF GLUTAMIC ASPARTIC AMINOTRANSFERASE*

by Irwin W. Sizer

Department of Biology,
Massachusetts Institute of Technology,
Cambridge, Massachusetts

and

W. Terry Jenkins

Department of Biochemistry,
University of California,
Berkeley, California

The mechanism of the transamination reaction discovered by Braunstein and Kirtzmann[1] is based largely on Snell's hypothesis[2] that the reaction does not occur between amino acids and keto acids directly but rather involves a prosthetic group pyridoxal phosphate or pyridoxamine phosphate. The indirect evidence of Schlenk and Fisher[3] that this shuttle reaction did in fact occur in the glutamic aspartic aminotransferase system was not generally accepted until Meister *et al.*[4] showed that both pyridoxal phosphate and pyridoxamine phosphate could reactivate the apoenzyme. Even after we were able to prepare the pyridoxal and pyridoxamine forms of the enzyme,[5] this fact alone did not prove the hypothetical mechanism because of Snell's demonstration of the facile interconversion of pyridoxal phosphate into pyridoxamine phosphate in non-enzymatic systems. The interconversion of the two forms of the enzyme, however, we found to be quite specific for the physiological substrates and appeared to be virtually instantaneous. Moreover, the rate of the known transamination from glutamate to keto-glutarate[6] could be shown to be faster than that from aspartate, in agreement with the hypothesis.[7] Subsequently it has been shown[8] that the reaction between glutamate alone and the pyridoxal enzyme is almost too fast to measure by stop–flow methods and occurs at a rate consistent with the postulated mechanism in the complete system.

*This work was aided by the National Institutes of Health (Grants No. A–1680, H–4417, RG–6315A and RG–8901).

Chemical studies of the mechanism of the reaction have depended to a large degree upon investigations of the reactivity of only pyridoxal phosphate and its derivatives. This is due to the fact that the derivatives of pyridoxal phosphate have characteristic spectra whereas those of pyridoxamine phosphate are very similar and in many cases are identical with those of other derivatives. We have encountered the same experimental difficulties in dealing with the glutamic aspartic aminotransferase and have therefore of necessity concentrated our attention on the properties of the pyridoxal enzyme and its derivatives, quite conscious of the fact that we are only looking at half the story. We believe that these studies throw light on the role of the phenolic and carboxyl groups in the reaction of the pyridoxal moiety of the enzyme with the substrate amino group.

Before proceeding it should be pointed out that in investigating these reactions we are perhaps studying the basis for the specificity of the enzyme rather than the mechanism of transamination as it is usually understood. We now know that the structure of the alanine aminotransferase differs from that of the glutamic aspartic enzyme[9,10] and that different isozymes have different pH optima.[11] It is likely, therefore, that the detailed mechanisms of the reactions of substrates with different aminotransferases are not necessarily similar.

## THE BEHAVIOR OF THE ENZYME AS A pH INDICATOR

The pyridoxal form of the glutamic aspartic aminotransferase changes color with pH. Contrary to the behavior of other pyridoxal enzymes this change is readily reversible and is consistent with the dissociation of a single proton.[12] The proton dissociation constant may be readily obtained spectrophotometrically by conventional methods or by calculations based upon the change in color with pH (see Appendix I).

The change in absorption due to the formation of the acidic species at any wavelength is proportional to the concentration of that species. The value of the p$K$ may be obtained from a few determinations by plotting the reciprocal of this change against the ratio of the basic to the acidic species of a buffer whose p$K$ is close to that of the chromophore. The negative intercept on the abscissa gives the composition of a buffer whose pH is numerically the same as the p$K$ of the chromophore. It is, of course, necessary to make sure that the concentration of the buffer does not affect the result. The principal advantage of this method is that the p$K$ may be determined over a very restricted pH range, a range which may be encompassed by a single buffer. Figure 1 shows the determination of the p$K$ of the pyridoxal enzyme chromophore obtained in this way from absorbency changes at 362 m$\mu$ and 430 m$\mu$. The p$K$ value of 6.3 obtained is the same as was found by more laborious methods.

## IDENTIFICATION OF THE CHROMOPHORE

Perhaps the most striking feature of this enzyme chromophore was that its spectra were not those of pyridoxal phosphate although the latter could readily be obtained from the pyridoxal form of the enzyme. Striking parallels to the spectra of the valine imines of pyridoxal phosphate reported by Metzler[13], led us to propose[14] that the chromophore was in fact the phenolic group of a pyridoxal imine derivative rather than that of pyridoxal phosphate with a free aldehydic group. However, the p*K* for the color change of the

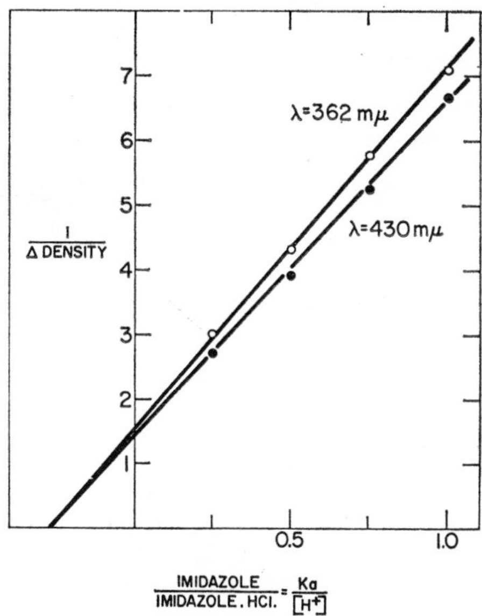


FIG. 1. Graphical determination of the p*K* of the pyridoxal form of the glutamic aspartic aminotransferase in 0.2 M imidazole buffers. In imidazole alone the solution had absorbencies of 0.991 and 0.050 at 362 mμ and 430 mμ, respectively. As the pH is lowered there is a decrease in absorbency at 362 mμ and a concomitant increase at 430 mμ. The reciprocals of these increments and decrements have been plotted against the ratio of imidazole to imidazole hydrochloride. The intercept on the abscissa is 0.27 and the pH of the buffer with this composition was found to be 6.3 which therefore is the p*K* of the chromophore.

imines was 10.5, four pH units higher than was observed for the enzyme. Since it was the p*K* of the imines which was unexpectedly high, Metzler had ascribed this to the formation of a very stable hydrogen bond between the imine nitrogen and the phenolic group. In short, it appeared that this did not occur in the enzyme in which the binding of the pyridoxal phosphate was such as to make the colorless zwitterion the predominant species at neutrality rather than the yellow, hydrogen-bonded form (Fig. 2). It is now known that the aldehyde group is bound to the ε-amino group of a lysine residue in the enzyme protein.[15,16]

## THE FORMATION OF COMPLEXES

The formation of a complex between the pyridoxal enzyme and a compound X must thus be thought of in terms of an interaction with the two observable species E and the protonated form H.E (Fig. 3).

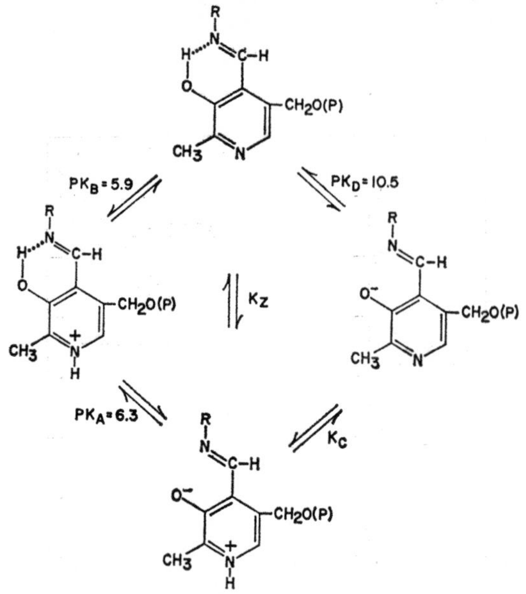

FIG. 2. Ionic forms of Schiff bases of pyridoxal phosphate present at different pH values. No attempt has been made to indicate which of the specific geometrical isomers are present in the system.

$$\begin{array}{rcccl} & X & & X & \\ & + & K_1 & + & \\ H^+ + & E & \rightleftharpoons & H\,.\,E & \\ K_2 & \updownarrow & K & \updownarrow & K_3 \\ H^+ + & E\,.\,X & \rightleftharpoons & H\,.\,E\,.\,X & \end{array}$$

FIG. 3.

It follows from the simple equilibria involved that if the affinities of E and H.E for X differ, the p$K$ of H.E.X will be different from that of E.X and that the dissociation constant of X will vary between the two extreme values in a predictable manner. In certain cases, E, H.E, E.X, and H.E.X all possess distinct spectra; hence any of the four reactions may be studied individually. In the case of carboxylic acids, however, it appears that the spectra of E.X resembles that of E and H.E.X resembles that of H.E so that only the hydrogen ion dissociation constants may be determined directly and the dissociation constants for the compound X have to be obtained indirectly from a theoretical analysis of the variation of the dissociation constant with pH.

Surprisingly it was found that the behavior of the system may be accurately and sufficiently described in these simple terms shown in Fig. 3. In many cases the values obtained indirectly could be shown to check with those obtained directly. On one occasion a discrepancy led to the discovery of an inhibitory effect due to the buffer.

## THE REACTION WITH DICARBOXYLIC ACIDS

It has long been known that carboxylic acid analogs of the substrates for specific aminotransferases are competitive inhibitors of the reaction.[17–19] It can be shown, in addition, that substrate inhibition is due to an effect of the keto acid on the enzyme affinity for the amino acid and vice versa.[20] It seems likely that the inability of some investigators to observe these effects was due to the fact that the degree of inhibition is dependent upon the pH.[7,19] In general, it appears that most competitive inhibitors of transaminases are more effective at low pH values.

The interaction between dicarboxylic acids and the pyridoxal form of the glutamic aspartic aminotransferase may be readily observed at pH 8[12,20] at which the free enzyme is colorless while the equilibrium mixture of complexes is colored yellow (Figs. 4A and 4B). This color arises from the fact that in all cases the protonated enzyme has a much higher affinity for dicarboxylic acids than the colorless form of the enzyme. Contrary to our original conclusion,[21] however, the colorless form does interact with these acids. This is apparent with high concentrations which permit hydrogen ion dissociation of the complex (i.e. reaction 4) to be studied. Notable features of this reaction are that the enzyme has a great affinity for maleate, succinate and mesotartarate but little affinity for fumarate and *dl*-tartarate. It is also significant that the affinity for *d*-malic acid is much greater than it is for the *l*-isomer. In the homologous series of dicarboxylic acids it is found that oxalic and pimelic acids do not react and that there is an optimum chain length with glutarate which produces maximum interaction.[12]

These unique characteristics appear to define the specificity requirements very closely. The fact that this inhibitor specificity, as with other transaminases[19] closely resembles the specificity of the enzyme for its physiological substrates suggests very strongly that the same groups of the enzyme are involved in binding both the competitive inhibitors and the substrates. It should be emphasized, however, that this binding of two carboxyl groups governs the substrate specificity but not the optical specificity, for only the *l*-isomer of alanine will react directly with the enzyme.[22] The low rate of transamination observed with alanine could be shown to be due to a very low affinity for this substrate.

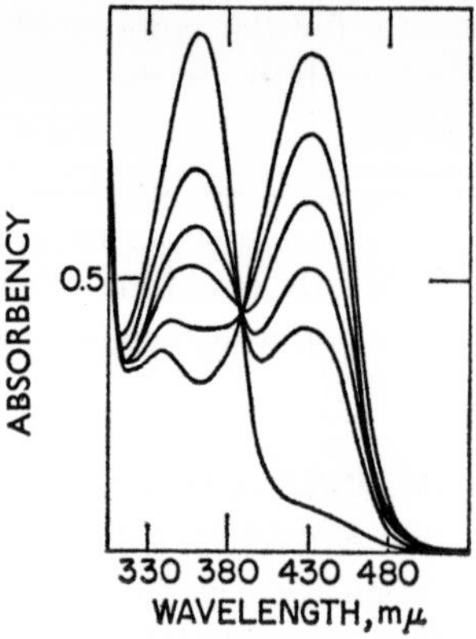


FIG. 4A. The reaction of *l*-malate with the pyridoxal form of the glutamic aspartic aminotransferase in 0.1 M Tris buffer pH 8.0. The spectra shown are the enzyme alone (top curve; $\lambda_{max}$, 362 mμ) and those obtained with increasing concentrations (0.006, 0.010, 0.014, 0.020 and 0.040 M) of *l*-malate.

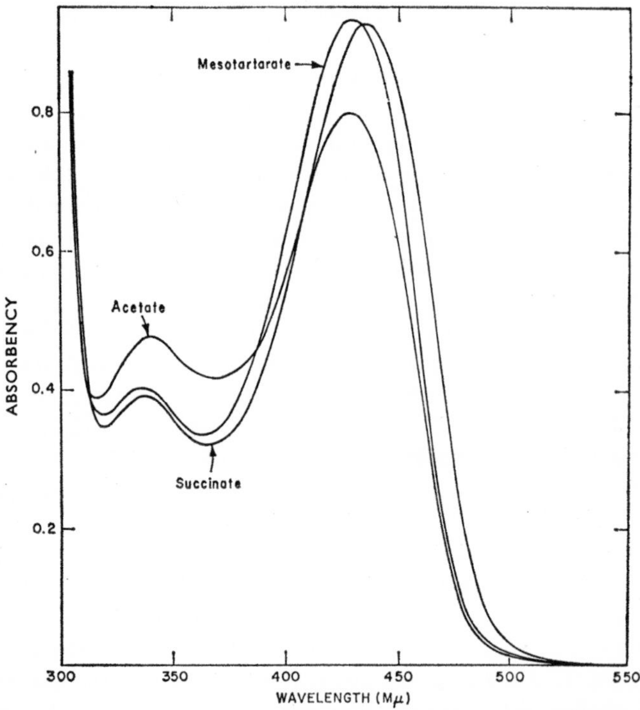


FIG. 4B. Interaction of the pyridoxal form of the pig heart glutamic aspartic aminotransferase with dicarboxylic acid substrate analogs demonstrated by spectral changes. Each curve represents the same concentration of enzyme, the same concentration of buffer (0.08 M) at the same pH of 5.1. Different dicarboxylic acids characteristically form complexes with different $\lambda_{max}$ values and different extinction coefficients.

## ANALYSIS OF THE EFFECT OF pH ON THE INTERACTION WITH DICARBOXYLIC ACIDS

As an extension of the method previously described to determine the hydrogen ion dissociation constant of the chromophore it can be shown (see Appendix II) that the apparent enzyme dissociation constant for X, measured spectroscopically from changes in the optical density at any wavelength due to the addition of X, is independent of the relative extinction coefficients of the species involved and is numerically equal to

$$K' = \frac{K_3(1 + H^+/K_4)}{(1 + H^+/K_4)}$$

TABLE 1. CORRECTION FOR COMPETITIVE INHIBITION BY IMIDAZOLE BUFFERS

| Imidazole.HCl / Imidazole | $1/K_{obs}$ 0.1 M Imidazole | $1/K_{obs}$ 0.2 M imidazole | $1/K_{true}$ | $1/K_1$ |
|---|---|---|---|---|
| 0.2 | 136 | 85 | 339 | 15 |
| 0.4 | 158 | 95 | 462 | 19 |
| 0.6 | 170 | 100 | 565 | 23 |
| 0.8 | 183 | 104 | 755 | 31 |
| 1.0 | 182 | 102 | 820 | 35 |

Values for $K_{obs}$ were determined from double reciprocal plots for the absorbency increases at 435 mμ due to the addition of succinate in concentrations from 0.004 to 0.02 M. The least squares straight line also gives a value for the maximum absorbency which would be obtained with an infinite concentration of succinate. These maximum absorbency values were used to determine the p$K$ of the succinate complex as in Fig. 1, yielding a value of 7.9. When the values for the succinate dissociation constant in imidazole buffers were used to determine this same p$K$ by the method of Fig. 5B, inconsistent results were obtained. One may assume that at each pH the inhibition is purely competitive and that the observed dissociation constants are described by the equation $K_{obs} = K_{true}(1 + 1/K_1)$. The $K_{true}$ and $K_1$ values can be derived from the data in the table. When the corrected $K_{true}$ values were used a value of 7.9 was obtained for p$K_4$ and 0.0065 M for $K_3$. Although the values for $K_1$ are subject to large experimental errors, the effect of the inhibition is much more marked at low pH values.

Since $K'$ may be determined at different values of $H^+$ where the ratio $H^+/K_1$ is known, the values of $K_4$ and $K_3$ may be readily determined graphically from a plot of $(1 + H^+/K_1)/K'$ against the ratio of the acidic to basic species of the buffer. It was found in the case of succinic acid in imidazole buffers that this leads to erroneous results unless the values of the dissociation constant are corrected for a competitive inhibitory action of the buffer itself (Table 1). This correction results in a value in agreement with the value of $K_4$ determined more directly from the experimental values for the maximum theoretical absorbency change.

## THE REACTION WITH CARBONYL REAGENTS

A unique feature of the pyridoxal enzyme is that it reacts with carbonyl reagents much more rapidly than does free pyridoxal phosphate.[21,23] It is possible in favorable cases to carry out an analysis of this interaction in the same way as has been outlined for the dicarboxylic acids. The product with the carbonyl antitubercular drug, Isoniazid, has a p$K$ much higher than that of the enzyme chromophore. This interaction may be measured directly because, although the two forms absorb at around 400 m$\mu$, there is a difference

TABLE 2

| Reaction | $\lambda_{max}$ reactant (m$\mu$) | $\lambda_{max}$ product (m$\mu$) | p$K_d$ |
|---|---|---|---|
| 1. $E + H^+ \rightleftharpoons H.E$ | 362 | 430 | 6.4 |
| 2. $E + X \rightleftharpoons E.X$ | 362 | 402 | 1.5 |
| 3. $H.E + X \rightleftharpoons H.E.X.$ | 430 | 410 | 2.6 |
| 4. $E.X + H^+ \rightleftharpoons H.E.X.$ | 402 | 410 | 7.6 |

All reactions were studied in 0.05 M pyrophosphate buffers.
$pK_1 + pK_3 = 9.0.$
$pK_2 + pK_4 = 9.1.$

in their molar absorbencies. Each of the four reactions shown in Fig. 3 (see Table 2) could be studied independently and it could be shown that the dissociation constant obeyed the theoretical equation $K_1 . K_3 = K_2 . K_4$.

Comparable results have now been obtained with thiosemicarbazide which is a more suitable carbonyl reagent for these studies because it does not absorb above 300 m$\mu$, it is more stable, its p$K$ values of 1.5 and 10.3 are removed from the experimental pH range, and finally its reaction with the enzyme is slow enough to be followed with a recording spectrophotometer.

It was found experimentally that the rate could be described by a pseudo first-order reversible reaction where the rate constant ($K_{-1} + K_{+1} . X$) yielded a dissociation constant $K_{-1}/K_{+1}$ in agreement with that obtained directly from the final absorbency increment (Figs. 5A and 5B). Although the product appeared to have two peaks at about 330 m$\mu$ and 400 m$\mu$, which suggests that it is an equilibrium mixture of more than one species, no direct evidence for the accumulation of an intermediate could be found (Fig. 6). In Figs. 5A and 7B it can be seen that in the pH range from 7 to 9.2, the rate-limiting reaction in the forward direction is dependent upon the hydrogen ion concentration but that the rate-limiting reaction for the decomposition of the complex is not dependent upon the pH. Thus it appears that the greater affinity of the yellow form of the enzyme is due solely to its greater reactivity with the carbonyl reagent. The values obtained for $K_4$ and $K_3$ (Fig. 5B) could again be checked directly in the presence of an excess of thiosemicarbazide (Fig. 7A) and at a high pH value (Fig. 7B), respectively.

The fact that both acidic and basic species of this complex have absorption maxima at about 400 m$\mu$ leads one to ascribe the dissociation to the pyridinium

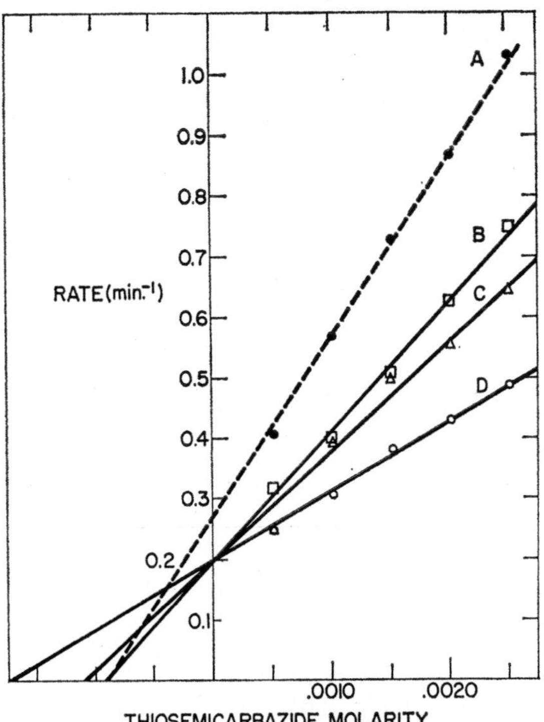


FIG. 5. Determination of the p$K$ of the enzyme thiosemicarbazide complex from the thiosemicarbazide dissociation constants at different pH values.

A. Rate constants (derived from semilogarithmic plots of ($D_\infty - Dt$) vs. time) are plotted against the thiosemicarbazide concentration. Since the rate constant has the form ($K_{-1} + K_1.X$) the straight lines have intercepts on the ordinate and the abscissa equal to $K_{-1}$ and the dissociation constant $K_{-1}/K_1$, respectively. The dissociation constant derived from the final increments in the absorbency in all cases was found to be the same. This is shown in line A which is a plot of 50X(thiosemicarbazide)/$\Delta D_{\lambda = 413\ m\mu}$. Lines B, C and D were for imidazole hydrochloride to imidazole ratios of 0.75, 0.50 and 0.25, respectively.

group. This behavior is contrary to that of pyridoxal phosphate and may imply that the protein $\epsilon$-amino group which was bound to the pyridoxal phosphate forces the hydrazide into the correct favorable position for hydrogen bonding.

The formation of the H . E . X type of complex may also be envisaged theoretically as a reaction of XH with E. It so happens that this reaction

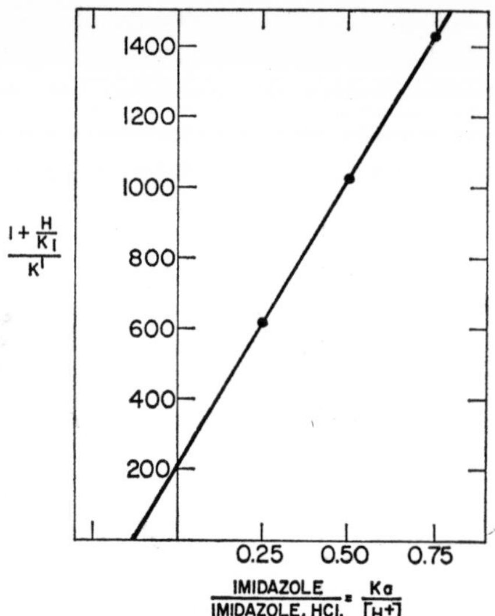


FIG. 5B. This is a graphical determination of $K_3 = 0.005$ M and p$K_4 = 7.9$ by the method outlined in Appendix II with data from Fig. 5A. A new determination of $K_1$ with these buffer solutions gave an imidazole/imidazole hydrochloride ratio of 0.19 and this value was used in the small correction $(1 + H^+/K_1)$ applied to the values of the dissociation constant $K'$. All experiments were carried out in 0.2 M imidazole buffers.

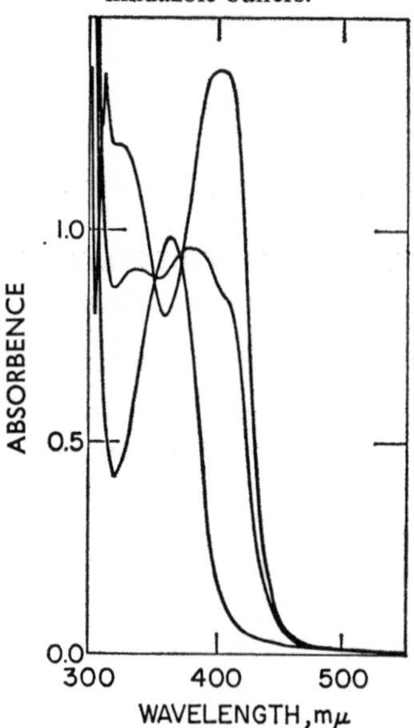


FIG. 6. Spectral changes produced by the addition of thiosemicarbazide to the pyridoxal form of the glutamic aspartic aminotransferase in 0.06 M borax, pH 9.2. Spectra shown are in the absence of thiosemicarbazide (lower curve: $\lambda_{max}$ 362 m$\mu$), and in the presence of 0.006 M (middle curve) and 0.06 M (upper curve) thiosemicarbazide, respectively.

cannot be observed directly but the equilibrium constant $K_5$ may be obtained theoretically from the expression $K_5 . K_6 = K_3 . K_4$ where $K_6$ is the hydrogen ion dissociation constant. We found a $pK_6 = 1.54$ which gives a $pK_5$ of 8.7. It can therefore be appreciated that the effect of the phenolic group is to give the pyridoxal enzyme an extremely high affinity for a protonated amino group of a substrate.

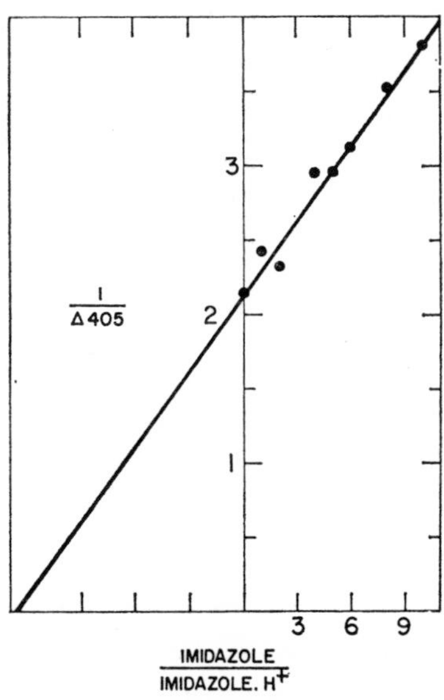


FIG. 7A. Determination of the p$K$ of the chromophore as in Fig. 1. In this case the chromophore is the thiosemicarbazide derivative of the pyridoxal form of the glutamic aspartic aminotransferase since the spectra are taken in 0.06 M thiosemicarbazide. The p$K$ of 8.0 determined from the value of the intercept on the abscissa agrees with that found indirectly from Fig. 5B.

## THE MECHANISM OF THE REACTION WITH CARBONYL REAGENTS

The rate of formation of simple Schiff bases from pyridoxal phosphate does not lend itself readily to experimental investigation. Recently Cordes and Jencks[24] have studied an analogous reaction, the formation of semicarbazones. Their finding that primary and secondary amines have a pronounced catalytic effect strongly implies that the greater reactivity of the pyridoxal enzyme is due to the fact that it exists as a Schiff base which is much more reactive than a free aldehydic group to nucleophilic attack.[25] They suggest that the Schiff base with a proton on the nitrogen would be the most reactive species. The apparent conflict with our observation that it is the basic form of the enzyme which is most reactive with substrates is readily resolved if it be accepted that the interaction is in fact a two-step process, the first step being an interaction with the two carboxyl groups to give an intermediate whose p$K$ is higher than the free enzyme. Hence this is a necessary step in promoting the displacement of the $\epsilon$-amino group by the substrate amino group. An absorption maximum has yet to be ascribed

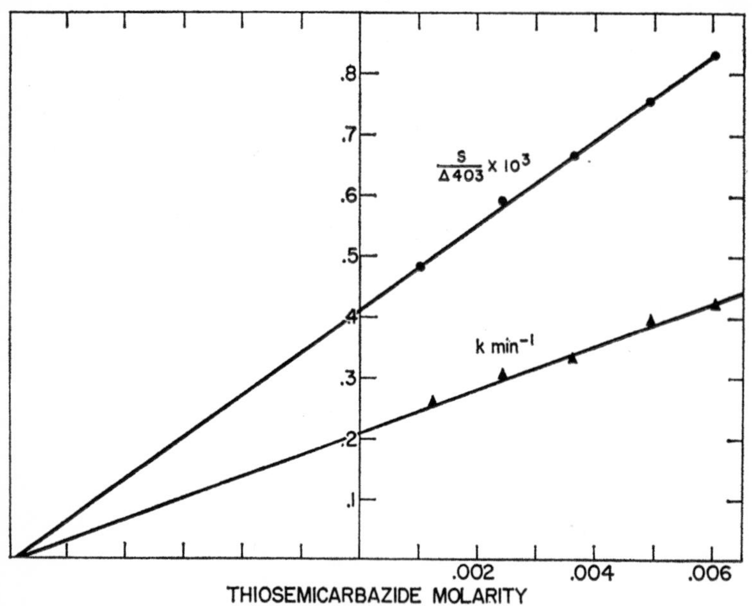


FIG. 7B. The dissociation constant ($K_3$) for thiosemicarbazide and the basic form of the pyridoxal enzyme determined from the variation in the rate constant of the reaction with thiosemicarbazide concentration and the final increments in the absorbency. The values for both $K_3 = 0.0058$ and $K_{-1} = 0.21$ min$^{-1}$ obtained in 0.06 M borax, pH 9.2, are in good agreement with those derived in Fig. 5.

to the protonated Schiff bases which have been implicated as intermediates in this displacement. We have reported evidence for intermediates with an absorption maximum of 492 m$\mu$[10,26] and it is possible that this maximum is due to this species, for the fluorescence maximum of Schiff bases absorbing around 400 m$\mu$ is at the same wavelength.

Since the early work of Herbst, the action of the carboxyl group in model systems has been little investigated.[27,32] His work suggests that it is the interaction of the carboxyl group which will distinguish the aminotransferases from the decarboxylases. There is some spectroscopic evidence for the interaction of acidic groups with Schiff bases[28,29] and for a specific effect of acetic acid upon Schiff base formation.[30] Because the copper chelates of pyridoxal phosphate glycine and ethanolamine imines have identical spectra, Matsuo concluded that in the glycine derivative a linkage involving the carboxyl group was unlikely.[31]

## SUMMARY

(1) A spectroscopic method is described for the determination of dissociation constants of glutamic aspartic aminotransferase plus substrates or inhibitors which is shown to be applicable even in the presence of four components.

(2) The method was used to investigate the effect of pH upon the stability of derivatives of the pyridoxal form of this enzyme formed upon the addition of certain dicarboxylic acids, Isoniaziol or thiosemicarbazide.

(3) It was shown that thiosemicarbazide reacts with the pyridoxal glutamic aspartic aminotransferase in a pseudo first-order reaction and that the ratio of the reaction constants agrees with the stability of the complex determined by an independent method. From these results it is concluded that changes in the stability of the product with pH reflect a difference in the reactivity of the acidic and basic forms of the enzyme with thiosemicarbazide.

(4) The significance of the finding that the acidic form of the enzyme has a greater affinity than does the basic form for both carboxyl groups and carbonyl reagents is discussed in relation to the mechanisms of specificity for substrates and inhibitors and the nature of the transamination reaction.

## APPENDIX I

### DETERMINATION OF p*K* VALUE COLORIMETRICALLY

Let the molar absorbencies for E and EH be $E_1$ and $E_2$.

The density increment $\Delta D$ is then defined as:

$$\Delta D = E_1(\mathrm{E}) + E_2(\mathrm{HE}) - E_1(\mathrm{E} + \mathrm{HE})$$
$$= (E_2 - E_1)\,(\mathrm{H}\,.\,\mathrm{E})$$

where the density of the basic solution is $E_1(\mathrm{E} + \mathrm{EH}) = E_1\, E_T$

The total enzyme concentration $E_T$ is given by

$$E_T = \mathrm{E} + \mathrm{EH} = \mathrm{EH}\left(1 + \frac{\mathrm{E}}{\mathrm{EH}}\right)$$

$$= \frac{\Delta D}{(E_2 - E_1)}\left(1 + \frac{K}{\mathrm{H}^+}\right) \text{ since } K = \frac{(\mathrm{E})\,(\mathrm{H}^+)}{(\mathrm{EH})}$$

If $R$ = the ratio of the concentration of the acidic species of buffer to the basic.

The dissociation constant of the buffer

$$K^1 = \frac{(\mathrm{B})(\mathrm{H}^+)}{\mathrm{BH}} = \frac{(\mathrm{H}^+)}{R}$$

Substitution for $(\mathrm{H}^+)$

$$E_T(E_2 - E_1) = (\Delta D)_{\max} = \Delta D\left(1 + \frac{K}{RK'}\right)$$

A plot of $1/\Delta D$ vs. $1/R$ has a negative intercept, $1/R^1$ such that a buffer with this composition has a p$H$

$$= -\log R^1K^1$$
$$= \text{p}K$$

## APPENDIX II

### THE EFFECT OF pH ON ENZYME–INHIBITOR DISSOCIATION CONSTANTS

Assume that the four species present, (E), (H.E), (EX) and (H.E.X) have molar absorbencies of $E_1$, $E_2$, $E_3$ and $E_4$.

The following dissociation constants may be defined:

$$K_1 = \frac{(\text{E})(\text{H})}{(\text{EH})}$$

$$K_2 = \frac{(\text{E})(\text{X})}{(\text{EX})}$$

$$K_3 = \frac{(\text{H.E})(\text{X})}{(\text{H.E.X})}$$

$$K_4 = \frac{(\text{EX})(\text{H})}{(\text{H.E.X})}$$

It follows that

$$\frac{(\text{E})(\text{X})(\text{H})}{(\text{H.E.X})} = K_1K_3 = K_2K_4$$

Upon the addition of X there will be an absorbency change $\Delta D$ and a change in $E$ $\Delta E$ where

$$\Delta D = \Delta E(E_1 + E_2\,\text{H}/K_1) + (\Delta\,\text{EX})(E_3 + E_4\,\text{H}/K_4)$$
$$= (\Delta E)(1 + \text{H}/K_1)\left(\frac{(E_1 + E_2\,\text{H}/K_1)}{(1 + \text{H}/K_1)} - \frac{(E_3 + E_4\,\text{H}/K_4)}{(1 + \text{H}/K_4)}\right) \tag{1}$$

$$\Delta\text{E} = E_T\left(\frac{1}{1 + \text{H}/K_1} - \frac{1}{1 + \text{H}/K_1 + \text{X}/K_3(1 + \text{H}/K_4)}\right) \tag{2}$$

(1) and (2) may be combined at constant pH to give

$$\frac{(\Delta D)_{\text{max}}}{\Delta D} = 1 + \frac{K^1}{\text{X}} \quad \text{where} \quad \frac{(1 + \text{H}/K_1)}{K^1} = \frac{(1 + \text{H}/K_4)}{K_3}$$

$$\Delta D_{\text{max}} = E_T\left(\frac{(E_1 + E_2\,\text{H}/K_1)}{(1 + \text{H}/K_1)} - \frac{(E_3 + E_4\text{H}/K_4)}{(1 + \text{H}/K_4)}\right)$$

$K^1$ is the negative intercept on the abscissa of a plot of $\text{X}/\Delta D$ vs. X.

## REFERENCES

1. A. E. BRAUNSTEIN and M. G. KIRTZMANN; *Enzymologia* **2**, 129 (1937).
2. E. E. SNELL; *J. Am. Chem. Soc.* **67**, 194 (1945).
3. F. SCHLENK and A. FISHER; *Arch. Biochem.* **12**, 69 (1947).
4. A. MEISTER, H. A. SOBER and E. A. PETERSON; *J. Biol. Chem.* **206**, 89 (1954).
5. W. T. JENKINS and I. W. SIZER; *J. Biol. Chem.* **235**, 620 (1960).
6. A. NISONOFF, F. W. BARNES, JR., T. ENNS and S. VON SUCHING; *Bull. Johns Hopkins Hosp.* **94**, 117 (1954).
7. W. T. JENKINS and I. W. SIZER; *J. Biol. Chem.* **234**, 1179 (1959).
8. H. GUTFREUND, K. E. EBNER and L. MENDIOLA; *Nature* **192**, 820 (1960).
9. Y. M. TORCHINSKII; *Doklady Akad. Nauk S.S.S.R.* **138**, 1464 (1961).
10. W. T. JENKINS; *Federation Proc.* **20**, 978 (1961).
11. G. A. FLEISHER, C. S. POTTER and K. G. WAKIM; *Proc. Soc. Exptl. Biol. Med.* **103**, 229 (1960).
12. W. T. JENKINS, D. A. YPHANTIS and I. W. SIZER; *J. Biol. Chem.* **234**, 51 (1959).
13. D. E. METZLER; *J. Am. Chem. Soc.* **79**, 485 (1957).
14. W. T. JENKINS and I. W. SIZER; *J. Am. Chem. Soc.* **79**, 2655 (1957).
15. E. H. FISCHER and E. G. KREBS; Abstract Am. Chem. Soc. meeting, Atlantic City (1959).
16. C. TURANO, P. FASELLA, P. VECCHINI and A. GIARTOSIO; *Atti accad. naz. Lincei, Classe sci. fis.* **30**, 532 (1961).
17. A. E. BRAUNSTEIN; *Enzymologia* **7**, 25 (1939).
18. L. S. DARLING; *Studier uber den Enzymatiske Transaminering*, Fischers Forlag, Copenhagen (1951).
19. M. MASON; *J. Biol. Chem.* **234**, 2770 (1959).
20. S. F. VELICK and J. VAVRA; *J. Biol. Chem.* **237**, 2109 (1962).
21. I. W. SIZER and W. T. JENKINS; *Methods in Enzymol.* **5**, 677 (1962).
22. W. T. JENKINS; *J. Biol. Chem.* **236**, 474 (1961).
23. W. T. JENKINS, S. ORLOWSKI and I. W. SIZER; *J. Biol. Chem.* **234**, 2657 (1959).
24. E. H. CORDES and W. P. JENCKS; *Biochemistry* **1**, 773 (1962).
25. E. E. SNELL and W. T. JENKINS; *J. Cell. Comp. Physiol.* **54**, suppl. 1, 161 (1959).
26. W. T. JENKINS; *J. Biol. Chem.* **236**, 1121 (1961).
27. R. M. HERBST; *Advances in Enzymol.* **4**, 75 (1944).
28. H. N. CHRISTENSEN; *J. Am. Chem. Soc.* **80**, 99 (1958).
29. A. W. BAKER and A. T. SHULGIN; *J. Am. Chem. Soc.* **81**, 1523 (1959).
30. C. S. MARVEL and N. TARKOY; *J. Am. Chem. Soc.* **79**, 6000 (1957).
31. Y. MATSUO; *J. Am. Chem. Soc.* **79**, 2011 (1957).
32. C. CENNAMO; *Boll. soc. ital. biol. sper.* **37**, 183 (1961).

## DISCUSSION

DR. CEDRANGOLO:

In relation to the demonstration of the dissociation of a proton in the mechanism of transamination I would like to recall some experiments of many years ago in which I demonstrated a repression of oxidative deamination of amino acids when the transamination occurs (addition of ketoglutarate in a mixture containing amino acid and tissue homogenate). Does Dr. Sizer think that some relationship may exist between deamination and transamination?

DR. SIZER:

The observation of Dr. Cedrangolo that in tissue homogenates there is a repression of oxidative deamination of amino acids when transamination occurs is most interesting. Since oxidative deamination is essentially irreversible it seems unlikely that any effect on this system would result from a reaction of keto acids with transaminases. On the other hand, one would expect that transaminases would compete directly with oxidative deaminases for amino acids which are substrates for both enzyme systems. In addition, however, we have found that glutamic amino transferase combines with certain monocarboxylic amino acids which are not substrates. In this way transaminases can compete with deaminases for amino acids in the metabolic pool. This would result in an overall repression of deamination by the transaminase systems.

DR. SENEZ:

Concerning the binding of the prosthetic group to the apoprotein, it seems that an enzyme such as β-aspartate decarboxylase, which can now be obtained in fairly large amounts by Dr. Meister, and which contains firmly bound pyridoxal-phosphate, could provide an excellent material for the study of the problem.

DR. SIZER:

One of the key problems of the pyridoxal enzymes is a consideration of the binding of the prosthetic group to the apoprotein. For such studies one needs relatively large amounts of a highly purified enzyme. The β-aspartate decarboxylase of Dr. Meister would be an excellent enzyme for such studies. Recently Dr. Evangelopoulos and I have been preparing glutamic-aminotransferase in fairly high yield and in excellent stage of purity from skeletal muscle. Since already so much is understood of the properties of this enzyme, we believe that it would serve ideally for studies of binding of coenzyme to apoprotein.

DR. METZLER:

Although the linkage between pyridoxal phosphate and an amino group is covalent, it is nevertheless a very weak linkage in aqueous solution by virtue of the rapid, reversible equilibrium with the free aldehyde and amino acid. The comparatively " strong " Schiff base between valine and pyridoxal has a free energy of formation from free pyridoxal and valine at pH 7 of only about −1112 kcal per mole (*J. Am. Chem. Soc.* **79**, 485, 1957). For pyridoxal phosphate this value is about 3 kcal more negative (Matsuo, *J. Am. Chem. Soc.* **79**, 2011, 1957), but the strength of the binding is still very low.

DR. SIZER:

No one has as yet measured the free energy of formation of the Schiff base formed by the reaction of pyridoxal phosphate and the apoenzyme of glutamic amino transferase. From certain indirect evidence we believe that the strength of binding of coenzyme to protein by Schiff base formation is also relatively low.

# BINARY COMPLEXES INVOLVED IN ENZYMIC TRANSAMINATION*

by W. TERRY JENKINS

Department of Biochemistry,
University of California, Berkeley

THE mechanism of transamination is, in reality, the mechanism of three dissimilar reactions: (1) the reaction of a protonated amino group ($—NH_3^+$) with the aldehyde group of enzyme-bound pyridoxal phosphate, the aldehyde group itself being linked to the protein through a Schiff base linkage; (2) the reaction of an $\alpha$-keto acid or carbonyl group with the amino group of an enzyme-bound pyridoxamine phosphate molecule, this amino group being also most likely in the $—NH_3^+$ form; and (3) the interconversion of the products of the first two reactions, a reaction which conceivably might involve many intermediates. These intermediates are of two kinds: pyridoxal phosphate Schiff bases and pyridoxamine phosphate bases.

The mechanism of the overall reaction is thus dependent upon the elucidation of the structures of the reactive enzymic species and of the binary intermediates involved in the third reaction.

## PARTICIPATION OF TERNARY COMPLEXES

The evidence for the occurrence of ternary intermediates, that is complexes of amino acid donor, keto acid acceptor and enzyme, is extremely superficial. The hypothesis that such complexes were involved in the reaction dates prior to the discovery of the role of vitamin $B_6$ in the reaction.[1,2] It was supported by the model experiments of Herbst[3] with amino acids and keto acids now superseded by those with amino acids and pyridoxal phosphate,[4] also by the hypothesis, now discarded,[5] that glutamate/ketoglutarate were obligatory participants,[6] by the requirement for both amino acid and keto acid for certain exchange reactions,[7–9] an observation shown to be irrelevant,[10] and lastly perhaps even by the name " transaminase " which implies some such mechanism.

A persistent form of this hypothesis suggests that there are two distinct substrate binding sites on the enzyme protein. In support it is commonly

*Original work in this investigation was supported in part by a U.S. Public Health Service research grant H 04417–05 from the Heart Institute.

shown that competitive inhibitors of the amino acid have no effect on the binding of the keto acid. This type of experiment is also irrelevant because of the evidence for the participation of " aldimine " and " pyridoxamine " forms of the enzymes. In fact it is very hard to demonstrate experimentally that a particular enzyme, for example, binds two dissimilar substrates in different ways although such a hypothesis does not seem unreasonable.[11] The principal difficulty encountered[12] is the fact that the effect of competitive inhibitors studied kinetically may be exerted either on the enzyme itself or upon a subsequent equilibration:

$$E + S = ES_1 = ES_2 \quad E + S' = ES_1' = ES_2'$$

A differential effect of an inhibitor with the two substrates S and S′ may be due to the unique nature of $ES_1$ rather than two distinct sites on the enzyme E.

Originally we thought that the experimental observation that both amino acid and keto acid could react with the pyridoxal form of the glutamic aspartic aminotransferase supported the idea of a ternary complex. Subsequent evidence[13] showed that the keto acid–" aldimine " enzyme complex was inactive. The groups which bind the carboxyl groups of the keto acid in fact appear to be the same as those which normally bind those of the amino acid, and this is really what one would expect.

## PARTICIPATION OF BINARY INTERMEDIATES

The " aldimine " and " pyridoxamine " forms of both the pig heart glutamic aspartic aminotransferase and the glutamic alanine aminotransferase (Fig. 1) are readily interconvertible by the addition of amino acid and keto acid substrates. It is not the interconversion itself which is so important but rather the fact that the physiological substrates are the most effective and react at a rate consistent with their reactivity in a more complete system.[14] Important also is the fact that the rate from an amino acid to its own analogous keto acid is comparable to that in a complete four substrate system.[13,15,16]

In theory observation of the binary intermediate complexes should be easy in the presence of both amino acid and keto acid. In practice spectroscopic observation of the binary intermediates is complicated by the following facts.

(1) The pyridoxal phosphate is bound to the enzyme in Schiff base linkage through an ε-amino group of a lysine residue.[17,18] The spectra of many of the intermediates therefore resemble those of the aldimine enzyme.

(2) Certain of the complexes may not be present in observable concentrations when the whole equilibrium mixture of binary complexes is present.

(3) As shown in Fig. 2 there appear to be three classes of binary complexes present in these equilibrium systems.

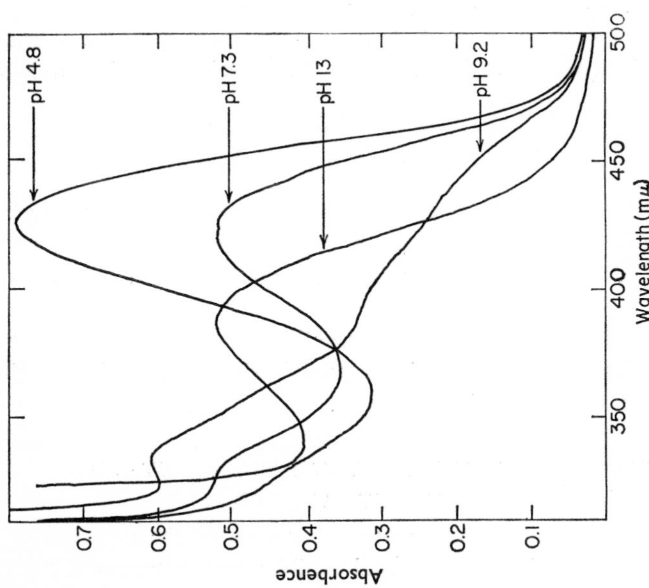


FIG. 1. A. Spectra of the " pyridoxal " (aldimine) form of the pig heart glutamic alanine aminotransferase at different pH values. Buffers: pH 4.8, 0.08 M acetate, pH 7.3, 0.08 M potassium phosphate, pH 9.2, 0.02 M sodium tetraborate, pH 13, 0.1 M NaCH.

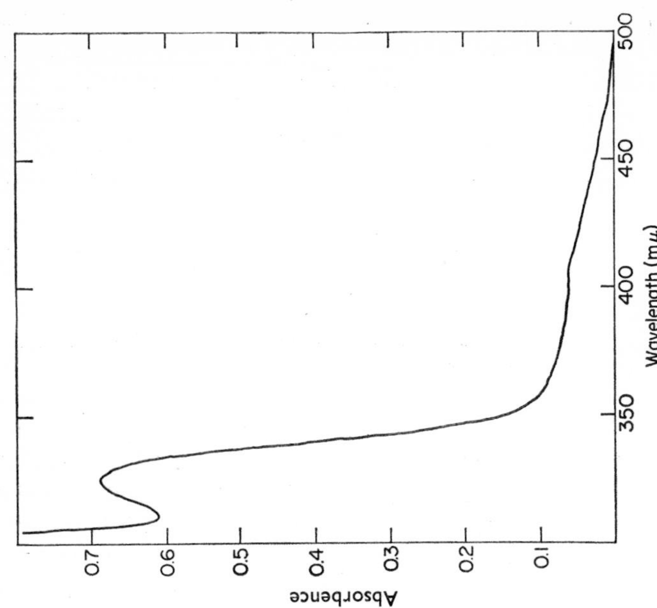


FIG. 1. B. Spectrum of the " pyridoxamine " form of the same transaminase in 0.01 M potassium phosphate buffer, pH 6.9.

In this formulation $E_1$, $E_2$, ESi, $E_1S_2$ and $E_2S_1$ are intended to represent equilibrium mixtures. The " aldimine " enzyme–keto acid complexes ($E_1S_2$) and the " pyridoxamine " enzyme–amino acid complexes are inactive and may be termed " abortive " complexes.[19,20] The total concentration of ESi complexes should be proportional to the rate of carbon chain or $\alpha$-hydrogen exchange in systems containing mixtures of amino acid and analogous keto acid. In favorable cases one of the ESi complexes absorbs

$$\begin{array}{ccccc} & E_1 + S_1 & \overset{K_2}{\leftrightharpoons} & \text{ESi} \overset{K_3}{\leftrightharpoons} & E_2 + S_2 \\ +S_2 \downarrow\uparrow & K_1 & & +S_1 \downarrow\uparrow & K_4 \\ E_1S_2 & & & E_2S_1 & \end{array}$$

FIG. 2. Summary scheme of the enzyme–substrate binary complexes theoretically possible with aminotransferases.

at an unique wavelength and the absorbency at this wavelength may be used as a measure of the total concentration of ESi complexes. This measure of the concentration of ESi complexes is termed X in the subsequent discussion.

For the determination of the constants $K_1$, $K_2$, $K_3$ and $K_4$ it is shown in the Appendix that one must study the effect on X of varying the concentrations of amino acid and keto acid together at a constant ratio $R = S_2/S_1$. Under such conditions a certain proportion of the enzyme will be converted into ESi complexes, the remainder of the $E_1$ and $E_2$ forms of the enzyme being converted into the " abortive " complexes $E_1S_2$ and $E_2S_1$. The slopes of a plot of $S_2/X$ vs. $S_2$ should reflect changes in the value of $R$ since they are proportional to $(1 + R.K_2/K_1 + K_3/R.K_4)$. The values of $K_1$, $K_2$, $K_3$ and $K_4$ may be determined from the intercepts on the abscissa which should be:

$$\frac{(R.K_2 + K_3)}{(1 + R.K_2/K_1 + K_3/R.K_4)}$$

A simpler although less rigorous test is to plot $S_1/X$ at constant levels of $S_2$ when it can be shown that the lines extrapolate to a single point on the Y-axis if $K_2S_2/K_1$ is negligible and will be straight lines if $K_3S_1/K_4$ is also negligible.

In practice it seems most practicable to use this latter method with enzymes which do not form abortive complexes, that is those which do not show substrate inhibition at high substrate levels.

## SPECTROSCOPIC STUDIES WITH THE GLUTAMIC ALANINE AMINOTRANSFERASE

The pig heart glutamic alanine aminotransferase in the presence of an excess of both amino acid and keto acid exhibits three absorption maxima at about 330, 360 and 490 m$\mu$ (Fig. 3). As judged by the criteria outlined in

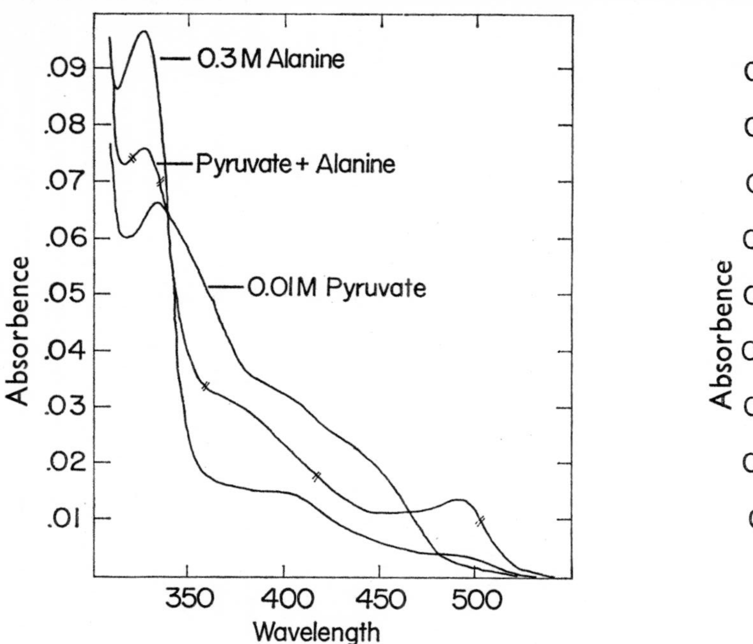


FIG. 3. A. Changes in the spectra of the "aldimine" form of the glutamic–alanine aminotransferase upon the addition of substrates. The addition of pyruvate alone caused no change in the spectrum. Buffer, 0.05 M sodium tetraborate, pH 9.2.

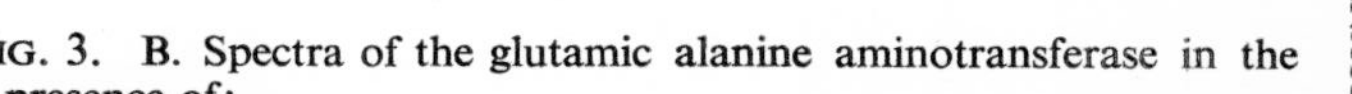


FIG. 3. B. Spectra of the glutamic alanine aminotransferase in the presence of:

(*a*) 0.3 M L-alanine + 0.01 M sodium pyruvate.

(*b*) 0.15 M L-glutamate + 0.01 M sodium ketoglutarate.

Both spectra taken in the presence of 0.05 M sodium tetraborate, pH 9.2.

the preceding paragraph the formation of abortive complexes does not appear to be significant in the range of pH from 7–9 and with alanine concentrations up to 0.2 M and pyruvate concentrations to 0.01 M. With very high levels of pyruvate at low pH values it was possible to observe an interaction with the pyridoxal form of the enzyme but this only confirms the belief that such interactions were not significant in the experiments to be described. An intermediate with $\lambda_{max} = 492\ m\mu$ had previously been observed with the glutamic–aspartic aminotransferase. Although the proportion of the ESi

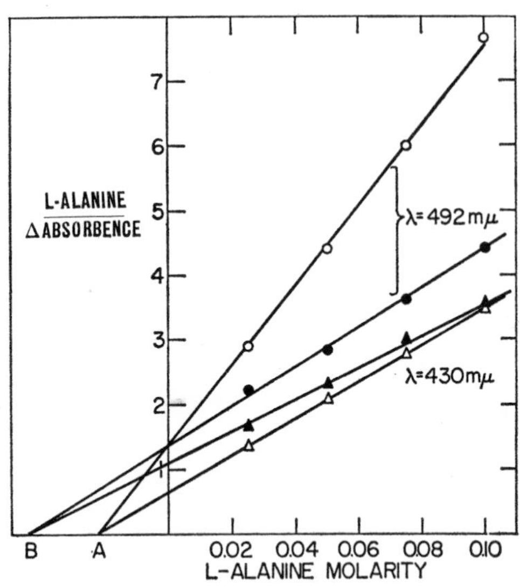


FIG. 4. Determination of the enzyme–substrate "dissociation constants" from spectral changes as described in the text. Buffer, 0.05 M sodium tetraborate, pH 9.2.
○, $\lambda = 492\ m\mu$. △, $\lambda = 430\ m\mu$, both 0.001 M in pyruvate.
●, $\lambda = 492\ m\mu$. ▲, $\lambda = 430\ m\mu$, both 0.01 M in pyruvate.
The absorbency increases at 492 mμ and decreases at 430 mμ due to the addition of alanine were taken from difference spectra recorded with a Cary 14 spectrophotometer fitted with an expanded 0–0.1 absorbency unit scale. The spectrophotometer was balanced at 0.05 absorbency units at 600 mμ. Spectra above 350 mμ were reproducible and did not vary with time.

complexes absorbing at 492 mμ is less than with the glutamic aspartic aminotransferase and erythro-β-hydroxy-L-aspartic acid, with high concentrations of the enzyme the absorbency at this wavelength could be used as a measure (X) of the total concentration of all the ESi complexes. The experiment was carried out with two levels of pyruvate at three pH values. One series is shown in Fig. 4. It can be seen in the figure that as predicted by theory the intercept on the ordinate is independent of the concentration of pyruvate for the Δ values at 492 mμ which are due only to one or more of the ESi complexes. This is not the case for the decrease at 430 mμ at which wavelength more than one species absorbs. Regardless of the wavelength chosen, however, the intercept on the abscissa is the same for any series at the same concentration of pyruvate. These intercepts yield four constants, the dissociation constants for the reactions

$$E_1 + S_1 \leftrightharpoons ESi \text{ and } E_2 + S_2 \leftrightharpoons ESi,$$

the overall equilibrium constant $K_2/K_3$ and perhaps most important the maximum value of the absorbency at 492 mμ representing the concentration of the species absorbing at 492 mμ when all of the enzyme is present as ESi complexes. The provisional data are shown in Table 1.

TABLE 1

| Buffer | pH | $K_2$ | $K_3$ | $(\Delta_{492})$max | $K_2/K_3$ |
|---|---|---|---|---|---|
| Potassium | | | | | |
| Phosphate | 6.9 | 0.180 | 0.0021 | 0.101 | 86 |
| I = 0.15 | 7.5 | 0.068 | 0.0015 | 0.085 | 45 |
| Borax 0.05 M | 9.2 | 0.057 | 0.0015 | 0.041 | 38 |

The greatest variation in values are for the dissociation constant for alanine. Much if not all of this variation is due apparently to the fact that only the basic form of the chromophore (p*K* 7.3) reacts with the zwitterionic form of the amino acid.

The variation in the values for $(\Delta_{492})_{max}$ are not consistent with the hypothesis that the equilibria amongst ESi complexes involve the addition and removal of a proton. These equilibria therefore appear to be tautomerizations or hydrogen atom translocations rather than ionizations. Two features of this table remain to be explained. They are the large values for the dissociation constant for alanine which appear to be larger than the reported $K_m$ values and the slight variation in the $(\Delta_{492})_{max}$ values which may be due to the effects of buffer ions on the ESi equilibria.

## THE USE OF SUBSTRATE ANALOGS

The large number of binary complexes and the rapidity of their interconversions pose formidable experimental problems. In an effort to elucidate some features of the reaction we have studied inhibitors such as carbonyl reagents and carboxylic acids.[21] A more satisfactory inhibitor is the substrate analog which itself undergoes a very slow rate of transamination and yet has a high affinity for the enzyme. Such inhibitors react with the enzyme rapidly to form a limited number of ESi type complexes.

We have studied two such inhibitors with the pig heart glutamic aspartic aminotransferase. Erythro-β-hydroxy-L-aspartic acid reacts with the "aldimine" form of the enzyme ($\lambda_{max}$ = 362 mμ) to form predominantly the complex with a maximum at 492 m$\mu$. Another analog, $\beta\beta$-difluoro-oxalacetate reacts with the " pyridoxamine " form of the enzyme ($\lambda_{max}$ = 332 m$\mu$) to yield a derivative with absorption maximum at 325 m$\mu$. With both these analogs our preliminary data suggest it will be possible to measure not only the loss of the binary complex but also its formation. These analogs appear therefore to represent extreme examples of the fact that the rate limiting step in the reaction is the interconversion of the " pyridoxal " Schiff bases into the " pyridoxamine " Schiff bases.

## LOCATION OF THE NITROGEN ATOMS IN ENZYME–SUBSTRATE BINARY COMPLEXES

Because of the unique stereochemistry of the reaction it would be nice to know the location of the nitrogen atoms of the amino acid and the $\epsilon$-amino group of the lysine residue which is bound to the pyridoxal phosphate originally.

Prevailing opinion favors a location for the amino acid nitrogen in the plane of the pyridine ring but there is no direct evidence to support this hypothesis except the mechanistic requirement for conjugation of the bonds on the $\alpha$-carbon atom of the amino acid with the electrons in the pyridine ring. One point seems certain and that is that if this nitrogen is in the plane of the ring the lysine nitrogen cannot be at the time that the formation of the amino acid pyridoxal phosphate Schiff base occurs. It seems unlikely that the nitrogen atoms move in going from one complex to another so that the spectra of the pyridoxal enzymes must be interpreted in the light of the fact that the lysine nitrogen is fixed somewhere out of the plane of the ring. Perhaps it is this fact which makes the spectra of the aldimine enzymes unique and different from those of the pyridoxal phosphate amino acid imines.

## SIGNIFICANCE OF THE RELATIVE AFFINITIES OF THE APOENZYME FOR PYRIDOXAL PHOSPHATE AND PYRIDOXAMINE PHOSPHATE

The relative affinities of the apoenzyme for pyridoxal phosphate and pyridoxamine phosphate governs what might be termed the " transfer potential " of the aminotransferase. By analogy with oxido-reduction enzymes each intracellular location is also characterized by a certain " transfer potential " which is measured in terms of the ratio of the concentrations of a particular amino acid to its analogous keto acid. The " transfer potential " of the particular transaminase is thought of in terms of the constant $K$ where, for example,

$$K = \frac{(E_L)(\text{Alanine})}{(E_M)(\text{Pyruvate})} = \frac{(\text{PlP})(\text{Alanine})}{(\text{PmP})(\text{Pyruvate})} \times \frac{(\text{PmP})(E)}{(E_M)} \times \frac{(E_L)}{(\text{PlP})(E)}$$

$$= \text{a constant} \times \frac{\text{Affinity of apoenzyme for pyridoxal P}}{\text{Affinity of apoenzyme for pyridoxamine P}}$$

This concept may be useful in the correlation of amino acid interconversions with the redox potential of different tissues because the latter governs the ratio of glutamate/ketoglutarate. The presence of different transaminases in mitochondria and supernatant may likewise be due to the fact that they have to operate at a different " transfer potential ".

## SUMMARY

(1) The unsatisfactory nature of the evidence for the participation of ternary complexes in transamination is discussed.

(2) A method is presented for the analysis of the different possible kinds of binary complexes occurring in steady-state transamination systems. This analysis was applied to the pig heart glutamic alanine aminotransferase where it was shown that the contribution of the abortive complexes was negligible.

(3) It was shown that this analysis indicates that none of the intermediary complexes is the conjugate base of any other observable complex. Such a hypothesis is also supported by the lack of Vm variation with pH and current experiments with substrate analogs.

(4) Binary complexes which have been identified as being of the intermediary type have maxima at about 325 mμ, 360 mμ and 492 mμ.

(5) It is suggested that substrate analogs may play an important role in the elucidation of the mechanism of transamination.

## APPENDIX

### STEADY STATE KINETIC ANALYSIS OF ENZYME SUBSTRATE BINARY COMPLEXES

The reaction scheme is that shown in Fig. 2 where it will be recalled $E_1$, $E_2$, ESi, $E_1S_2$ and $E_2S_1$ represent equilibrium mixtures of complexes. The equilibrium constants are defined as follows:

$$K_1 = \frac{(E_1)(S_2)}{(E_1S_2)} \quad K_2 = \frac{(E_1)(S_1)}{(ESi)} \quad K_3 = \frac{(E_2)(S_2)}{(ESi)} \quad K_4 = \frac{(E_2)(S_1)}{(E_2S_1)}$$

Solving the equations for ESi in terms of the total enzyme concentration Et gives:

$$\frac{(Et)}{(ESi)} = 1 + \frac{K_2}{S_1}\left(1 + \frac{S_2}{K_1}\right) + \frac{K_3}{S_2}\left(1 + \frac{S_1}{K_4}\right) \qquad (1)$$

If it is possible to measure some quantity X where $k.X = ESi$ and if the ratio $S_2/S_1$ is kept constant at $R$ then

$$S_2/X = A.S_2 + B$$

a straight line where the gradient is equal to

$$k.(1 + R.K_2/K_1 + K_3/R.K_4)/Et$$

and the negative intercept on the abscissa is

$$\frac{(R.K_2 + K_3)}{(1 + R.K_2/K_1 + K_3/R.K_4)}$$

## REFERENCES

1. E. E. SNELL; *J. Biol. Chem.* **154**, 313 (1954).
2. F. SHLENK and E. E. SNELL; *J. Biol. Chem.* **157**, 425 (1945).
3. R. HERBST; *Advances in Enzymol.* **4**, 75, (1954).
4. E. E. SNELL; *Vitamins and Hormones* **16**, 77 (1957).
5. A. MEISTER; *Biochemistry of the Amino Acids*, p. 185, Academic Press, New York (1957).
6. A. E. BRAUNSTEIN; *Advances in Protein Chem.* **3**, 1 (1947).
7. A. S. KONIKOVA, N. N. DOBBERT and A. E. BRAUNSTEIN; *Nature* **159**, 67 (1947).
8. P. PEYSER; Doctoral Dissertation Columbia University, N.Y. (1954).
9. A. NISONOFF, F. W. BARNES, JR. and T. ENNS; *J. Biol. Chem.* **204**, 957 (1953).
10. J. B. LONGENECKER and E. E. SNELL; *Proc. Natl. Acad. U.S.* **42**, 221 (1956).
11. S. HOPPER and H. L. SEGAL; *J. Biol. Chem.* **237**, 3189 (1962).
12. C. TURANO, P. FASELLA and A. GIARTOSIO; *Biochim. et Biophys. Acta* **58**, 255 (1962).
13. W. T. JENKINS and I. W. SIZER; *J. Biol. Chem.* **234**, 1179 (1959).
14. H. GUTFREUND, K. E. EBNER and L. MENDIOLA; *Nature* **192**, 820 (1961).
15. E. M. SCOTT and W. B. JAKOBY; *J. Biol. Chem.* **234**, 932 (1959).
16. R. G. HILLER and D. A. WALKER; *Biochem. J.* **78**, 56 (1961).
17. C. TURANO, P. FASELLA, P. VECHINI and A. GIARTOSIO; *Atti. accad. Lincei, Classe sci. fis.* **30**, 532 (1961).
18. R. C. HUGHES, W. T. JENKINS and E. H. FISCHER; *Proc. Natl. Acad. U.S.* **48**, 1615 (1962).
19. V. ZEWE and H. J. FROMM; *J. Biol. Chem.* **237**, 1668 (1962).
20. S. F. VELICK and J. VAVRA; *J. Biol. Chem.* **237**, 2109 (1962).
21. I. W. SIZER and W. T. JENKINS; This volume, p. 123.

## DISCUSSION

DR. HOLZER:

What is known about the quotients PLP-enzyme/PMP-enzyme?

DR. JENKINS:

In the presence of equimolar concentrations of both amino acid and keto acid substrates the overall equilibrium with the two forms of the transaminases lies far in the direction of the aldimine species. This is consistent with the fact that pyridoxal phosphate is bound tighter than pyridoxamine phosphate to the apoenzyme.

# STRUCTURAL FEATURES OF GLUTAMIC ASPARTIC TRANSAMINASE

by C. Turano, A. Giartosio, F. Riva and P. Vecchini

Institute of Biological Chemistry,
The University of Rome and Centro Studi di Enzimologia del C.N.R.,
Rome (Italy)

Glutamic aspartic transaminase from pig heart has been prepared in highly purified form by different methods; the enzyme prepared according to Lis[1], by fractional acetone precipitations and passages on carboxymethylcellulose and electrophoresis columns, behaves as a homogeneous protein in electrophoresis carried out at different pH values, and at the ultracentrifuge. Furthermore, the molecular weight calculated from the coenzyme content (2 moles of coenzyme per 116,000 g of protein) corresponds closely to the molecular weight calculated from ultracentrifugation analysis by Jenkins *et al.*[2] and Fasella[3].

The homogeneity of this preparation has permitted us to begin a study of its chemical features; in addition the importance for the catalytic activity of some functional groups in the protein has been investigated.

## AMINO ACID COMPOSITION

The amino acid composition of the protein has been studied by the technique of Moore *et al.*[4]; the results are shown in Table 1.

Ammonia has been determined also by an independent method,[5] and tryptophan has been estimated by a spectrophotometric procedure on the apoenzyme in 0.1 N NaOH.[6]

The noteworthy features in the pattern of the amino acid composition of transaminase are the relatively low content of serine, and the relatively high content of proline, arginine and tryptophan. Otherwise, the content of individual amino acids is within the limits generally encountered.

Cystine was present in the hydrolyzates, but in order to obtain quantitative data it was necessary to determine the cysteic acid content of the performic acid oxidized protein: the technique of Schram *et al.*[7] was used. The results of these determinations indicate that fourteen residues of cysteic acid are present in 1 mole of protein, i.e. 7 per mole of coenzyme.

## DETERMINATION OF SULFHYDRYL GROUPS

In order to assign the residues of cysteic acid found in the oxidized protein to sulfhydryl or disulfide groups present in the original protein the SH groups have been determined by titration with paramercuribenzoate (pMB), following the spectrophotometric method of Boyer[8]. The results of such titrations are summarized in Table 2.

TABLE 1. AMINO ACID COMPOSITION OF GLUTAMIC ASPARTIC TRANSAMINASE

| Amino acid | Amino acid residues per 100 g protein (g) | Calculated no. of residues for m.w. 58,000 | No. of residues to nearest integer |
|---|---|---|---|
| Lysine | 5.18 | 23.4 | 23 |
| Histidine | 2.11 | 8.9 | 9 |
| Ammonia | | 56.0 | 56 |
| Arginine | 8.57 | 31.8 | 32 |
| Half cystine | 1.23 | 6.9 | 7 |
| Aspartic acid | 10.75 | 54.2 | 54 |
| Threonine | 5.42 | 31.1 | 31 |
| Serine | 4.86 | 32.4 | 32 |
| Glutamic acid | 11.46 | 51.5 | 51 |
| Proline | 5.04 | 30.1 | 30 |
| Glycine | 3.16 | 32.1 | 32 |
| Alanine | 4.51 | 36.8 | 37 |
| Valine | 5.63 | 32.9 | 33 |
| Methionine | 1.60 | 7.1 | 7 |
| Isoleucine | 4.11 | 21.1 | 21 |
| Leucine | 8.90 | 45.6 | 46 |
| Tyrosine | 4.51 | 16.0 | 16 |
| Phenylalanine | 6.66 | 26.3 | 26 |
| Tryptophan | 4.44 | 13.8 | 14 |
| | 98.14 | | |

It should be pointed out that when titrations were performed at pH 7, in 0.12 M phosphate buffer, only about 4* SH groups were titratable, instead of 5–6, as found at pH 4.6. In 8 M urea, 7 groups were titrated; the same result was obtained upon addition of an excess of pMB to the protein in 8 M urea, followed by back titration of free pMB with cysteine.

Furthermore, no increase in SH titer was found after borohydride treatment of the protein.

There is a close correspondence between the number of cysteic acid residues in oxidized protein and the number of cysteine residues titrated by the mercurial; the existence of disulfide bridges in our preparation seems accordingly ruled out.

*The number of SH groups from now on will be referred to 58,000 g of protein.

It is rather surprising that this enzyme, although devoid of the stabilizing influence of disulfide cross-linkages, is rather stable towards some denaturing agents; in 5 M urea it retains more than 70 per cent of its activity, and the inactivation caused by 8 M urea is nearly completely reversible.

Upon leaving enzyme solutions at pH 8–9 exposed to an atmosphere of oxygen for 24 hr, no more than 5 SH groups were titratable in urea, but enzymatic activity was practically unaffected. It could therefore be assumed that oxidation of some SH groups can take place, without any significant structural alterations of the protein.

TABLE 2. DETERMINATION OF SULFHYDRYL GROUPS IN GLUTAMIC ASPARTIC TRANSAMINASE

| | SH groups per 58,000g of protein |
|---|---|
| In acetate buffer, pH 4.6, 0.25 M | 5.0 ± 0.2;[a] 5.9 ± 0.2[b] |
| In 8 M urea, and acetate buffer pH 4.6, 0.25 M | 6.0 ± 0.1;[c] 6.8 ± 0.1[b] |

[a] Mean value (± average deviation) from five different enzyme preparations.

[b] Mean values (± average deviations) from three different enzyme preparations; these values have been calculated from the increase in optical density 1 hr after the addition of an excess of pMB to the enzyme solution.

[c] Mean value (± average deviation) from three different enzyme preparations.

From the data that have been presented in Table 2, differences in reactivity among the various SH groups appear to be present: while five sulfhydryl groups seem to react readily with pMB in the native protein at pH 4.6, the sixth reacts more slowly and the seventh only in urea. Moreover, following the increase in optical density upon addition of the mercurial to the protein solution, it has been possible to detect a greater reactivity of 3 out of 7 SH groups; this finding has been confirmed by the results of acetylation experiments, that will be described later.

In conclusion, 3 SH groups show the greatest reactivity, 3 others can be considered as sluggish, while the seventh is masked in the native protein.

## N-TERMINAL AMINO ACIDS

The N-terminal residues of polypeptide chains were determined, both by the fluorodinitrobenzene (FDNB) and the Edman methods.

By the FDNB method, only dinitrophenyl-alanine (DNP-alanine) was found in the ethereal extracts of FDNB treated and hydrolysed protein, and no α-DNP-amino acid was found in the acqueous phase. No traces of the labile DNP-amino acids were found even after hydrolysis performed in concentrated HCl for 4 hr at 105°C; no DNP-cysteic acid was found after dinitrophenylation of the oxidized protein.

The Edman procedure was performed following the paper strip procedure[9] with slight modifications. By chromatography in heptane–pyridine (70/30) only one phenylthiohydantoin (PTH) derivative was obtainable from transaminase, and this was undistinguishable from synthetic PTH-alanine. It can be concluded that alanine is the only terminal residue in glutamic aspartic transaminase.

A quantitative determination of the terminal alanine residues, by the FDNB method, showed that there are 2 moles of alanine per mole of protein, i.e. 1 per mole of coenzyme. The enzyme (m.w. 116,000) appears, therefore, to be composed of two polypeptide chains.

Further studies are needed to ascertain the identity of the two chains. The information so far available reveals no differences between them: in fact alanine is the N-terminal residue for both chains, and also the composition of the peptide that binds pyridoxal–phosphate is probably the same, since only one type of pyridoxyl-peptide has been found, both by Hughes *et al.*[10] and by ourselves.[11]

## ACTIVITY OF THE PROTEIN WITH BLOCKED SULFHYDRYL GROUPS

It has long been known that transaminase is inhibited by heavy metals and in general by sulfhydryl group reagents.[12,13] We have determined the activity of the enzyme after addition of various amounts of pMB and the results are shown in Fig. 1. Activity decreases gradually as the number of blocked groups increases, and when pMB is present in excess the enzyme is completely inactivated.

With present data it is not possible to decide whether the reaction of pMB with the enzyme occurs in a random way or if the reaction of pMB with 1 SH group modifies the reactivity of the other SH groups on the same molecule. Anyway, since 3 SH groups have been shown to be more reactive than the others, after the addition of three equivalents of pMB the protein should be homogeneously combined with the mercurial.

The activity of the pMB treated protein can be at least partially restored by the addition of an excess of glutathione. The degree of reactivation cannot be increased by addition of pyridoxal phosphate; therefore dissociation of the coenzyme does not appear to be the cause of inactivation, and this is further demonstrated by the unmodified peak at 430 mμ shown at pH 4.6 by the aldimine form of the enzyme after pMB treatment. It should be pointed out that the failure to obtain complete reactivation by sulfhydryl compounds occurs when more than 2–3 SH have been blocked by pMB, i.e. when also the sluggish sulfhydryl groups have reacted. This fact is in accordance with the hypothesis that these less reactive SH groups are situated in the interior of the protein molecule: their reaction with the mercurial would cause a pronounced and partially irreversible structural alteration of the protein.

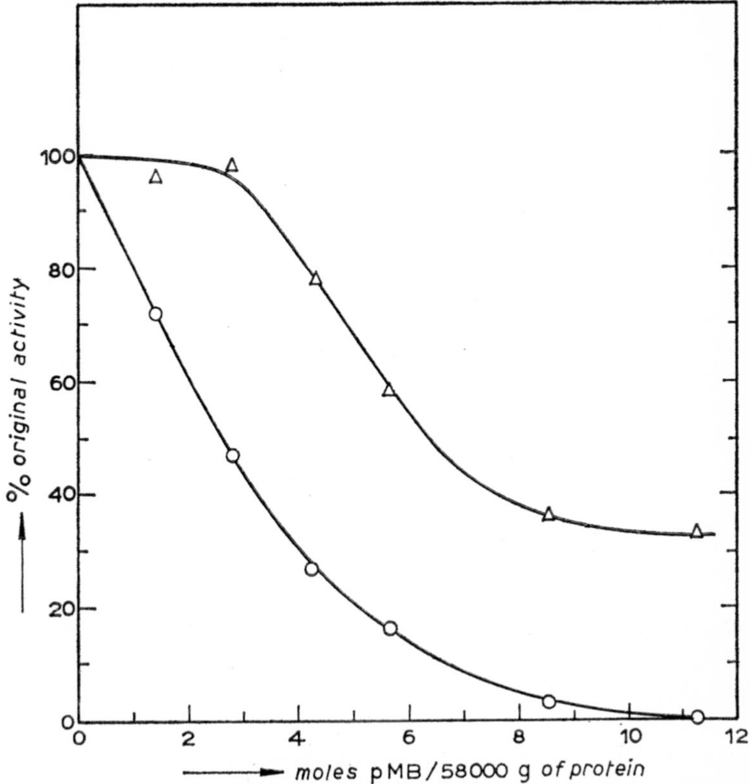


FIG. 1. Effect of addition of pMB on the activity of glutamic aspartic transaminase. Activities were determined as previously described.[14] For other experimental details, see Turano *et al.*[15]

○: enzyme + pMB.

△: enzyme + pMB + glutathione ($1.7 \times 10^2$ fold excess on a molar basis, referred to coenzyme).

Further investigation is needed to decide whether at least some of these SH groups are situated in the proximity of the enzymatic active site.

## ACTIVITY OF THE PROTEIN WITH BLOCKED AMINO GROUPS

Acetic anhydride has been employed in order to modify the amino groups of the protein. This reagent can be considered quite specific for amino groups, although it may be expected to acetylate also free SH groups. The reaction was carried out either in 0.5 M $K_2HPO_4$ or in half saturated sodium acetate, at 0°C.* It was possible to obtain modified protein with a maximum of about 80 per cent acetylated amino groups. As expected, 3 out of 7 SH groups were acetylated too. The inhibition of enzymatic activity in preparations that had from 58 to 79 per cent acetylated amino groups was about

TABLE 3. ACETYLATION OF TRANSAMINASE WITH PROTECTED SULFHYDRYL GROUPS

| Equivalents of pMB added | Acetylated amino groups (per cent) | Inhibition (per cent) |
|---|---|---|
| 2 | — | 20 |
| 3 | 31 | 10 |
| 3 | 68 | 11 |
| 3 | 70 | 10 |
| 4 | 72 | 39, 18[a] |

Activities were determined as previously described.[14] For other experimental details, see Turano *et al.*[16]

[a] Inhibition referred to the enzyme treated with pMB and glutathione, but not acetylated.

50 per cent (44–51 per cent); when the pyridoxamine form of the enzyme was acetylated, inhibition was practically complete.

Since it is known that the blockage of SH groups produces a marked decrease of the catalytic activity of transaminase, it seemed worthwhile to obtain an acetylated enzyme with free SH groups, and this was achieved by treating the enzyme before acetylation with pMB, and then removing the mercurial with glutathione. Experiments (shown in Table 3) were performed adding 2, 3 or 4 equivalents of pMB; in all cases from 80 to 90 per cent of the original activity could be recovered after removal of the mercurial.

As expected, the best conditions for the recovery of the original enzymatic activity were given by the addition of 3 equivalents of pMB; in this case the acetylated enzyme, that after treatment with glutathione was shown to have all of its SH groups free, was 90 per cent active. The slight degree of inhibition remained constant even when activity was tested under different conditions, i.e. with different substrates or enzyme concentrations, and at pH values that ranged from 7 to 9.

*The enzyme subjected to the acetylation procedure was entirely in the form of pyridoxal phosphate enzyme, unless otherwise stated.

It can be concluded that the freely reacting amino groups of transaminase e not essential for enzymatic activity; the ε-amino group of lysine that nds pyridoxal phosphate is not, of course, taken into consideration here, ice it is masked by its linkage with the aldehydic group of the coenzyme d therefore unaffected by the acylating reagent; this is further demon-ated by the unmodified absorption spectrum of the acetylated enzyme.

Before discussing such experiments, it should be recalled that good bstrates of glutamic aspartic transaminase are dicarboxylic acids, or iyway have two negative charges, as cysteinsulfinic acid, so that it could be asonable to assume that some positively charged groups on the protein ight act as substrate binding sites; since the acetylation of the more active amino groups of the protein does not affect significantly the catalytic tivity, it looks rather improbable that these positive charges are furnished ε-amino groups of lysine residues or by terminal amino groups.

Alternatively, it could be possible that lysine amino groups are in fact esent at the binding sites, but that they are scarcely reactive towards mmon reagents, as acetic anhydride. In this case the slight inhibition of e acetylated enzyme with free sulfhydryl groups could mean that only a nall fraction of the groups at the active site have reacted; this looks improb-le, however, in view of the constancy of the inhibition value (about 10 per nt) in enzyme preparations acetylated to a different extent (from 31 to ) per cent acetylated amino groups); furthermore the presence of keto acid ibstrates failed to reduce the degree of inhibition; finally, even a different ylating reagent, acetyl chloride, produced no more than 10–15 per cent hibition.

Beside the implications regarding the role of amino groups, acetylation periments show that SH groups in the free form are necessary for complete izymatic activity, since when they are blocked, inhibition is produced, pparently independently from the size of the blocking agent; it appears robable, moreover, that they have a specific role in the maintenance of otein configuration, since a chemical modification of other groups, no atter how extensive, is not sufficient to affect enzymatic activity significantly.

## REFERENCES

. H. Lis; *Biochim. et Biophys. Acta* **28**, 191 (1958).
. W. T. Jenkins, D. A. Yphantis and I. W. Sizer; *J. Biol. Chem.* **234**, 51 (1959).
. P. Fasella; Unpublished data.
. S. Moore, D. H. Spackman and W. H. Stein; *Anal. Chem.* **30**, 1185 (1958).
. C. H. W. Hirs, W. H. Stein and S. Moore; *J. Biol. Chem.* **211**, 941 (1954).
. T. W. Goodwin and R. A. Morton; *Biochem. J.* **40**, 628 (1946).
. E. Schram, S. Moore and E. J. Bigwood; *Biochem. J.* **57**, 33 (1954).
. P. D. Boyer; *J. Am. Chem. Soc.* **76**, 4331 (1954).
. H. Fraenkel-Conrat; *J. Am. Chem. Soc.* **76**, 3606 (1954).
). R. C. Hughes, W. T. Jenkins and E. H. Fischer; *Proc. Natl. Acad. U.S.* **48**, 1615 (1962).

11. C. TURANO, P. FASELLA and A. GIARTOSIO; *Proc. Vth Int. Cong. Biochem., Mosc* 1961, Abstract of Comm., p. 128.
12. E. S. G. BARRON and T. P. SINGER; *Science* **97**, 356 (1943).
13. F. SCHLENK and A. FISHER; *Arch. Biochem.* **12**, 69 (1947).
14. H. LIS, P. FASELLA, C. TURANO and P. VECCHINI; *Biochim. et Biophys. Acta* 529 (1960).
15. C. TURANO, A. GIARTOSIO and F. RIVA; *Enzymologia* **xxv**, 196 (1963).
16. C. TURANO, A. GIARTOSIO and P. VECCHINI; *Arch. Biochem. Biophys.* **99**, 191 (19

# THE ROLE OF THIOL GROUPS IN ASPARTATE–GLUTAMATE TRANSAMINASE

by O. L. POLYANOVSKY and YU. M. TORCHINSKY

Institute of Radiobiology and Physico-Chemical Biology,
Academy of Sciences of the U.S.S.R.

ANSAMINASES and many other PLP enzymes are inhibited by sulfhydryl gents, particularly by heavy metal compounds. Inactivation of partially rified aspartate–glutamate transaminase* and alanine–glutamate trans- inase from pig heart due to blocking of thiol groups has been observed Wada *et al.*[1] in 1957; their data have been confirmed elsewhere.[2–4] her transaminases reported to be sensitive to the action of sulfhydryl gents include liver glutamine transaminase, hepatic and bacterial tyrosine– tamate transaminase, ornithine–glutamate transaminase from *Neurospora* ).[5–8] However, the mechanism of inhibition of transaminases by sulfhydril agents is still unknown. It has been suggested[2] that these reagents (specific- y, *p*-CMB) may cause the breaking of bonds between PLP and the oenzymes. This idea and other suggestions can be verified only in periments with highly purified enzyme preparations.

The purpose of the present work was to determine the content and function thiol groups in practically pure preparations of AS-transaminase.

AS-transaminase activity was determined at 37° in 3-ml test samples ntaining 20 μmoles each of α-ketoglutarate and L-aspartate (1/15-molar osphate buffer, pH 8.3) by measurement of the increase in optical density 280 mμ due to formation of oxaloacetate. One unit is the amount of zyme that increases the O.D. at 280 mμ by 0.001 per min (initial rate).

AS-transaminase was prepared from pig heart as the PLP protein. The st steps of purification–preparation and heat treatment, ammonium lfate fractionation, were those of the method reported by Jenkins *et al.*[9] solution of the protein fraction precipitated from 0.50 to 0.67 $(NH_4)_2SO_4$ turation was desalted by gel filtration through a column of Sephadex G-25. was further chromatographed on CM-cellulose according to Lis[10]. dditional purification was achieved by fractionation on a DEAE-cellulose lumn equilibrated with 0.01 M acetate buffer (pH 5.4); the enzyme was

*Abbreviations: AS-transaminase, aspartate–glutamate transaminase; *p*-CMB, *p*-loromercuribenzoate; PLP, pyridoxal phosphate; TCA, trichloroacetic acid.

eluted with 0.04–0.06 M acetate buffer (pH 5.4). In the final purificati step the enzyme was subjected to column electrophoresis on cellulo powder.[10]

The purest AS-transaminase preparations thus obtained had a speci activity of 3.5–4.0 × $10^4$ units per mg of protein. In the electrophoretica homogeneous preparations of AS-transaminase the PLP content (calculat from the $E_{388}$ value in 0.1 N NaOH) was 16.7 $\mu$moles per 1 g prote in fair agreement with the data of Lis *et al.*[11], who reports 17.2 $\mu$mol of PLP per 1 g protein. The AS-transaminase preparations used in t following experiments were $\geqslant$95 per cent pure, as indicated by ultracentrifug analysis and PLP content.

The quantitative estimation of SH groups in AS-transaminase was pe formed by means of spectrophotometric titration with *p*-CMB[12] and amperometric titration with $AgNO_3$.[13] On titration with *p*-CMB we fou 5–6 equivalents of SH groups per 1 mole protein (assuming the molecul weight of AS-transaminase to be 110,000[9]). Titration of the enzyme wi silver nitrate in ammonia buffer (0.08 M $NH_4NO_3$ 0.01 M $NH_4OH$; pH 8.6 indicated 6 equivalents of SH groups, and on titration in 0.133 M tr nitric acid buffer (pH 7.35) we found 6.9 equivalents of SH-groups per m protein. Storage of the enzyme solution for several weeks at +2° leads to decrease of the amount of titratable SH groups. The same content of S groups was found in experiments with the PMP-form of AS-transamina or with the pure apoenzyme.

Preliminary tests had shown that AS-transaminase was highly sensitive inhibition by heavy metals (*p*-CMB; $HgCl_2$; $AgNO_3$) but only sligh susceptible to inactivation by reagents alkylating thiol groups (iodoacetat acrylonitril; acrylamide). This differential sensitivity to different ager blocking SH groups is due to lowered reactivity of the SH groups of A transaminase towards the alkylating reagents. As shown in Table 1 or partial blocking of SH groups is achieved by treatment of the enzyme wi high concentration of alkylating agents. The number of reacting SH grou was controlled as follows. After incubation with the inhibitor at pH 8 the enzyme solution was gel-filtered through a column of Sephadex G- to remove the excess of non-reacted inhibitor, whereupon the amount free SH groups was determined in the filtered protein fraction by titrati with *p*-CMB according to Boyer[12]. AS-transaminase activity was measur before and 30 min after the addition of *p*-CMB. As shown in Table 1 t major part of AS-transaminase activity is retained so long as at least tw SH groups remain free in the enzyme treated with iodoacetate or acrylonitr These experiments thus indicate that the thiol groups of AS-transamina differ in chemical properties. Those SH groups that are most important f AS-transaminase activity are apparently the least readily accessible alkylating reagents.

Ninety per cent of the activity of AS-transaminase, on the average, are lost when all the six thiol groups of the enzyme are blocked with *p*-CMB. It was of interest to find out if the loss of activity is associated with the blockage of only some of the thiol groups or if it proceeds smoothly in the course

TABLE 1. INTERACTION OF ALKYLATING REAGENTS WITH ASPARTATE–GLUTAMATE TRANSAMINASE

| Reagent | Concentration of reagent (M) | Preincubation time (hr) | Preincubation Temperature (°C) | Free SH groups after alkylation | Inhibition (%) Before CMB-treatment | Inhibition (%) After CMB-treatment |
|---|---|---|---|---|---|---|
| Iodoacetate | $10^{-2}$ | 2 | 30 | 6 | 0 | 95 |
| Iodoacetate | $10^{-1}$ | 3.5 | 38 | 2.5 | 37 | 91 |
| Acrylonitril | $10^{-1}$ | 3 | 30 | 6 | 0 | 98 |
| Acrylonitril | $6 \times 10^{-2}$ | 3 | 38 | 2 | 35 | 98 |
| Acrylonitril | $5 \times 10^{-3}$ | 2 | 42 | 1 | 50 | — |
| Acrylamide | $6 \times 10^{-2}$ | 3 | 30 | 5 | 0 | 98.5 |

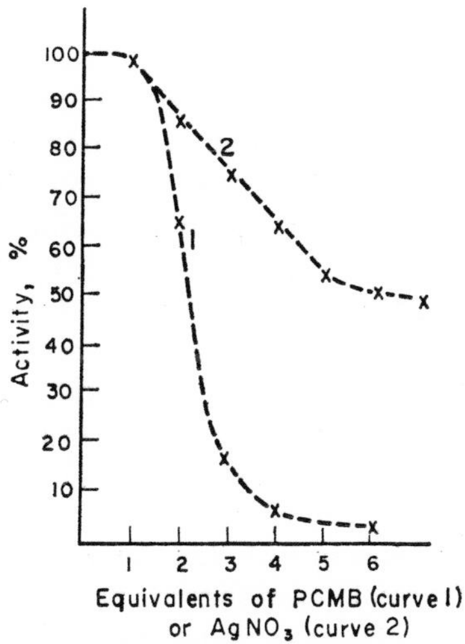


FIG. 1. *p*-CMB- and $AgNO_3$-inhibition curves of AS-transaminase. Curve 1, *p*-CMB; curve 2, $AgNo_3$.

of titration with *p*-CMB. To this aim stepwise additions of 1 equivalent of *p*-CMB at a time were made to a $5 \times 10^{-6}$ M solution of the enzyme. After completion of mercaptide formation following each addition, as checked by measuring the increase in O.D. at 250 m$\mu$, transaminase activity was determined in aliquots of the solution. The curve of enzyme inhibition in the course of titration with *p*-CMB is represented in Fig. 1 (curve 1).

It is evident from this graph that binding of the first equivalent of *p*-CMB does not significantly impair the activity. The major part of inactivation (down to 15 per cent of the original activity) occurs upon binding of the second and third equivalents of *p*-CMB. These data imply that two of the thiol groups of the enzyme are particularly essential for its catalytic activity.

Curve 2 of the same figure (Fig. 1) shows the decrease in AS-transaminase activity in the course of titration of thiol groups with $Ag^+$ ions. Samples of 1 ml enzyme solution (each containing 0.55 mg protein, i.e. $5 \times 10^{-9}$ mole of the enzyme) were added with from 1 to 7 equivalents of $AgNO_3$; the samples were incubated with 0.133 M tris-$HNO_3$ buffer (pH 7.35) for 1 hr at 22°. It was found that the reaction of $Ag^+$ ions with the enzyme went to completion during this time, since no further change in activity occurred on prolongation of the incubation period. It is evident from curve 2 (Fig. 1) that practically no inhibition of AS-transaminase occurs when 1 equivalent of $AgNO_3$ has reacted (just as in the case of *p*-CMB); in the other samples there is a smooth gradual increase of inhibition as the amount of $Ag^+$ ions added is raised from 2 to 5 equivalents per mole of enzyme protein. These results suggest that in the transaminase molecule the thiol groups most essential and those less essential for catalytic activity are sterically accessible in equal measure for $Ag^+$ ions in contrast to *p*-CMB. This is a plausible explanation of the fact that titration of the thiol groups (from the second to the fifth group) with $AgNO_3$ results in gradual inactivation of the enzyme. Moreover, the maximum degree of inactivation reached upon addition of 7 equivalents of $Ag^+$ ions did not exceed 50 per cent, as a rule whereas the average degree of inhibition resulting from complete blocking of SH groups with *p*-CMB was 90 per cent. The dissimilarities in the inhibitory action of *p*-CMB and of silver ions most probably depend on their different dimensions and charge. The inhibition of AS-transaminase by *p*-CMB and by $Ag^+$ ions is reversible; the activity can be largely restored with the aid of thiol compounds (Fig. 2).

There are several possible mechanisms that might account for the inactivation of AS-transaminase by *p*-CMB or $AgNO_3$: viz. (1) inhibition is due to disruption of bonds between PLP and the apoenzyme; (2) inhibition is caused by blocking of a thiol group forming part of the substrate anchoring site; and (3) inhibition depends on impairment of the native conformation of the active centre of the enzyme.

Conjecture (1) could be discarded since treatment with *p*-CMB or $AgNO_3$ did not affect the spectral properties of AS-transaminase. Moreover, transaminase with completely blocked SH groups can be reactivated to an equal extent ($\sim$70 per cent) with cysteine prior or following gel filtration on a Sephadex column (if the inhibitor caused dissociation of PLP from the

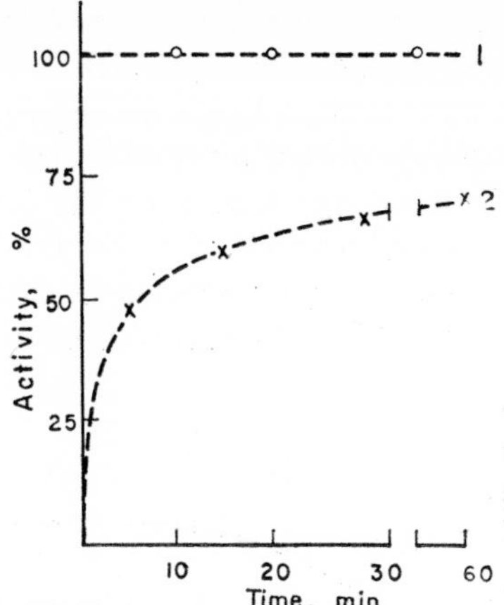


FIG. 2. Reactivation of *p*-CMB-inhibited AS-transaminase with cysteine.

1. Control.
2. Restitution by cysteine ($5 \times 10^{-3}$ M) of the activity of AS-transaminase ($5 \times 10^{-6}$ M) inhibited with *p*-CMB ($5 \times 10^{-5}$ M). Cysteine added at zero time.

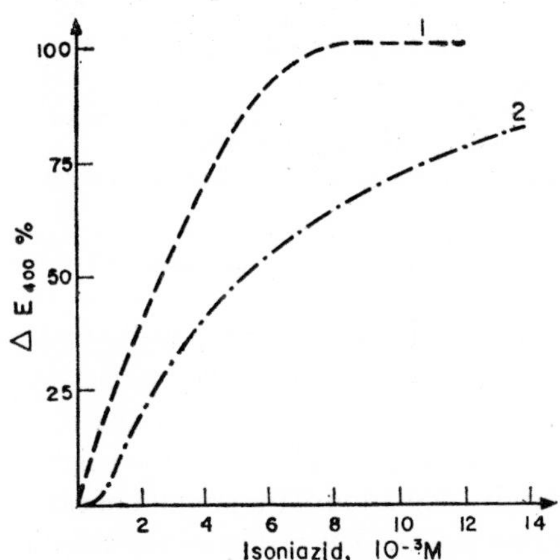


FIG. 3. Effect of *p*-CMB treatment on the interaction of AS-transaminase with isoniazid.

Ordinates: $E_{400}$ as percentage of $E_{max}$ (reached on saturation of the enzyme with isoniazid).

Curve 1, increase of $E_{400}$ on addition of isoniazid to native enzyme solution; curve 2, same with *p*-CMB-inhibited enzyme solution.

enzyme protein, no reactivation should occur after passage of the solution through the Sephadex column). The second conjecture is likewise improbable, because it was found that presence of the specific substrates failed to protect AS-transaminase against inhibition with *p*-CMB.

In our opinion the third explanation is the most probable one. Further evidence favouring it was provided by experiments concerning the effects of blocking with *p*-CMB or $Ag^+$ ions upon the interaction of AS-transaminase with certain carbonyl reagents. It is well known that the absorption spectra of AS-transaminase undergo characteristic changes when the protein-bound PLP combines with carbonyl reagents (isoniazid shifts the absorption

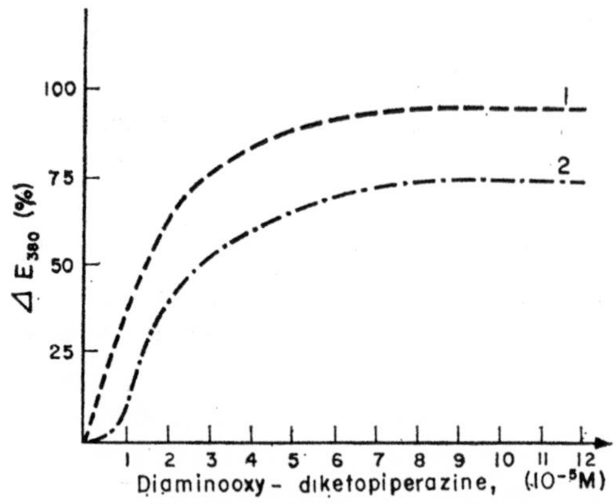


FIG. 4. Effect of *p*-CMB treatment on the interaction of AS-transaminase with di(amino-oxymethyl)diketopiperazine (DADP).

Ordinates: $E_{380}$ as percentage of $E_{max}$ (reached on saturation of the enzyme with DADP).

Curve 1, increase of $E_{380}$ on addition of DADP to native enzyme solution; curve 2, same with *p*-CMB-inhibited enzyme solution.

maximum of the enzyme to 400–410 m$\mu$, while hydroxylamine, $\beta$-amino-oxy-$\alpha$-alanine or di(amino-oxymethyl)diketopiperazine (DADP) displaces it to 370–380 m$\mu$.[14,15] Either the decrease of the characteristic absorption maximum of the original enzyme solution or the height of the new maximum that appears can permit calculation of the amount of enzyme–inhibitor complex formed from the components. The results of our experiments are represented in Figs. 3 and 4. As evident from these graphs, the affinity of *p*-CMB-inhibited transaminase for isoniazid or DADP is substantially lowered. The differences in interactions with the two forms of transaminase (active and inhibited) are particularly marked at low concentrations of isoniazid or DADP.

The $K_i$ values of isoniazid and DADP were computed, using the formula $K_i = [E].[I]/[EI]$. The concentration of the enzyme–inhibition complex,

[EI], was calculated from the increase in O.D. at the characteristic $\lambda_{max}$ of the respective complexes. The concentration of AS-transaminase was $10^{-5}$ M (based on m.w. = 110,000) in all experiments. The concentration of free enzyme $[E] = [E]_{initial} - [EI]$; the concentration of non-bound inhibitor $[I] = [I]_{initial} - [EI]$. For isoniazid and DADP we found $K_i$ values of $2.5 \times 10^{-3}$ and $0.9 \times 10^{-5}$ M, respectively. Upon treatment of AS-transaminase with *p*-CMB these $K_i$ values rose to $7 \times 10^{-3}$ (isoniazid) and $3 \times 10^{-5}$ (DADP). An increase of $K_i$ of isoniazid was also observed with Ag-inhibited transaminase. In contrast to the data just reported, the $K_i$ values of hydroxylamine and of β-amino-oxy-α-alanine were not altered upon inhibition of the enzyme with *p*-CMB. These results suggest that the binding of mercuribenzoate or of silver ions to the thiol groups of AS-transaminase is associated with appearance at the enzyme's active site of steric hindrance for the access of isoniazid or DADP to the protein-bound PLP. The less bulky molecules of hydroxylamine or β-amino-oxy-α-alanine apparently can easily overcome this obstacle.

The above experiments, however, provide no answer to the question whether the mentioned hindrance is caused by the bound inhibitor molecules themselves or by a change in configuration of the protein moiety of the enzyme. The latter conjecture is supported by the results of experiments concerning the influence of *p*-CMB treatment upon the hydrolysis of AS-transaminase by the crystalline bacterial proteinase, Nagase (of the firm Nagarse, Japan). Determination of the susceptibility of proteins to attack by proteolytic enzymes is a very sensitive method for the detection of relatively slight alterations in the structure of protein molecules.[16,17] Exploratory experiments had shown that native AS-transaminase was very resistant to the action of trypsin and chymotrypsin. As seen on Fig. 5 (curve 1) the native enzyme is also fairly resistant to attack by Nagase (increase of O.D. at $\lambda_{280}$ in the supernatant obtained after deproteinization of the digest with TCA served as a measure of the rate of hydrolysis); however, AS-transaminase inhibited with *p*-CMB is hydrolysed by Nagase at an appreciable rate (Fig. 5, curve 2). In the latter case the transaminase was preincubated at 37° with 6 equivalents of *p*-CMB for 20–30 min before the addition of Nagase (completion of the reaction with *p*-CMB was checked by the lack of further increase of O.D. at 250 mμ). The splitting of AS-transaminase by Nagase is particularly rapid in the presence of an excess of *p*-CMB (Fig. 5, curve 3), probably owing to non-specific interaction of *p*-CMB with the protein. Similar phenomena (increased rates of denaturation by *p*-CMB added in excess) have been reported for aldolase[16] and serum albumin.[18]

It thus appears from the results of our experiments that treatment with *p*-CMB induces alterations in the conformation of the transaminase molecule that render this molecule accessible to cleavage by Nagase. It seems plausible that these alterations, probably involving the tertiary structure of the enzyme, are responsible for the inhibition of its activity by *p*-CMB or $Ag^+$. Finally, it should be stated that ultracentrifugal investigations have failed to reveal any dissociation of the molecule of AS-transaminase to smaller subunits upon treatment with *p*-CMB.

A considerable amount of evidence is already available, in the literature, concerning alterations of the structure of enzymes and other proteins caused by *p*-CMB or other heavy metal compounds specifically interacting with SH groups.[19,20] Up till now the question remained unsolved as to whether

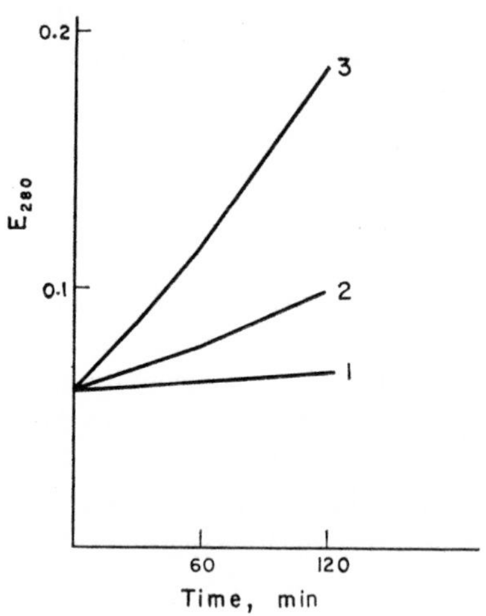


FIG. 5. Effect of *p*-CMB upon hydrolysis of AS-transaminase (0.16 per cent solution) by Nagase (7 $\mu$g/ml); incubation in 0.03 M phosphate buffer at 37°, pH 8.0.

Curve 1, native transaminase; curve 2, transaminase preincubated with *p*-CMB equivalent in amount to the thiol group content of the solution; curve 3, digestion of transaminase in the presence of a 2.5-fold excess of *p*-CMB above the equivalent amount.

the structural alterations of enzyme proteins induced by *p*-CMB were a result of immediate deforming action of the bound inhibitor upon neighbouring parts of the protein molecule, or rather a consequence of the rupture of intramolecular bonds involving the thiol groups of the protein.

The data reported in the present paper, providing evidence for a dependence of the degree of AS-transaminase inhibition upon the molecular dimensions and charge of the inhibitor, evidently lend support to the first of these propositions.

## SUMMARY

(1) By means of spectrophotometric titration with *p*-CMB and amperometric titration with $AgNO_3$ aspartate–glutamate transaminase of high purity (from pig heart) was shown to contain about six to seven SH groups per 110,000 g of protein.

(2) AS-transaminase activity is strongly inhibited by mercaptide-forming reagents (*p*-CMB, $HgCl_2$, $AgNO_3$) and weakly inhibited by alkylating agents (iodoacetate, acrylonitril, acrylamide).

(3) The curves of inhibition of AS-transaminase with increasing amounts of *p*-CMB and of $Ag^+$ ions are dissimilar; the dissimilarity is probably due to differences in the molecular dimensions and charge of the two inhibitors.

(4) The inhibition of AS-transaminase by *p*-CMB or $AgNO_3$ is not due to the rupture of bonds between PLP and the apoenzyme. The specific substrates do not protect the enzyme against inhibition.

(5) Inhibition of AS-transaminase with *p*-CMB increases its susceptibility to attack by a bacterial proteinase (Nagase) and lowers the affinity of the enzyme for isoniazid and di(amino-oxymethyl)diketopiperazine. These data suggest that the inhibition of AS-transaminase activity by *p*-CMB (and by $Ag^+$ ions) is probably due to impairment of the native conformation of the active centre.

## REFERENCES

1. H. WADA *et al.*; *Proc. Int. Symp. Enzyme Chemistry*, Tokyo and Kyoto, 1957, p. 148, Maruzen, Tokyo (1958).
2. L. GREIN and G. PFLEIDERER; *Biochem. Z.* **330**, 433 (1958).
3. YU. M. TORCHINSKY; *Biokhimia* **27**, 916 (1962).
4. O. L. POLYANOVSKY; *Biokhimia* **27**, 734 (1962).
5. HSU TING SENG; *Biokhimia* **25**, 1113 (1960).
6. S. SENTHESHANMUGANATHAN; *Biochem. J.* **77**, 619 (1960).
7. F. T. KENNY; *J. Biol. Chem.* **234**, 2707 (1959).
8. R. H. VOGEL and M. J. KOPAC; *Biochem. et Biophys. Acta* **37**, 539 (1960).
9. W. T. JENKINS, D. A. YPHANTIS and I. W. SIZER; *J. Biol. Chem.* **234**, 51 (1959).
10. H. LIS; *Biochim. et Biophys. Acta* **28**, 191 (1958).
11. H. LIS, P. FASELLA, C. TURANO and P. VECCHINI; *Biochim et Biophys. Acta* **45**, 529 (1960).
12. P. D. BOYER; *J. Am. Chem. Soc.* **76**, 4331 (1954).
13 R. E. BENESCH, H. A. LARDY and R. BENESCH; *J. Biol. Chem.* **216**, 663 (1955).
14. W. T. JENKINS, S. ORLOWSKI and I. W. SIZER; *J. Biol. Chem.* **234**, 2657 (1959).
15. I. W. SIZER and W. T. JENKINS; *Methods in Enzymol.* **5**, 677 (1962).
16. G. SZABOLCSI and E. BISZKU; *Biochim. et Biophys. Acta* **48**, 335 (1961).
17. P. ELODI; *Biochim. et Biophys. Acta* **40**, 272 (1960).
18. H. K. FRENSDORFF, M. T. WATSON and W. KAUZMANN; *J. Am. Chem. Soc.* **75**, 5167 (1953).
19. N. B. MADSEN and C. F. CORI; *J. Biol. Chem.* **223**, 1055 (1956).
20. P. D. BOYER; *The Enzymes* (edited by P. BOYER, H. A. LARDY and K. MYRBÄCK), vol. 1, p. 511, Academic Press, New York and London (1959).

# THE RESOLUTION OF ASPARTATE AMINOTRANSFERASE

by V. Scardi, P. Scotto, M. Iaccarino and E. Scarano

Laboratorio di Chimica delle Fermentazioni, Istituto di Chimica Organica, and Istituto di Fisiologia Umana, Universita di Napoli, Italia

A possible regulation of enzyme levels in cells may be effected through the inhibitory action of a hormone upon the reconstitution of a holoenzyme from its coenzyme and apoenzyme. We have shown the competitive action that oestrogen sulphates and phosphates exert on the reconstitution of two pyridoxal-5-phosphate-dependent enzymes, namely kynurenine aminotransferase and aspartate aminotransferase.[1,2] Figures 1 and 2 describe the findings.

In the experiments with oestrogen esters we used an aspartate apoaminotransferase obtained by resolving the holoenzyme prepared according to O'Kane and Gunsalus[3]. In subsequent experiments we tried the same resolving procedure on the aspartate aminotransferase prepared according to Jenkins *et al.*[4] In contrast with the results obtained with the preparation of O'Kane and Gunsalus[3] it was not possible to resolve the enzyme prepared according to Jenkins *et al.*[4], notwithstanding variation of temperature, incubation time and ammonium sulphate concentration. In Table 1 are summarized the attempts made to resolve the aspartate aminotransferase prepared by Jenkins *et al.*[4]

This unexpected result raised the problem of finding the general conditions for resolving any aspartate aminotransferase preparation, independently of its purification procedure.

Our preliminary experiments seemed to indicate that it is not possible to resolve the aspartate aminotransferase by the procedures described in Table 1 if the enzyme is in the " pyridoxal " form. As a matter of fact, the enzyme prepared by Jenkins *et al.*[4] is in the " pyridoxal " form as a consequence of the addition of an excess of α-ketoglutarate during the preparation. The same authors have found that the " pyridoxamine " form of the enzyme is more labile than the " pyridoxal " form to heat inactivation.

On the assumption that the binding of coenzyme to apoenzyme is weakened in the " pyridoxamine " enzyme, because of the absence of the azomethine linkage whose existence was previously indicated by Bonavita and Scardi[6],

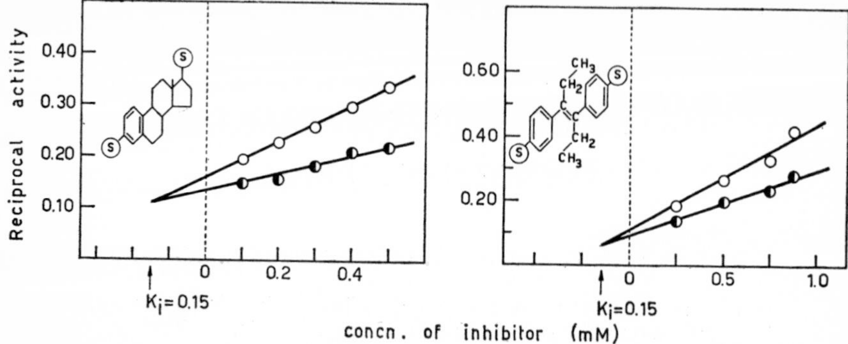


FIG. 1. Dixon plots of the inhibition of aspartate aminotransferase reconstitution by: oestradiol disulphate (*left*) and stilboestrol disulphate (*right*). In the formulas S stands for $-OSO_3H$. The concentration of pyridoxal-5-phosphate in the preincubation mixture was 8 μM (○) and 25 μM (◑), respectively. For experimental details, see Scardi *et al.*[1]

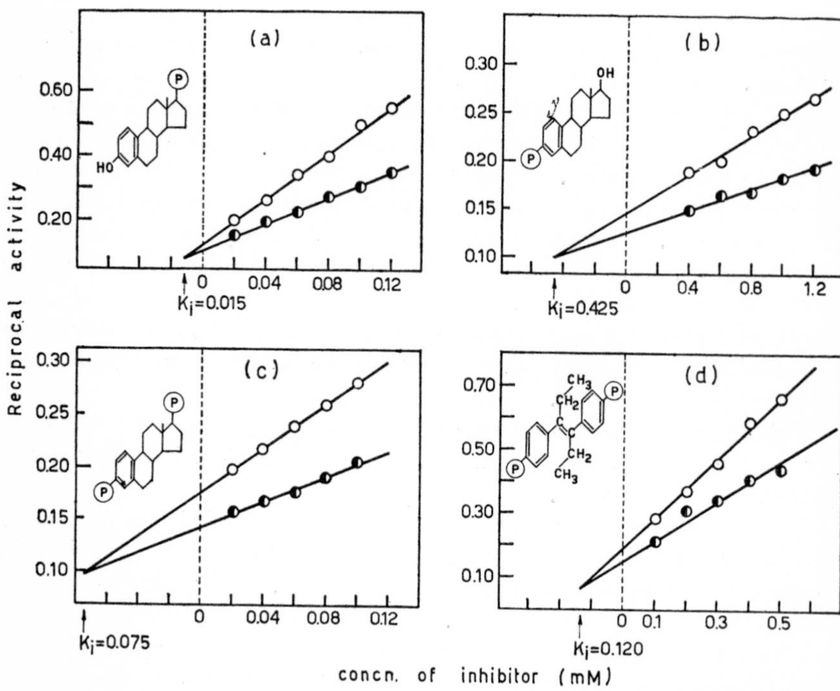


FIG. 2. Dixon plots of the inhibition of aspartate aminotransferase reconstitution by: (a) oestradiol-17-phosphate, (b) oestradiol-3-phosphate, (c) oestradiol diphosphate, and (d) stilboestrol diphosphate. In the formulas P stands for $-OPO_3H_2$. The concentration of pyridoxal-5-phosphate in the preincubation mixture was 20 μM (○) and 40 μM (◐), respectively. For experimental details, see Scardi *et al.*[2]

an excess of aspartate or glutamate was added to the enzyme in order to convert it into the " pyridoxamine " form.

The " pyridoxamine " enzyme was obtained by incubating 20 $\mu$l aliquots of the enzyme (20.5 mg/ml) at room temperature for 15 min with 40 $\mu$moles

TABLE 1. EXPERIMENTAL CONDITIONS UNDER WHICH RESOLUTION OF ASPARTATE AMINOTRANSFERASE (" PYRIDOXAL " FORM)[4] WAS ATTEMPTED

| Incubation | | | % Resolutions |
|---|---|---|---|
| at | for | in the presence of | |
| 60° | 2 min | 20–30% $(NH_4)_2SO_4$[b] | 0 |
| 65° | 2 min | 20–30% $(NH_4)_2SO_4$ | 0 |
| 65° | 80 min | 15% $(NH_4)_2SO_4$ | 0 |
| 60° | 50 min | M-phosphate buffer pH 6[c] | 27 |

[a]% Resolution = $(A - a/A)$ 100, where $A$ is the activity determined in the presence of pyridoxal-5-phosphate, and $a$ is the activity determined without pyridoxal-5-phosphate.
[b]Scardi *et al.*[1]
[c]Banks and Vernon[5].

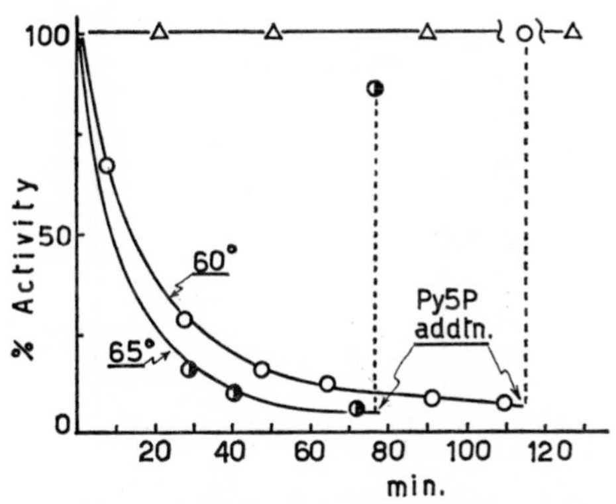


FIG. 3. Effect of incubation in 20 per cent ammonium sulphate on the aspartate aminotransferase resolution. (△) " Pyridoxal " form, 60° temp., (○) (◑) " Pyridoxamine " form at temperatures of 60° and 65°, respectively. Py5P = pyridoxal-5-phosphate.

aspartate adjusted at pH 7.4 with 1 N NaOH in a final volume of 2 ml. This preparation, unless otherwise stated, was submitted to the action of different anions, under various experimental conditions.

Figure 3 shows the resolution at 60° and 65° in the presence of 20 per cent ammonium sulphate: while the " pyridoxamine " enzyme is completely resolved under these conditions, the " pyridoxal " enzyme is unaffected. At 65° a partial denaturation occurs, since the addition of excess of pyridoxal-5-phosphate does not recover the full activity.

The experimental conditions described by Banks and Vernon[5] which resulted in a partial resolution of the " pyridoxal " enzyme (see Table 1) were used for the " pyridoxamine " enzyme. However, after 10 min

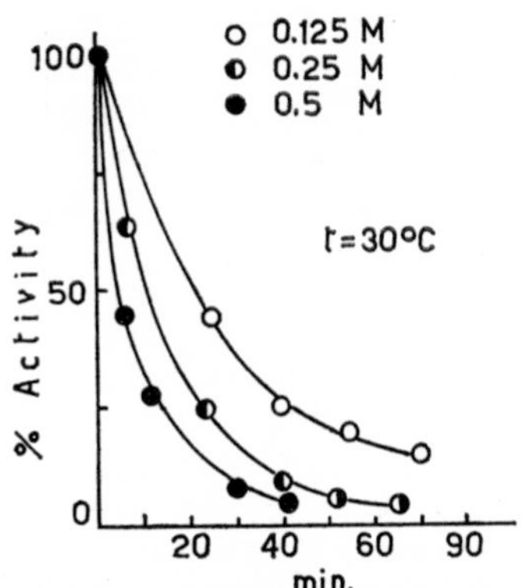


FIG. 4. Effect of phosphate concentration on the resolution of aspartate aminotransferase (" pyridoxamine " form) at pH 6.0.

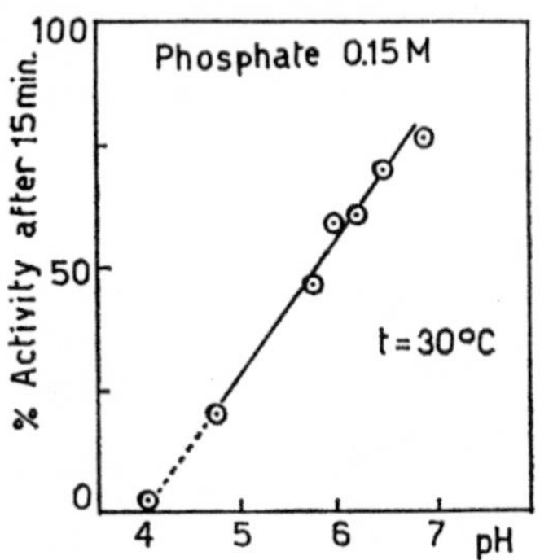


FIG. 5. Effect of pH on the resolution of aspartate aminotransferase (" pyridoxamine " form). Below pH 4.75 irreversible inactivation occurs.

incubation only a 60 per cent recovery of the inactivated enzyme was obtained, thus showing a partial denaturation along with resolution. For this reason the incubation temperature was decreased and a standard temperature of 30° was chosen for all other experiments reported here, unless otherwise stated.

Figures 4 and 5 show the resolution as a function of phosphate concentration and of the pH, respectively.

Figures 6 and 7 show the influence of acetate, arsenate and sulphate at two different pH values, as compared to the resolving action of phosphate; at pH 4.75 arsenate caused irreversible inactivation. Irreversible inactivation was also obtained by incubating aspartate aminotransferase with either quinolinate and phthalate. Chloride, borate, formate and citrate were without resolving effect.

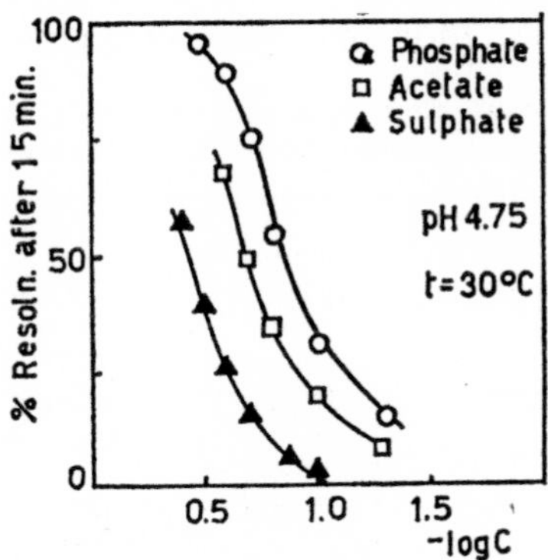


FIG. 6. Resolving action of phosphate, acetate and sulphate at pH 4.75 as a function of the molarity (C).

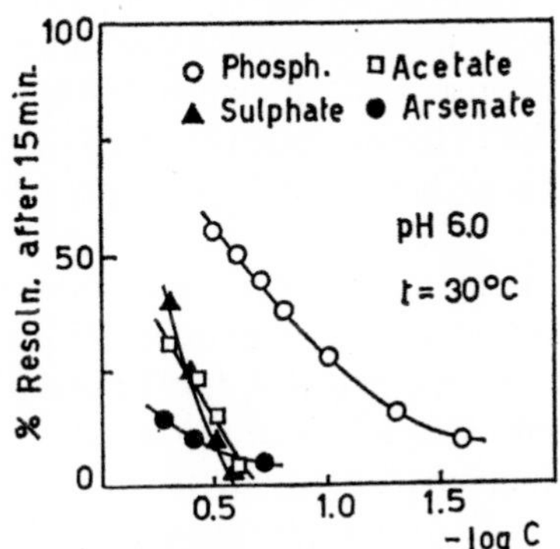


FIG. 7. Effect of phosphate, acetate, sulphate and arsenate at pH 6.0 as a function of the molarity (C).

On the basis of these experiments phosphate appears to be the most active resolving anion. In Table 2 standard conditions, under which complete resolution of aspartate aminotransferase can be obtained, are reported.

Aspartate cannot be replaced by any other amino acid except glutamate, or by any other dicarboxylic acid such as succinate. DL-Aspartate or DL-glutamate can replace only 50 per cent L-aspartate or L-glutamate. α-Ketoglutarate or oxaloacetate are without effect.

In order to confirm that the resolution of aspartate aminotransferase was possible provided the enzyme was in the " pyridoxamine " form and that the presence of aspartate or glutamate was unnecessary, the " pyridoxamine " enzyme was reconstituted by adding synthetic pyridoxamine-5-phosphate to aspartate apoaminotransferase obtained by resolving the holoenzyme as above described. Special care was taken to eliminate any trace of keto acid which is formed during the conversion of the " pyridoxal " form of the enzyme into the " pyridoxamine " form and which could rapidly reconvert this latter

TABLE 2. STANDARD CONDITIONS UNDER WHICH RESOLUTION OF ASPARTATE AMINOTRANSFERASE IS PERFORMED.

| Incubation | | |
|---|---|---|
| at | for | in the presence of |
| 1. Room temperature | 15 min | L-aspartate or L-glutamate (15 μmoles/mg protein) |
| 1. 30° | 30 min | $KH_2PO_4$ (final conc. 0.5 M) pH 4.75 |

into the original form. Spectrophotometric and enzymatic analyses were performed in order to confirm the conversion. The reconstituted " pyridoxamine " enzyme was readily resolved by addition of phosphate under standard conditions, whereas the " pyridoxal " form obtained by addition of pyridoxal-5-phosphate to the untreated apoenzyme required preincubation with aspartate or glutamate before addition of phosphate to obtain 100 per cent resolution.

The present results strengthen the point that an azomethine linkage does exist between the 4-formyl group of pyridoxal-5-phosphate and an $NH_2$ group of the enzymic protein, and that this linkage is rather strong being broken only by a specific enzymic interaction between the 4-formyl group and L-aspartate or L-glutamate, namely by the amino acid substrates. When the azomethine linkage disappears, the remaining linkages (probably salt linkages) can be easily loosened by intervention of anions, such as phosphate.

It seems interesting to speculate that the reversible resolution of the aminotransferase might have a physiological meaning and be a mechanism by which the cell can regulate its pool of amino acids. Indeed, it does not seem too unlikely that in some compartmentalized regions of the cell conditions may arise under which the " pyridoxamine " enzyme can be reversibly resolved.

*Acknowledgment*—The research reported in this document has been made possible through the support and sponsorship of the U.S. Department of Army, through its European Research Office.

## REFERENCES

1. V. Scardi, S. Magno and E. Scarano; *Boll. soc. ital. biol. sper.* **36**, 1719 (1960).
2. V. Scardi, M. Iaccarino and E. Scarano; *Biochem. J.* **83**, 413 (1962).
3. D. E. O'Kane and I. C. Gunsalus; *J. Biol. Chem.* **170**, 425 (1947).
4. W. T. Jenkins, D. A. Yphantis and I. W. Sizer; *J. Biol. Chem.* **234**, 51 (1959).
5. E. C. Banks and C. A. Vernon; *J. Chem. Soc.*, 1698 (1961).
6. V. Bonavita and V. Scardi; *Experientia* **14**, 7 (1958).

## DISCUSSION

Dr. Vernon:

If I understand you correctly you are saying that the procedure described by Dr. Banks and myself does not work on the pyridoxal enzyme but does work on the pyridoxamine enzyme. Our procedure was, of course, arrived at quite empirically and was intended to resolve the enzyme at an earlier stage in the purification. We regularly achieve *ca.* 98 per cent resolution and then go on to purify the apoenzyme. Your results must mean that the enzyme which we extract from the heart muscle is nearly completely in the pyridoxamine form. I was interested to see that you have found, as we did, that phosphate ions at high concentration helps the resolution. This is presumably consistent with Dr. Wootton's finding that phosphate inhibits the recombination.

Dr. Snell:

Perhaps attention should be called here to the method Dr. Wada and I developed for the resolution of both the PMP and the PLP-forms of the glutamic–aspartic transaminase. PMP is much more readily removed from the holoenzyme than is PLP (H. Wada and E. E. Snell; *J. Biol. Chem.* **237**, 127, 1962).

# THE DIFFERENCES BETWEEN THE GLUTAMIC OXALOACETIC APOTRANSAMINASES OF MITOCHONDRIA AND THE SUPERNATANT FRACTION OF BEEF LIVER

by YOSHIMASA MORINO and HIROSHI WADA

Department of Biochemistry, Medical School Osaka University, Osaka, Japan

IN THIS paper we describe the transamination of pyridoxamine with certain keto acids catalyzed by glutamic oxalacetic apotransaminase and its relationship to the normal transamination.

As previously reported,[1] Wada and Snell found pyridoxamine oxaloacetic transaminases in rabbit liver and *E. coli*. They also found that the apoenzyme of GOT* from pig heart muscle catalyzes the transamination between pyridoxamine and either α-ketoglutarate or oxaloacetate.[1] This finding, together with the fact that the pyridoxamine oxaloacetic transaminase of rabbit liver and *E. coli* was strongly inhibited by addition of PLP,* drove them to speculate whether the enzyme of rabiit liver and *E. coli* is not actually an unidentified apotransaminase.

During the course of the present investigation, Katsunuma[2] and Boyd[3] independently presented evidence that there exist GOT's with different properties in the mitochondrial and supernatant fractions of some mammalian livers.

Hence, it was very interesting to see how these GOT's from different locations would behave with respect to the transamination between pyridoxamine and α-keto acids, when each was converted to its apoenzyme.

## PURIFICATION AND PROPERTIES OF GOT'S FROM SUPERNATANT AND MITOCHONDRIAL FRACTIONS

Listed in Table 1 are the procedures used for purification of GOT's from the mitochondrial (Table 1, *a*) and supernatant (Table 1, *b*) fractions of beef liver. The mitochondrial and supernatant fractions were prepared by differential centrifugation of a 16 per cent homogenate of beef liver in

*Abbreviations used are: GOT, glutamic oxaloacetic transaminase; PLP, pyridoxal phosphate.

0.25 M sucrose solution containing 0.001 M EDTA essentially according to the method of Schneider and Hogeboom.[4]

The assay of GOT was carried out by determining oxaloacetate formed during enzymatic reaction as previously reported.[1] In kinetic studies with purified enzymes, the activity was determined by method II of Jenkins.[5] The activity of pyridoxamine transaminases was determined as previously reported.[1]

TABLE 1.

A. PURIFICATION OF GOT FROM MITOCHONDRIA

| Steps | Specific activity[a] | Recovery (%) |
|---|---|---|
| Sonic extract | 10.6 | 100 |
| Heat treatment (72°) | 109.3 | 90 |
| $(NH_4)_2SO_4$ fractionation | 630.0 | 62 |
| Column eluate (0.12 M, pH 6.8) | 4050.0 | 50 |

B. PURIFICATION OF GOT FROM SUPERNATANT

| Steps | Specific activity[a] | Recovery (%) |
|---|---|---|
| Crude extract | 16.0 | 100 |
| 1st $(NH_4)_2SO_4$ fractionation | 67.0 | 75 |
| Heat treatment (85°) | 361.0 | 60 |
| 2nd $(NH_4)_2SO_4$ fractionation | 1960.0 | 40 |
| Column eluate (0.018 M, pH 6.8) | 11,000.0 | 35 |

[a] $\mu$mole oxaloacetate per hour per mg protein.

As was demonstrated on pig heart GOT,[5] the presence of maleate (pH 6.0), $\alpha$-ketoglutarate and PLP (especially for mitochondrial GOT) was found to protect both GOT's from inactivation during heat treatment (Fig. 1).

By sonic disruption of mitochondrial pellets, heat treatment at 72° in the presence of stabilizers, ammonium sulfate fractionation and finally hydroxylapatite column chromatography, about 400-fold purification was achieved for mitochondrial GOT.

By similar procedures, supernatant GOT was purified 700-fold.

Photographs of typical sedimentation patterns of both GOT's are shown in Fig. 2. The final preparation of mitochondrial GOT showed a single symmetrical boundary on ultracentrifugal analysis. The sedimentation coefficient was calculated to be 4.8 S. The final preparation of supernatant GOT was almost homogeneous. The sedimentation coefficient of the major component was 5.4 S.

The purest preparation of both GOT's have a deep yellow color. The variation in their absorption spectra with pH were shown in Fig. 3.

The absorption maximum of the cationic form of mitochondrial GOT was at 430 mμ, and that of anionic form at 350 mμ, with an isobestic point at 382 mμ. These seem to be characteristic spectra of the pyridoxal enzyme. On addition of 0.1 M glutamate to the pyridoxal enzyme, a new peak appeared at 330 mμ. This indicates its conversion to the pyridoxamine form.

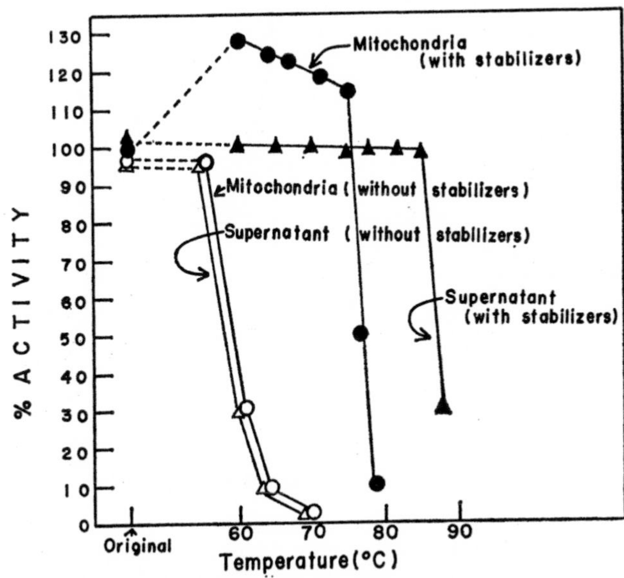


FIG. 1. Heat stability of enzymes. The enzyme preparations used were those of step 1 (mitochondrial GOT) and step 2 (supernatant GOT). The activity of the original preparations was taken as 100 per cent. Stabilizers used were 0.05 M maleate (pH 6.0), 0.001 M α-ketoglutarate, and 0.00001 M pyridoxal phosphate. Enzyme preparations were maintained for 5 min at indicated temperatures.

The supernatant GOT shows an absorption maximum at 430 mμ at an acidic pH, and at 360 mμ at an alkaline pH, with an isobestic point at 390 mμ. The absorption maximum of the pyridoxamine form which was prepared by addition of 0.1 M glutamate was at 330 mμ, The spectrum was very similar to that of pig heart GOT obtained by Jenkins[5].

Supernatant GOT had a sharp pH optimum at 8.5. As is shown in Fig. 4, a close correlation was observed between the increase in reaction rate and of absorbency at 360 mμ with pH, as was demonstrated by Jenkins on pig heart GOT.[5] On the other hand, the mitochondrial GOT showed optimal activity over a broad range of pH, that is, 6.0 to 8.5. However, the spectral change with pH at 350 mμ was very similar to that of the supernatant GOT. Thus, in the case of mitochondrial GOT, a discrepancy was observed between the variation in activity and spectrum with pH. No explanation has been obtained for this phenomenon.

Lineweaver–Burk plots of the substrate concentration curves gave $K_m$ values of 8.0 mM for α-ketoglutarate, and 0.7 mM for L-aspartate with mitochondrial GOT; and 2.4 mM for α-ketoglutarate, and 2.3 mM for

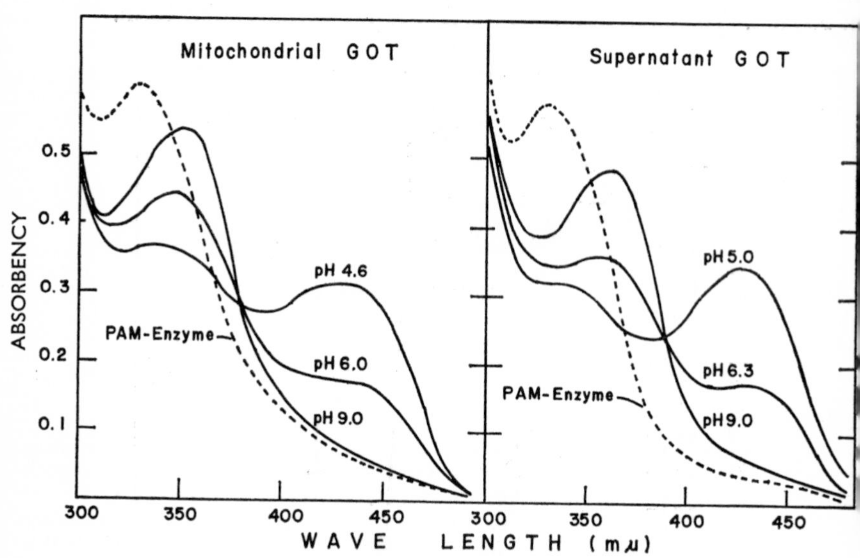


FIG. 3. Absorption spectra of GOT's.

Mitochodrial GOT. The solid lines show the spectra of the pyridoxal enzyme. Numbers indicate the pH at which spectra were measured. The buffers used were 0.1 M sodium acetate (pH 4.6 or 5.0), potassium phosphate (pH 6.0 or 6.3), and Tris-HCl (pH 9.0). The dotted lines show the spectra of the pyridoxamine enzyme.

Supernatant GOT. Conditions as above.

L-aspartate with the supernatant GOT. It should be noted that the apparent affinity of mitochondrial GOT for aspartate is much higher than that for α-ketoglutarate and, on the other hand, the affinities of supernatant GOT for both substrates are of a similar order.

## CATALYTIC ACTIVITY OF APOPROTEINS OF GOT'S FROM MITOCHONDRIAL AND SUPERNATANT FRACTIONS

Apo-GOT's were prepared by resolution of pyridoxamine phosphate from the corresponding holo-GOT's (in pyridoxamine forms) by treatment with acidic (pH 5.0) ammonium sulfate.[6]

Figure 5 shows that on addition of various concentrations of PLP to each apo-GOT the appearance of GOT activity was just parallel to the disappearance of pyridoxamine oxaloacetic transaminase activity (POT). In this

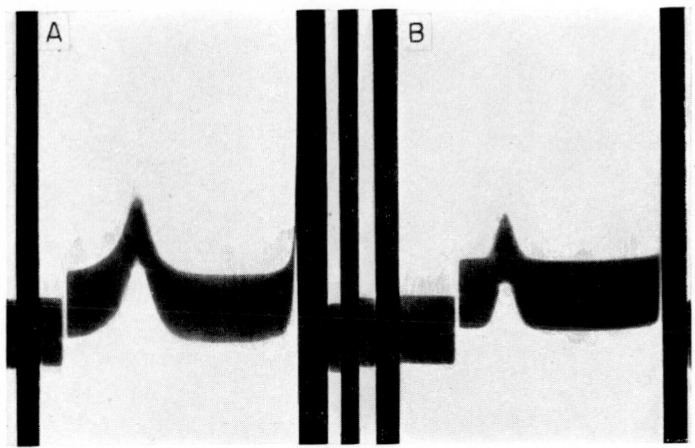


FIG. 2. Schlieren patterns of purified GOT's.

A. Supernatant GOT. The photograph was taken after 60 min at 51,200 rev/min in the Hitachi analytical ultracentrifuge. Protein 1.2 per cent in 0.025 M potassium phosphate buffer, pH 6.8.

B. Mitochondrial GOT. The photograph was taken after 32 min at 59,820 rev/min in the Hitachi analytical ultracentrifuge. Protein 0.8 per cent in 0.025 M potassium phosphate buffer, pH 6.8.

experiment, PLP was pre-incubated with apoenzymes for 15 min at 25°. The apparent affinity of the coenzyme for the mitochondrial GOT ($K_m$ or $K_I = 3.3 \times 10^{-4}$ M) was much lower than that of the supernatant GOT ($K_m$ or $K_I = 5.0 \times 10^{-7}$ M).

Mitochondrial apo-GOT was specific for oxaloacetate in transamination with pyridoxamine. α-Ketoglutarate and pyruvate were ineffective as amino

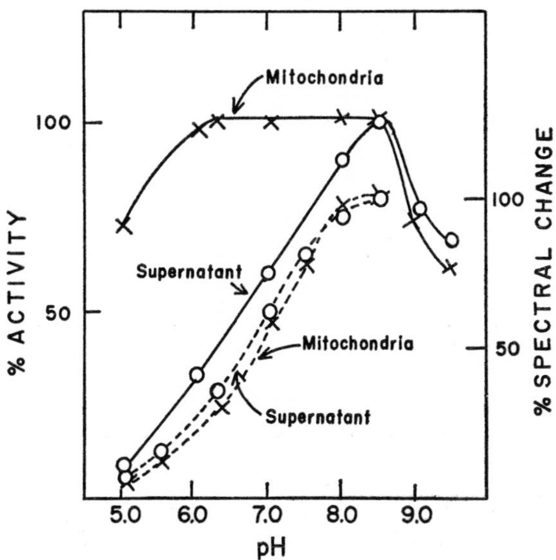


FIG. 4. Variation of enzymic activity and spectra with pH. Enzyme activity was determined as described in the experimental section. The buffers used were 0.1 M sodium acetate, potassium phosphate, Tris-HCl and sodium carbonate. The spectral change was followed at 360 mμ with supernatant enzyme and at 350 mμ with mitochondrial enzyme. The activity and absorbency at pH 8.5 in both cases were taken as 100 per cent. Solid lines indicate the GOT activity and dotted lines show the spectral change. Crosses represent data obtained with mitochondrial GOT and open circles those obtained with supernatant GOT.

group acceptors. The pH optimum is near 8.5. In contrast to the mitochondrial apo-GOT, supernatant apo-GOT utilized oxaloacetate and α-ketoglutarate equally well as amino group acceptors. The pH optimum of the reaction was 8.5.

It is very interesting that phosphate ion has a diverse influence on the catalytic activity of these apo-GOT'S (Fig. 6). In transamination with pyridoxamine catalyzed by mitochondrial apo-GOT, a sufficient amount of phosphate ion was essentially required. Here, it may be stated that these properties of mitochondrial apo-GOT are quite similar to those of the pyridoxamine oxaloacetic transaminases of *E. coli* and rat liver which were reported by Wada and Snell[1]. On the contrary, supernatant apo-GOT did not require phosphate ion but rather inhibited the reaction. In this case, the inhibition by phosphate ion is much stronger for transamination with α-ketoglutarate than with oxaloacetate.

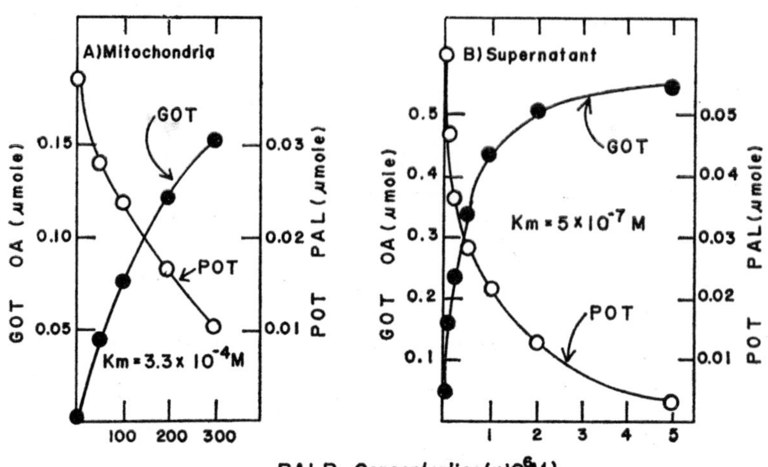


FIG. 5. Enhancement of GOT activity and depression of pyridoxamine oxaloacetate transaminase activity on the addition of pyridoxal phosphate to the apoenzymes of mitochondrial and supernatant GOT.

Enzyme activity was determined as described in the Experimental section. Pyridoxal phosphate was preincubated with apoenzymes for 15 min at 25°.

## CONCLUDING REMARKS

Table 2 summarizes the results of our investigations of these transaminases.

Absorption maximum of the anionic form of mitochondrial glutamic oxaloacetic transaminase lies at 10 mμ shorter wavelength than that of supernatant transaminase.

Although neither the diffusion coefficient nor the partial specific volume have not yet been determined, the molecular weight of mitochondrial enzyme seems to be lower than that of supernatant enzyme.

On the basis of these assumed molecular weight, the turnover number of mitochondrial enzyme is much smaller than that of supernatant enzyme. For the transamination with pyridoxamine, the turnover number of mitochondrial apoenzyme is much larger than that of supernatant apoenzyme.

The affinity of pyridoxal phosphate for mitochondrial apoenzyme is much lower than that for supernatant apoenzyme.

Although the supernatant enzyme has an equal affinity for α-ketoglutarate and L-aspartate, the mitochondrial enzyme shows much higher affinity for L-aspartate than that for α-ketoglutarate. This property of mitochondrial

GOT might have some physiological significance as suggested by Gutfreund *et al.*[7]

The most distinct are the differences in catalytic properties of the two apoproteins. That is, the supernatant apoenzyme catalyzes the transamination between pyridoxamine and either oxaloacetate or α-ketoglutarate in the absence of phosphate ion, but, on the other hand, the apoenzyme of mitochondrial origin fails to use α-ketoglutarate as an amino group acceptor whether phosphate ion is present or not.

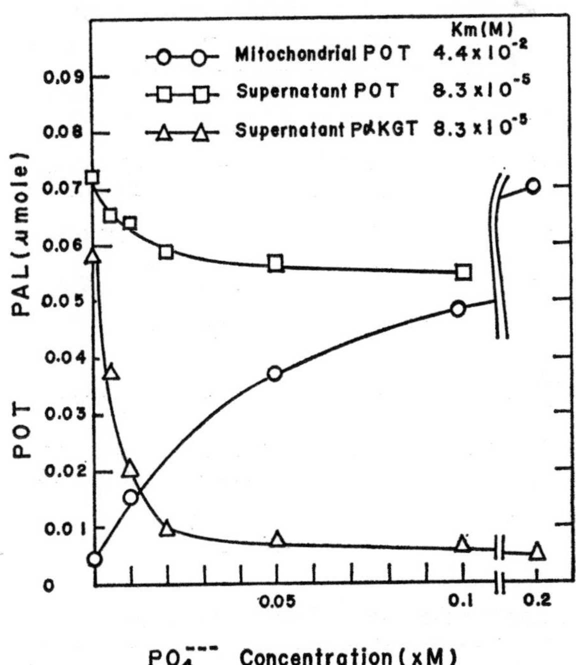


FIG. 6. Effect of phosphate ion on the transamination with pyridoxamine.

Enzyme activity was determined under standard conditions but the phosphate ion concentration was varied. The enzyme preparations used were apoenzymes of step 4 (supernatant GOT) and step 3 (mitochondrial GOT).

POT, pyridoxamine oxaloacetate transamination; PαKGT, pyridoxamine α-ketoglutarate transamination.

It is very interesting to note that, α-ketoglutarate, which is utilized as an amino group acceptor in the normal transamination, loses its reactivity in the transamination with pyridoxamine catalyzed by the mitochondrial apoenzyme. We would like to consider two possibilities to explain this phenomenon. First, the affinity of α-ketoglutarate for the mitochondrial holoenzyme is much lower than that for L-aspartate (or oxaloacetate) and this may be reflected in the inability of the mitochondrial apoenzyme to utilize α-ketoglutarate as substrate. Second, it may be assumed that on the surface of the holoproteins of glutamic oxaloacetic transaminase there are two distinct sites binding, 4-carbon substrates (that is, oxaloacetate and aspartate) and 5-carbon substrates (that is, α-ketoglutarate and glutamate) respectively, besides a site binding the coenzyme. On the dissociation of pyridoxal phosphate, then, the conformation of the apoprotein moiety is influenced so that, in the case of mitochondrial enzyme, neither the 4-carbon

TABLE 2. COMPARISON OF PROPERTIES OF HOLOPROTEINS AND APOPROTEINS OF MITOCHONDRIAL AND SUPERNATANT GOT'S

| | Mitochondrial GOT | | Supernatant GOT | |
|---|---|---|---|---|
| | Holoenzyme | Apoenzyme | Holoenzyme | Apoenzyme |
| Spectral maxima ($\lambda_{max}$) | 430 (pH 5.0)<br>350 (pH 9.0) | — | 430 (pH 5.0)<br>360 (pH 9.0) | — |
| Molecular weight | 90,000 | | 110,000 | |
| Turn-over number | 6000 | 23 | 20,000 | 8.0 |
| Optimum pH | 8.5 (6.0–8.5) | 8.5 | 8.5 | 8.5 |
| $K_m$ or $K_i$ for pyridoxal phosphate ($\times 10^4$ M) | 3.3 | (3.3) | 0.005 | (0.005) |
| $K_m$ for substrate ($\times 10^3$ M) | α-KG 8.0<br>Asp. A 0.7 | OA 0.16<br>α-KG — | α-KG 2.4<br>Asp. A 2.3 | OA 0.05<br>α-KG 0.05 |
| Effect of phosphate ion $K_m$ or $K_i$ | | Essential<br>$4.4 \times 10^{-2}$ M | | Inhibitory<br>$8.3 \times 10^{-5}$ M |

substrates site nor the 5-carbon substrates site is any longer accessible to the pyridoxamine site and, only when a sufficient amount of phosphate ion is present, 4-carbon substrates site becomes sufficiently accessible to the pyridoxamine site. It is possible that phosphate ion acts in a favorable rearrangement of the steric configuration of a part near the pyridoxamine site and the 4-carbon substrate site on the apoprotein.

Further investigations are needed to answer the questions raised above.

## ADDENDUM

### *Apo-GOT of E. coli*

Cells of *E. coli* (K 12) grown on a common medium containing 4-desoxypyridoxine (3 mg/dl) were found to contain three to four times as high pyridoxamine oxaloacetate transaminase activity as those grown on the ordinary medium. These $B_6$ deficient cells also contained a higher amount of apo-GOT than normal cells. We tried to purify pyridoxamine oxaloacetate transaminase and check the apo-GOT activity at each stage of the purification. The procedure used consists of sonic disruption of cells, removal of nucleoproteins by streptomycin, ammonium sulfate fractionation and elution from a hydroxylapatite column. On this column, the elution pattern of the enzyme was identical with that of the protein. The purification factor was 100 (specific activity of crude extract = 0.082, that of the purest enzyme = 8.9). This fact strongly supports the idea that the pyridoxamine oxaloacetate transaminase[1] is the glutamic oxaloacetic apotransaminase.

A further confirmation of this proposition was obtained by extensive purification of GOT from normal cells of *E. coli* and the appearance of pyridoxamine transaminase activity on the resolution of pyridoxal phosphate from the purest GOT preparation.

*Acknowledgment*—The authors wish to express their gratitude to Drs. Esmond E. Snell and Osamu Hayaishi for their continuous interest, advice and criticism.

## REFERENCES

1. H. Wada and E. E. Snell; *J. Biol. Chem.* **237**, 127 (1962).
2. N. Katsunuma, T. Matsuzawa and A. Fujino; *J. Vitaminol. (Kyoto)* **8**, 74 (1962).
3. J. W. Boyd; *Biochem. J.* **81**, 434 (1961).
4. W. C. Schneider and G. H. Hogeboom; *J. Biol. Chem.* **183**, 123 (1950).
5. W. T. Jenkins, D. A. Yphantis and I. W. Sizer; *J. Biol. Chem.* **234**, 51 (1959).
6. H. Wada and E. E. Snell; *J. Biol. Chem.* **236**, 2089 (1961).
7. H. Gutfreund, K. E. Ebner and L. Mendiola, *Nature* **192**, 820 (1961).

## DISCUSSION

Dr. Christensen:

I wonder, Dr. Snell, if you can tell us whether Dr. Wada tried to substitute other aniont for phosphate as a co-factor for the mitochondrial enzyme. I assume that the phosphase ion serves as a cofactor by joining to a cationic site on the enzyme, thereby interfering with the addition of PLP or PMP, thereby in turn permitting pyridoxal or pyridoxamine to serve as the substrate. This action is reminiscent of the one observed by Dempsey and Christensen (*J. Biol. Chem.* **237**, 1113, 1962) of various anions in competing with pyridoxal phosphate in combining with a specific site on the bovine serum albumin molecule. Phosphate was one of the less effective inhibitors, aromatic phosphates, sulfates and carboxylates being more effective in blocking the specific reaction. I wonder, for example, if Dr. Wada has tried benzylphosphate, which might bind to the site more tightly. It might of course also interfere with the entry of pyridoxal into its presumably adjoining site on the enzyme. In such a way the effect of a phosphate in decreasing the affinity for pyridoxal phosphate might perhaps be dissociated from its effect in permitting the action on pyridoxal. This enzyme should be a valuable additional model for comparative study to help discover the critical features of the coenzyme-binding sites on $B_6$ enzymes.

Dr. Wada (answer submitted in written form only):

As already reported by Wada and Snell (*J. Biol. Chem.* **237**, 127, 1926), arsenate was about 50 per cent as effective as phosphate with the rabbit and *E. coli* enzymes, which appear to have all of the properties described herein for the mitochondrial enzyme. Thus arsenate would be expected to serve as an activator for the mitochondrial enzyme. Although we have not yet tried benzylphosphate, pyridoxine phosphate at a low concentration ($10^{-4}$ M) completely suppressed the catalytic activities of the mitochondrial and supernatant GOT's. In these cases phosphate ion did not show any detectable effect. The real answer to a proposal by Dr. Christensen must await further investigations.

DR. JENKINS:

The presence of two different glutamic aspartic transaminases has now been shown in a wide variety of different tissues.

It is of great interest that the one exclusively located in mitochondria always has a pH activity curves and $K_m$ values characteristically different from those of the enzyme exclusively present in the easily extracted proteins. I believe this important paper will lead to a much greater understanding of the mechanism of the reaction and the metabolic function of isozymes.

# THE MECHANISM OF ENZYMATIC TRANSAMINATION*

by GORDON G. HAMMES and PAOLO FASELLA†

Department of Chemistry and Research Laboratory of Electronics,
Massachusetts Institute of Technology, Cambridge 39, Massachusetts

## INTRODUCTION

THE mechanism of enzymatic transamination has been studied by many different workers.[1] In all cases investigated (with one exception[2]) pyridoxal phosphate is utilized as a coenzyme, and the overall transamination was found to occur in two steps :

$$E_L + AA\,I = X_1 = \ldots X_n = E_M + KA\,I \quad (1)$$

$$E_M + KA\,II = Y_n = \ldots Y_1 = E_L + AA\,II \quad (2)$$

Here $E_L$ is the pyridoxal form of the enzyme, $E_M$ is the aminic form, AA designates an amino acid, KA designates a keto acid, and $X_n$ and $Y_n$ are reaction intermediates. In no case thus far has it been possible to unequivocally determine the nature or number of the intermediates in the mechanism.

The problem involved in determining the nature of the reaction intermediates is universal in enzymatic systems. Equilibrium measurements (e.g. spectrophotometric, etc.) are difficult to interpret because the physical and chemical properties of the intermediates may be quite similar to those of the native enzyme. On the other hand, kinetic studies at enzyme levels where the concentrations of intermediates become appreciable are limited by the resolution time of conventional techniques. In the work we shall describe, the recently developed temperature jump technique[3] has been used to partially overcome this problem. The principle of this method is to begin with a system at equilibrium and then to raise the temperature of the reaction mixture rapidly by discharging a large voltage ($\sim$30,000V) through the solution. Since chemical equilibria are in general temperature-dependent, the reactant concentrations will decay to new equilibrium values at the higher temperature. The rate of decay of the reactants is characterized by a

*This work was supported in part by the U.S. Army Signal Corps, Air Force, Office of Scientific Research, and Office of Naval Research and in part by the National Institutes of Health.

†Permanent address: Istituto di Chimica Biologica dell' Universita di Roma e Centro di Enzimologia del C.N.R., Italy.

spectrum of relaxation times (reciprocal first-order rate constants) which are known functions of the rate constants and equilibrium concentrations.[4]

Since glutamic–aspartic transaminase is now available pure in relatively large quantities,[5,6] it was chosen for an intensive study. This enzyme has a molecular weight of about 115,000, has two coenzyme molecules per protein molecule, and is pure as judged by the usual sedimentation and electrophoretic criteria. The general mechanism conforms to that given in Eqs. (1)–(2) with aspartate–oxalacetate and glutamate–ketoglutarate as the substrate amino–keto acid pairs. The aminic form of the enzyme has been isolated,[7,8] and the results of steady state kinetic studies are consistent with this mechanism.[9,10]

By combining equilibrium and kinetic measurements at high enzyme concentrations, we shall show that a quite detailed picture of the enzymatic mechanism can be obtained.

## THE ENZYMATIC TRANSAMINATION

Each of the half reactions described by Eqs. (1) and (2) was studied separately with the temperature jump. For each half reaction, three relaxation times were seen, ranging from less than 50 $\mu$sec to about 20 msec. Altogether, five of the relaxation times were determined unequivocally as a function of substrate and enzyme concentrations. Only an upper limit of 50 $\mu$sec could be assessed for the sixth relaxation time.[11]

The minimal mechanism consistent with the temperature jump results is as follows:

$$E_L + As \underset{k_{-1}}{\overset{k_1}{\rightleftharpoons}} X_1 \underset{k_{-2}}{\overset{k_2}{\rightleftharpoons}} X_2 \underset{k_{-3}}{\overset{k_3}{\rightleftharpoons}} E_M + Oa \tag{3}$$

$$E_M + Kg \underset{k'_3}{\overset{k'_{-3}}{\rightleftharpoons}} Y_2 \underset{k'_2}{\overset{k'_{-2}}{\rightleftharpoons}} Y_1 \underset{k'_1}{\overset{k'_{-1}}{\rightleftharpoons}} E_L + Gm \tag{4}$$

Here As, Oa, Kg and Gm designate aspartate, oxalacetate, ketoglutarate and glutamate respectively.

Since the slowest relaxation time is relatively independent of enzyme and substrate concentrations it can be identified with the intramolecular interconversion of intermediates. Assuming this equilibrium to be adjusted slowly relative to the other steps, the relaxation times for the mechanism in Eq. (3) are

$$1/\tau_1 = k_{-1} + k_1(\overline{As} + \overline{E}_L) \tag{5}$$

$$1/\tau_2 = \frac{k_2}{1 + [K_1(\overline{E}_L + \overline{As})]^{-1}} + \frac{k_{-2}}{1 + [K_3(\overline{E}_M + \overline{Oa})]^{-1}} \tag{6}$$

$$1/\tau_3 = k_3 + k_{-3}(\overline{Oa} + \overline{E}_M) \tag{7}$$

Here the bars indicate equilibrium concentrations, $K_1 = k_1/k_{-1}$ and $K_3 = k_{-3}/k_3$. A more detailed calculation of the relaxation times under less restrictive assumptions has been presented elsewhere,[11] but the results differ very little from the above equations. Similar equations can be written for the mechanism in Eq. (4) simply by inserting the primed rate constants and exchanging $\overline{\text{Gm}}$ and $\overline{\text{Kg}}$ for $\overline{\text{As}}$ and $\overline{\text{Oa}}$ respectively. Altogether some thirty equations were obtained containing ten unknown rate constants and one unknown equilibrium constant plus the equilibrium concentrations dependent on these quantities; these equations included mass conservation requirements, measured relaxation times and the equilibrium constant for the overall reaction (=1/7).[12]

In addition, the equilibrium spectrum of the reaction mixture places a stringent restriction on the rate constants. The absorbency of the reaction mixture containing aspartate and oxalacetate as substrates in the region 300–400 mμ is given by

$$a = \epsilon_L(E_L) + \epsilon_M(E_M) + \epsilon_{X_1}(X_1) + \epsilon_{X_2}(X_2) \tag{8}$$

where $a$ is the absorbency, the $\epsilon$'s are extinction coefficients, and a 1-cm path length has been assumed. Since $\epsilon_L$ and $\epsilon_M$ can be determined independently, $\epsilon_{X_1}(X_1) + \epsilon_{X_2}(X_2)$ can be readily calculated. Dividing this quantity by $(X_2)$ gives the quantity $\epsilon_{X_2} + K_2\epsilon_{X_1}(K_2 = k_{-2}/k_2)$ which must be constant for every reaction mixture. Similar expressions for the substrates glutamate–ketoglutarate are obvious. A method of successive approximations was used to find the rate constants and equilibrium constants which best described the data. The following parameters permit all of the experimental relaxation times and spectral quantities (e.g. $\epsilon_{X_2} + K_2\epsilon_{X_1}$) to be calculated to within 10–15 per cent, which is within the expected experimental uncertainty.

| | |
|---|---|
| $k_1/k_{-1} = 1.8 \times 10^3\ \text{M}^{-1}$ | $k'_1 = 3.3 \times 10^7\ \text{M}^{-1}\ \text{sec}^{-1}$ |
| | $k'_{-1} = 2.8 \times 10^3\ \text{sec}^{-1}$ |
| $k_2 = 80\ \text{sec}^{-1}$ | $k'_2 = 61\ \text{sec}^{-1}$ |
| $k_{-2} = 26\ \text{sec}^{-1}$ | $k'_{-2} = 30\ \text{sec}^{-1}$ |
| $k_3 = 1.4 \times 10^2\ \text{sec}^{-1}$ | $k'_3 = 70\ \text{sec}^{-1}$ |
| $k_{-3} = 7 \times 10^7\ \text{M}^{-1}\ \text{sec}^{-1}$ | $k'_{-3} = 2.1 \times 10^7\ \text{M}^{-1}\ \text{sec}^{-1}$ |

The above values were determined at 25°C, pH 8.0 in 0.16 M phosphate buffer. These constants can be considered precise to ±25 per cent within the framework of the proposed mechanism. However, it should be pointed out that a more complex mechanism could undoubtedly explain the data equally well, although a detailed analysis in terms of a definite number of intermediates would not then be possible. In addition the following lower bounds could be obtained :

$$k_1 > 10^7 \text{ M}^{-1} \text{ sec}^{-1}$$

$$k_{-1} > 5 \times 10^3 \text{ sec}^{-1}$$

The enzyme–substrate binding constants which can be calculated from the rate constants are quite large, being about $10^3$–$10^4$ M$^{-1}$ for the enzyme and amino acids, and about $10^5$ M$^{-1}$ for the enzyme and keto acids. Note that the difference between the binding constants for the amino and keto acids is reflected mainly in their rates of dissociation. The bimolecular rate constants characterizing the rate of formation of intermediates are all about $10^7$ M$^{-1}$ sec$^{-1}$. Although this is a quite large value for a bimolecular rate constant, the maximum value is considerably greater, being about $10^9$ M$^{-1}$ sec$^{-1}$ for a diffusion controlled reaction.[13] This implies that each of the four intermediates must be preceded by at least one additional intermediate. (However, such an assertion is not unequivocal since we do not know which ionized form of the enzyme and/or substrate is the actual reactant. For example, if an amino acid with a neutral amino group is the reactant, then the actual bimolecular rate constant would be about $10^9$ M$^{-1}$ sec$^{-1}$, which would indicate an essentially diffusion controlled rate of reaction.) Note that the interconversion of one intermediate into another is a relatively slow process.

In principle, one should be able to calculate steady state kinetic parameters with the rate constants obtained in the temperature jump studies. The agreement between temperature jump data and steady state kinetic data is not perfect. One possible explanation could be that at high concentrations, the enzyme exists in a form different from the one existing at great dilution. The occurrence of a monomer–dimer equilibrium between protein molecules would be compatible with this hypothesis. Disagreement between the values for the substrate-binding constants determined at high enzyme concentrations and the upper bounds for the same deduced from steady state kinetics has been reported for glutamic–aspartic transaminase[7] and for alanine–glutamic transaminase.[14]

A partial check on the rate constants and binding constants can be made using the stopped flow and equilibrium dialysis techniques. The results obtained are consistent with the temperature jump data; however, this system extends both techniques to their utmost so that a detailed analysis of the results must be accepted with caution. A more comprehensive discussion of these data is available elsewhere.[11]

Finally, the spectral parameters obtained are shown in Fig. 1. For both half reactions, two spectral peaks are found, one at 330 m$\mu$ and another of lower intensity at 360 m$\mu$. Since the difference in height between the two peaks is larger for the aspartate–oxalacetate system, where the equilibrium is more in favor of the second enzyme–substrate intermediate, $X_2$, the intermediates $X_2$ and $Y_2$ can probably be identified with the 330 peaks, and $X_1$ and $Y_1$ with the 360 peaks. These spectra are consistent with the intermediates being Schiff bases since absorption peaks around 360–370 mμ are characteristic of Schiff bases between amino acids and pyridoxal phosphate,[17] while pyridoxine derivatives with no double bond conjugated to the ring have absorption maxima around 310–330 mμ.

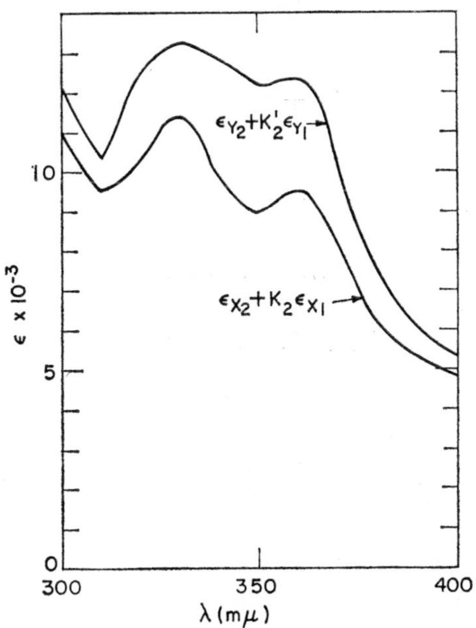


FIG. 1. Spectra of transamination reaction intermediates. See text for explanation of symbols.

## THE INTERACTION OF $E_L$ WITH $H^+$, $NH_2OH$, AND KETO ACIDS

The pyridoxal form of the enzyme can exist in two forms depending on the pH.[16] At low pH's (<5), an absorption peak at 430 mμ is found. As the hydrogen ion concentration is decreased, this peak gradually disappears and a new peak at 360 mμ appears. The transformation is complete at about pH 8. This reaction has been ascribed to the dissociation of the phenol group on the pyridoxal, with a p*K* of approximately 6.3.[16] In addition, the protonated form was shown to be catalytically inactive. (This apparent inactivity may be related to keto acid inhibition which increases greatly as the pH decreases.) However, it should be pointed out that this assignment of the proton binding site may not be correct since the reason for such an extremely large decrease in the phenol group p$K$ from its normal value of about 10 is not clear and, in fact, is not found in model compounds.[17] At first glance, this p$K$ would ordinarily be ascribed to the ring nitrogen; however, such a reaction does not cause a change in the absorption spectra of model compounds at wavelengths greater than 300 m$\mu$. In point of fact, the ionizable group in question need not even be on the coenzyme ring: any protein group interacting strongly with the coenzyme is a possibility.

Because of these factors, an exact interpretation of the observed spectral changes in terms of the active site structure must be viewed cautiously. In any case, the rate constants for the reaction

$$E_L + H^+ \underset{k_{-H^+}}{\overset{k_{H^+}}{\rightleftharpoons}} E_LH^+ \tag{9}$$

can be determined unambiguously in unbuffered solutions with the temperature jump method. In strongly buffered solutions, the equilibrium is established very fast (in less than $10^{-6}$ sec) through proton transfer reactions between the enzyme and buffer. The rate constants obtained at 25°C and in 0.1 M $KNO_3$ are[18]

$$k_{H^+} = 5.4 \times 10^8 \text{ M}^{-1} \text{ sec}^{-1}$$

$$k_{-H^+} = 240 \text{ sec}^{-1}$$

The value of the bimolecular rate constant is quite revealing since it is much smaller than normally observed for protolytic reactions.[4] In fact in all model systems of normal acids and bases, the rate of protonation is diffusion controlled ($k_{H^+} \sim 10^{10}$ M$^{-1}$ sec$^{-1}$) *unless* the non-protonated group interacts strongly with a neighboring group or its immediate environment.[19] Therefore, the non-protonated form of the pyridoxal (or protein) apparently interacts strongly with its environment. This data, of course, does not permit a decision to be made between the ring nitrogen and the phenolic group as the acid or base involved. If $10^{10}$ M$^{-1}$ sec$^{-1}$ is taken as the "normal" bimolecular rate constant, then the p$K$ calculated from this value and the measured rate constant for dissociation is about 7.6.

Hydroxylamine was previously observed to interact with the coenzyme, as judged by absorbency changes when hydroxylamine is added to the enzyme.[9,20] By analogy with model systems, a Schiff base is presumably formed. A quantitative evaluation of the equilibrium constant at different pH's showed that $E_L$ binds hydroxylamine much less strongly than $E_LH^+$, the association constants being $9 \times 10^4$ M$^{-1}$ (25°C, 0.16 M phosphate buffer) and $1.5 \times 10^6$ M$^{-1}$ (25°C, 0.2 M acetate buffer) respectively.[20] A kinetic study of these reactions with the temperature jump was carried out at pH 8 and the rate constant for complex formation was found to be $3.7 \times 10^6$ M$^{-1}$ sec$^{-1}$, and that for complex dissociation 38 sec$^{-1}$. Unfortunately decomposition of reaction mixtures in the temperature jump cell at low pH's precluded determination of the kinetic constants for the reaction of $E_LH^+$ with $NH_2OH$. Note that the bimolecular rate constant is only slightly less than those found for the corresponding substrate reactions.

These results indicate that Schiff base formation occurs both with $E_L$ and $E_LH^+$, but apparently the interconversion of the intermediate Schiff bases is catalyzed only by the non-protonated form of the enzyme.[9] This hypothesis is further substantiated by the results of Jenkins, Orlowski and Sizer who found that isonicotinic acid hydrazine formed a more stable hydrazone with $E_LH^+$ than with $E_L$ by a factor of more than ten.[21] The Schiff base formation between $E_LH^+$ and the amino acids is apparently not observed because the spectral properties of the Schiff bases and the native enzyme are practically identical. Of course another possible explanation is simply that a protonated amino group may not react appreciably with $E_LH^+$.

The interaction of keto and dicarboxylic acids with the pyridoxal enzyme has been reported by several workers.[9,22] Addition of these pseudo-substrates to the enzyme at neutral pH's causes an increase in the absorbency at 430 mμ, with a corresponding decrease at 360 mμ. If the spectral changes are studied as a function of pH and keto acid concentration, the following reaction scheme can be used to describe the experimental data :

$$
\begin{array}{ccc}
E_L + H^+ + KA & \overset{K_1}{\rightleftharpoons} & E_LKA + H^+ \\
\downarrow\uparrow K_A & & \downarrow\uparrow K'_A \\
E_LH^+ + KA & \overset{K_2}{\rightleftharpoons} & E_LKAH^+
\end{array}
$$

where the equilibrium constants for the system are defined as

$$
\begin{aligned}
K_1 &= \frac{(E_LKA)}{(E_L)(KA)} \\
K_2 &= \frac{(E_LKAH^+)}{(E_LH^+)(KA)} \\
K_A &= \frac{(E_LH^+)}{(E_L)(H^+)} \\
K'_A &= \frac{(E_LKAH)}{(E_LKA)(H^+)}
\end{aligned}
\qquad (10)
$$

The constants obtained for ketoglutarate and oxalacetate at 25°C and 0.16 M phosphate buffer are summarized in Table 1.

Since no major enzyme spectral changes are found for the enzyme–keto acid complexes, this interaction presumably characterizes a protein–keto acid interaction rather than a coenzyme–keto acid interaction. This hypothesis is further strengthened by recent optical rotary dispersion measurements where keto acids were found not to change the enzyme rotary power in the spectral region 300–600 mμ.[25] According to the results obtained with hydroxylamine, however, both $E_L$ and $E_LH^+$ complexes can form Schiff bases with a subsequent change in spectral and optical dispersion curves.

An attempt to study the kinetics of these reactions showed that the reaction proceeded too fast to be studied with the temperature jump method. However, a lower bound can be obtained for the bimolecular rate constant of complex formation; this constant is really a composite constant containing

TABLE 1. ENZYME–KETO ACID BINDING CONSTANTS

| | Ketoglutarate | Oxalacetate |
|---|---|---|
| $K_A(\text{M}^{-1})$ | $2.4 \times 10^6$ | $2.4 \times 10^6$ |
| $K'_A(\text{M}^{-1})$ | $>5 \times 10^7$ | $>2.5 \times 10^7$ |
| $K_1(\text{M}^{-1})$ | $<1 \times 10^2$ | $<7 \times 10^1$ |
| $K_2(\text{M}^{-1})$ | $2.0 \times 10^3$ | $8.0 \times 10^2$ |

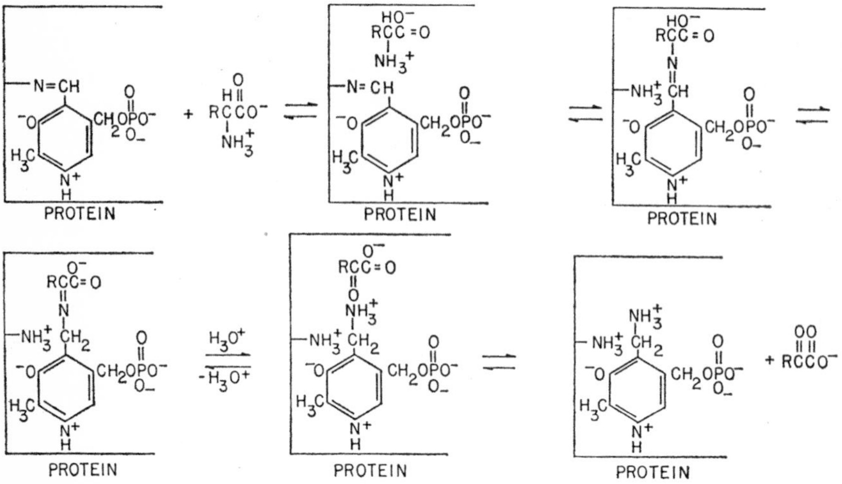

FIG. 2. A schematic mechanism for enzymatic transamination derived from kinetic and equilibrium studies. For aspartate–oxalacetate R is $CH_2COO^-$, while for glutamate–ketoglutarate R is $CH_2CH_2COO^-$.

the two rate constants characterizing $E_LKA$ and $E_LKAH^+$ formation, the largest rate constant essentially determining the composite constant. The lower bound obtained for the composite constant is $k > 5 \times 10^8\ \text{M}^{-1}\ \text{sec}^{-1}$. The rate of formation of these complexes, therefore, is essentially diffusion controlled.

The minimal mechanism, at pH 8, consistent with all the experimental facts and present knowledge of the active site is shown schematically in Fig. 2 for a single half reaction. Actually, the appropriate mechanism for *any* pH is somewhat more complex and can be written for each half reaction as

$$\begin{array}{l} E_L + AA \leftrightarrows X_1 \leftrightarrows X_2 \leftrightarrows X_3 \leftrightarrows X_4 \leftrightarrows E_M + KA \\ H^+ \upharpoonleft\downharpoonright \qquad H^+ \upharpoonleft\downharpoonright \qquad H^+ \upharpoonleft\downharpoonright \\ E_LH^+ + AA \leftrightarrows X_1H^+ \leftrightarrows X_2H^+ \end{array} \tag{11}$$

The initial enzyme–substrate complexes ($X_1$, $X_1H^+$ and $X_4$) apparently are present in very small concentrations even in our concentrated enzyme solutions. This mechanism is presented with the quite important reservation that we are still not certain which ionized species of enzyme and substrates are most important kinetically.

## COMPARISON OF ENZYMATIC AND MODEL REACTIONS

Some insight into the enzymatic mechanism can be obtained by comparing the results reported above with the results of studies of model reactions. The overall mechanism appears quite similar in both cases : namely the formation of a Schiff base between pyridoxal phosphate and the amino acid followed by a relatively slow shift of the double bond to form another Schiff base which then decomposes into pyridoxamine and the keto acid. However, a typical bimolecular rate constant for Schiff base formation is about $1\ \text{M}^{-1}\ \text{sec}^{-1}$ (pyridoxal plus valine),[24] so that the enzymatic process is a factor of $10^7$ more efficient. Even in the case of hydroxylamine, the Schiff base formation is a factor of $10^6$ faster. The transformation of one Schiff base into the other proceeds about $10^8$ times faster in the enzymatic process.[25]

A predominant feature of model reactions is the marked catalytic effect of metal ions on the transamination. In the case of glutamic–aspartic transaminase, metal ions do not enhance the catalytic activity, and chemical analysis shows that this transaminase does not meet the criteria for a metalloenzyme.[26]

Therefore even though the gross aspects of the model systems are similar to the enzymatic reaction, the details are obviously quite different. As usual the unanswered question is what is the role of the protein molecule? Although a definite answer to this question is presently impossible, the protein conformation is probably all important. Here static and dynamic effects should be differentiated. In the case of static conformational effects, the protein may simply bring the substrate into a critical configuration. For example, if ion-induced dipole interactions are important for polarizing the appropriate chemical bonds, positioning would be very important since the potential energy of this interaction falls off inversely as the fourth power of the distance.

Alternatively, localized acid–base catalysis might occur. In this case the rate of catalysis is limited by the rate of dissociation of the acidic or basic group involved. If the p$K$ of the group (or groups) involved is between 6 and 7, the maximum rate of acid–base catalysis is about $10^3$ sec$^{-1}$ (assuming a diffusion controlled rate of protonation).[27] This number, of course, is only a rough order of magnitude, but the rate constants previously presented indicate that the interconversion of Schiff bases occurs slowly enough for acid–base catalysis to be involved.

Another possible role of the protein is that dynamic conformational changes could actually involve a physical straining of the chemical bonds. In either dynamic or static conformational effects, the rate of conformational change could be kinetically important. Although almost no information is available about the rates of such processes, conformational changes can occur very fast as judged by the fact that the helix-coil transition in polyglutamic acid occurs in less than $10^{-6}$ sec.[28,29]

Although glutamic–aspartic transaminase has been specifically discussed, other enzymatic transaminations probably involve similar mechanisms. Further investigation of the conformational aspects of enzymatic transamination should produce an even more detailed picture of the enzymatic mechanism.

## REFERENCES

1. E. E. Snell; *Vitamins and Hormones* **16**, 77 (1958); A. E. Braunstein; *The Enzymes* (edited by P. D. Boyer, H. Lardy and K. Myrbäck), vol. II, p. 113, Academic Press, New York (1960).
2. E. E. Snell; *J. Biol. Chem.* **239**, 127 (1962).
3. G. Czerlinski and M. Eigen; *Z. Elektrochem.* **63**, 652 (1959).
4. M. Eigen; *Z. Electrochem.* **64**, 115 (1960).
5. H. Lis; *Biochim. et Biophys. Acta* **28**, 191 (1958).
6. W. T. Jenkins, D. A. Yphantis and I. W. Sizer; *J. Biol. Chem.* **234**, 51 (1959).
7. W. T. Jenkins and I. W. Sizer; *J. Biol. Chem.* **235**, 620 (1960).
8. H. Lis, P. Fasella, C. Turano and P. Vecchini; *Biochim. et Biophys. Acta* **45**, 529 (1960).
9. S. F. Velick and J. Vavra; *J. Biol. Chem.* **237**, 2109 (1962).
10. C. Turano, P. Fasella and A. Giartosio; *Biochim. et Biophys. Acta* **58**, 255 (1962).
11. G. G. Hammes and P. Fasella; *J. Am. Chem. Soc.* **84**, 4644 (1962).
12. B. E. C. Banks, K. C. Oldham, E. H. Thain and C. A. Vernon; *Nature* **183**, 1084 (1959).
13. R. A. Alberty and G. G. Hammes; *J. Phys. Chem.* **62**, 154 (1958).
14. W. T. Jenkins; This volume, p. 139.
15. Y. J. Matsuo; *J. Am. Chem.* **79**, 2011 (1957).
16. W. T. Jenkins and I. W. Sizer; *J. Am. Chem. Soc.* **79**, 2655 (1957).
17. D. E. Metzler; *J. Am. Chem. Soc.* **79**, 485 (1957).
18. G. G. Hammes and P. Fasella; In preparation.
19. M. Eigen; *Proc. of VIIIth Int. Cong. Coord. Chem.*, Stockholm, 1962.
20. W. T. Jenkins and I. W. Sizer; *The Enzymes* (edited by P. D. Boyer, H. Lardy and K. Myrbäck), vol. V, p. 677, Academic Press, New York (1961); O. L. Polyanovskii and Yu. M. Torchinskii; *Doklady* (*Bioch.*) **141**, 488 (1961).
21. W. T. Jenkins, S. Orlowski and I. W. Sizer; *J. Biol. Chem.* **234**, 2657 (1959).
22. W. T. Jenkins and I. W. Sizer; *J. Biol. Chem.* **234**, 1179 (1959).

23. P. FASELLA and G. G. HAMMES. To be published.
24. P. FASELLA; Unpublished results.
25. B. E. C. BANKS, A. A. DIAMANTES, C. A. VERNON; *J. Chem. Soc.* 4235 (1961).
26. P. FASELLA, G. G. HAMMES and B. VALLEE; *Biochim. et Biophys. Acta* **65**, 142 (1962).
27. M. EIGEN and G. G. HAMMES; *Advances in Enzymol.* In press.
28. M. EIGEN, G. G. HAMMES, R. LEGARE and R. LUMRY. In preparation.
29. G. G. HAMMES and J. J. BURKE. In preparation.

## SUMMARY

The mechanism of enzymatic transamination has been investigated using purified glutamic–aspartic transaminase as a particular example. Both the kinetic and equilibrium properties of the enzyme–substrate systems were investigated at high enzyme concentrations ( $> 10^{-5}$ M). The kinetic studies were carried out over a time range from 5 $\mu$sec to 1 sec. At pH 8.0, the minimal mechanism consistent with all of the data is as follows

$$E_L + As = X_1 = X_2 = E_M + Oa$$
$$E_M + Kg = Y_2 = Y_1 = E_L + Gm$$

Here $E_L$ is the aldehydic form of the enzyme, $E_M$ is the aminic form, As is aspartate, Oa is oxalacetate, Kg is ketoglutarate, Gm is glutamate, and the X's and Y's are reaction intermediates. All of the rate constants or lower bounds thereof were obtained; the second-order rate constants are all about $10^7$ $M^{-1}sec^{-1}$, while the rate constants for the interconversion of intermediates lie between 10–100 $sec^{-1}$. The enzymes–substrate binding constants are about $10^3$–$10^4$ $M^{-1}$ for the amino acids and about $10^5$ $M^{-1}$ for the keto acids. Spectral properties of the intermediates were measured and are consistent with their being Schiff bases.

A study of the interaction of hydroxylamine with the enzyme revealed that the equilibrium constant for Schiff base formation is more favorable for the combination of hydroxylamine with the enzyme at low pH's, although the enzyme is catalytically inactive at these same pH's. This suggests that a basic form of the enzyme is necessary for the catalytic interconversion of intermediates, but not for Schiff base formation. In addition, the kinetic constants of the protolytic reaction were determined and indicated that the non-protonated site interacts strongly with its immediate environment.

A quantitative study of the interaction of keto acids with the pyridoxal form of the enzyme indicated that the rate constant characterizing the formation of $E_L$KA and $E_L$KAH$^+$ complexes (KA designates the keto acid) is essentially diffusion controlled ($> 5 \times 10^8$ $M^{-1}sec^{-1}$). In the case of actual substrates, these pseudo enzyme–substrate complexes probably represent a process preceding Schiff base formation; therefore the mechanism above should be modified to include another intermediate between each Schiff base and the corresponding free enzyme and substrate. Possible roles of the protein molecule in the catalytic process are also discussed.

# KINETIC STUDIES OF GLUTAMIC–ASPARTIC TRANSAMINASE (PIG HEART MUSCLE)

by BARBARA E. C. BANKS, A. J. LAWRENCE, C. A. VERNON and J. F. WOOTTON

Chemistry Department, University College, London

## 1. KINETIC METHODS

AQUEOUS solutions of oxaloacetic acid absorb relatively strongly in the ultraviolet ($\epsilon$, 550; $\lambda$, 2800 Å) due to the presence of the enolic form (16 per cent, 25°).[1] This is the basis of the most convenient and commonly used analytical method for following the enzyme-catalysed reaction between L-aspartic (A) and $\alpha$-oxoglutaric acids (K) (Eq. I)

$$\mathrm{A} + \mathrm{K} \underset{}{\overset{v_t}{\rightleftharpoons}} \mathrm{G} + \begin{array}{c}\mathrm{COOH}\\ |\\ \mathrm{CH_2}\\ |\\ \mathrm{CO}\\ |\\ \mathrm{COOH}\end{array} \underset{k_1}{\overset{k_{-1}}{\rightleftharpoons}} \begin{array}{c}\mathrm{COOH}\\ |\\ \mathrm{CH}\\ \|\\ \mathrm{COH}\\ |\\ \mathrm{COOH}\end{array} \qquad \text{(I)}$$

$v_t$ is the overall velocity of formation of products (mole l.$^{-1}$ sec$^{-1}$) at time $t$, and $k_{-1}$ and $k_1$ are first-order rate coefficients.

Typically, the initial rate of increase in optical density at some suitable wavelength, of a solution containing substrate, buffer and enzyme is measured using a photoelectric spectrophotometer, and is taken as a measure of the initial velocity ($v$) of the enzyme-catalysed reaction (direct method).

However, a recent study by one of us[1,2] of the keto–enol transformation in oxaloacetic acid showed that under a variety of commonly used experimental conditions, the rate of enolization is relatively slow. This suggested that if the overall reaction is correctly represented by Eq. (I), i.e. if the enol form of oxaloacetic acid is not a substrate for the enzyme, then measurements of $v$ obtained by the direct spectrophotometric method might be in error by an amount depending on the extent to which the enolization step is rate-limiting. We have investigated this point using a homogeneous preparation of glutamic–aspartic transaminase from pig cardiac muscle and have shown that: (*a*) oxaloacetic acid is produced in the keto form by the enzymic reaction; (*b*) low values of $v$ are obtained by using low buffer concentrations or by using buffers which are not effective catalysts for the enolization reaction (e.g. barbiturate, pyrophosphate); and (*c*) many of the kinetic results reported for this enzymic reaction are seriously in error.

The analytical method introduced by Greenwood and Greenbaum[3] depends, like the direct spectrophotometric method, on the enolization of oxaloacetic acid, but the possibility that this process may be rate-limiting is avoided. Essentially the procedure consists of stopping the enzymic reaction in successive aliquots of reaction mixture by the addition of strong acid. The amounts of oxaloacetic acid present in the aliquots are then determined spectrophotometrically under conditions where equilibrium between the keto and enol forms has been reached. The method is inconvenient and unsuitable for routine work but gives, unambiguously, the true value of $v_{(t)}$ at any time. Figure 1 shows typical results obtained using a modification of the originally described method. It was found that curves representing

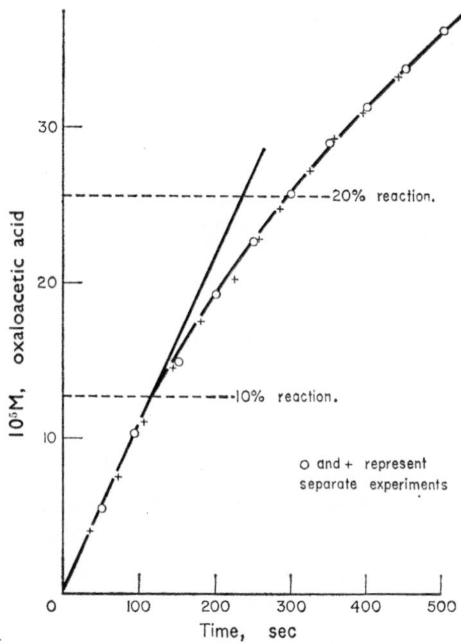


FIG. 1. Aliquot method (0.01 M asp. 0.0025 M $\alpha$-oxoglutaric, 0.1 M phosphate, pH 7.38, 25°C).

the time course of the reaction for given substrate concentrations could always be superimposed (by adjusting the time scale) irrespective of temperature, of the concentration of the enzyme or of the concentration and nature of the buffer. The initial velocity ($v$) can be found easily since velocity is sensibly independent of time over at least the first 10 per cent of the reaction. The error is *ca.* ±5 per cent, but increases markedly as the time for 10 per cent reaction falls below 2 min.

The sum of the first-order rate coefficients ($k_T = k_1 + k_{-1}$) describing the keto–enol tautomerism of oxaloacetic acid in any given medium can be found from spectrophotometric measurements of the decrease in optical density with time of a solution of the enol form in that medium. The individual coefficients can then be calculated using the known equilibrium constant.[1,2] Values of $k_T$ obtained under a variety of the buffer conditions used for the enzymic reaction are given in Table 1. Aspartic acid has a small catalytic effect: the quoted values refer, therefore, to solutions containing this substance (0.01 M). The enzyme has no catalytic effect except in large concentration.

TABLE 1

| Buffer | Conc (M) | pH | $10^2\, k_T$ (sec$^{-1}$) |
|---|---|---|---|
| Phosphate ($Na_2HPO_4/KH_2PO_4$) | 0.02 | 7.38 | 0.6 (0.09)[a] |
| | 0.05 | 7.38 | 1.8 |
| | 0.10 | 7.38 | 4.2 (0.54)[a] |
| | 0.10 | 7.90 | 2.5 |
| Pyrophosphate (Na salt/HCl) | 0.10 | 7.38 | 1.27 |
| β-glycerophosphate (Na salt/HCl) | 0.10 | 7.38 | 1.94 |
| Triethanolamine (hydrochloride/NaOH) | 0.02 | 7.38 | 3.4 |
| | 0.04 | 7.38 | 4.6 |
| | 0.06 | 7.38 | 6.1 |
| Imidazole (base/HCl) | 0.10 | 6.6 | 10.0 |
| | 0.10 | 7.38 | 10.0 |
| | 0.10 | 8.0 | 9.5 |
| Barbiturate (Na salt) | 0.10 | 8.0 | 0.7 |
| Arsenate (Na salt/HCl) | 0.04 | 7.4 | 2.4 |

[a]25° except a (0°)

From each set of values of $v_{(t)}$, $k_1$ and $k_{-1}$ measured as described, it is possible to calculate the optical density–time relationship to be expected from the first spectrophotometric method. Let $x_e$ and $x_k$ be the amounts of the enol and keto forms of oxaloacetic acid present at time $t$. Then:

$$\frac{dx_e}{dt} + \frac{dx_k}{dt} = v_{(t)} \tag{1}$$

$$x_e + x_k = \int_0^t v_t \, dt \tag{2}$$

$$\frac{dx_e}{dt} = k_{-1}x_k - k_1 x_e \tag{3}$$

Hence

$$\frac{dx_e}{dt} + k_T x_e = k_{-1} \int_0^t v_t \, dt \tag{4}$$

Let

$$x_e = y \exp(-k_T t)$$

Then

$$\frac{dx_e}{dt} = \exp(-k_T t)\frac{dy}{dt} - k_T y \exp(-k_T t)$$

and

$$\frac{dy}{dt} = \exp(k_T t) k_{-1} \int_0^t v_t dt$$

By substitution and integrati on

$$x_e = \exp(-k_T t) k_1 \int_0^t \exp(k_T t) \int_0^t v_t \, dt . dt \quad (5)$$

From the time course of the reaction as determined by the aliquot method, the value of the function

$$\int_0^t v_t \, dt$$

can be found at successive times by using Eq. (2). The values of the function

$$\int_0^t \exp(k_T t) \int_0^t v_t \, dt . dt$$

can then be found by numerical integration. For comparison purposes it is convenient to plot $x_T$ against time where $x_T$ is given by

$$x_T = x_e \left(\frac{k_T}{k_{-1}}\right) = x_e(K_e + 1)$$

where $K_e$ is the equilibrium constant for the keto–enol transformation and $x_T$ gives the total amount of oxaloacetic acid if, and only if, the keto and enol forms are at equilibrium. Comparison of the values of $x_T$ obtained in this way and those obtained from the aliquot method indicates for any given conditions the extent to which this assumption is justified.

Figure 2 shows the results obtained under conditions deliberately chosen to be extreme. It can be seen that (*a*) the direct method does not give the true velocity of the enzymic reaction, and (*b*) the agreement between the observed and calculated points proves conclusively that the keto form of oxaloacetic acid is the true substrate for the enzyme.

Since, however, the direct method has the advantage of convenience it is important to discover under what conditions it may be used. If only the first 10 per cent of the enzymic reaction is considered, then Eq. (4) becomes

$$\frac{dx_e}{dt} + k_T x_e = k_{-1} v . t$$

and by integration

$$x_e = v \frac{k_{-1}}{k_T^2} \{k_T t + \exp(-k_T t) - 1\}$$

whence,

$$\left(\frac{k_1 + k_{-1}}{k_{-1}}\right) \frac{dx_e}{dt} \bigg/ v = \{1 - \exp(-k_T t)\} \tag{6}$$

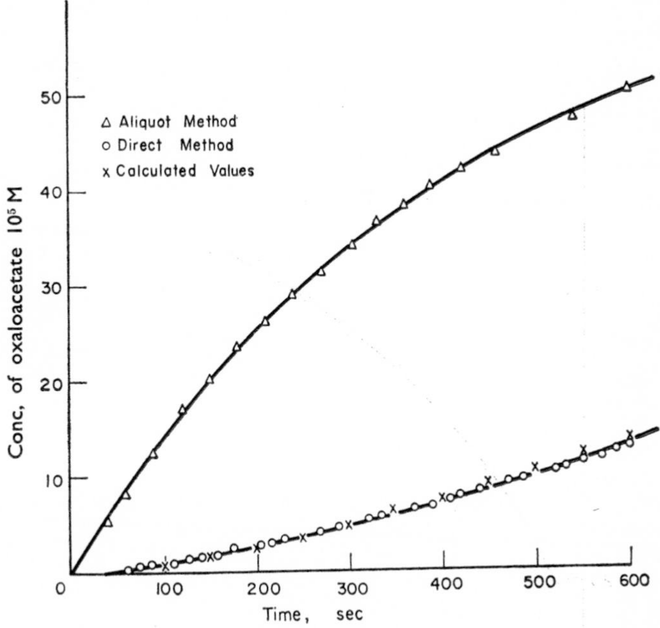


FIG. 2. (0.01 M asp., 0.0025 M α-KG, 0.02 M phosphate buffer pH 7.38. $T = 1.5°C$, $k_1 + k_{-1} = 0.0009\ \text{sec}^{-1}$.)

Clearly the direct method measures $v$ correctly only as $\exp(-k_T t)$ approaches zero. Table 2 shows the time required under different conditions for the measured velocity to be within 5 per cent of the true velocity. It can be seen that barbiturate buffer and phosphate buffer at low concentrations are

TABLE 2

| Buffer | $t$ (sec) |
|---|---|
| Phosphate 0.1 M, pH 7.38 25°C | 71 |
| Phosphate 0.05 M, pH 7.38 25°C | 167 |
| Phosphate 0.02 M, pH 7.38 25°C | 500 |
| Barbiturate 0.1 M, pH 8.0 25°C | 429 |
| Imidazole 0.1 M, pH 7.38 25°C | 30 |

unsuitable and will lead to erroneous results. In imidazole buffer (0.1 M) the direct method gives the true value of $v$ provided that 10 per cent reaction does not occur in less than about 2 min. We have checked the correctness of this by comparison with results obtained using the malic dehydrogenase method.

Exactly the same objections apply to the use of the direct method for following the reverse reaction (i.e. starting with L-glutamic acid and oxalo-acetic acid). A detailed analysis of this will be given elsewhere.

Effects have been reported for the glutamic–aspartic transaminase reaction which are spurious and originate from a failure to use the direct method correctly. Figure 3 illustrates an apparent buffer catalysis of the reaction.

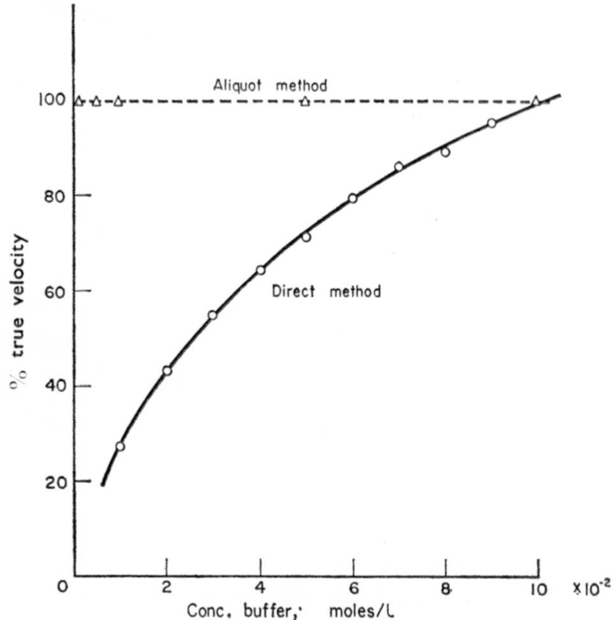


FIG. 3. Apparent buffer catalysis of transamination. (Phosphate pH 7.38, 25°C, 0.01 M asp., 0.0025 M $\alpha$-KG.)

As the buffer concentration is lowered the enolization of oxaloacetic acid becomes progressively slower and the error in the estimation of the velocity of enzymic reaction becomes progressively larger. Measurements using the aliquot method show that there is no catalysis of the enzymic reaction by phosphate buffer. This result has been confirmed with other buffer systems.

Errors can also arise even at high buffer concentrations if the time for 10 per cent reaction becomes short, i.e. at high enzyme concentrations. Under these circumstances the direct method measures the true enzyme velocity only when this is considerably less than the initial rate. The effect is to give an apparent non-linear dependence of rate on enzyme concentration

Figure 4 shows that this effect can be correctly predicted from the equations already given.

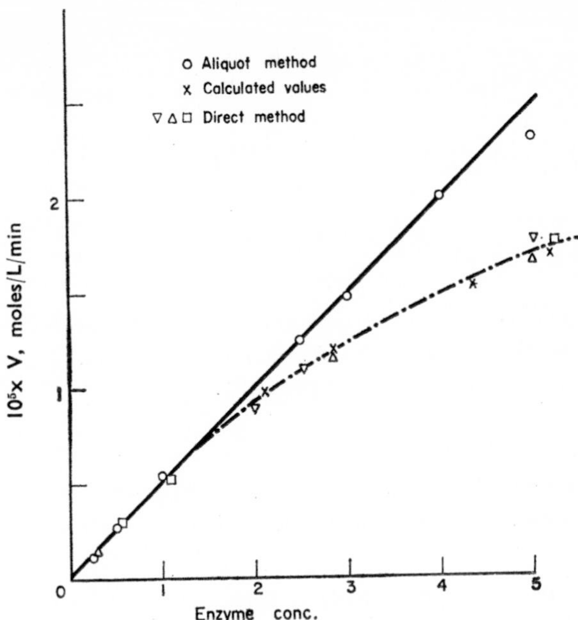


FIG. 4. Experimental and theoretical calibration curves (0.1 M phosphate buffer, pH 7.38, 25°C.)

## 2. STEADY STATE KINETICS

Two models for the interpretation of steady state kinetics suggest themselves.

### A. *The Binary Mechanism*

This supposes that the enzyme undergoes interconversion between the pyridoxal and pyridoxamine forms in a cyclic process, and is analogous to the mechanism proposed for the non-enzymic model systems.[4,5] The annexed scheme shows the intermediates involved and gives the appropriate steady state equations for the initial velocity.

$$E + A_1 \underset{k_2}{\overset{k_1}{\rightleftharpoons}} EA_1 \underset{k_4}{\overset{k_3}{\rightleftharpoons}} E'K_1 \underset{k_6}{\overset{k_5}{\rightleftharpoons}} E' + K_1$$

$$E' + K_2 \underset{k_8}{\overset{k_7}{\rightleftharpoons}} E'K_2 \underset{k_{10}}{\overset{k_9}{\rightleftharpoons}} EA_2 \underset{k_{12}}{\overset{k_{11}}{\rightleftharpoons}} E + A_2$$

Initial rate

$$\frac{1}{v} = \frac{1}{V_M[\mathrm{E}]}\left\{1 + \frac{K_{\mathrm{A}_1}}{[\mathrm{A}_1]} + \frac{K_{\mathrm{K}_2}}{[\mathrm{K}_2]}\right\} \tag{7}$$

$$V_M = \frac{k_3k_5k_9k_{11}}{k_9k_{11}(k_3 + k_4 + k_5) + k_3k_5(k_9 + k_{10} + k_{11})}$$

$$K_{\mathrm{A}_1} = V_M\left(\frac{k_2k_4 + k_2k_5 + k_3k_5}{k_1k_3k_5}\right)$$

$$K_{\mathrm{K}_2} = V_M\left(\frac{k_8k_{10} + k_8k_{11} + k_9k_{11}}{k_7k_9k_{11}}\right)$$

E and E′ are the pyridoxal and pyridoxamine forms of the enzyme respectively. $A_1$ and $A_2$ are aspartic and glutamic acids respectively. $K_1$ and $K_2$ are oxaloacetic and-oxoglutaric acids respectively.

## B. *The Ternary Mechanism*

This supposes that both substrates must combine with the enzyme before reaction can occur. The annexed scheme shows the intermediates involved.

$$\mathrm{E} + \mathrm{P} \underset{k_2}{\overset{k_1}{\rightleftharpoons}} \mathrm{EP} + \mathrm{Q} \underset{k_4}{\overset{k_3}{\rightleftharpoons}} \mathrm{EPQ} \underset{k_6}{\overset{k_5}{\rightleftharpoons}} \mathrm{ERS} \underset{k_8}{\overset{k_7}{\rightleftharpoons}} \mathrm{ES} + \mathrm{R} \underset{k_{10}}{\overset{k_9}{\rightleftharpoons}} \mathrm{E} + \mathrm{S}$$

Initial rate

$$\frac{1}{v} = \frac{1}{V_M[\mathrm{E}]}\left(1 + \frac{K_{\mathrm{P}}}{[\mathrm{P}]} + \frac{K_{\mathrm{Q}}}{[\mathrm{Q}]} + \frac{K_{\mathrm{PQ}}}{[\mathrm{P}][\mathrm{Q}]}\right) \tag{8}$$

$$V_M = \frac{k_5k_7k_9}{k_9(k_5 + k_6) + k_7(k_5 + k_9)}$$

$$K_{\mathrm{P}} = V_M\left(\frac{V_M}{k_1}\right)$$

$$K_{\mathrm{Q}} = V_M\left(\frac{k_7(k_4 + k_5) + k_4k_6}{k_3k_5k_7}\right)$$

$$K_{\mathrm{PQ}} = V_MK_Q\left(\frac{k_2}{k_1}\right)$$

P and Q, and R and S, are appropriate substrate pairs.

Both mechanisms predict a linear relationship between the reciprocals of the initial velocity and the independently varied concentration of each substrate. A ternary mechanism involving random addition of the substrates does not lead to such linear relationships.

Distinction between the two mechanisms is made as follows: if for the two substrates P and Q, $1/v$ is plotted against $1/[P]$ for a series of fixed concentrations of Q, the resulting straight line will be parallel when and only when $K_{PQ} = 0$, i.e. when the binary mechanism is operative. Figures 5 and 6 show the results obtained at different pH values by varying the concentration

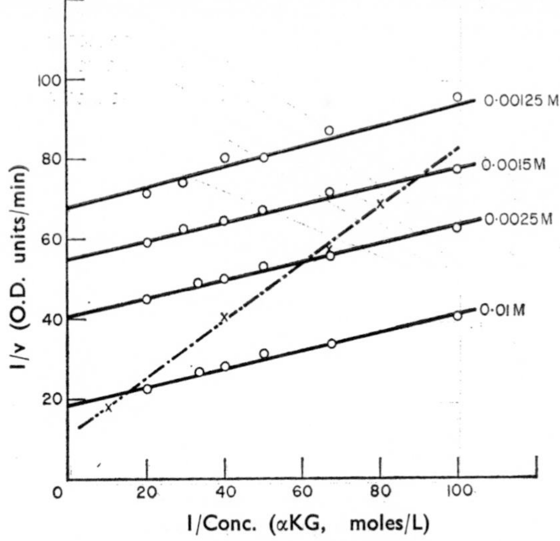


FIG. 5. Forward reaction (0.1 M imidazole/Cl$^-$, 8.0, 25°C.)

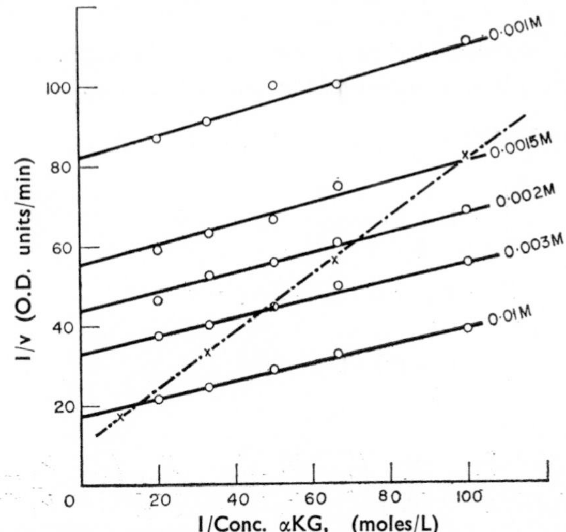


FIG. 6. Forward reaction. (0.1 M imidazole/Cl$^-$, pH 7.1, 25°C.)

of α-oxoglutaric acid at a series of fixed concentrations of aspartic acid. These results do not, of course, exclude the ternary mechanism. However, they show that the kinetic behaviour under the conditions studied can be adequately represented by equations derived from the binary mechanism and that the constant $K_{PQ}$, even if it has physical significance, must be very small.

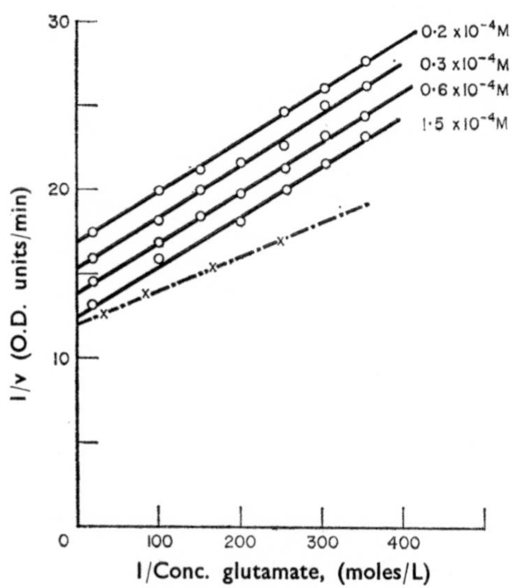


FIG. 7. Reverse reaction (0.1 M imidazole/Cl⁻, pH 7.8, 25°C.)

Competitive inhibition by an inhibitor I can be expressed, in terms of the binary mechanism, as shown in the annexed scheme.

$$\mathrm{E}\left[\begin{array}{l} + \mathrm{A}_1 \rightleftharpoons \mathrm{EA}_1 \rightleftharpoons \mathrm{E'K}_1 \rightleftharpoons \mathrm{E'} + \mathrm{K}_1 \\ \quad k_1 \\ + \mathrm{I} \rightleftharpoons \mathrm{EI} \\ \quad k_2 \end{array}\right.$$

$$\mathrm{E'}\left[\begin{array}{l} + \mathrm{K}_2 \rightleftharpoons \mathrm{E'K}_2 \rightleftharpoons \mathrm{EA}_2 \rightleftharpoons \mathrm{E} + \mathrm{A}_2 \\ \quad k_3 \\ + \mathrm{I} \rightleftharpoons \mathrm{E'I} \\ \quad k_4 \end{array}\right.$$

$$\frac{1}{v} = \frac{1}{V_M[\mathrm{E}]}\left[1 + \frac{K_{\mathrm{A}_1}}{[\mathrm{A}_1]}\left(1 + \frac{k_1}{k_2}[\mathrm{I}]\right) + \frac{K_{\mathrm{K}_2}}{[\mathrm{K}_2]}\left(1 + \frac{k_3}{k_4}[\mathrm{I}]\right)\right] \tag{9}$$

The ratios $k_1/k_2$ and $k_3/k_4$ are the inhibitor constants describing the combinations of the inhibitor with the pyridoxal and pyridoxamine forms of the enzyme respectively. The values can clearly be found by determining the apparent Michaelis parameters, i.e. $K_{A_1}$ and $K_{K_2}$ of the equation describing the binary mechanism, for each pair of substrates in the presence and absence of the inhibitor. Typical results for the inhibitor glutaric acid are shown in Figs. 8 and 9. Analysis leads to the kinetic parameters shown in Table 3 (pH, 6.9, imidazole buffer, $\mu$0.05, 25°).

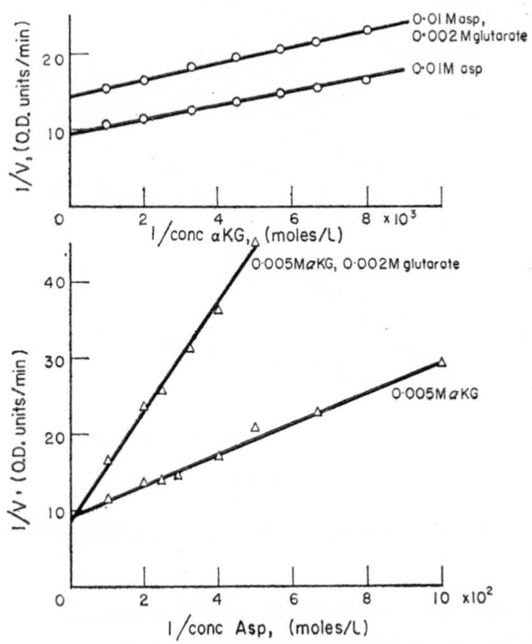


FIG. 8. Glutarate inhibition (forward reaction). (0.1 M imidazole/Cl$^-$, pH 6.9, 25°C.)

TABLE 3

| Substrate | Michaelis parameters ($10^{3-1}$ M) | Inhibitor parameters($10^{-3}$ M$^{-1}$) |
|---|---|---|
| Aspartate | 2.78 | 1.22 |
| Glutamate | 4.05 | 1.47 |
| α-Oxoglutarate | 0.13 | 0.05 |
| Oxaloacetate | 0.013 | 0.00 |

The results show that glutaric acid combines with the pyridoxal form of the enzyme, but not appreciably with the pyridoxamine form. This conclusion, the mechanistic significance of which will be discussed elsewhere, is at variance with the recent findings of Velick and Vavra[6].

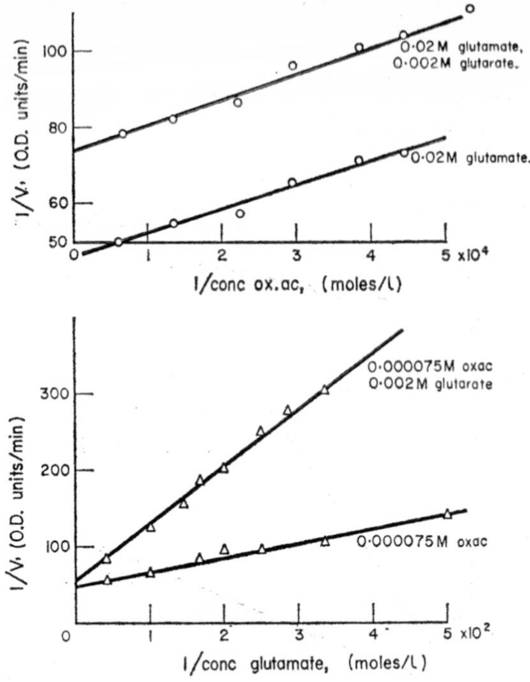


FIG. 9. Glutarate inhibition (reverse reaction). (0.1 M imidazole/$Cl^-$, pH 6.9, 25°C.)

Consistent results were obtained by studying substrate inhibition. If, in the binary mechanism, a substrate $\alpha$ competes with a substrate A then the appropriate steady state equation can be shown to be

$$\frac{1}{v} = \frac{1}{V_M}\left\{1 + \frac{K_\alpha}{[\alpha]} + \frac{K_A}{[A]}(1 + K'_\alpha[\alpha])\right\} \tag{10}$$

where $K_\alpha$, $K_A$ and $K'_\alpha$ are functions of rate coefficients. If [A] is kept constant and $[\alpha]$ is varied, the relationship between $1/v$ and $1/[\alpha]$ will be linear where the inhibition is unimportant and will depart from linearity as the inhibition becomes appreciable. The results in Fig. 10 show that whereas $\alpha$-oxoglutarate is an inhibitor (i.e. combines with the pyridoxal form of the enzyme), aspartate is not (i.e. does not combine with the pyridoxamine form of the enzyme). In Fig. 11 the data are plotted differently and it can be seen that, as required by the equation, $1/v$ is proportional to $[\alpha]$ in the region where inhibition is important.

One of the difficulties of kinetic work with glutamic–aspartic transaminase is that the reaction is sensitive to changes in ionic strength. This is illustrated

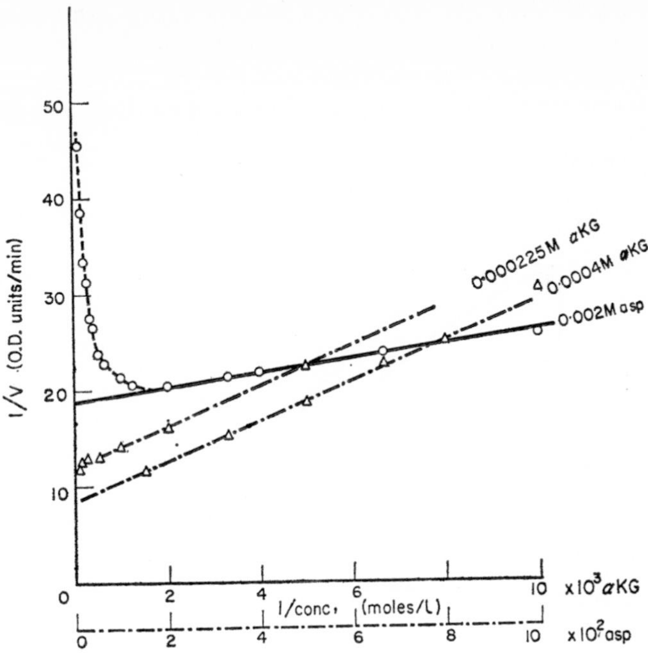


FIG. 10. Substrate inhibition. (0.1 M imidazole/Cl⁻, pH 6.9, 25°C.)

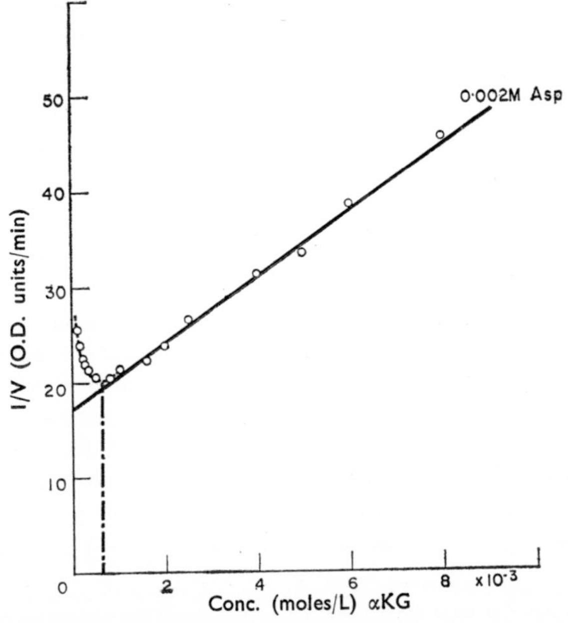


FIG. 11. Substrate inhibition. (0.1 M imidazole/Cl⁻, pH 6.9, 25°C.)

$$\frac{1}{v}=\frac{1}{V_M}\left\{1+\frac{K_a}{[a]}+\frac{K_A}{[A]}(1+K'_a[a])\right\}$$

in Figs. 12 and 13, where it is shown that increasing salt concentration depresses the rate.* The effect is mainly on the so-called Michaelis parameters and is greater for that associated with the keto acids. Kinetic experiments in which concentrations or pH are varied must, therefore, be carried

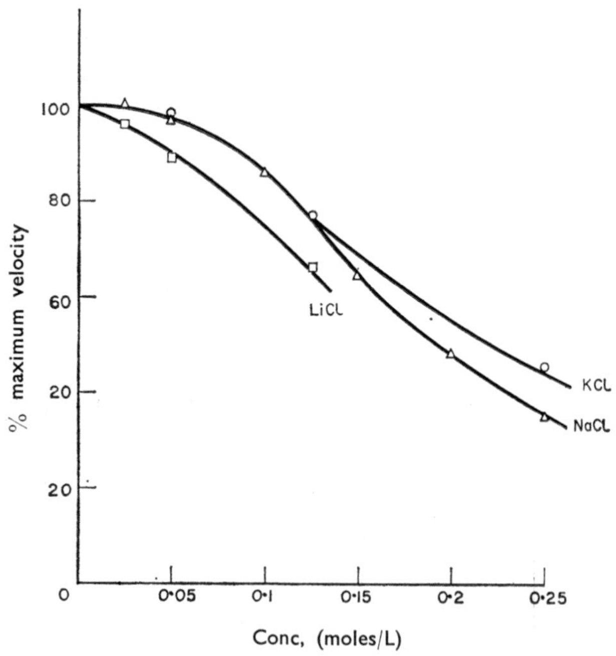


FIG. 12. Effects of cations on transamination rate. (0.1 M imidazole/$Cl^-$, pH 8.0, 25°C, 0.01 M asp. 0.0025 M α-KG.)

out at constant ionic strength if spurious results are to be avoided. Figure 14 shows how the kinetic parameters calculated on the basis of the binary mechanism vary with pH. The data refer to media of constant ionic strength and indicate that $V_{max}$ and the Michaelis parameter for α-oxoglutarate vary only slightly over the range pH 6–8. The variation in the Michaelis parameter for aspartate is difficult to interpret because this parameter includes the constant describing the binding of α-oxoglutarate with the pyridoxal form of the enzyme (see Eq. 10). This constant is approximately $2 \times 10^2$ $M^{-1}$ at pH 7 but appears to increase as the pH is lowered. This may account for the variation of $K_{asp}$ with pH shown in Fig. 14 and is being further investigated.

*The large effect produced by the perchlorate ion is not understood and is being further investigated. It does not arise from metal impurities, since the sodium perchlorate used was repeatedly recrystallized from solutions containing EDTA.

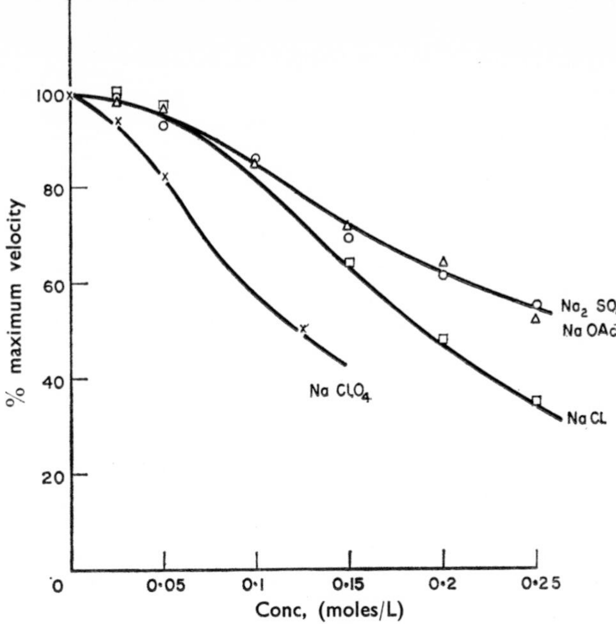


FIG. 13. Effect of salts on transamination rate. (0.1 M imidazole/$Cl^-$ asp., 0.0025 M α-KG.)

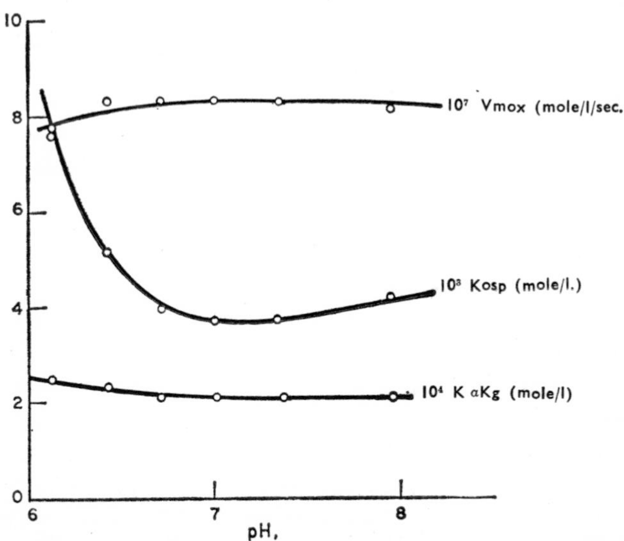


FIG. 14. Forward reaction. (0.1 M imidazole/$Cl^-$[NaCl], $\mu = 0.09$, 25°C.)

The effect of using glutamic acid in which the hydrogen at the $C_1$-position is replaced by deuterium is to reduce the overall rate of the transamination reaction. If it is assumed that a tautomeric shift of the type :

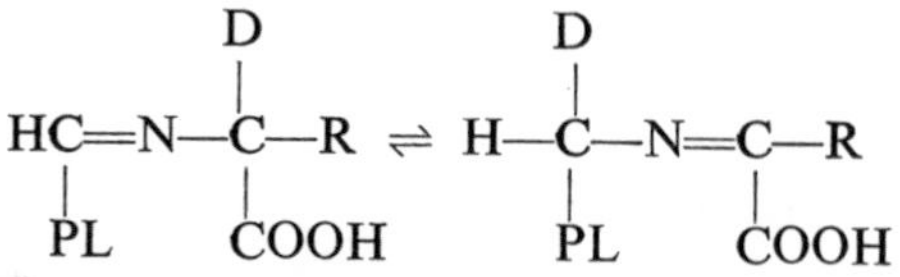

$$\mathrm{HC{=}N{-}C(D)(COOH){-}R \;(\text{HC bearing PL}) \rightleftharpoons H{-}C(D)(PL){-}N{=}C(COOH){-}R}$$

occurs in the transamination reaction (as required by the binary mechanism and by the study of model systems) it can be shown that the value of $K_K/V_{max}$ should remain unchanged, whereas the value of $K_A/V_{max}$ should show an isotope effect. This has been found to be the case. A full analysis will be presented elsewhere.

## 3. THE COMBINATION OF APOENZYME AND COFACTORS

The apoenzyme has been purified to a high degree.[7] Preparations have been obtained which appear homogeneous to free-flow electrophoresis, ultracentrifugation and starch gel ionophoresis. Using such preparations a kinetic study of the combination of the apoenzyme and its cofactors has been made.

The technique employed involves incubation of apoenzyme and coenzyme mixtures at 0°C under various conditions, removal of aliquots at intervals during the activation and estimation of the concentration of active holoenzyme. This is accomplished by spectrophotometric determination of the rate of formation of oxaloacetate in the transamination reaction between aspartate and α-oxoglutarate in 0.1 M phosphate buffer, pH 7.38, 25°C. By choosing appropriate concentrations of enzyme and coenzyme, it is possible to follow the time course of activation at 0° in detail under a variety of conditions.

This study is still in progress. However, several useful relationships have been ascertained. The initial rate of activation is directly proportional to both coenzyme and apoenzyme concentrations and, therefore, is first-order with respect to each. This is demonstrated by the constant values of the apparent second-order rate constant with ten-fold changes in either apoenzyme or coenzyme concentration.

The initial rate is inhibited by phosphate buffer. The degree of inhibition at any pH is proportional to total phosphate concentration. Furthermore, when the results at several pH's and phosphate concentrations are compared, the inhibition can be demonstrated to depend principally on phosphate monoanion concentration. This is consistent with competition between coenzyme and phosphate monoanion. It offers supporting evidence for the conclusion of Meister *et al.* that the phosphate moiety of the coenzyme, presumably with one negative charge, is the primary group involved in binding to the protein.

Evidence against the postulate that pyridoxal phosphate is attached to the protein through the carbonyl group as a substituted aldimine (at least at physiological pH's where the enzyme is active) comes from studies of the effect of added pyridoxal upon the rate of activation with pyridoxal phosphate. If such a linkage were essential in the attachment of this form of the coenzyme to the protein, or were responsible for the greater rate of activation with pyridoxal phosphate, addition of pyridoxal, which contains the carbonyl moiety but not the phosphate group, should retard activation due to competition for the binding site. However, the rates of activation in the presence and absence of a ten-fold excess of pyridoxal were found to be identical throughout the time course of the reaction.

For detailed study of the time course of activation, the kinetics were simplified by the isolation method of employing a large excess of coenzyme. From the first-order dependence of the initial rate on apoenzyme concentration, it was expected that this would result in pseudo first-order kinetics. However, this did not prove to be the case. Apparent first-order rate constants calculated either by the differential method or by the method of integration decreased dramatically with time under all conditions, indicating that the reaction is complex. Studies at present are being directed toward testing the possible reasons for these kinetic complexities.

Possibilities which have been ruled out are : (1) an approach to equilibrium and a contribution from the reverse reaction ($K_{eq} > 1 \times 10^8$ l.mole$^{-1}$); (2) denaturation of either apoenzyme or holoenzyme; and (3) a decrease in coenzyme concentration due to decomposition or secondary binding on the protein.

The findings are consistent with the following general reaction type :

$$\text{Apoenzyme} + \text{Coenzyme} \xrightarrow{k_1} \text{B} \xrightarrow{k_2} \text{C}$$

where C is fully active holoenzyme and B is a partially active intermediate with a specific activity coefficient of $\alpha$ (relative to the specific activity coefficient of C taken as 1.0). Thus the enzymic activity ($A_t$) at any time is proportional to $\alpha C_B + C_C$, where $C_B$ and $C_C$ are the concentrations of C and B respectively.

Mathematical analysis results in the following rate expression :

$$\frac{A_t}{A_\infty} = (\alpha - 1)\frac{k_1}{k_2 - k_1}\{\exp(-k_1 t) - \exp(-k_2 t)\} + \{1 - \exp(-k_1 t)\} \quad (1)$$

where $A_\infty$ is the final level of enzymic activity.

It can also be demonstrated that:

$$ak_1 = \left(\frac{dA_t}{dt}\right)_{t=0} \tag{2}$$

and

$$k_2 = \left(\frac{dA_t}{dt}\right)_{t=\infty} \tag{3}$$

which are the initial and late slopes, respectively, of a plot of $A_t$ versus time ($t$) divided by $A_\infty - A_t$. Furthermore

$$(k_1 - ak_1)(k_2 - ak_1) = \left(\frac{d^2A_t}{dt^2}\right)_{t=0} \tag{4}$$

or the initial slope of a plot of $dA_t/dt$ versus $t$.

From Eqs. (2), (3) and (4) one can determine $k_1$, $k_2$ and $a$ and calculate a theoretical curve of $A_t/A_\infty$ versus $t$ from Eq. (1). This can then be compared with the experimental curve to determine whether or not the proposed mechanism is consistent with the data. Results so far obtained show good agreement with the theoretical curve.

While this does not constitute proof that this kinetic scheme is correct, the proposed mechanism does appear to be consistent with the data.

Studies presently underway are directed toward further testing of this and alternative mechanisms and toward the identification of ionizing groups, either on the protein or the coenzyme, which may be involved in binding.

## REFERENCES


1. B. E. C. BANKS; *J. Chem. Soc.* 5043 (1961).
2. B. E. C. BANKS; *J. Chem. Soc.* 63 (1962).
3. GREENWOOD and GREENBAUM; *Biochim. et Biophys. Acta* **10**, 623 (1953).
4. METZLER, IKAWA and SNELL; *J. Am. Chem. Soc.* **76**, 648 (1954).
5. B. E. C. BANKS, DIAMANTIS and C. A. VERNON; *J. Chem. Soc.* 4235 (1961).
6. VAVRA and VELICK; *J. Biol. Chem.* **237**, 2109 (1962).
7. B. E. C. BANKS and C. A. VERNON; *J. Chem. Soc.* 1698 (1961).


## DISCUSSION

DR. FASELLA:

Some time last year we reported an activating effect of phosphate on glutamic-aspartic transaminase, which we found to be competitive for aspartate and oxaloacetic acid. I think we should now re-examine those findings in the light of what Dr. Vernon has just told us. In the course of kinetic work on transaminase we had also run into the effect of the enol–keto equilibrium of oxaloacetic acid. Though we did not study the phenomenon as thoroughly as Dr. Vernon did, we had derived an equation to establish the effects of this phenomenon on the direct method of determining initial velocities. The equation, though different in form, was obviously analogous to that presented by Dr. Vernon. As shown in the paper we have just heard, the enol–keto equilibration rate practically effects the determination of initial velocities only if, during the lag phase, transamination progresses to more than 10 per cent of the final equilibrium. In a first scanning of salt effect on transaminase we had indeed used excessively high enzyme concentration. In later work, by using low enzyme concentration ($\simeq 10^{-9}$ M enzyme) it was possible to carry out the assay so that even during a 500 sec lag phase the reaction proceeds to equilibrium only of a few per cent. It was under the latter conditions that the effect of phosphate was studied quantitatively on our enzyme preparation. I am grateful to Dr. Vernon for having let me read his manuscript and use his very accurate data to check once more the correctness of our assumptions.

We were particularly interested in his figure showing that in the presence of aspartate $2 \times 10^{-2}$ M no phosphate activation is observed with the correct aliquots method while a spurious activation effect is observed with the incorrectly used direct method. Under our experimental conditions (low enzyme concentration and exclusion of the lag phase) and at the above high concentrations of aspartate we got results corresponding to those obtained by Dr. Vernon with the correct aliquot method. We take this as further evidence that under our conditions the direct method had been correctly used. In conclusion, therefore, we still think that with our enzyme, phosphate may act as a competitive activator. Anyway we shall now proceed to check our results by Vernon's direct method. The difference respecting Dr. Vernon's enzyme might be due to the effect of acetone which we use during purification or to the fact that we prepare a different enzyme. The difference observed in the molecular weight (116,000 against his 85,000) would indeed support the latter explanation.

We were also interested in hearing of the inhibitory effects of high ionic strength on transaminase. In particular, we had observed that at high sodium chloride concentrations the optical dispersion curve of transaminase presents changes which, in the light of Dr. Vernon's kinetic findings, can be ascribed to the enzyme assuming a configuration unfavourable to enzyme activity.

DR. VERNON:

I should certainly hesitate to say that the results reported by Dr. Fasella and his colleagues were due, in part, to troubles with the analytical method. I am sure, however, that our particular preparation of glutamic–aspartic transaminase is not activated by phosphate ions. On the contrary, the activity of our preparation is reduced by any increase in ionic strength and, to a first approximation, this is independent of whether the ionic strength is increased by phosphate buffer or by sodium chloride. I am also sure that the direct method can give spurious results unless the enolization of oxaloacetic acid is effectively catalyzed.

However, as Dr. Fasella points out, there may be differences between his enzyme and ours, and this raises a number of very interesting questions. I should not want to place too much reliance on our provisional figure (85,000) for the molecular weight of our enzyme. I know that Dr. Banks is, at the moment, doing some careful measurements on this and we shall soon know if this apparently gross difference between Dr. Fasella's enzyme and ours really exists. If it does then I think we should get together with Dr. Fasella's group and find out exactly what the differences are and how they arise.

# PURIFICATION AND PROPERTIES OF THE β-ASPARTIC DECARBOXYLASE OF *DESULFOVIBRIO DESULFURICANS*

by Jeanne Cattanéo and Jacques C. Senez

Laboratoire de Chimie Bactérienne du CNRS,
Marseille (9), France

## INTRODUCTION

Most strains of non-sporulating, vibrion-like sulfate-reducing bacteria (*Desulfovibrio*) have a very restricted amino acid metabolism. They all possess transaminases and cysteine desulfhydrase activities[11,13] but are devoid of usual amino acid dehydrogenases and decarboxylases. Some years ago, however, it was found in this laboratory that the strain El Agheila Z isolated by Adams *et al.*[1] is unique amongst all the tested strains of *Desulfovibrio* in possessing besides transaminases an α-glutamic and a β-aspartic decarboxylase.[12] The last enzyme, converting L-aspartate into L-α-alanine, and first demonstrated by Meister *et al.*[8] in another strict anaerobe (*Clostridium welchii*), has the remarkable property of being inhibited by several inorganic salts and reactivated by catalytic amounts of pyridoxal phosphate and/or α-keto acids.

The purification of the β-aspartic decarboxylase of *D. desulfuricans* has been undertaken in order to get further information on the constitution of the enzyme and on the mechanism of its inactivation and reactivation.

## MATERIAL AND METHODS

### 1. *Organism*

The organism studied (*Desulfovibrio desulfuricans*, El Agheila Z, NCIB 8380) is a halophilic strain whose morphological and physiological characters have been described elsewhere.[1] The bacteria were grown anaerobically at +32°C in a culture medium of the following composition: $NH_4Cl$, 2 g; $MgSO_4.7H_2O$, 4 g; $Na_2SO_4$, 2 g; $K_2HPO_4$, 1 g; sodium lactate, 20 g; Difco yeast extract, 5 g; $CaCl_2.2H_2O$, 0.05 g; NaCl, 20 g; distilled water, 1 l.; pH adjusted to 6.5.

### 2. *Extraction and Purification*

The cells were harvested by centrifugation from a 40-l. culture in the stationary phase of growth, washed, resuspended in distilled water and sonically disrupted (Raytheon, 500 kc, 15 min). Cellular debris was discarded by centrifugation (30,000 rev/min, 60 min) and the supernatant, containing about 12 mg of total protein per ml and a high amount of nucleoprotein (*ca.* 17 per cent), was collected. Most nucleic acid contaminants were precipitated by addition of streptomycin sulfate (4 mg/ml) and eliminated by low-speed centrifugation (3000 rev/min, 10 min). The supernatant was dialyzed against distilled water for 1 hr and then a considerable amount of inactive proteins was precipitated by acidification to pH 5.0 with 0.1 M acetate buffer.

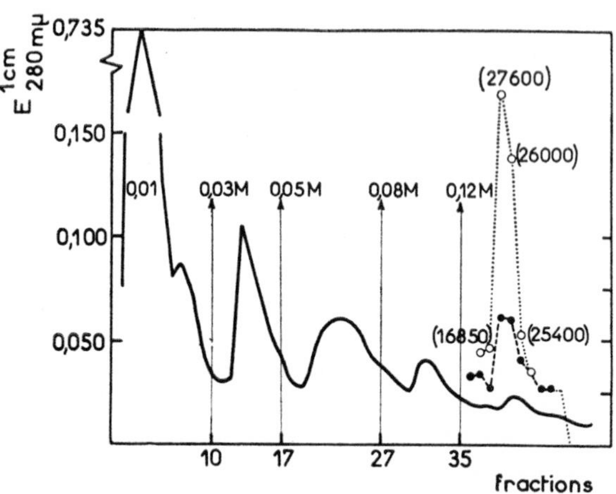


FIG. 1. Elution diagram of a CM-cellulose column loaded with 40 mg of total protein. Flow rate 70 ml/hr at 0°C. Effluent collected in 10-ml fractions. Discontinuous elution by 0.01 M phosphate buffer (pH 6.4) with increasing concentrations of NaCl (0.01 to 0.12 M) as indicated on the diagram. Solid line: optical density at 280 mμ. Dotted line: specific activity ($Q_{CO_2}$).

By conventional precipitation with ammonium sulfate two fractions were separated, the first one (0–0.6 S) containing the α-glutamic decarboxylase and the second (0.6–0.8 S) containing both transaminases and β-aspartic decarboxylase. This last precipitate was redissolved and dialyzed against distilled water.

In a previous procedure, subsequent purification was obtained by column chromatography on brushite gel.[4] More recently, however, chromatography on carboxymethyl (CM)-cellulose was preferred because of better reproducibility. Ten millilitres of ammonium sulfate-free preparation were applied to a refrigerated column (1.5 cm i.d.) packed with 3 g of CM-cellulose in equilibrium with 0.01 M sodium phosphate buffer (pH 6.4). Adsorbed materials were eluted by successive application of the same buffer with increasing concentrations of NaCl (0.01 M, 0.03 M, 0.05 M, 0.08 M and 0.12 M), at a flow rate of about 70 ml/hr. Each NaCl solution was passed through the column until complete elution of the corresponding peak was attained as judged by spectrophotometric readings at 280 mμ. The bulk of inactive proteins and all transaminase activity is eluted by the first NaCl solution (0.01 M). The β-aspartic decarboxylase comes out from the column with the last NaCl solution (0.12 M) with an average recovery of 42 per cent (Fig. 1, Table 1).

TABLE 1. PURIFICATION OF THE ENZYME

| | Protein (mg/ml) | Specific activity[a] ($Q_{CO_2}$) | Purification | Yield (%) |
|---|---|---|---|---|
| Crude extract | 12.34 | 82.5 | — | — |
| Supernatant from streptomycin step | 7.7 | 95.4 | ×1.15 | 56 |
| Supernatant from acidification to pH 5.0 | 4.6 | 145.00 | ×1.75 | 53 |
| Precipitate 0.6 to 0.8 saturated ammonium sulfate | 4.0 | 540.00 | ×6.55 | 21 |
| Chromatography on CM-cellulose (10 ml fractions) | | | | |
| fraction 39 | 0.012 | 27.600 | ×336.00 | |
| fraction 40 | 0.011 | 26.000 | ×310.00 | 10 |

[a]Activities measured in the presence of 10 μmoles aspartate and $10^{-4}$ M pyruvate.

### 3. *Measurement of Activity*

Enzyme activity was routinely measured by conventional Warburg method at 37°C, in acetate buffer at the optimum pH 5.0. The manometric systems contained 10 μmoles of L-aspartate with or without addition of $10^{-4}$ M pyruvate. Activities ($+Q_{CO_2}$) are expressed in terms of μl of $CO_2$ evolved per hr and per mg of protein. Protein was determined both spectrophotometrically at 260 and 280 mμ[15] and by Folin's method as modified by Lowry *et al.*[7]

### 4. *Pyridoxal Phosphate*

This was determined enzymatically by the *Streptococcus faecalis* apodecarboxylase, as described by Gunsalus and Smith[6]. This method is specific for PLP. However, the dried cells of *S. faecalis* contain a pyridoxal-kinase and can utilize PL in the presence of exogenous ATP.

It has been verified that tyrosine apodecarboxylase is inactive in the presence of added pyridoxamine phosphate unless an α-keto acid is added. The conversion of PMP and PLP in these systems is obviously related to the non-enzymic transamination we have described elsewhere.[5]

## RESULTS

### 1. *Inactivation by Inorganic Salts*

The preparations resulting from ammonium sulfate fractionation have a low aspartic decarboxylase activity and are reactivated by catalytic amounts of PLP, non-phosphorylated pyridoxal (PL) and/or α-keto acids (Fig. 2, Table 2). Pyridoxamine and pyridoxamine phosphate have no reactivating effect.

TABLE 2. REACTIVATION OF THE PREPARATIONS AFTER AMMONIUM SULFATE FRACTIONATION

Activities ($+Q_{CO_2}$) measured in acetate buffer (pH 5.0), *t*, 37°, concentration of the activating agents 3.3 : $10^{-4}$ M (unless differently stated)

| Addition | $+Q_{CO_2}$ | Activation |
|---|---|---|
| None | 18 | — |
| pyridoxal | 68 | ×3.8 |
| pyridoxal phosphate | 128 | ×7.1 |
| pyridoxamine | 16 | ×(0.9) |
| pyridoxamine phosphate | 23 | ×1.3 |
| α-ketoglutarate | 210 | ×11.7 |
| α-ketoglutarate + pyridoxal phosphate | 210 | ×11.7 |
| α-ketoglutarate + pyridoxamine phosphate | 153 | ×8.5 |
| α-ketoglutarate[a] + pyridoxamine phosphate | 214 | ×11.9 |

[a] $10^{-3}$ M.

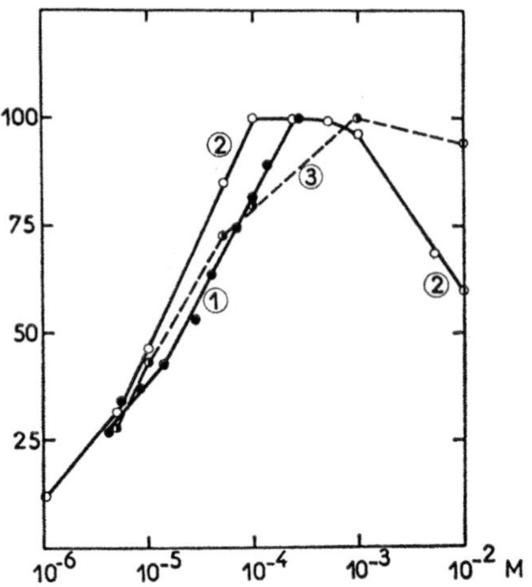


FIG. 2. Reactivating effect of pyridoxal-phosphate (curve 1), α-keto glutarate (curve 2), and pyruvate (curve 3) on the β-aspartic decarboxylase activity of a preparation partially purified by ammonium sulfate precipitation at 0.6 to 0.8 saturation and not dialyzed. Abscissa: molar concentration of the reactivating agents. Ordinates: percentage of maximum activity.

The fact that reactivation by PLP is not specific suggests that the inactivation is not due, as it could be postulated, to enzyme resolution during the purification procedure, but rather to the reversible conversion of the holo-

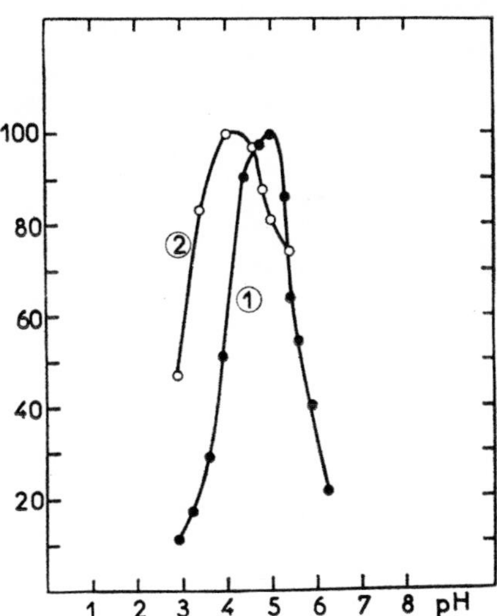


FIG. 3. Influence of pH on the β-aspartic decarboxylase activity. Preparation reactivated by $10^{-3}$ M concentration of pyridoxal-phosphate (curve 1) and of α-ketoglutarate (curve 2). Ordinates: percentage of maximum activity.

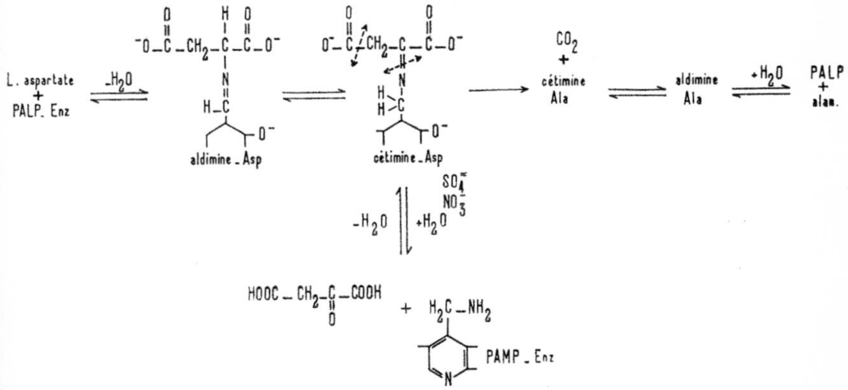

L. aspartate + PALP. Enz
$-H_2O$
$^-O-C(=O)-CH_2-C(H)(-N=CH-)-C(=O)-O^-$
aldimine _ Asp
$O^--C(=O)-CH_2-C(=N-CH_2-)-C(=O)-O^-$
cetimine _ Asp
$CO_2$ + cetimine Ala
aldimine Ala
$+H_2O$
PALP + alan.
$SO_4^=$ $NO_3^-$
$-H_2O$ $+H_2O$
$HOOC-CH_2-C(=O)-COOH$ + $H_2C-NH_2$ PAMP _ Enz

FIG. 4. Postulated mechanism for enzyme inactivation and reactivation.

enzyme from an active to an inactive form. Moreover, these observations suggest that reactivation is caused by the only common character of all the reactivating agents, i.e. their carbonyl group. This interpretation is consistent with the fact that the effects of PLP and of keto acids are not additive (Table 2).

However, it must be noted that optimum pH for the reactivation of the enzyme (Fig. 4) is different in the case of PLP (pH 5.0) and in the case of keto acids (pH 4.0). At the present time we have no explanation for this difference of behaviour.

TABLE 3. EFFECT OF DIALYSIS ON THE ACTIVITY OF THE PREPARATIONS AFTER AMMONIUM SULFATE FRACTIONATION

| Time of dialysis (min) | Activity ($Q_{CO_2}$ per ml of enzyme solution) | |
|---|---|---|
| | Without addition | +α-ketoglutarate $10^{-3}$ M +PLP 0.8 $10^{-4}$ M |
| 30 | 142 | 580 |
| 60 | 216 | 500 |
| 90 | 264 | 464 |
| 120 | 308 | 500 |
| 150 | 420 | 436 |
| 180 | 364 | 332 |

TABLE 4. EFFECT OF AMMONIUM SULFATE ON THE ACTIVITY OF β-ASPARTIC DECARBOXYLASE AFTER AMMONIUM SULFATE FRACTIONATION

| Enzyme preparation | $Q_{CO_2}$ | | |
|---|---|---|---|
| | Without addition | +α-ketoglutarate $10^{-3}$ M | +PLP 0.8 $10^{-3}$ M |
| non-dialyzed | 82 | 690 | 220 |
| dialyzed (4 h) | 436 | 436 | 404 |
| id° + $(NH_4)_2SO_4$ $10^{-3}$ M | 320 | 448 | 368 |
| id° + $(NH_4)_2SO_4$ $10^{-2}$ M | 172 | 460 | 292 |
| id° + $(NH_4)_2SO_4$ 0.1 M | 32 | 448 | 112 |

Prolonged dialysis of preparations previously treated by ammonium sulfate fractionation results in considerable reactivation of the enzyme (Table 3). After 3 hr dialysis, the activity of the preparation is identical to that of the non-dialyzed enzyme in the presence of added PLP and is not further increased by the addition of PLP and/or keto acids.

When reactivated by dialysis, the preparations are inactivated again by addition of $(NH_4)_2SO_4$ and are protected against this secondary inactivation when assays are performed in the presence of keto acid or of PLP (Table 4).

TABLE 5. EFFECT OF INORGANIC SALTS ON THE ACTIVITY OF β-ASPARTIC DECARBOXYLASE PREVIOUSLY REACTIVATED BY DIALYSIS

| Salt[a] | Activity[b] (%) | |
|---|---|---|
| | Without pyruvate | +Pyruvate ($10^{-4}$ M) |
| none | 100.0 | 136 |
| $(NH_4)_2SO_4$ | 19.0 | |
| $NH_4NO_3$ | 16.5 | |
| $NH_4Cl$ | 85.2 | |
| $Na_2SO_4$ | 13.6 | 110 |
| $Na_2S_2O_3$ | 11.0 | 120 |
| NaCl | 100.0 | 136 |
| $KNO_3$ | 25.0 | 133 |

[a] Salt concentration: 0.1 M.
[b] Manometric systems containing L-aspartate 10 μmoles, ±pyruvate $10^{-4}$ M enzyme preparation.

TABLE 6. EFFECT OF INORGANIC SALTS ON THE ACTIVITY OF THE α-GLUTAMIC DECARBOXYLASE OF DESULFOVIBRIO DESULFURICANS

| Addition | Activity (%) |
|---|---|
| none | 100 |
| $(NH_4)_2SO_4$ | 118 |
| $Na_2SO_4$ | 118 |
| $Na_2S_2O_4$ | 100 |
| NaCl | 123 |
| $NaNO_3$ | 80 |
| $NaNO_3$ + pyruvate | 70 |

Enzyme partially purified by ammonium sulfate precipitation (0–0.6 S), redissolved and dialyzed. Activities measured at pH 5.0 (citrate–phosphate buffer) in the presence of L-glutamate 6.6 $10^{-3}$ M ± salts 0.1 M ± pyruvate $10^{-4}$ M.

The data reported in Table 5 demonstrate that the inactivation of the enzyme by ammonium sulfate is due to sulfate ions. From these observations, it is clear that $SO_4^{2-}$, $S_2O_3^{2-}$ and $NO^-_3$ are inhibitory, whereas $Cl^-$, $Na^+$

and $NH_4^+$ are not. It is interesting to note that the anions which inactivate the β-aspartic decarboxylase have little or no effect on the activity of the α-glutamic decarboxylase extracted from the same organism (Table 6). Actually, a slight inhibitory effect of $NO_3^-$ on glutamic decarboxylase was observed, but this effect, instead of being supressed by pyruvate, seems to be rather reinforced in the presence of keto acid.

### 2. *Properties of the Purified Enzyme*

In the presence of $10^{-4}$ M pyruvate, the specific activity ($Q_{CO_2}$) of the preparation obtained by chromatography on CM-cellulose averaged 27,000, corresponding to a purification of about 330-fold over the original extracts. The chromatographic peak is fairly homogeneous (Fig. 1) in regard to its specific activity. A slightly lower specific activity can be noted at the beginning

TABLE 7. EFFECT OF PYRUVATE AND PLP ON THE ACTIVITIES OF PURIFIED ENZYME

| Addition | Specific activity ($Q_{CO_2}$) | |
|---|---|---|
| | Before filtration on Sephadex | After filtration on Sephadex |
| none | 13,000 | 23,000 |
| pyruvate $10^{-3}$ M | 23,010 (+77%) | 26,680 (+16%) |
| PLP $10^{-3}$ M | 16,900 (+30%) | 25,300 (+10%) |
| pyruvate + PLP | 21,190 (+63%) | 24,610 (+7%) |

of the elution peak, but this could be explained by the fact that the protein concentration in the corresponding fractions is the same order of magnitude as the inherent error in the method of estimation.

The purified fractions are active even in the absence of added PLP or keto acid. However, these compounds consistently increase the specific activity. The importance of inorganic ions for the activity of the purified enzyme is emphasized by the fact that the elimination of mineral salts by filtration on Sephadex gel results in preparations with higher specific activity and which are not significantly activated by the addition of PLP and/or keto acids (Table 7).

### 3. *PLP Content of Purified Enzyme Preparations*

Determinations of PLP were performed on pooled and concentrated batches of chromatographically purified preparations with similar specific activities. In diluted solutions, the purified enzyme is unstable, even when kept at −15°C. For this reason the eluants had to be concentrated immediately after the elution from the CM-columns. The enzyme is completely denaturated by freeze-drying. The best procedure for concentrating the enzyme was found to be a simple overnight vacuum concentration over $CaCl_2$, with the precaution that the preparation should not be completely desiccated.

As estimated by the tyrosine apodecarboxylase method, the PLP content of the purified preparations is very low (*ca.* 4.8 mμg/mg protein), but much higher in preparations previously submitted to alkaline hydrolysis. This shows that the cofactor is tightly bound to the apoprotein and in this form is not available for the activation of the test enzyme. Alkaline hydrolysis was routinely performed in 0.1 N NaOH for 5 min in a boiling water bath, and followed by acidification to pH 5.0 with 0.1 N $SO_4H_2$. The average PLP content determined on these hydrolyzed samples was 330 mμg/mg of protein. Comparatively, the PLP content of the initial crude extract after alkaline hydrolysis is only of 34 mμg/mg of total protein.

## DISCUSSION

The cellular content of β-aspartic carboxylase in *Desulfovibrio desulfuricans* has been found to be unexpectedly low. In a typical purification experiment, from a crude extract containing 4900 mg of protein, only 0.3 mg of active protein was recovered after CM-cellulose chromatography, with a total enzyme recovery of about 10 per cent. This would correspond to about 0.05 per cent of β-aspartic decarboxylase in the crude extract. Quite similar observations have recently been made by Nishimura *et al.*[10] who have extracted and purified the same enzyme from *Clostridium welchii.* According to the figures reported by these authors, the final aspartic decarboxylase fraction represented only 0.02 per cent of the protein in the initial crude extract which had a specific activity ($Q_{CO_2} = 67$) very close to the activity of our *D. desulfuricans* crude extracts ($Q_{CO_2} = 77$).

These results are in contrast with what has been found for other PLP-dependent enzymes in other bacterial species. Shukuya and Schwert[14] have extracted and purified from *Escherichia coli* a PLP dependent glutamic decarboxylase. This enzyme represented as much as 2.5 per cent of total protein and had a specific activity, after a ten-fold purification, of 92,000.

The quantities of purified enzyme we could obtain were far too low for measurements of homogeneity, molecular weight determination, and estimation of PLP content by conventional methods. Biological determinations of PLP in the purified preparations have demonstrated, however, that pyridoxal phosphate is the cofactor of the enzyme and is tightly bound to the specific apoprotein. The average PLP content found by us (330 mμg/mg protein) is close to the result independently obtained by Nishimura *et al.*[10] for the same enzyme extracted and purified from *C. welchii* (250 mμg/mg protein.)

Assuming only one PLP group per active enzyme unit, it can be calculated a minimum molecular weight of about 800,000. In comparison, Shukuya and Schwert[14] have found that their glutamic decarboxylase contains two PLP groups per mole and has a molecular weight of 300,000 as determined by ultracentrifugation. In the light of available information on the structure of other active proteins, it seems most unlikely that these figures correspond to the actual molecular weight of the considered enzymes. It may be that, in the course of the purification procedure, a large proportion of the enzyme irreversibly loses its capacity for binding with the cofactor or that only a part of the bound PLP is liberated by alkaline hydrolysis. An alternative interpretation would be that the active enzyme unit consists in several smaller protein molecules bound to a single PLP group.

The mechanism of enzyme inhibition by some inorganic anions and of its reactivation by carbonylic compounds is an interesting problem. Several years ago, Meister *et al.*[8] pointed out that the activating effect of keto acids could correspond to a mechanism in which aspartic acid would be decarboxylated through a complex series of intermediary transaminations. However, from experiments with $C^{14}$-labelled pyruvate, he considered this hypothesis as most unlikely. Such an interpretation seems to be definitively eliminated by the complete separation of transaminases and aspartic decarboxylase activities during the purification procedure.

More recently, Nishimura *et al.*[10] suggested that the inactive form of the enzyme could result from a chemical reaction between the aldehydic group of PLP and a free amino group on the apoprotein molecule, as in the case of phosphorylase where PLP carbonyl is bound to the $\epsilon$-amino group of a lysine residue.[2] This hypothesis, however, does not provide an explanation for the reactivating effect of keto acids.

According to Braunstein and Shemyakin[3], the $\beta$-decarboxylation of aspartic acid involves a preliminary tautomerization of the aldimine to the ketimine form of the amino acid–PLP–enzyme complex. As schematically represented in Fig. 4, one may postulate that the inactivating anions interfere with this process and catalyse the hydrolysis of the ketimine complex to the corresponding keto acid and PMP–enzyme. The PMP–enzyme would then be the inactive form of the decarboxylase. Exogenous keto acids in sufficient concentration would revert the process and restore the enzyme to its active PLP-form.

The fact that glutamic decarboxylase is not inhibited by anions nor activated by carbonylic compounds supports this interpretation since, according to Mendeles *et al.*[9], $\alpha$-decarboxylation of glutamate does not involve the intermediary formation of a ketimine complex. In order to check this hypothesis, it would be required to obtain quantities of the purified enzyme sufficient for direct spectrophotometric examination.

## SUMMARY

The β-aspartic decarboxylase of *Desulfovibrio desulfuricans* (strain El Agheila Z, NCIB 8380) has been purified 330-fold by ammonium sulfate fractionation and chromatography on CM-cellulose.

The purified preparations contain per mg of protein, 330 mμg of PLP tightly bound to the enzyme.

The enzyme is inactivated by several inorganic anions ($SO_4^{2-}$, $S_2O_3^{2-}$, $NO_3^-$) and is reactivated by catalytic amounts of PLP, PL or α-keto acids.

A postulated mechanism of enzyme inactivation, involving hydrolysis of a ketimine–PLP–enzyme complex, is discussed.

## REFERENCES

1. M. E. ADAMS, K. R. BUTLIN, S. J. HOLLANDS and J. R. POSTGATE; *Research* **4**, 245 (1951).
2. T. BARANOWSKI, B. ILLINGWORTH, D. H. BROWN and C. F. CORI; *Biochim. et Biophys. Acta* **25**, 16 (1957).
3. A. E. BRAUNSTEIN and M. M. SHEMYAKIN; *Biokhimija* **18**, 393 (1953).
4. J. CATTANÉO, J. C. SENEZ and P. BEAUMONT, *Biochim. et Biophys. Acta* **30**, 458 (1958).
5. J. CATTANÉO, J. C. SENEZ and P. BEAUMONT; *Biochim. et Biophys. Acta* **44**, 543 (1960).
6. I. C. GUNSALUS and R. A. SMITH; *Methods in Enzymology*, vol. III, p. 963, Academic Press, New York (1957).
7. O. H. LOWRY, N. J. ROSENBROUGH, A. C. FARR and R. J. RANDALL; *J. Biol. Chem.* **193**, 265 (1951).
8. A. MEISTER, H. A. SOBER and S. V. TICE; *J. Biol. Chem.* **189**, 577 (1951).
9. S. MENDELES, R. KOPPELMAN and M. E. HANKE; *J. Biol. Chem.* **209**, 327 (1954).
10. J. S. NISHIMURA, J. M. MANNING and A. MEISTER; *Biochemistry* **1**, 442 (1962).
11. J. C. SENEZ; *Ann. Inst. Pasteur* **83**, 786 (1952).
12. J. C. SENEZ and J. CATTANÉO; *Compt. Rend.* **242**, 943 (1956).
13. J. C. SENEZ and J. LEROUX-GILLERON; *Bull. Soc. Chim. Biol.* **36**, 553 (1954).
14. R. SHUKUYA and G. W. SCHWERT; *J. Biol. Chem.* **235**, 1649 (1960).
15. E. LAYNE; *Methods in Enzymology*, vol. III, p. 447, Academic Press, New York (1957).

# α-KETO ACID-ACTIVATED ENZYMATIC DECARBOXYLATION OF L-ASPARTATE TO L-ALANINE*

by ALTON MEISTER, JONATHAN S. NISHIMURA and ABRAHAM NOVOGRODSKY

Department of Biochemistry, Tufts University School of Medicine, Boston, Massachusetts, U.S.A.

THE α-keto acid activation of aspartic acid β-decarboxylase was first observed in 1950 in the course of studies in which cell suspensions of *Clostridum perfringens*† were used for determination of glutamate formed by transamination from aspartate to α-ketoglutarate.[1]‡ Subsequent studies showed that preparations of *C. perfringens* catalyzed formation of carbon dioxide from aspartate, and that the rate of decarboxylation was greatly increased by the addition of small quantities of α-ketoglutarate, pyruvate, and a number of other α-keto acids (Table 1). The product of the reaction was shown to be L-alanine and not β-alanine. Alanine was formed even when α-keto acids other than pyruvate were added, and in such experiments detectable amounts of the amino analogs of the added α-keto acids were not formed. Acceleration of decarboxylation was also observed when small quantities of pyridoxal-5′-phosphate were added; pyridoxal-5′-phosphate activated aspartic acid decarboxylation to approximately the same extent as did pyruvate, and the rate of carbon dioxide formation in the presence of both pyruvate and pyridoxal-5′-phosphate was not appreciably greater than when either of these was added alone. The possibility that the formation of carbon dioxide and alanine from aspartate was due to transamination between aspartate and pyruvate to yield alanine and oxaloacetate, followed by

*The authors acknowledge the generous support of the National Science Foundation and of the National Institutes of Health, Public Health Service, Department of Health, Education and Welfare.

†Formerly referred to as *Clostridium welchii* SR 12.

‡Aspartic β-decarboxylase has been found in a number of micro-organisms (e.g. mycobacteria,[2–5] *Desulfovibrio desulfuricans*,[6] and *Nocardia globerula*[7]). It may also be present in the silkworm,[8] and the possibility exists that it may also occur in mammalian tissues. The aspartic β-decarboxylases of *Desulfovibrio desulfuricans* and of *Nocardia globerula* are also activated by α-keto acids.

decarboxylation of the latter to give pyruvate and carbon dioxide according to Eqs. (1–3), was excluded by experiments with radioactive pyruvate.

$$\text{Aspartate} + \text{pyruvate} \leftrightharpoons \text{alanine} + \text{oxaloacetate} \quad (1)$$

$$\text{Oxaloacetate} \leftrightharpoons CO_2 + \text{pyruvate} \quad (2)$$

$$\textit{Sum}: \text{Aspartate} \leftrightharpoons \text{alanine} + CO_2 \quad (3)$$

TABLE 1. EFFECT OF KETO ACIDS ON CARBON DIOXIDE FORMATION FROM ASPARTIC ACID[a]

| Keto acid | Original preparation | Treated preparation[b] |
|---|---|---|
| None | 60.5 | 0.0 |
| Pyruvic | 225. | 56.0 |
| α-Ketobutyric | 232. | 53.6 |
| α-Ketovaleric | 228. | 55.5 |
| α-Ketocaproic | 190. | 50.4 |
| α-Ketoheptanoic | 172. | 42.9 |
| α-Ketoisovaleric | 241. | 40.2 |
| Phenylpyruvic | 230. | 42.5 |
| α-Ketoisocaproic | 208. | 45.6 |
| *p*-Hydroxyphenylpyruvic | 203. | 41.2 |
| αKetoglutaric | 236. | 58.6 |
| γ-Ketovaleric | 60.0 | 0.0 |
| Triacetic lactone | 59.0 | 0.0 |
| Dehydroacetic | 58.0 | 0.0 |
| α, γ-Diketovaleric | 221. | 47.0 |
| β-Acetylacrylic | 63.0 | 0.0 |
| d-α-Keto-β-methylvaleric | 106. | 10.1 |
| l-α-Keto-β-methylvaleric | 108. | 8.9 |

[a] The values are expressed as microliters of carbon dioxide per 30 min. The vessels contained 20 μmoles of aspartic acid, 0.5 μmole of keto acid, and 13 mg of *C. perfringens* cells in 1.4 ml of 0.2 M acetate buffer (pH 4.9).
[b] Cells treated with semicarbazide as described.[1]

Thus, equivalent concentrations of unlabeled aspartate and $C^{14}$-pyruvate were incubated with the cell suspension, and samples were removed during the course of the reaction. These studies revealed that the alanine formed did not contain detectable amounts of radioactivity, indicating that the reaction was a direct β-decarboxylation of aspartate :

$$\text{L-Aspartate} \rightarrow CO_2 + \text{L-alanine} \quad (4)$$

The finding that pyridoxal-5′-phosphate activated the enzyme was consistent with observations indicating that pyridoxal-5′-phosphate was the prosthetic group of other amino acid decarboxylases. Pyridoxamine-5′-phosphate did not activate the enzyme unless an α-keto acid was also present. Although it was suggested at that time[1] that the α-keto acid activation was due to transamination of pyridoxamine-5′-phosphate (present in the enzyme preparation or attached to the enzyme) with added α-keto acid, subsequent analytical studies (described below) did not support this belief.

The problem of the mechanism of activation of aspartic β-decarboxylase by α-keto acid was taken up again in our laboratory in 1960 by Nishimura *et al.*[9], who achieved a much greater purification of the enzyme from *C. perfringens*. In the earlier work[1] preparations were employed which exhibited specific activities of approximately 20 μl of $CO_2$ per mg of protein per hr. The procedure subsequently developed[9] involved autolysis of the cells to give a preparation of specific activity 60–70. The steps in the purification included treatment with protamine sulfate, low temperature ethanol fractionation, ammonium sulfate precipitation of the enzyme, and column chromatography on carboxymethylcellulose. The final preparation was almost 500 times more active than the preparation employed in the earlier work. Assay of the fractions of protein obtained from the carboxymethylcellulose column for vitamin $B_6$ with *Saccharomyces carlsbergensis*[10–12] indicated that the enzymatic activity and vitamin $B_6$ were eluted together. The purified enzyme was also assayed with *Streptococcus faecalis* R, which responds to either pyridoxamine or pyridoxal (and their phosphorylated forms), and *Lactobacillus casei*, which responds specifically to pyridoxal.[10–12] Several comparative assays with these organisms and with *S. carlsbergensis*, which responds to pyridoxine, pyridoxamine, or pyridoxal, were in essential agreement. Since the values obtained with *L. casei* were substantially the same as those observed with the other organisms, it appears that virtually all of the vitamin $B_6$ present in the enzyme is in the pyridoxal form. Furthermore, poor responses were obtained with *L. casei* when the enzyme was not hydrolyzed with dilute hydrochloric acid; it may therefore be concluded that pyridoxal-5′-phosphate rather than pyridoxal is present in the enzyme. The data do not provide evidence for the presence of pyridoxamine-5′-phosphate.

The purified *C. perfringens* aspartic decarboxylase was activated by low concentrations of either pyridoxal-5′-phosphate or pyruvate. When both activators were used together at a concentration of $3.33 \times 10^{-4}$ M, the activity was only from 10 to 20 per cent greater than when either was used alone (Table 2). The findings indicate that the effects of keto acid and pyridoxal-5′-phosphate are not additive. When preparations of the purified enzyme were incubated with either pyridoxal-5′-phosphate or pyruvate and then dialyzed, the enzyme after dialysis was not appreciably active except on addition of further keto acid or pyridoxal-5′-phosphate. Experiments with $C^{14}$-aspartate and unlabeled pyruvate (analogous to those reported above) failed to reveal significant transamination between aspartate and pyruvate to give alanine.

A number of attempts were made to remove the vitamin $B_6$ from the enzyme by precipitation and dialysis of the enzyme, but in no case was resolution of

TABLE 2. EFFECTS OF PYRIDOXAL-5′-PHOSPHATE AND PYRUVATE ON ACTIVITY OF THE PURIFIED ENZYME FROM *C. perfringens*[a]

| Additions | Activity |
|---|---|
| None | 8.6 |
| Pyridoxal-5′-phosphate | 47.0 |
| Pyruvate | 49.7 |
| Pyridoxal-5′-phosphate + pyruvate | 56.9 |

[a] Activity is expressed in terms of microliters of carbon dioxide liberated in 15 min. The reaction mixtures consisted initially of L-aspartic acid (15 μmoles), sodium pyruvate (0.5 μmole), pyridoxal-5′-phosphate (0.5 μmole), enzyme (51 μg), and sodium acetate buffer (pH 5.0; 1100 μmoles) in a final volume of 1.5 ml; incubated at 38°.

TABLE 3. RESOLUTION OF THE *C. perfringens* ENZYME[a]

| Additions | Before radiation | After radiation | After radiation and treatment with pyridoxal-5′-phosphate[b] |
|---|---|---|---|
| None | 8.6 | 5.6 | 12.4 |
| Pyruvate | 49.7 | 7.8 | 46.9 |
| Pyridoxal 5′-phosphate | 47.0 | 49.2 | 44.8 |

[a] Activity values were obtained under conditions described in Table 2; 51 and 102 μg, respectively, of enzyme were used for assay of the enzyme before and after radiation. The enzyme contained 6.8 mμg of vitamin $B_6$ (as pyridoxal HCl) per 51 μg of protein.

[b] Radiated enzyme (0.58 mg in 2 ml of 0.1 M sodium acetate buffer, pH 4.8) was incubated with 0.14 ml of buffer containing 0.7 μmole of pyridoxal-5′-phosphate for 30 min at 38°, and then dialyzed at 5° against 5 changes of 500 ml each of 0.2 M sodium acetate buffer (pH 4.6) over 3 days. The radiated enzyme contained no vitamin $B_6$ as determined by microbiological assay.

the enzyme achieved. However, radiation of the enzyme with an unfiltered ultraviolet lamp (under specific conditions previously described[1]) gave an enzyme which was very largely resolved with respect to pyridoxal-5′-phosphate. The isolated enzyme was activated approximately equally by pyridoxal-5′-phosphate and pyruvate. After radiation, activation by pyridoxal-5′-phosphate was observed, but little if any effect was observed on addition of pyruvate (Table 3). Assay of the radiated enzyme with *L. casei* and *S. carlsbergensis* failed to indicate the presence of vitamin $B_6$. When the radiated enzyme was treated with pyridoxal-5′-phosphate and then exhaustively dialyzed, the dialyzed preparation responded to both pyridoxal-5′-phosphate and pyruvate in a manner typical of the original preparation.

The properties of the purified enzyme from *C. perfringens* may be briefly summarized as follows[9]: The enzyme contains firmly bound vitamin $B_6$, which on microbiological assay fulfills the requirements for pyridoxal-5′-phosphate. This vitamin $B_6$ is not removed by dialysis. Addition of either pyridoxal-5′-phosphate or an $\alpha$-keto acid is required for enzymatic activity, and the effects of these are not additive. Enzymes to which either pyridoxal-5′-phosphate or pyruvate have been added are inactive after dialysis, but may be activated by subsequent addition of either activator. The resolved enzyme is not activated by $\alpha$-keto acids, but can be activated by pyridoxal-5′-phosphate. When the apoenzyme is reconstituted by addition of pyridoxal-5′-phosphate followed by extensive dialysis, either pyridoxal-5′-phosphate or pyruvate will restore activity.

The data indicate that enzyme-bound pyridoxal-5′-phosphate is required for activation by $\alpha$-keto acids. Pyridoxal-5′-phosphate therefore appears to exhibit two functions: One requires that it be tightly bound to the enzyme, and the other, which involves a more labile linkage, may be fulfilled also by $\alpha$-keto acids. The evidence provides no basis for the belief that pyridoxamine-5′-phosphate is present in the isolated enzyme.

Although the enzyme obtained from *C. perfringens*[9] was considerably more active than the earlier preparation,[1] it was not available in sufficient quantity to permit spectrophotometric and other studies. For this reason, an attempt was made to obtain a micro-organism that possessed a higher concentration of the enzyme. Such an organism, a strain of *Alcaligenes faecalis*, was isolated by enrichment culture from soil obtained from the Boston Common.[13] The organism was grown on a medium containing ammonium aspartate as the sole source of nitrogen and carbon. Purification was achieved by sonication of the cells and treatment of the extract with protamine sulfate followed by precipitation of the enzyme at pH 4.6; after dissolving the enzyme, it was precipitated with ammonium sulfate. Further purification was achieved by ultracentrifugation and by centrifugation in a sucrose gradient. The final preparation, which was obtained in approximately 20 per cent yield, exhibited a specific activity of about 75,000; the initial extracts gave specific activities of approximately 1000. The enzyme sedimented as a nearly homogeneous component representing approximately 90 per cent of the total protein present; sedimentation coefficients of from 18 to 22 S were observed. This indicates that the enzyme is a relatively large molecule possessing a molecular weight of the order of 800,000.

Like the enzyme from *C. perfringens*, the *A. faecalis* enzyme was activated by α-keto acids. However, in contrast to the *C. perfringens* enzyme, the *A. faecalis* enzyme was isolated in partially resolved form. Incubation of the isolated enzyme with pyridoxal-5′-phosphate followed by dialysis gave a preparation which was not significantly activated by further addition of pyridoxal-5′-phosphate ($3.33 \times 10^{-4}$ M), but which required the addition of α-keto acid for full activity (Table 4). Similarly, the partially resolved

TABLE 4. EFFECT OF PYRIDOXAL-5′-PHOSPHATE (PLP) AND PYRUVATE ON THE PURIFIED ENZYME FROM *Alcaligenes faecalis*

| Reaction mixtures | Relative activity[a] | |
|---|---|---|
| | Original enzyme | Holoenzyme |
| Enzyme + PLP + pyruvate | (100) | (100) |
| Enzyme + pyruvate | 43 | 100 |
| Enzyme + PLP | 11 | 13 |
| Enzyme alone | 9 | 6 |

[a] Per cent of activity observed with $3.33 \times 10^{-4}$ M pyruvate plus $3.33 \times 10^{-4}$ M PLP.

enzyme was significantly active only in the presence of added α-keto acids. These observations indicate another difference between the two enzymes; i.e. the *A. faecalis* enzyme exhibits a requirement for keto acid which cannot be replaced by an equivalent concentration of pyridoxal-5′-phosphate. Pyridoxal-5′-phosphate was not readily removed from the holoenzyme of *A. faecalis* by dialysis. It was shown by experiments with $C^{14}$-pyruvate similar to those described above with the enzyme from *C. perfringens* that the enzyme does not catalyze appreciable transamination from aspartate to pyruvate.

The other properties of this enzyme are currently being investigated. Preliminary study has indicated that the spectrum of the isolated *A. faecalis* exhibits a small peak at 350 mμ and a small shoulder at 415 mμ. When pyridoxal-5′-phosphate was added, the peak absorbency increased considerably and shifted to 355 mμ, and after dialysis the spectrum was essentially unchanged (Fig. 1). We have thus far not observed a shift in the band at 355 mμ after addition of pyruvate or by alteration of pH over the range 4.6–8.5. On addition of strong alkali, an absorption curve characteristic of pyridoxal-5′-phosphate with a broad band in the 380–400 mμ region was observed. The sedimentation behavior of the partially resolved enzyme in a sucrose gradient (5–20 per cent) was not changed by addition of pyruvate or pyridoxal-5′-phosphate.

It is evident that additional study is required before the mechanism of activation by α-keto acids can be fully understood. Such experiments are now in progress. However, at least two possibilities can be eliminated on the basis of presently available data. Thus, it has been conclusively shown that there is no significant transamination between pyruvate and aspartate

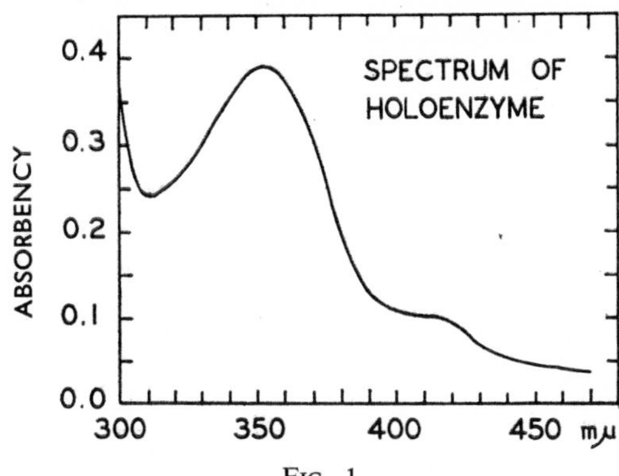


FIG. 1

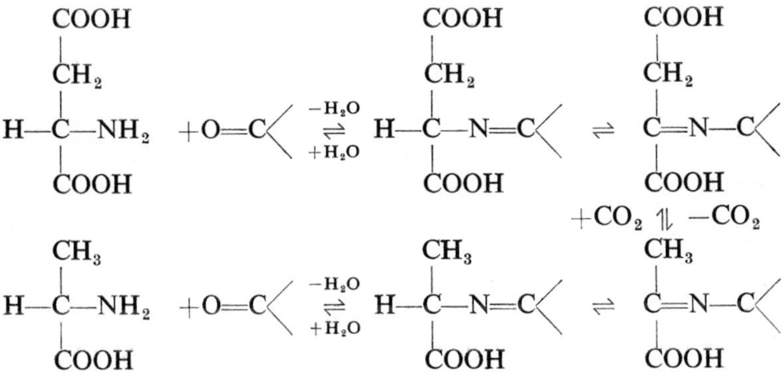

$$\begin{array}{c}COOH\\|\\CH_2\\|\\H-C-NH_2\\|\\COOH\end{array} + O=C\langle \; \underset{+H_2O}{\overset{-H_2O}{\rightleftharpoons}} \; \begin{array}{c}COOH\\|\\CH_2\\|\\H-C-N=C\langle\\|\\COOH\end{array} \rightleftharpoons \begin{array}{c}COOH\\|\\CH_2\\|\\C=N-C\langle\\|\\COOH\end{array}$$

$$+CO_2 \; \upharpoonleft\!\downharpoonright \; -CO_2$$

$$\begin{array}{c}CH_3\\|\\H-C-NH_2\\|\\COOH\end{array} + O=C\langle \; \underset{+H_2O}{\overset{-H_2O}{\rightleftharpoons}} \; \begin{array}{c}CH_3\\|\\H-C-N=C\langle\\|\\COOH\end{array} \rightleftharpoons \begin{array}{c}CH_3\\|\\C=N-C\langle\\|\\COOH\end{array}$$

FIG. 2

at the substrate level (as in Eqs. (1)–(3), above). Furthermore, the data do not support the belief that the isolated enzyme contains bound pyridoxamine-5′-phosphate, which is converted to bound pyridoxal-5′-phosphate by transamination with the added α-keto acid.

We have previously considered the hypothesis that the added pyridoxal-5′-phosphate or α-keto acid might in some way alter the enzyme-bound pyridoxal-5′-phosphate as to allow it to react with aspartate; this suggestion has been considered in detail elsewhere.[9] A scheme for the decarboxylation of aspartate that is consistent with the generally accepted Schiff base mechanism of vitamin $B_6$ catalysis is given in Fig. 2. In contrast to that postulated for $\alpha$-decarboxylation of amino acids,[14,15] this mechanism involves labilization of the $\alpha$-hydrogen atom of aspartate, and therefore more closely resembles transamination. The requirement for catalytic amounts of an $\alpha$-keto acid as well as for pyridoxal-5′-phosphate is of particular interest. At least three general types of mechanisms may be considered :

(*a*) Schiff base formation may occur between enzyme-bound pyridoxal-5′-phosphate and aspartate and the $\alpha$-keto acid may serve in another (essential) function.[9]

(*b*) Schiff base formation may take place only between aspartate and $\alpha$-keto acid, with pyridoxal-5′-phosphate functioning in some other way. The studies on the enzyme from *C. perfringens* demonstrated two types of vitamin $B_6$, and it appears that the loosely bound vitamin $B_6$ of this system is analogous to the $\alpha$-keto acid of the *A. faecalis* enzyme. Although it is perhaps somewhat unconventional to postulate that a vitamin $B_6$-enzyme that acts on an amino acid substrate does not act by a mechanism involving Schiff base formation between pyridoxal-5′-phosphate and the amino group of the amino acid, the presently available experimental data do not conclusively exclude such a possibility. Thus, an enzyme-bound $\alpha$-keto acid might serve as a coenzyme (cf. Fig. 2), and the pyridoxal-5′-phosphate might function in some other way. The bound pyridoxal-5′-phosphate of phosphorylase is essential for enzymatic activity; yet it appears reasonably certain that this vitamin $B_6$ does not form a Schiff base by reaction with substrate.[16–18] Should further work support a mechanism of type (*b*), a fundamentally new function of vitamin $B_6$ would be indicated.

(*c*) The mechanism may be more complex than indicated in either (*a*) or (*b*); for example, both the $\alpha$-keto acid as well as pyridoxal-5′-phosphate may participate in Schiff base formation. A mechanism of this general type seems most likely at the present time (see Addendum).

In very recent experiments we have observed that treatment of the holoenzyme with L-aspartate led to an immediate shift of the absorption peak to the region of 325 m$\mu$. On subsequent addition of pyruvate, the spectrum reverted to its original form with an absorbency maximum at 355 m$\mu$. These observations suggest that the holoenzyme can react with L-aspartate under conditions which do not permit significant decarboxylation, i.e. in the absence of added $\alpha$-keto acid.

In summary, study of these bacterial aspartic acid $\beta$-decarboxylases has indicated that both enzymes contain firmly bound pyridoxal-5′-phosphate, and that the addition of $\alpha$-keto acid is necessary for decarboxylase activity. In the case of the enzyme from *Clostridium perfringens*, the $\alpha$-keto acid may be replaced by pyridoxal-5′-phosphate. There is thus evidence that enzyme from *Clostridium perfringens* utilizes two types of pyridoxal-5′-phosphate. Studies on the *Alcaligenes faecalis* enzyme, which is now available in highly purified form, may be expected to shed further light on the reaction mechanism since detailed spectrophotometric observations and studies with stoichiometric amounts of enzyme are now experimentally feasible.

## ADDENDUM

Experiments carried out shortly after the Symposium was held appear to have clarified considerably the mechanism of activation of aspartic decarboxylase by pyridoxal phosphate and $\alpha$-keto acids. These studies have followed closely upon the observation reported by us at the Symposium (see page 236) that treatment of the enzyme with L-aspartate led to an immediate shift in peak absorbency from 355 to 325 m$\mu$, and that on subsequent addition of pyruvate the spectrum reverted to its original form. We have also found that under certain conditions the rate of aspartate decarboxylation (with aspartate alone or aspartate plus low concentrations of $\alpha$-keto acid) declined rapidly, reaching a plateau within 15–45 min. Subsequent addition of keto acid did not reactivate the enzyme, but addition of pyridoxal phosphate did. The rapid decline in the rate of decarboxylation could be prevented or decreased by initial addition of pyridoxal phosphate or a high concentration of $\alpha$-keto acid. The tendency of the rate of decarboxylation to decline was accelerated by high concentrations of buffer or salts, and under certain conditions this could be prevented by adding more pyridoxal phosphate or $\alpha$-keto acid initially.

Although experiments with $C^{14}$-pyruvate exclude a mechanism of decarboxylation according to Eqs. (1)–(3) (see page 230 above), a very small but definite quantity of $C^{14}$-alanine was invariably found in experiments with $C^{14}$-pyruvate. Similar results were obtained with $C^{14}$-$\alpha$-ketoglutarate, and it was found that the rate of formation of $C^{14}$-amino acid from the corresponding $C^{14}$-$\alpha$-keto acid was proportional to that of decarboxylation of aspartic acid; however, decarboxylation occurred much more rapidly than did transamination.

Incubation of the enzyme with other L-amino acids which are not substrates for decarboxylation (e.g. L-glutamate, L-alanine, L-$\beta$-methylaspartate), led to inactivation, i.e. after incubation no $CO_2$ was formed on addition of aspartate plus $\alpha$-keto acid. However, when the enzyme was incubated with these L-amino acids plus an $\alpha$-keto acid, no inactivation occurred. Transamination of the other L-amino acids (D-amino acids were inactive) with $C^{14}$-$\alpha$-keto acids was demonstrated. Enzyme preparations inactivated by incubation with various L-amino acids could decarboxylate L-aspartate provided that pyridoxal phosphate was added.

The experimental findings can now be explained in terms of a mechanism (see Fig. A) in which the enzyme-bound ketimine (III) can undergo decarboxylation (pathway A) or hydrolysis (pathway B). As larger amounts of the coenzyme are converted to the pyridoxamine form (VI), decarboxylase activity is decreased. We may ascribe activation by α-keto acids to reaction of VI with α-keto acid to form I. α-Keto acids do not reactivate enzyme incubated with L-aspartate and other L-amino acids because there is dissociation of pyridoxamine phosphate from the enzyme. The activation by pyridoxal phosphate is due to reconstitution of the apoenzyme formed in this manner. Dissociation of pyridoxamine phosphate from the enzyme occurs more rapidly in the presence of high concentrations of salt, which also decrease affinity of the enzyme for α-keto acid.

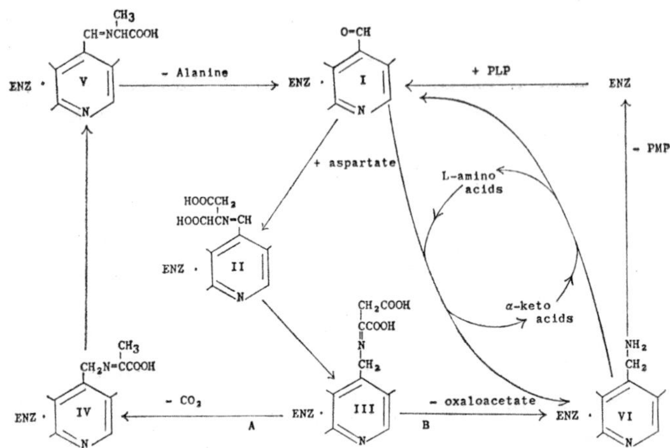


FIG. A. (From NOVOGRODSKY, A., NISHIMURA, J. S. and MEISTER, A., *J. Biol. Chem.*, **238**, PC1903, 1963).

The data therefore indicate that aspartate β-decarboxylase acts both as an aspartate decarboxylase and as an amino acid transaminase of relatively low specificity. The diagram given in the accompanying figure explains why activation by α-keto acid and pyridoxal phosphate is not additive and suggests that the enzyme should catalyze transamination of added pyridoxamine phosphate, a reaction that has recently been demonstrated spectrophotometrically. These observations and the proposed mechanisms are interesting in relation to earlier suggestions that the activating effect of α-keto acids was due to transamination. Our observations are in general agreement with those reported by Dr. Senez at this meeting on the effects of salts on the reaction. The additional function attributed to pyridoxal phosphate observed in our earlier studies seems now to be explained by its ability to reconstitute the apoenzyme, but we have not yet excluded the possibility that pyridoxal phosphate can transaminate with enzyme-bound pyridoxamine phosphate.

Aspartate β-decarboxylase is therefore an unusual vitamin $B_6$ enzyme in that the same active site can participate in two reactions, one of which is capable of converting the coenzyme necessary for the other to an inactive form. Transamination leading to enzyme-pyridoxamine phosphate, although much slower than decarboxylation, results in inability of the enzyme to act as a decarboxylase; restoration of decarboxylation activity may be accomplished by transamination of enzyme-pyridoxamine phosphate to enzyme-pyridoxal phosphate or by reconstitution of the apoenzyme. There appear to be certain differences in the relative effectiveness of α-keto acids and pyridoxal phosphate in activating various preparations of the enzyme; these and other differences that have been observed may be due at least in part to differences in the relative rates of transamination and dissociation of the pyridoxamine phosphate from the enzyme.

The ability of this enzyme to catalyze two types of reactions may serve as a significant metabolic control mechanism. It will be of interest to see whether the relative rates of these reactions are altered by variation of conditions. It would also be of interest to learn whether other vitamin $B_6$ enzymes that catalyze reactions involving similar ketimine intermediates are inactivated by substrate in this way, and whether such inactivation can be prevented or reversed by transamination with α-keto acids.

Dr. Jerry L. Hedrick in Dr. Fischer's laboratory has recently determined the emission spectrum of the Hanovia lamp used in the studies of Meister *et al.* and of Nishimura *et al.* on aspartate β-decarboxylase and in some of those of Fischer *et al.* on phosphorylase. Dr. Hedrick found that the major emisssion bands were at 313, 334, 367, 407, 438 and 547 mμ. It seems probable that one or more of the bands between 300 and 400 mμ may be responsible for destruction of the aspartate β-decarboxylase pyridoxal phosphate. That other lamps have not been useful in duplicating such destruction of pyridoxal phosphate suggests that they have considerable emission below 300 mμ so that there is an effect on the protein leading to denaturation.

## REFERENCES

1. A. Meister, H. A. Sober and S. V. Tice; *J. Biol. Chem.* **189**, 577, 591 (1951).
2. S. R. Mardashev; *Mikrobiologiia* **16**, 469 (1947).
3. S. R. Mardashev and R. N. Etinhof; *Biokhimiia* **13**, 402 (1948).
4. S. R. Mardashev and V. N. Gladkova; *Biokhimiia* **13**, 315 (1948).
5. S. R. Mardashev, L. A. Semina, R. N. Etinhof and A. I. Baliasnaia; *Biokhimiia* **14**, 44 (1949).
6. J. Cattanéo-Lacombe, J. C. Senez and P. Beaumont; *Biochim. et Biophys. Acta* **30**, 458 (1958).
7. L. V. Crawford; *Biochem. J.* **68**, 221 (1958).
8. B. Bheemeswar; *Nature* **176**, 555 (1955).
9. J. S. Nishimura, J. M. Manning and A. Meister; *Biochemistry* **1**, 442 (1962).
10. J. C. Rabinowitz and E. E. Snell; *Anal. Chem.* **19**, 277 (1947).
11. J. C. Rabinowitz and E. E. Snell; *J. Biol. Chem.* **169**, 631 (1947).
12. J. C. Rabinowitz, N. I. Mondy and E. E. Snell; *J. Biol. Chem.* **175**, 147 (1948).
13. Unpublished data.
14. A. E. Braunstein; *The Enzymes* (edited by P. D. Boyer, H. Lardy and K. Myrbäck), vol. II, p. 113, Academic Press, New York (1960).

15. E. E. SNELL; *Vitamins and Hormones* **16**, 77 (1958).
16. T. BARANOWSKI, B. ILLINGWORTH, D. H. BROWN and C. F. CORI; *Biochim. et Biophys. Acta* **25** 16 (1957).
17. E. H. FISCHER, A. B. KENT, E. R. SNYDER and E. G. KREBS; *J. Am. Chem. Soc.* **80**, 2906 (1958).
18. A. B. KENT, E. G. KREBS and E. H. FISCHER; *J. Biol. Chem.* **232**, 549 (1958).

## DISCUSSION

DR. CHRISTENSEN:

A proposal made by both Drs. Senez and Meister that the decarboxylation of aspartate occurs as the ketimine derivative of the substrate and the enzyme, yielding a ketimine derivative of the product, should be accessible to a simple test, as has probably occurred to the authors. If the experiments were made in the presence of some heavy water, deuterium should enter the $\alpha$-position of the product alanine, in place of a part of the $\alpha$-hydrogen. Confirmation of this point should place the further exploration of the role of the keto acid on a secure basis.

DR. SNELL:

Dr. Meister's observation on the equivalent action of added PLP or of the keto acid in promoting action of the aspartic $\beta$-decarboxylase recalls one of our unpublished findings with the histidine decarboxylase of *Lactobacillus* 30 a. We reported that this enzyme was activated several fold by addition of PLP plus $Fe^{3+}$. Subsequently, we have found that the added PLP apparently is not functioning catalytically because its effect can be duplicated by the addition of much larger quantities of certain non-ionic detergents such as Tween 40. The effect has not yet been studied in detail, but suggests that PLP and Tween are active by virtue of inducing a common configurational change in the decarboxylase protein.

GUNSALUS:

The last figure presented contained arrows in both directions. Has the addition as well as loss of $CO_2$ been measured; that is, both the decarboxylation and the reverse reaction?

MEISTER:

It is probable that the decarboxylation of aspartate is measurably reversible, but we have not yet examined this. It has been reported that glutamate decarboxylase can be made to go in the reverse direction, although the equilibrium constant favors decarboxylation.

GUNSALUS:

Could a $CO_2$ transfer reaction occur in this case, is the system avidin sensitive; or in other words, it is a biotin enzyme?

MEISTER:

I believe that this is unlikely. However, although I favor the "classical" vitamin $B_6$-type mechanism, I must admit that we have never carried out analyses for biotin, or studies with avidin. Perhaps now that a highly-purified enzyme is available this will become possible.

GUNSALUS:

Will the enzyme exchange $CO_2$ in an oxalacetate–pyruvate + $CO_2$ reaction; are any of the several mechanisms studied by Utter catalyzed by your system?

MEISTER:

We have not studied reactions of this type.

GUNSALUS:

A point of semantics, if you add pyridoxal phosphate to the enzyme and increase the catalytic rate, are you really talking about a pyridoxamine phosphate enzyme? I should be included to say pyridoxal phosphate enzyme. If there were a feedback inhibition, that is, is the system sensitive to $\alpha$-alanine or to pyridoxal? One could ask experimentally if there were feedback inhibition of the enzyme by α-L-alanine or pyridoxal. Has the sensitivity of the enzyme to these reactants been measured?

MEISTER:

In view of the recent work (see addendum) on the mechanism of activation of aspartate β-decarboxylase it appears that the coenzyme must shuttle back and forth between pyridoxamine phosphate and pyridoxal phosphate as in a transaminase. Thus, transaminases and aspartate β-decarboxylase, in contrast to other vitamin $B_6$-catalyzed enzymatic reactions, use both forms of the coenzyme. Perhaps there should be a terminology to distinguish these types. We have not carried out studies directed to detection of "feedback" inhibition. The enzyme might be inhibited by a very high concentration of L-alanine. Pyridoxal is inactive when substituted for pyridoxal phosphate; this result differs from that reported by Dr. Senez, who found that there was some activation by free pyridoxal.

# STUDIES ON AMINOMALONATE

by MARGARET MATTHEW and A. NEUBERGER

Department of Chemical Pathology,
St. Mary's Hospital Medical School, London, W.2

WE BECAME interested in aminomalonate some years ago when we investigated the condensation of glycine and succinyl-coenzyme A to give aminolaevulic acid (ALA). This condensation requires pyridoxal phosphate, but this was shown several years ago by ourselves[1] and various other groups, especially Shemin and his co-workers in the United States.[2] However, both the avian systems and microbial preparations which were used were not highly purified, mainly because the enzyme responsible is very labile and activity is readily lost during the various purification procedures employed. However, working with ALA synthetase of *Rhodopseudomonas spheroides*, we found a biotin requirement for the formation of this enzyme,[3] and this suggested that the actual substrate might not be glycine, that the carboxylation of glycine may precede the actual condensation with succinyl-CoA and the real substrate might be aminomalonate. Later evidence[3] clearly demonstrated that biotin was not specifically concerned with the synthesis of the enzyme, but we had in the meantime prepared aminomalonate and various derivatives thereof, and this led to an investigation of the enzymology of this substance. I wish to report today on some of the observations made.

First of all I would like to say something about the purely chemical synthesis of aminomalonate. This substance was first prepared by Baeyer[4] and later by Piloty and Finckh[5], and various other syntheses have been reported more recently.[6,7] Our method followed the method of Lutz[8], who started from malonic acid. He converted malonic acid into the monobromo compound, and then treated the bromomalonic acid with ammonia which gave the ammonium salt of aminomalonic acid. Treatment with Zeokarb 225 in the $H^+$ form gave aminomalonic acid, which is fairly unstable, at least in the form of the free acid. It loses carbon dioxide at a measurable rate if kept in solution at room temperature,[5,6] and is also somewhat unstable in the solid state. It is fairly strong acid and the p$K_1$ has never been determined. Its p$K_2$ is approximately 3.2[9] and the p$K$ corresponding to the amino group is approximately 9.4. The compound therefore has a 1-unit negative charge, between the pH values of 5.5 to about 7.7. This property has been used in separation and identification by high-tension paper electrophoresis. Salts such as potassium or ammonium salts of aminomalonic acid are quite stable and the compound has therefore been stored in the form of one of these salts.

We have also prepared the ethyl and methyl half esters by partial saponification of N-benzyloxycarbonyldiethyl or dimethyl aminomalonate, and in a similar manner we have synthesized the monoamide (Fig. 1). These compounds are of course neutral at a pH of approximately 6.0 with a $pK_2$ corresponding to the amino group of about 7.5 for the monoesters or 8.1 for the monoamide. This shift of the dissociation constant of the ammonium ion is of the expected order of magnitude, if the changes of the charge from the di-acid to the mono-acid are taken into account.

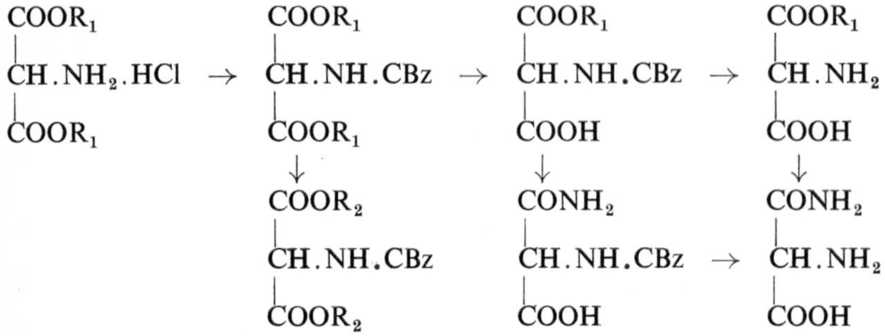

$$
\begin{array}{ccccccc}
COOR_1 & & COOR_1 & & COOR_1 & & COOR_1 \\
| & & | & & | & & | \\
CH.NH_2.HCl & \rightarrow & CH.NH.CBz & \rightarrow & CH.NH.CBz & \rightarrow & CH.NH_2 \\
| & & | & & | & & | \\
COOR_1 & & COOR_1 & & COOH & & COOH \\
 & & \downarrow & & \downarrow & & \downarrow \\
 & & COOR_2 & & CONH_2 & & CONH_2 \\
 & & | & & | & & | \\
 & & CH.NH.CBz & & CH.NH.CBz & \rightarrow & CH.NH_2 \\
 & & | & & | & & | \\
 & & COOR_2 & & COOH & & COOH
\end{array}
$$

$R_1 = C_2H_5.$

$R_2 = CH_3.$

$CB_Z$ = Benzyloxycarbonyl.

FIG. 1. Outline of the synthesis of the monoesters and monoamide of aminomalonate.

## EFFECTS OF AMINOMALONATE AND DERIVATIVES ON ENZYMES

When we tried the effect of the addition of aminomalonate on a system containing either avian or bacterial ALA synthetase, glycine, pyridoxal phosphate, and succinyl-CoA, an intense colour was obtained suggesting formation of ALA. However, it was soon realized that this was misleading. The reaction used for estimation of ALA was a condensation of this acid with acetylacetone to give a pyrrole which could be estimated by the Ehrlich reagent. It was soon found that aminomalonic acid itself condenses in a slightly different manner with acetylacetone to give a pyrrole which can react with Ehrlich's reagent to give a colour differing little from the accepted characteristic given by ALA. We therefore had to modify our reaction for ALA. This was done by using ethyl acetoacetate for acetylacetone. The former compound reacts with ALA, but not aminomalonate, to form a pyrrole. Having now a reliable method we could investigate more fully the reaction of aminomalonate with succinyl-CoA in the presence of the enzyme. It was found that aminomalonate, if completely freed from glycine, does not react with succinyl-CoA to give an aminoketone. If glycine was present in the system, it was found that aminomalonate inhibited the reaction (Table 1). About a 50 per cent inhibition was observed if the molar ratio of amino-

TABLE 1. INHIBITION OF AMINOLAEVULATE SYNTHETASE BY AMINOMALONATE

Aminomalonate was incubated in the standard assay system containing 40 $\mu$moles of glycine. Inhibition was determined by comparing amounts of $\delta$-aminolaevulate formed in the absence and presence of aminomalonate.

| Aminomalonate ($\mu$moles) | Aminomalonate : glycine (molar ratio) | Inhibition (%) |
|---|---|---|
| 0.0 | — | 0 |
| 0.5 | 0.0125 | 16 |
| 1.0 | 0.025 | 36 |
| 2.0 | 0.05 | 43 |
| 4.0 | 0.1 | 54 |
| 10.0 | 0.25 | 65 |
| 20.0 | 0.5 | 86 |

TABLE 2. COMPARISON OF THE INHIBITION OF AMINOLAEVULATE SYNTHETASE BY SOME AMINES WITH THE STABILITY OF THE IMINES WHICH THESE FORM WITH PYRIDOXAL PHOSPHATE *in vitro*

The ability of compounds to inhibit aminolaevulate synthetase was tested at pH 7.4 in a system containing 40 $\mu$moles of glycine and a crude enzyme extract from *Rps. spheroides*. The affinity constant ($K_d$) of the imine which these compounds form *in vitro* at pH 7.4 with pyridoxal phosphate is analagous to $K_m$ and is measured spectrophotometrically.

| Compound added | Quantity required for 50% inhibition of aminolaevulate synthetase ($\mu$moles) | $K_d$ (mM) |
|---|---|---|
| Aminomalonate | 4, 16 | 50.3 |
| Monoethyl aminomalonate | 10, 30 | 44.4 |
| Monomethyl aminomalonate | 44 | 44.5 |
| Ethanolamine | 23 | 9.5 |
| Isobutylamine | 26 | 2.7 |
| Ethyl aminomalonate | 56 | 71.4 |
| Aminomalonic acid monoamide | >100 | 126.0 |
| Sarcosine | >200 | — |

malonate to glycine was 1 : 10. With a molar ratio of 1 : 2 the inhibition was almost 90 per cent. Some slightly different results were obtained with the chicken erythrocyte ALA synthetase preparation, but even in this case the inhibitory power of aminomalonate was found to be very high. We then tried other compounds as potential inhibitors (Table 2). The monomethyl aminomalonate was a less powerful inhibitor, but still quite strong, and surprisingly the monomethyl ester was weaker than the monoethyl ester and aminomalonic monoamide had practically no inhibitory powers. Ethanolamine showed about the same degree of inhibition as monomethyl aminomalonate and was a more powerful inhibitor than diethyl aminomalonate. Isobutylamine was also a fairly powerful inhibitor but L-serine was completely ineffective, whilst L-alanine and L-threonine were quite strong inhibitors.

Lineweaver and Burk[10] plots of the inhibition of aminolaevulate synthetase by aminomalonate and monomethyl aminomalonate gave the following average values :

$$K_m \text{ for glycine} = 1.42 \times 10^{-4}\ \text{M}$$

$$K_i \text{ for aminomalonate} = 2.25 \times 10^{-5}\ \text{M}$$

$$K_i \text{ for monoethyl aminomalonate} = 3.11 \times 10^{-5}\ \text{M}$$

We next studied the influence of the pyridoxal phosphate concentration on this inhibition. Unfortunately the concentration of pyridoxal phosphate could not be increased beyond a relatively low value as high concentrations of this coenzyme interfered with the colour reaction which we used. However, it could be shown that inhibition of the synthetase reaction by a constant amount of aminomalonate decreased from about 60 to 30 per cent as the concentration of pyridoxal phosphate decreased from 0.138 to 0.0043 mM. In other words, the inhibitory power of aminomalonate on the synthetase reaction was more marked at a higher pyridoxal phosphate concentration. We have also tried to relate the inhibitory power of aminomalonate to the affinity constant[11] for pyridoxal phosphate and the amines and amino acids used in these assays (Table 2). The results show no clear correlation between these two sets of values.

We may assume that the general mechanism of reactions catalysed by pyridoxal phosphate-containing enzymes follows the pattern first suggested by Braunstein[12] and Snell[13]. In other words, the initial reaction is a formation of an aldimine between the aldehyde group of pyridoxal phosphate and the primary amine. We may also assume that the pyridoxal phosphate which reacts enzymically is not the free coenzyme but pyridoxal phosphate bound to the enzyme protein. In order to explain the aminomalonate inhibition, we may also assume that aminomalonate competes with glycine for a position on the enzyme–pyridoxal phosphate complex. The fact that the inhibition is competitive between aminomalonate and glycine supports this conclusion. The great efficiency of aminomalonate as an inhibitor and its superiority in that respect over the monomethyl and monoethyl esters and monoamide or the di-ester may partly be explained by steric factors, but it may also be due to the fact that the possession of two negatively charged carboxyl groups assists in the anchoring of the aminomalonate molecule in the enzyme–coenzyme complex. It is particularly interesting that the monomethyl and monoethyl and monoamide derivatives of aminomalonate which have a lower p$K$ for the amino group than the parent compound, and will therefore contain a higher proportion of the nitrogen in the form of a free amine, are less effective than aminomalonate itself, which has a much higher p$K_3$. Braunstein pointed out[14] that amino acids can act as inhibitors of specific enzymic reactions catalysed by pyridoxal phosphate-requiring enzymes, and some general inhibition was indeed found in the present work by many amino acids tested. However, some compounds such as ethanolamine or threonine seem to be particularly effective, and at the moment it seems to us impossible to explain the relative potency of all these compounds by one hypothesis. It seems that apart from the p$K$ values of the amino group, other factors must play a part, such as the particular fit of the compound in question on the enzyme surface, the presence of carboxyl group, and other factors at present not capable of a qualitative analysis. I should mention here that some other enzymes have been shown to be inhibited by aminomalonate. Thus, the serine transhydroxymethylase is significantly inhibited by aminomalonate, but transaminases such as glutamic–oxaloacetic transaminase are not affected by aminomalonate. Aminomalonate has only a very slight inhibitory action towards the glycine N-acylase or glycinamide ribotide kinosynthase, neither of which requires pyridoxal phosphate, and aminomalonate has also relatively little action on tyrosine decarboxylase, which does require pyridoxal phosphate. It would therefore seem that aminomalonate is inhibitory mainly in reactions in which it can compete with glycine in the reaction of this with a pyridoxal phosphate–enzyme complex.

## NON-ENZYMIC REACTIONS OF AMINOMALONATE

I will now deal briefly with some non-enzymic reactions which came to our attention in studies on various enzyme reactions described above. The reaction between aminomalonate and its derivatives with formaldehyde, benzaldehyde and acetaldehyde was studied in the presence of pyridoxal (Table 3). Incubations were done at room temperature at various pH values. In the absence of pyridoxal phosphate or pyridoxal there is no reaction with any aldehyde in the case of aminomalonate. The monoethyl ester, however, forms even without pyridoxal phosphate significant quantities of the $\beta$-hydroxy monoesters, particularly of phenylserine. The diethyl ester is relatively negative and so is glycine ester. In the presence of pyridoxal aminomalonate forms significant amounts of serine, threonine and phenylserine on addition of the appropriate aldehyde, and the same applies to the monoethyl compound. This condensation was found to go best at a pH slightly above 7.0 (Table 4). At acid pH aminomalonate was largely decarboxylated to form glycine and at pH 10.5 it was almost unreactive in spite of pyridoxal phosphate being present. These reactions were in general not inhibited by EDTA, apart from very high concentrations which had some effect. The non-enzymic condensations were not affected by any of the metals studied with the exception of copper and iron, which increased formation of serine, and aluminium which decreases the formation of

TABLE 3. CONDENSATIONS BETWEEN VARIOUS ALDEHYDES AND COMPOUNDS RELATED TO AMINOMALONATE

Amino acid derivative (10 μmoles), aldehyde (10 μmoles) and $NaHCO_3$ (2.8 μmoles) were incubated in a volume of 0.2 ml with and without pyridoxal hydrochloride (1.5 μmoles) for 1 hr at 37°. The α-amino-β-hydroxy acids formed were measured semiquantitatively.

| Compound | Pyridoxal | % Conversion of compound to | | |
|---|---|---|---|---|
| | | Serine | Threonine | Phenylserine |
| Aminomalonate | + | 14 | 6 | 38 |
| Aminomalonate | — | Nil | Nil | Nil |
| Monoethyl aminomalonate | + | 25 | 25 | 18 |
| Monoethyl aminomalonate | — | 8 | 4 | 35 |
| Ethyl aminomalonate | + | 4 | Nil | Nil |
| Ethyl aminomalonate | — | 4 | Nil | Nil |

TABLE 4. EFFECT OF pH ON THE CONDENSATION OF FORMALDEHYDE WITH AMINOMALONATE

Glycine (15 μmoles), formaldehyde (6 μmoles) and pyridoxal phosphate (0.3 μmoles) were incubated in a volume of 0.2 ml for 1 hr at 37° in the presence of various buffers at concentrations of 0.05 M.

| Buffer | pH | Glycine | Serine |
|---|---|---|---|
| Citrate–phosphate | 3.0 | +++ | + |
| Acetate | 4.5 | ++ | ++ |
| Phosphate | 6.0 | ++ | ++ |
| Phosphate | 7.5 | + | +++ |
| Bicarbonate–carbonate | 9.0 | + | ++ |
| Bicarbonate–carbonate | 10.5 | + | — |

serine but caused the appearance of an acidic spot which probably consisted of a β-hydroxymethyl aminomalonate. In other words, it was probably a metal complex of the serine precursor.

It may also be mentioned that the non-enzymic formation of serine, even in the absence of metals, involved the β-hydroxymethyl ester of aminomalonate as intermediate and could be clearly demonstrated on paper electrophoresis.

## AMINOMALONATE DECARBOXYLASE

The last item I want to discuss is aminomalonate decarboxylase which was first discovered by Shimura *et al.*[15] in preparations of silk gland. We have found relatively high concentrations of this enzyme in a number of micro-organisms, such as *Rps. spheroides*, *Rps. Rubrum* and *Pr. Vulgaris* (Table 5). The enzyme seems to be constitutive and not adaptive. We have also found the enzyme in the soluble fraction of rat liver, but we could not observe any activity in blood, brain, kidney or spleen, or in liver nuclei, mitochondria or microsomes. We have examined various other possible

TABLE 5. AMINOMALONATE DECARBOXYLASE ACTIVITY OF SOME BACTERIA

Bacteria were grown on media rich or poor in organic materials and crude dialysed extracts were assayed for enzymic activity.

| Organism | Enzyme activity (μmole/mg per hr) | |
|---|---|---|
| | Depleted medium | Nutrient medium |
| *Rps. spheroides* | 2.27 | 0.47 |
| *Pr. vulgaris* | 1.65 | 2.02 |
| *B. subtilis* | 0.85 | 0.67 |
| *Myco. smegmatis* | 0.0 | 0.41 |
| *E. coli* | 0.27 | 0.34 |
| *Cl. welchii* | No growth | 0.14 |

TABLE 6. THE EFFECT OF INHIBITORS OF PYRIDOXAL PHOSPHATE ON AMINOMALONATE DECARBOXYLASE

| Compound added | Final concentration (mM) | Enzyme activity (%) |
|---|---|---|
| None | — | 100 |
| KCN | 2.5 | 55 |
| Isoniazid | 2.5 | 34 |
| Aminoxyacetic acid | 2.5 | 24 |
| L-Penicillamine | 2.5 | 12 |

substrates such as aspartic and glutamic acids, serine, threonine and a number of other likely compounds, but the enzyme appears to be quite specific for aminomalonic acid. The decarboxylation activity is inhibited by cyanide, isoniazid, aminoxyacetic acid and L-pencillamine, which is a particularly powerful inhibitor (Table 6). These data suggested that this enzyme, in common with other amino acid decarboxylases, has pyridoxal phosphate as a coenzyme, and it was found that the activity of undialysed extracts was stimulated by added pyridoxal phosphate (Fig. 2). This enzyme also acted

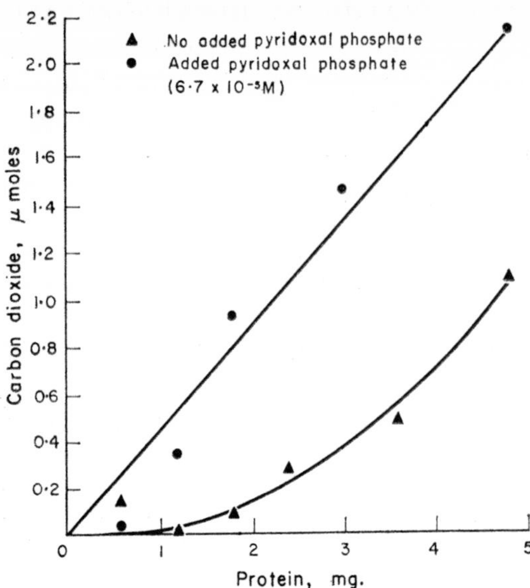


FIG. 2. Activation of aminomalonate decarboxylase by pyridoxal phosphate. Enzyme activity was measured in crude undialysed extracts of *Rps. spheroides*.

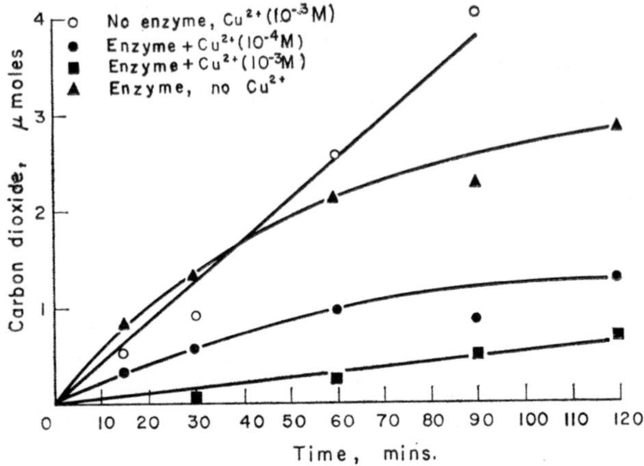


FIG. 3. Effect of copper on the enzymic and non-enzymic decarboxylation of aminomalonate.

The enzyme was a crude undialysed preparation of *Rps. spheroides*. Control flasks containing boiled enzyme were run for each concentration of $Cu^{2+}$, and the $CO_2$ released in these was subtracted from that released in the corresponding experimental flasks.

on monoethyl aminomalonate and it was inhibited by L-serine, but no other compound tested by us had any significant inhibition.

The decarboxylase appears to require sulphydryl groups for activity. The enzyme is also inhibited by a variety of di- and tri-valent metals and it is particularly interesting that copper, which is a very powerful cofactor of the non-enzymic decarboxylation of aminomalonate catalysed by pyridoxal phosphate, is a strong inhibitor of the enzymic decarboxylation (Fig. 3).

Finally I wish to say that the presence of this enzyme in a variety of cells may indicate that aminomalonate has an important and as yet undisclosed part to play in intermediary metabolism. One can speculate on this point, but so far no definite information is available which would be helpful, and we are at present engaged in searching for other enzymic and metabolic reaction in which aminomalonate might participate.

## REFERENCES

1. K. D. GIBSON, W. G. LAVER and A. NEUBERGER; *Biochem. J.* **70**, 71 (1958).
2. G. KIKUCHI, A. KUMAR, P. TALMAGE and D. SHEMIN; *J. Biol. Chem.* **233**, 1214 (1958).
3. K. D. GIBSON, A. NEUBERGER and G. H. TAIT; *Biochem. J.* **83**, 539 (1962).
4. A. BAEYER; *Ann. Chem. Liebigs* **131**, 291 (1864).
5. O. PILOTY and C. FINCKH; *Ann. Chem. Liebigs* **333**, 71 (1904).
6. S. RUHEMAN and K. J. P. ORTON; *J. Chem. Soc.* **67**, 1002 (1895).
7. T. B. JOHNSON and B. H. NICOLET; *J. Am. Chem. Soc.* **36**, 355 (1914).
8. O. LUTZ; *Ber. deut. chem. Ges.* **35**, 2549 (1902).
9. G. SCHWARZENBACH, E. KAMPITSCH and R. STEINER; *Helv. Chim. Acta* **28**, 1133 (1945).
10. H. LINEWEAVER and D. BURK; *J. Am. Chem. Soc.* **56**, 658 (1934).
11. N. LUCAS, H. K. KING and S. J. BROWN; *Biochem. J.* **83**, 118 (1962).
12. A. E. BRAUNSTEIN and M. M. SHEMYAKIN; *Doklady Akad. Nauk S.S.S.R.* **85**, 1115 (1952).
13. E. E. SNELL; *Vitamins and Hormones* **16**, 77 (1958).
14. A. E. BRAUNSTEIN; *The Enzymes* (edited by P. D. BOYER, H. LARDY and K. MYRBÄCK), vol. II, p. 113, Academic Press, New York (1960).
15. K. SHIMURA, H. NAGAYAMA and A. KIKUCHI; *Nature* **177**, 935 (1956).

## DISCUSSION

DR. CHRISTENSEN:

Have you by any chance looked to see whether pyridoxal or pyridoxal phosphate are fully recovered when they serve as catalysts for the cleavage of monoethyl aminomalonate and for its condensation with aldehydes?

The case strikes me as rather similar to one studied by Gregerman and myself (*J. Biol. Chem.* **220**, 765, 1956), namely the catalytic dehydrochlorination of β-chloroalanine. But in that case the reactivity at the β-carbon extend to the carbonyl group of pyridoxal itself: a proportionate loss of pyridoxal and of the product, pyruvate, relative to the release of chloride ion, signalled an interaction undoubtedly involving fusion of the β-carbon chain of the substrate to the formyl group of pyridoxal.

Similarly Snell and his associates have observed that the aluminium chelate of pyridoxylidene glycine passes partially to an addition product of glycine with the formyl group, which he called pyridoxylserine. In the present instance I wonder whether the carbonyl group of the catalyst itself escapes attack of the type that you observed on several added aldehydes.

# STUDIES ON LEUCINE DECARBOXYLASE

by H. K. King

Department of Chemistry, The University, Liverpool, England

The amino acid decarboxylases of bacteria described by Gale[1] share the common characteristics of an acid pH optimum; formation by the organism only under culture at low pH; and strict specificity for a single amino acid. Gale described decarboxylases only for amino acids with more than two polar groups (e.g. glutamic acid, arginine, tyrosine). When, therefore, Proom and Woiwod[2] reported the formation of amines from valine and leucine by *Proteus* strains under neutral conditions of culture, it seemed likely that Gale's list of bacterial decarboxylases was incomplete, and that the newly reported system might differ considerably in its properties from Gale's enzymes. On investigation[3,4] this proved to be the case.

*Proteus vulgaris* contains an enzyme which decarboxylates leucine, iso-leucine, valine, norvaline, and α-amino-n-butyric acid to yield the respective amines. There is a rather broad pH optimum at about pH 7. The classical

Table 1. Activity of Leucine Decarboxylase towards Various Substrates, in I.U. per Mg Dry Wt., following Growth in Presence of Inducers.

| | Substrate | | |
|---|---|---|---|
| Inducer | Leucine | Valine | Isoleucine |
| None | 5 | 5 | 0 |
| Leucine | 108 | 70 | 52 |
| Valine | 48 | 33 | 28 |
| Isoleucine | 33 | 26 | 19 |

Michaelis constants ($K_m$) are of about the same order of magnitude for each substrate, viz. 0.01 M when measured at pH 6.[5] As with Gale's decarboxylases, the enzyme is inducible. Only a trace of activity is obtained unless the organism is grown in presence of one of the known substrates. It is noteworthy that the relative activity towards the various substrates is independent of which of them is employed as inducer.[4] The enzyme indeed proved useful material for the study of enzyme induction,[6] but this lies outside the scope of the present paper.

The induction results did, however, remove any doubts whether we were dealing with a single enzyme of broad specificity or with several separate but specific enzymes which we had failed to separate. The latter possibility had to be considered carefully in view of our early results with both intact cells and cell-free preparations. These showed markedly different behaviour with leucine and valine, the two substrates most frequently employed in our studies. Decarboxylation of valine proceeded at a steady rate for up to 1 hr; but leucine decarboxylation started at a high rate in the first few minutes and then dropped to a steady but much slower level within 10–15 min of addition of the substrate. Addition of pyridoxal phosphate did not affect the valine reaction, but with leucine it permitted the initial rapid rate of decarboxylation to be maintained. Some pyridoxal phosphate decarboxylases had already been described in which the initial rate of reaction was not maintained, through loss of the coenzyme by spontaneous resolution of the system on addition of the substrate.[7–9]

Two points of interest arise here. First is the implication that since spontaneous resolution appears to take place more readily when leucine is the substrate rather than valine, the coenzyme–apoenzyme link must be less stable when leucine is being attacked. Such a situation is rare in enzymology and it was necessary to apply a number of rigorous criteria to ensure that our results could not be explained by the presence of two or more separate decarboxylases in our preparation, rather than a single enzyme of broad specificity and a substrate-dependent coenzyme affinity.

If the coenzyme affinity is determined from reciprocal plots of the rate of action at various coenzyme concentrations we find that the affinity constants (i.e. concentrations of pyridoxal phosphate permitting half-maximal velocity) are 0.07 $\mu$M during valine decarboxylation, but 0.9 $\mu$M for leucine decarboxylation. In pyridoxal phosphate enzymes one point of attachment is usually the coenzyme itself, through Schiff base formation between the amino group and the carbonyl of the pyridoxal; there is evidence that in many cases it is this point of attachment which largely determines the substrate affinity (see p. 264 and Ref. 10). We are therefore not dealing with the simple classical concept :

$$E + S = ES \tag{1}$$

(where E = enzyme and S = substrate) but with something more complex involving the equilibria

$$E + PLP = E{-}PLP \tag{2}$$

$$E{-}PLP + S = E{-}PLP{-}S \tag{3}$$

$$E{-}PLP{-}S = E + PLP{-}S \tag{4}$$

and also the non-enzymic reaction :

$$PLP + S = PLP{-}S \tag{5}$$

It might be possible to obtain the true enzyme–coenzyme affinity (equilibrium 2) if changes occur in fluorescence[11] or absorption spectra[12] when apoenzyme and coenzyme are mixed in absence of substrate. So far we have not obtained the leucine decarboxylase sufficiently pure for such observations. The reciprocal plots therefore probably represent equilibrium (4). The position of this equilibrium will depend on the nature of the substrate S, and hence we might well expect to find that the coenzyme affinity varied according to the substrate undergoing decarboxylation. We can, however, hazard a guess that the true coenzyme affinity constant may well be of the same order as the figure obtained in the presence of valine. We have seen that when leucine undergoes decarboxylation there is liable to be a rapid fall in reaction rate due to dissociation of the coenzyme. This is not seen with valine decarboxylation, even when the coenzyme level is well below that required for full saturation of the *valine* system.

One of the more curious results of the action of leucine in lowering the coenzyme affinity is an unusual form of competitive inhibition (Figs. 1 and 2). If we add valine to a preparation of the enzyme in presence of just sufficient pyridoxal phosphate to saturate the system, we get a steady output of carbon dioxide (Fig. 1). If we now add leucine, the reaction is progressively inhibited, although leucine itself normally undergoes even more rapid decarboxylation than valine. But under conditions of limiting coenzyme concentration, leucine causes displacement of the coenzyme from the enzyme surface and the reaction slows down. If the experiment is repeated at a higher level of pyridoxal phosphate, leucine does not exert this inhibitory action (Fig. 2).

The second important point is that displacement of the coenzyme seems to be a relatively slow phenomenon. In the leucine decarboxylation the initial rapid rate settles down to the slower reaction only after a period of the order of 10 min, and the same applies in Fig. 1 where the leucine drives the coenzyme off a system already decarboxylating valine. On the other hand the *combination* of coenzyme with apoenzyme is rapid. If additional pyridoxal phosphate is added to a system not previously saturated with coenzyme, maximum activity is achieved immediately. The enzyme–coenzyme interaction may thus be slow and not fully reversible. This is going to make interpretation of the kinetics of the reactions (1)–(5) very difficult.

Experience with inhibitor-analogues of pyridoxal phosphate has also suggested that enzyme–coenzyme union is not readily reversible. The analogue " toxopyrimidine phosphate " will inhibit tyrosine decarboxylase if added to the apoenzyme previously to or simultaneously with pyridoxal phosphate; but it is relatively ineffective if added to the system after apoenzyme and coenzyme have been allowed to interact.[13] Other workers have had similar experience with desoxypyridoxin phosphate.[14]

The slow reaction between pyridoxal phosphate and an enzyme is also seen in the inhibition of leucine decarboxylase by pyridoxal phosphate

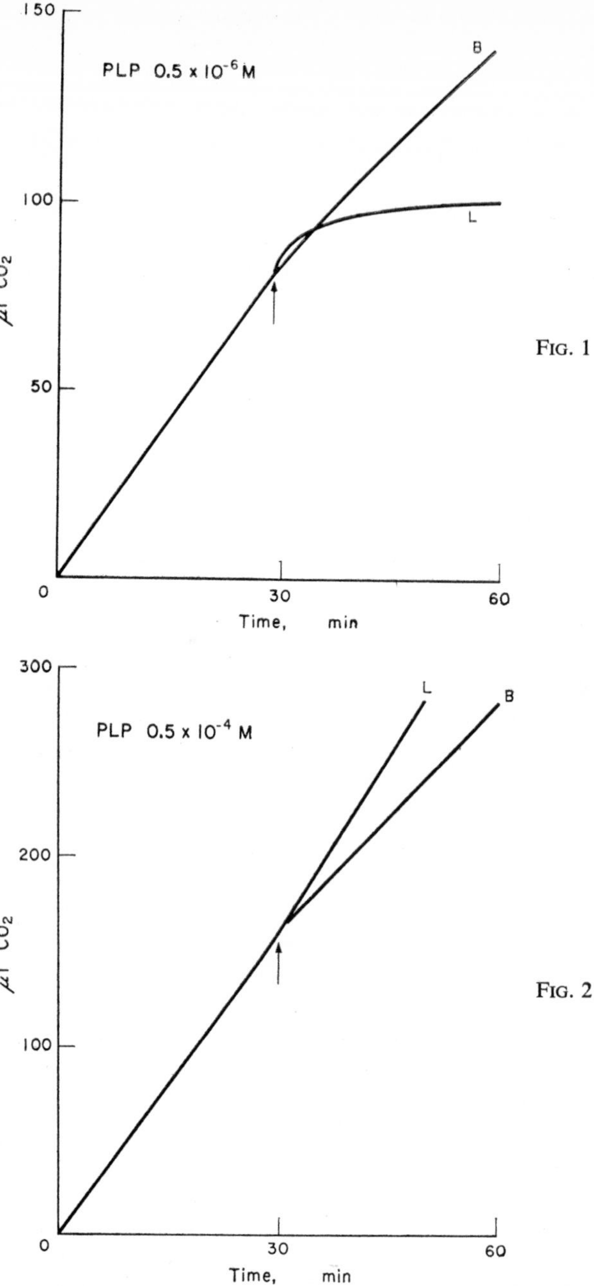


Figs. 1 and 2. Inhibition of leucine decarboxylase by coenzyme dissociation. Valine added at $t = 0$ to enzyme + pyridoxal phosphate ($0.5 \times 10^{-6}$ M in Fig. 1 $0.5 \times 10^{-4}$ M in Fig. 2); leucine (L) or buffer (B) added at $t = 30$ min.

oxime; the action of the inhibitor is slow, and so also is the restoration of activity on addition of excess pyridoxal phosphate (Fig. 3[15].)

The relations between apoenzyme and coenzyme became of considerable interest when the action of various inhibitors on the enzyme was investigated.[16] Iodoacetate behaved in a peculiar manner. It brought about a slow and progressive inhibition of decarboxylation, which was much more severe

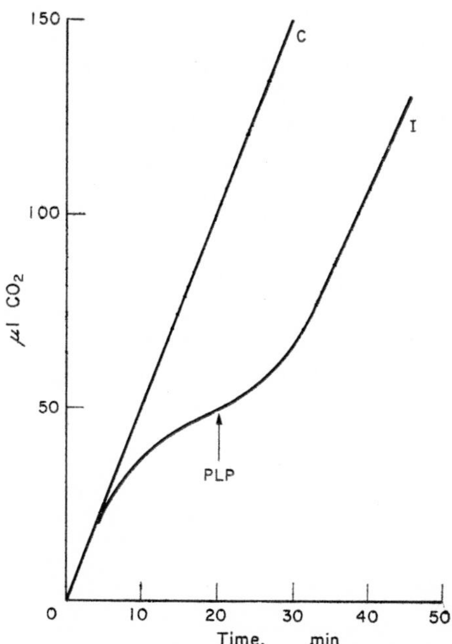


FIG. 3. Inhibition of leucine decarboxylase by pyridoxal phosphate oxime and reversal by pyridoxal phosphate. Control (C); enzyme, leucine and pyridoxal phosphate ($5 \times 10^{-6}$ M); Experiment (I), pyridoxal phosphate oxime ($5 \times 10^{-6}$ M) also added at $t = 0$; inhibition reversed by increasing pyridoxal phosphate concentration to $10^{-4}$ M at $t = 20$ min.

with leucine than with the other substrates (Fig. 4). It thus seemed to accentuate the loss of activity arising from coenzyme dissociation already noted during leucine decarboxylation. The inhibitory action of iodoacetate was much less apparent at higher pyridoxal phosphate concentrations. The coenzyme was not able to *reverse* inhibition. In Fig. 5 addition of excess pyridoxal phosphate at the point indicated by the arrows did not alter the course of the reaction. It did not reverse the inhibition already established, nor even retard its further progress.

Iodoacetate inhibition could not be regarded as a straightforward case of competitive inhibition since it was not reversed by pyridoxal phosphate.

Nevertheless, it has some of the characteristics of competition. When decarboxylation was carried out in presence of excess leucine and at varying levels of pyridoxal phosphate, a reciprocal plot of the initial reaction velocities followed closely the characteristics of a competitive inhibitor.[16] There was no evidence, however, of the iodoacetate competing with the substrate. Determination of reaction rates in presence of excess coenzyme and varying leucine concentrations gave a typical " non-competitive " plot.

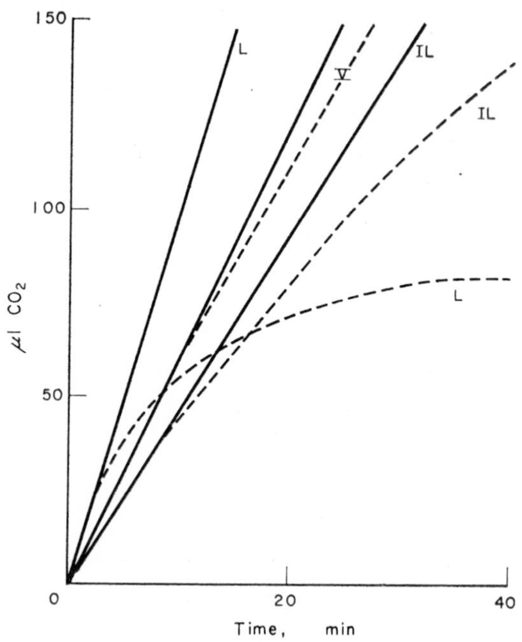


FIG. 4. Inhibition of leucine decarboxylase by iodoacetate. Full lines: substrates added to enzyme + $7 \times 10^{-6}$ M pyridoxal phosphate at $t = 0$. Broken lines: 0.002 M iodoacetate also added at $t = 0$. Substrates: L, leucine; V, valine, IL, isoleucine.

Experiments were also performed to determine whether the substrate would protect the enzyme to any degree against inhibition by iodoacetate. Surprisingly, substrates—particularly leucine—appeared to sensitize rather than to protect the enzyme. This is shown in the experiment illustrated by Fig. 6. In curve A substrate (leucine) was added to the enzyme at $t = 0$; no decarboxylation occurred owing to absence of the coenzyme. Pyridoxal phosphate was then added at $t = 30$ min, and a normal reaction followed. In curve B, following the same course, pyridoxal phosphate was added to the enzyme at $t = 0$ and leucine at $t = 30$ min. In curve C the iodoacetate was added to the enzyme at $t = 0$, and both leucine and pyridoxal phosphate at

$t = 30$ min. The enzyme is severely inhibited. In D, the enzyme was incubated with pyridoxal phosphate and inhibitor prior to addition of substrate at $t = 30$; coenzyme has afforded considerable protection. But in E, where enzyme and substrate were incubated in presence of inhibitor

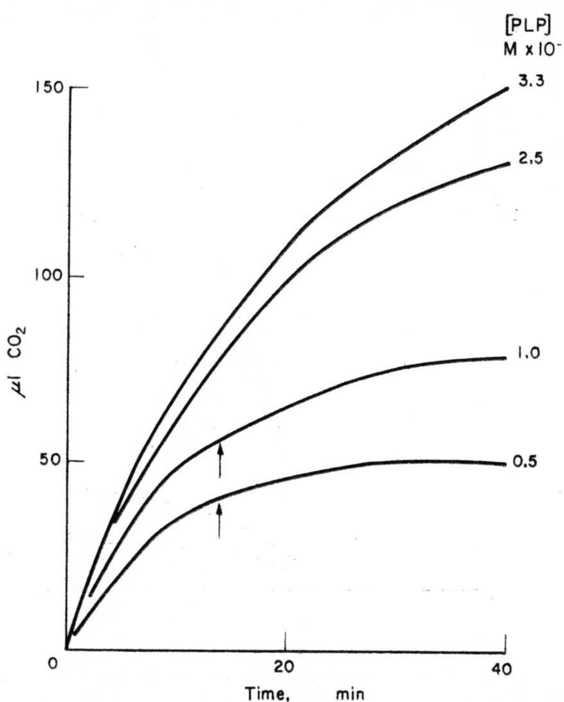


FIG. 5. Inhibition of leucine decarboxylation by iodoacetate at varying pyridoxal phosphate (PLP) concentrations. Iodoacetate (0.002 M) added at $t = 0$. Addition of excess ($0.5 \times 10^{-4}$ M) pyridoxal phosphate at $t = 15$ min as shown by arrows did not increase activity.

and the reaction initiated by addition of the coenzyme, inhibition is much more severe even than when the enzyme was treated with the inhibitor only. It is unusual for an enzyme to be rendered *more* susceptible to the action of an inhibitor through the presence of its substrate.

This effect was more closely examined in the experiments shown in Fig. 7. The lower curve indicates the rate of decarboxylation at intervals after simultaneous addition of pyridoxal phosphate, leucine, and iodoacetate to the apoenzyme. In the upper curve, the enzyme was exposed to iodoacetate (in the presence of pyridoxal phosphate) for the time indicated on the abscissa and leucine then added, and the initial reaction rate recorded. This indicates clearly how the inhibition of the enzyme occurs more rapidly if the substrate is present. In Table 2 we compare the time required for 50 per cent inactivation in presence of various substrates, at two different pyridoxal phosphate levels. The lower level is about the minimum required to saturate the enzyme for valine decarboxylation, but is well below the saturating level

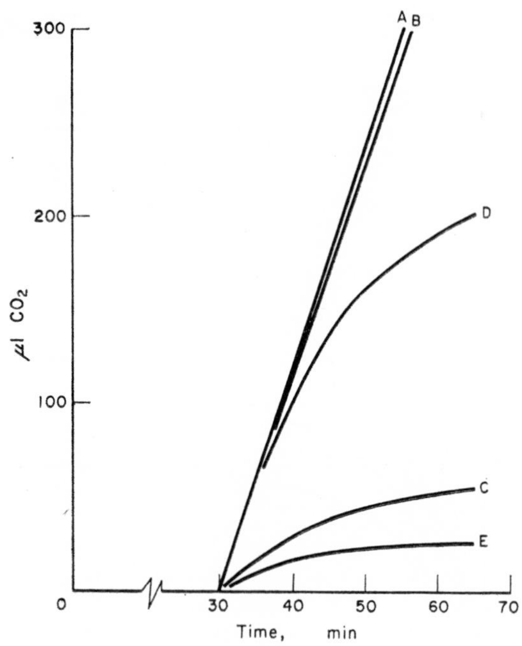


FIG. 6. Influence of substrate and coenzyme on iodoacetate inhibition of leucine decarboxylase. The following additions were made to the enzyme at the stated times:

A. $t = 0$, leucine;
$t = 30$, pyridoxal phosphate.
B. $t = 0$, pyridoxal phosphate ($2.7 \times 10^{-5}$ M);
$t = 30$, leucine (0.047 M).
C. $t = 0$, iodoacetate (0.002 M);
$t = 30$, pyridoxal phosphate + leucine.
D. $t = 0$, iodoacetate + pyridoxal phosphate;
$t = 30$, leucine.
E. $t = 0$, iodoacetate + leucine;
$t = 30$, pyridoxal phosphate.

for reaction with leucine. Valine does not potentiate the inhibitor at all, even at the lower coenzyme concentration. Leucine has a very deleterious action; the other substrates show intermediate behaviour.

These results suggested that Pyridoxal phosphate might be attached to the apoenzyme either through the iodoacetate-sensitive group, or possibly at a point so close to the latter as to shield it from the inhibitor. This situation was explored further by using derivatives of pyridoxal phosphate which compete with the latter for the enzyme centre. Those employed were

TABLE 2. TIME REQUIRED FOR RATE OF DECARBOXYLATION TO FALL TO HALF INITIAL VALUE IN PRESENCE OF 0.002 M IODOACETATE

| | Pyridoxal phosphate | |
|---|---|---|
| | 6.7 μM (min) | 1.35 μM (min) |
| A. No substrate present | 35 | 16 |
| B. In presence of leucine | 7 | 2 |
| valine | 40 | 17 |
| isoleucine | 25 | 10 |
| norvaline | 20 | 6 |
| α-aminobutyric acid | 25 | 10 |

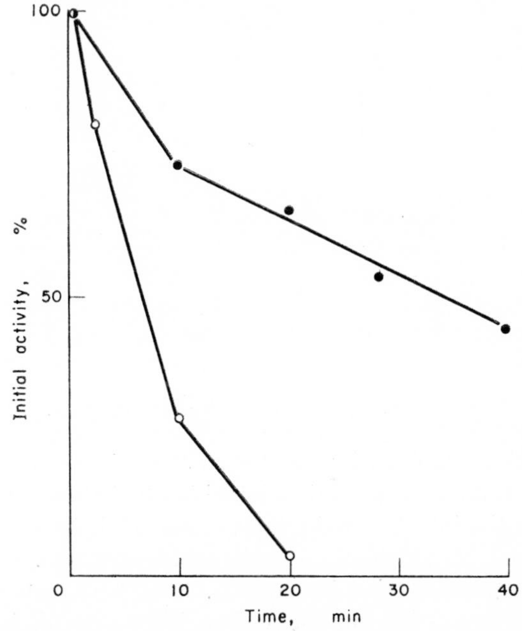


FIG. 7. Potentiation of iodoacetate inhibition by leucine. Upper line, activity of enzyme after incubation with iodoacetate (0.002 M) and pyridoxal phosphate ($6.7 \times 10^{-6}$ M) for time stated. Lower line, same conditions but leucine (0.047 M) present.

pyridoxal phosphate oxime and cyanhydrin, pyridoxamine phosphate, and pyridoxal. None of these protected the enzyme against iodoacetate. But neither did any of them block the protective action of pyridoxal phosphate itself, even when used at concentrations which (judging from competitive inhibition of the enzyme) must have displaced a substantial amount of the pyridoxal phosphate from the enzyme surface.

A number of substrate analogues were also examined as potential modifiers of iodoacetate inhibition. Some of these permitted differentiation between different points of substrate attachment. Thus, isobutylamine presumably

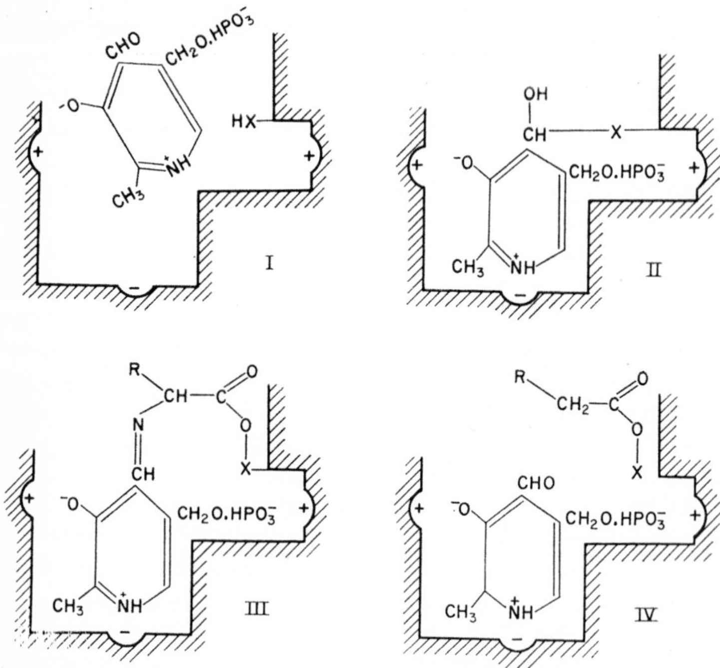


FIG. 8. Active centre of leucine decarboxylase.

exerts competitive inhibition by attachment through the carbonyl group of the coenzyme. It does not potentiate inhibition by iodoacetate. Isovalerate, another competitive inhibitor, must, however, attach itself to a different point on the enzymes—presumably a carboxyl-binding site. This afforded considerable protection against iodoacetate. Since both pyridoxal phosphate and isovalerate protect the enzyme against iodoacetate, it is possible that both are attached to the enzyme at the same point.

This suggestion is represented diagrammatically in Fig. 8. Here, X is the iodoacetate-sensitive group. In (I), the coenzyme is dissociated from the apoenzyme and X is exposed. In (II), the coenzyme is in position and its carbonyl group is linked to X. X is thus protected against iodoacetate. In (III) a substrate has attached itself to the enzyme. This is consistent with the mechanism suggested by Snell[17] for substrate-attachment in pyridoxal phosphate enzymes. The carbonyl group of the coenzyme is now required for formation of the Schiff base and no longer covers X, but the latter is now binding the COOH of the substrate. The substrate might not protect X if the substrate–X link is much weaker than the coenzyme–X link. We have already noted that leucine tends to cause dissociation of the coenzyme from the apoenzyme: this would suggest that (for this substrate) proceeding from (II) to (III) results in the replacement of a strong link by a weaker one. In this case, we might also expect X to become more accessible to the inhibitor; i.e. this substrate will potentiate the inhibitor action.

One might expect, in this case, that leucine would be significantly less firmly bound to the enzyme than other substrates (e.g. valine). We have, however, already noted that the Michaelis affinity constant is about the same for all substrates tested. On the other hand, we shall also show that the value of the Michaelis constant is largely determined by the stability of the Schiff base link. The other point or points of enzyme–substrate attachment—important though they may be in activating the enzyme–substrate complex and in determining specificity—presumably do not form strong linkages since they have little effect on the overall affinity constant. On the other hand, isovalerate is a competitive inhibitor with an affinity greater, by a factor of 10, than that of the substrates. Presumably it must form a relatively stable link with X; and we find that it protects the enzyme against iodoacetate.

Interpretation of the results with the other inhibitors analogues is less straightforward. None of the coenzyme analogues offer protection against iodoacetate. In the case of those which lack a carbonyl group (the oxime and cyanhydrin of pyridoxal phosphate, and pyridoxamine phosphate) the implication would be that actual combination between the coenzyme and X is necessary, and that steric coverage does not suffice. On the other hand, pyridoxal itself offers no protection. Pyridoxal competes with its phosphate only at concentrations over 1000 times greater than the latter, so it would be rash to assert that both fit into the same place on the enzyme surface and in the same way.

The results with isobutylamine also suggest that steric factors can come into play. On purely chemical grounds this substrate analogue would be expected to potentiate inhibition. It combines with the coenzyme in the same manner as a substrate and its affinity constant for the enzyme as inhibitor is close to the stability constant for the isobutylamine-pyridoxal phosphate Schiff base[10]; see p. 265. But it lacks a carboxyl group to react with X. The latter might therefore be expected to be left exposed and sensitive to attack by iodoacetate. Isobutylamine does not potentiate iodoacetate inhibition however; presumably its presence prevents access to the sensitive site. This serves to emphasize that the effect of leucine in increasing inhibition is probably due to its tendency to bring about dissociation of the coenzyme.

The nature of the group X is unknown. Iodoacetate is classically a reagent for — SH groups, but it is far from being specific; and in any case the chemical properties of a radicle when part of a protein may differ radically from its properties in simpler compounds. The relatively slow action of the inhibitor would be consistent with reaction with an — SH group, but might equally be explained by the previously noted sluggish reaction between the pyridoxal phosphate and its apoenzyme proteins, if we assume that dissociation of the coenzyme is necessary for inhibition. We therefore turned to *p*-chlormercuribenzoate (PCMB), usually regarded as relatively specific for — SH residues.

PCMB proved to be a highly effective inhibitor, active at levels of the order $10^{-6}$ M, but its characteristics proved very different from those of iodoacetate. Inhibition is established almost immediately on adding the PCMB. When an experiment similar to Fig. 6 was performed, it was found that—as with iodoacetate—the coenzyme afforded some protection against the inhibitor. But the substrates provided even better protection—leucine being slightly more effective than valine. When we attempted to determine whether competitive or non-competitive relationships existed between PCMB, the substrate and the coenzyme, the results of the reciprocal plots were ambiguous, though tending to suggest that inhibition was competitive with respect to the substrate and non-competitive with respect to the coenzyme. Moreover, isovalerate, which protects the enzyme against iodoacetate, was quite ineffective against PCMB.

It thus seems unlikely that iodoacetate and PCMB interact with the same enzyme grouping. Yet the latter must attack a group near the active centre of the enzyme and essential for its function. The protection afforded by both coenzyme and substrate may arise through steric hindrance of the approach of the relatively large inhibitor molecule.

Frequent reference has been made to the carbonyl group of the coenzyme as the site of substrate attachment which is mainly responsible for the binding of the latter to the enzyme. This concept is based on a comparison of the stability constants of the Schiff bases formed between amino acids and pyridoxal phosphate, with the classical Michaelis constants of pyridoxal phosphate enzymes operating with the same amino acids. Figure 9 shows that for the majority of enzymes investigated the correlation is very close. The situation is more complex than Fig. 9 indicates, since classical Michaelis constants are not necessarily a direct measure of enzyme–substrate affinity. There is also the question of the possible role of the tertiary chelate complexes formed between pyridoxal derivatives, amino acids, and divalent metals; for a fuller discussion, see Ref. 10. With leucine decarboxylase itself very interesting results were obtained.[18] The Michaelis constant was determined by the usual reciprocal plot method at pH values 5, 6 and 7; the latter is the pH optimum.

Table 3 shows that the Michaelis constant for the enzyme is rather lower than the stability constant for the leucine – pyridoxal phosphate Schiff base (suggesting that other sites of enzyme attachment add appreciably to the

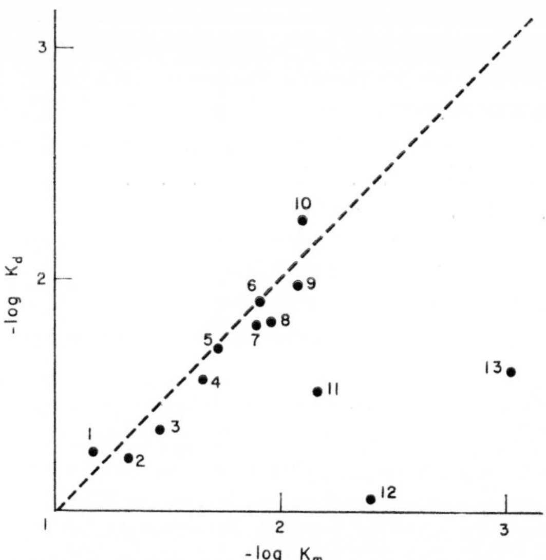


FIG. 9. Relation between stability constants ($K_d$) for amino acid–pyridoxal phosphate complexes and Michaelis constants ($K_m$) of corresponding enzymes. (1) Serine deaminase (pH 8.3); (2) leucine decarboxylase (pH 5.0); (3) glutamic decarboxylase (bacterial) (pH 4.5); (4) leucine decarboxylase (pH 6.0); (5) glycine, conversion to serine (pH 7.2); (6) alanine transaminase (pH 7.0); (7) leucine decarboxylase (pH 7.0); (8) glutamic acid transaminase (pH 7.0); (9) isobutylamine inhibitor constant for leucine decarboxylase (pH 6.0); (10) alanine racemase (pH 8.0); (11) glutamic decarboxylase (brain), (pH 6.3); (12) ornithine decarboxylase (pH 5.2); (13) arginine decarboxylase (pH 5.2).

TABLE 3. STABILITY CONSTANT ($K_d$) OF LEUCINE–PYRIDOXAL PHOSPHATE SCHIFF BASE AND MICHAELIS CONSTANT ($K_m$) OF LEUCINE DECARBOXYLASE AT pH 5, 6, 7

| pH | $K_m$(mM) | $K_m$ (mM) |
|---|---|---|
| 5.0 | 85 | 45 |
| 6.0 | 52 | 27 |
| 7.0 | 27 | 16 |

binding of the substrate) but both show the same reduction in stability as the pH moves to lower values. The $-NH_2-CHO$ bond is thus the main determinant of enzyme–substrate affinity. Moreover examination of the reciprocal plots shows that all three intersect the $1/V$ axis at the same point. This means that the rate of enzyme action under conditions of substrate saturation is independent of pH over this range, and the fall in enzyme activity which occurs below pH 7 under conditions of normal enzyme function is entirely attributable to a decrease in enzyme–substrate affinity which in turn is due to the reduced stability of the pyridoxal phosphate–amino acid Schiff base.[10,18]

*Acknowledgments*—I would wish to pay tribute ot my collaborators in these investigations, especially Dr. L. Ekladius, Dr. B. G. Haughton, Mr. N. Lucas and Dr. C. R. Sutton.

## REFERENCES

1. E. F. Gale; *Advances in Enzymol.* **6**, 1 (1946).
2. H. Proom and A. J. Woiwod; *J. Gen. Microbiol.* **5**, 930 (1951).
3. H. K. King; *Biochem. J.* **54**, xi (1954).
4. L. Ekladius, H. K. King and C. R. Sutton; *Biochem. J.* **17**, 602 (1957).
5. B. G. Haughton; Thesis, Liverpool (1958).
6. B. G. Haughton and H. K. King; *Biochem. J.* **60**, 268 (1961).
7. E. S. Taylor and E. F. Gale; *Biochem. J.* **39**, 52 (1945).
8. H. M. R. Epps; *Biochem. J.* **38**, 242 (1944).
9. O. Schales and S. S. Schales; *Arch. Biochem.* **11**, 155 (1946).
10. N. Lucas, H. K. King and S. J. Brown; *Biochem. J.* **84**, 118 (1962).
11. R. Shukuya and G. W. Schwert; *J. Biol. Chem.* **235**, 1653 (1960).
12. W. T. Jenkins and I. W. Sizer; *J. Biol. Chem.* **234**, 1179 (1959).
13. B. G. Haughton and H. K. King; *Biochem. J.* **70**, 660 (1958).
14. A. Meister, H. A. Sober and E. A. Peterson; *J. Biol. Chem.* **206**, 89 (1954).
15. C. R. Sutton; Thesis, Liverpool (1959).
16. C. R. Sutton and H. K. King; *Arch. Biochem. Biophys.* **96** 360 (1962).
17. E. E. Snell; *Vitamins and Hormones* **16**, 77 (1958).
18. H. K. King and S. J. Brown; *Biochem. J.* **74**, 3P (1960).

# MAMMALIAN AROMATIC L-AMINO ACID DECARBOXYLASE

by SIDNEY UDENFRIEND

Laboratory of Clinical Biochemistry, National Heart Institute,
Bethesda, Maryland

ABOUT 25 years ago Holtz[1] reported finding a potent decarboxylase for 3,4-dihydroxyphenylalanine (dopa) in guinea pig kidney. The great interest in catecholamines at that time focused attention on this enzyme as one of the key catalysts in adrenaline biosynthesis (Fig. 1).

The requirement of pyridoxal phosphate (PLP) for decarboxylation of dopa was demonstrated many years ago[2] and in fact crude preparations of this enzyme were used to detect and determine PLP in other systems.

There are present in animal tissues and urine many other amines, each of which requires a decarboxylation step for biosynthesis. Histamine is a potent physiologic agent and histidine decarboxylation activity was demonstrated in mammalian tissues even before dopa decarboxylation.[3] More recently 5-hydroxytryptamine (5HT) was isolated and 5-hydroxytryptophan decarboxylation was shown to be an intermediate step in its biosynthesis.[4] Reports of the presence of phenethylamine, tyramine and tryptamine in urine[5] suggested that decarboxylation of the dietary aromatic amino acids occurred in animal tissues. There had been earlier reports of tyrosine and tryptophan decarboxylases in animal tissues, but these were not corroborated.[6,7] When the question was raised whether decarboxylation of 5-HTP and dopa were catalyzed by the same enzyme,[8–10] it was decided to reinvestigate the problem of mammalian amino acid decarboxylases more carefully.

Initial studies showed that if the problem were to be explored standard manometric procedures were not sufficiently sensitive. Fortunately most of the aromatic amino acids and their corresponding amines are highly fluorescent or can be converted to fluorescent derivatives. By introducing simple chromatographic procedures it was possible to determine traces of decarboxylated products in the presence of the substrate amino acids. Using such sensitive procedures it was found that the guinea pig kidney and other tissues, prepared as previously described for dopa decarboxylation[1] or 5-HTP decarboxylation,[4] were capable of decarboxylating all the dietary amino acids, including histidine. During further purification the relative decarboxylation rates of all the biologically important amino acids were found to remain constant (Table 1). Even on column chromatography the enzyme activity eluted as a single component with respect to all the amino acid substrates (Fig. 2). In addition the amino acids mutually inhibited decarboxylation of one another and compounds such as α-methyldopa inhibited decarboxylation of all the substrate amino acids even in the most purified preparations. All these findings convinced us that we were dealing with a single enzyme which was in effect an aromatic L-amino acid decarboxylase.

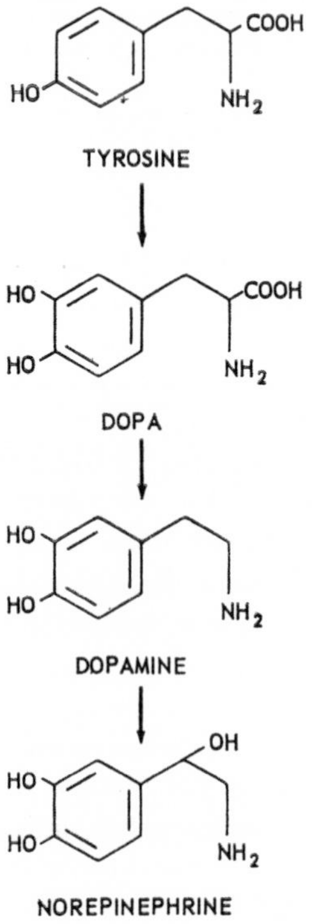

FIG. 1. Pathway for biosynthesis of norepinephrine (noradrenaline).

As shown in Table 2, dopa and 5-HTP are the most active of the substrates. However, it should be kept in mind that under physiologic conditions tissue levels of phenylalanine, tyrosine and tryptophan are about $10^{-4}$ M, well below their $K_m$ values. Following ingestion of protein their levels can increase several-fold for a short time, thereby increasing the rates of decarboxylation. This becomes apparent when one measures tissue or urinary amines[11] following ingestion of tyrosine or tryptophan. In patients with phenylketonuria, where tissue levels of phenylalanine are 20 to 40 times normal, the production of phenethylamine is markedly increased.[12] Since the decarboxylase is present in brain and phenethylamine is a potent pharmacologic agent with properties like amphetamine, this must be considered as one of the possible etiologic agents in the production of the central nervous system lesion in this disorder.

TABLE 1. PURIFICATION OF AROMATIC L-AMINO ACID DECARBOXYLASE FROM GUINEA PIG KIDNEY

| Substrate | Specific activity: High speed supernatant fraction | Specific activity: Alumina Cγ eluate | Specific activity: DEAE-cellulose eluate | Overall purification |
|---|---|---|---|---|
| DOPA | 700 | 7500 | 38,800 | 56 |
| 5-HTP | 85 | 792 | 5030 | 56 |
| Tryptophan | 11 | 135 | 695 | 63 |
| Phenylalanine | 6.2 | 59 | 375 | 60 |
| Tyrosine | 1.5 | 15.8 | 89 | 59 |
| Histidine | 0.47 | 4.5 | 29 | 62 |

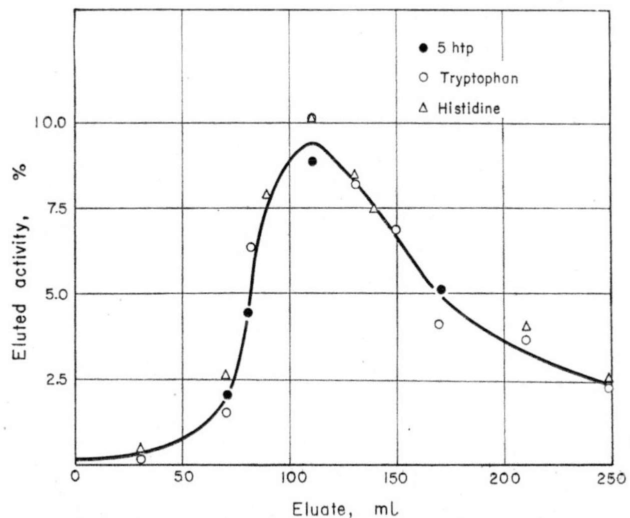


FIG. 2. Chromatography of aromatic L-amino acid decarboxylase on a DEAE–cellulose column.

It has also been shown that tryptophan produces marked central effects in humans following administration of monoamine oxidase inhibitors, due to the accumulation of its decarboxylated product tryptamine.[13]

Since aromatic L-amino acid decarboxylase is involved in the production of so many physiologically active products it is not surprising that attempts have been made to develop inhibitors for use as pharmacologic agents. One of the most obvious hopes was to be able to produce a chemical sympathectomy by blocking production of the sympathetic hormone, noradrenaline. Being a pyridoxal phosphate enzyme one can, of course, inhibit it with various carbonyl agents such as semicarbizide and various hydrazine derivatives. One of the drugs used for treatment of hypertension, hydralazine, does inhibit pyridoxal enzymes *in vitro* and there have been some claims that its action is due to blocking catecholamine formation at this step. However, there is no evidence that hydralazine acts in this way *in vivo* at therapeutic doses.

TABLE 2. $K_m$ OF VARIOUS SUBSTRATES FOR AROMATIC L-AMINO ACID DECARBOXYLASE

| Substrate | $K_m \times 10^5$ | $V_{max}$ |
|---|---|---|
| DOPA | 40 | 6400 |
| 5-HTP | 2 | 1000 |
| Tryptophan | 300 | 220 |
| *p*-Tyrosine | 1300 | 34 |
| Phenylalanine | 2000 | 104 |
| Histidine | 2200 | 10 |
| α-Methyl-dopa | 54 | 32 |

Clark and associates[14] produced a series of chalcone derivatives which inhibit aromatic L-amino acid decarboxylases by what is described as a competitive mechanism. These compounds have not been studied by many other groups. In 1954 Sourkes[15] demonstrated that α-methyl-dopa was a potent inhibitor of dopa decarboxylation. At that time he reported that the inhibition was competitive with respect to substrate and that α-methyl-dopa blocked decarboxylation of administered dopa in animals. In 1959 Sjoerdsma *et al.*[11] showed that α-methyl-dopa blocked amine formation in patients and effectively lowered blood pressure. It appeared then that inhibitors of this enzyme could produce a chemical sympathectomy. These findings excited more interest in this inhibitor and in the mechanism of its inhibition. Smith[16] reported that contrary to Sourkes' original claim, α-methyl-dopa interacted with pyridoxal phosphate and that the inhibition was non-competitive with substrate. Others seemed to support this claim. We have reinvestigated this problem and have found that with the guinea pig kidney enzyme exogenous pyridoxal phosphate does influence the degree of inhibition produced by the α-methyl amino acids but that with or without added coenzyme the inhibition is essentially competitive with substrate.

In attempting to understand the inhibition it must first be pointed out that L-α-methyl-dopa is itself decarboxylated by the enzyme and that it is now generally believed that it is the corresponding amine which is responsible for the antihypertensive effect in man.[17] The $K_m$ for decarboxylation of $\alpha$-methyl-dopa is in the same range as for dopa but the $V_{max}$ is very low. The decarboxylation of this $\alpha$-methyl amino acid corroborates current concepts of amino acid decarboxylation,[18] which are summarized in Fig. 3. According to this scheme one of the $\alpha$-hydrogens should remain undissociated during the interaction with pyridoxal phosphate attending decarboxylation. Substitution of this hydrogen by a methyl group should therefore not abolish activity.

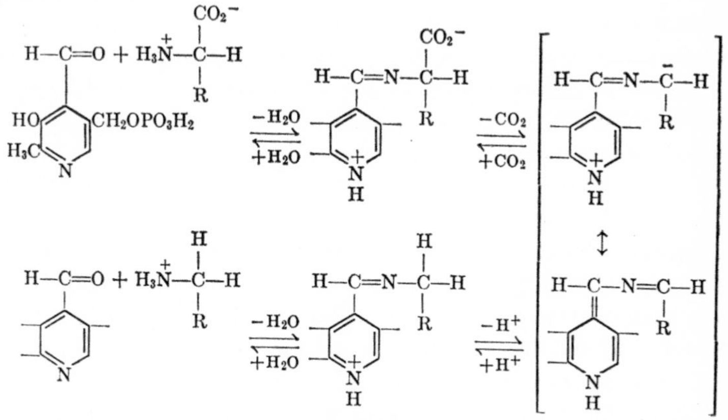

FIG. 3. Mechanism of pyridoxal phosphate catalyzed decarboxylation of amino acids, according to Mandeles *et al.*[18]

Since $\alpha$-methyl amino acids are substrates of the decarboxylase there is no question that they interact with the enzyme as well as with the coenzyme. Being substrates one would expect them to inhibit competitively the decarboxylation of other amino acids, as reported by Sourkes[15].

Mammalian aromatic amino acid decarboxylase obtained from guinea pig kidney is not appreciably dissociated from the coenzyme. Even after extensive purification one can show little stimulation of activity with respect to the common amino acids by addition of coenzyme. In the case of dopa, of course, the non-enzymic interaction with coenzyme requires additional coenzyme for maximal activity.[19] On the other hand, $\alpha$-methyl 5-HTP and $\alpha$-methyl-dopa, which do not react with coenzyme in the same manner, show absolute requirements for added pyridoxal phosphate. At extremely high concentrations of coenzyme decarboxylation of all substrates is inhibited, presumably through interaction with substrate.

Having found this marked difference in pyridoxal phosphate requirement by amino acids and their $\alpha$-methyl analogs it became of interest to examine the inhibition of amino acid decarboxylation by $\alpha$-methyl amino acids with and without added coenzyme. It was found that the character of the inhibition varies with the sequence of addition of substrate and inhibitor to the enzyme. When both were added simultaneously the inhibition was found to be typically competitive. When the α-methyl amino acid was preincubated with the enzyme, for as short a time as 3 min, the inhibition was then non-competitive. With simultaneous addition of inhibitor and substrate exogenous pyridoxal phosphate decreased the degree of inhibition but its character remained competitive. Thus, in the absence of coenzyme $10^{-6}$ M α-methyl-dopa produced 50 per cent inhibition of 5-HTP decarboxylation, with coenzyme, $3 \times 10^{-6}$ M α-methyl-dopa was required for the same degree of inhibition using the same amount of substrate ($2 \times 10^{-5}$ M). When inhibitor was preincubated with enzyme for 3 min before adding substrate (in the absence of added coenzyme), the degree of inhibition was increased several fold. Under these conditions the character of the inhibition was also different, being non-competitive in nature. Upon addition of pyridoxal phosphate much of the inhibition produced by preincubation with inhibitor could be reversed.

It is apparent from these findings that interaction of α-methyl amino acids with mammalian aromatic amino acid decarboxylase is rather complex, involving both enzyme and coenzyme. However, even the interaction with the coenzyme of the decarboxylase is unique. Thus, α-methyl-5-HTP and α-methyl-dopa do not inhibit other pyridoxal enzymes such as tyrosine transaminase. Of even greater significance is the observation that the aromatic L-amino acid decarboxylase obtained from *S. faecalis*, which catalyzes decarboxylation of many of the same substrates as does the mammalian enzyme, is not inhibited by α-methyl amino acids. Comparison of the effects of α-methyl-dopa on the mammalian and bacterial systems was made utilizing the same substrate and at the same pH.[20]

Unlike the mammalian enzyme the bacterial decarboxylase is readily dissociated into apoenzyme and pyridoxal phosphate. This led us to consider that the inhibition of the mammalian enzyme somehow entailed a firmly-bound pyridoxal phosphate. If this were so and if the α-methyl amino acids interacted with both enzyme and substrate, the following scheme could be envisaged (Fig. 4). In the absence of added coenzyme the inhibitor (I) combines with both enzyme (E) and enzyme-bound pyridoxal phosphate ($P_E$). This ternary combination is apparently very stable and does not undergo decarboxylation to an appreciable extent. Once formed it is not readily reversed by substrate. Addition of sufficiently large amounts of substrate along with inhibitor prevents the formation of the ternary complex and competes with enzyme for active decarboxylase sites. In the form of the ternary complex the inhibitor is apparently still able to interact with added pyridoxal phosphate ($P_A$). Addition of exogenous coenzyme would then open the ternary complex and increase the dissociation of the inhibitor–enzyme complex. This would permit decarboxylation of the inhibitor.

Under such conditions substrate would compete more favorably thereby lowering the observed potency of the inhibitor. Obviously such a mechanism is only conjecture at this time and considerable purification of the enzyme will be required before it can be verified.

What is the significance of mammalian aromatic L-amino acid decarboxylase?

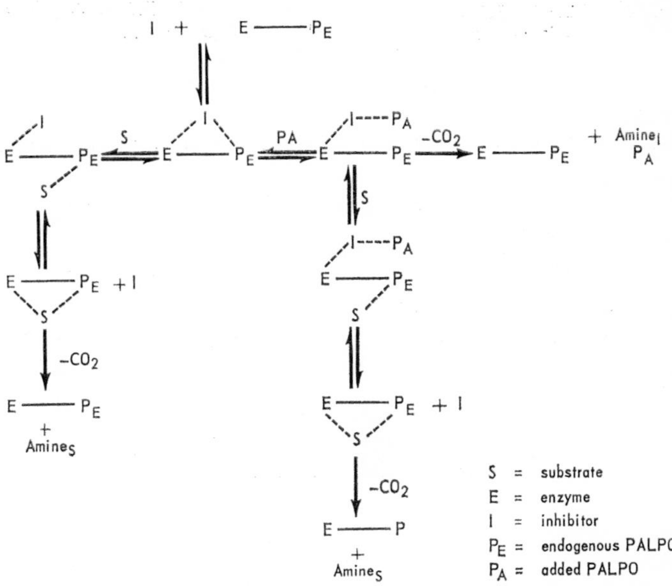


FIG. 4. Mechanism of inhibition of aromatic L-amino acid decarboxylase by α-methyl-dopa and α-methyl 5-HTP.

First, it is without doubt involved in the biosynthesis of two classes of hormonal agents, the adrenalines and serotonin. Just why nature should have economized in this manner is not clear unless it is indicative of the close physiologic relationship between these two agents.

Can production of one or both of these hormones be blocked *in vivo* by inhibiting aromatic L-amino acid decarboxylase? Under normal conditions this would not appear to be likely since in both instances the decarboxylase step is apparently the most active or most abundant enzyme in the biosynthetic sequence. This is schematically shown for noradrenaline biosynthesis in Fig. 5. In this case both oxidative enzymes, preceding and following the decarboxylation, are much less active. As can be seen it would therefore require almost complete inhibition of the decarboxylase *in vivo* to have any effect on endogenous adrenaline formation. Similar reasoning holds for serotonin biosynthesis. It is for this reason that even the most active decarboxylase inhibitors have not been able to lower endogenous levels of the adrenalines and serotonin in tissues by virtue of their inhibitory action. It would appear that efforts to produce a chemical sympathectomy by inhibition at this point are not likely to be successful.

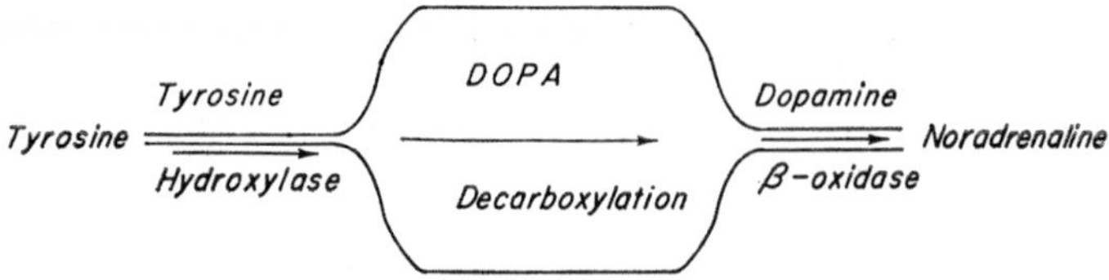


FIG. 5. Relative activities of catalytic steps in noradrenaline biosynthesis.

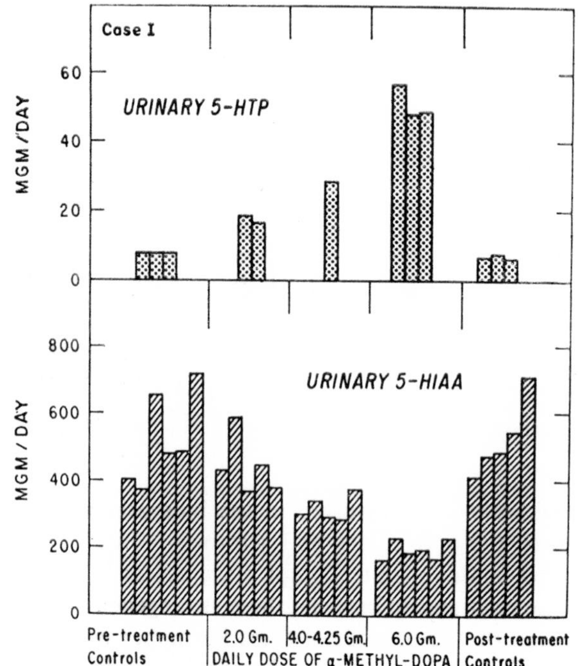


FIG. 6. Effect of α-methyl-dopa on 5-hydroxyindole metabolism in a patient with malignant carcinoid, according to Sjoerdsma *et al.*[21]

Under certain conditions the decarboxylase can become limiting, as when one of the substrates is administered experimentally or when there is overproduction of a substrate resulting from some pathologic state. An example of the latter occurs in patients with malignant carcinoid, a tumor which produces 5-HT. In these patients hydroxylation of tryptophan and subsequent decarboxylation of the resulting 5-hydroxytryptophan is a major route of metabolism. Under such conditions (as shown in Fig. 6) administration of the inhibitor, α-methyl-dopa, can decrease 5-HT formation, as evidenced by a fall in its end-product, 5-hydroxyindoleacetic acid. More than that it can bring about an accumulation of the amino acid 5-hydroxytryptophan.[21] Use of decarboxylase inhibitors in this and related conditions may be of some therapeutic value.

Although aromatic L-amino acid decarboxylase catalyzes the decarboxylation of histidine this activity appears to have little physiologic significance. A specific and more potent histidine decarboxylase, which is present in mast cells, is apparently responsible for production of histamine.[22]

The significance of the amines derived through decarboxylation of the dietary amino acids is not clear. However, tryptamine, phenethylamine and tryamine are pharmacologically active and have not been shown to be present in tissues of many animal species.

*Acknowledgment*—This review includes unpublished studies carried out in collaboration with Dr. Herbert Weissbach, Dr. Walter Lovenberg and Dr. Jack D. Barchas.

## REFERENCES

1. P. Holtz; *Naturwissenschaften* **27**, 724 (1939).
2. P. Holtz and F. Bachmann; *Naturwissenschaften* **39**, 116 (1952).
3. E. Werle and H. Herrmann; *Biochem. Z.* **291**, 105 (1937).
4. C. T. Clark, H. Weissbach and S. Udenfriend; *J. Biol. Chem.* **210**, 139 (1954).
5. A. Sjoerdsma, W. Lovenberg, J. A. Oates, J. R. Crout and S. Udenfriend; *Science* **130**, 225 (1959).
6. P. Holtz; *Naturwissenschaften* **25**, 457 (1937).
7. E. Werle and J. Sell; *Biochem. Z.* **326**, 110 (1954).
8. A. Yuwiler, E. Geller and S. Eiduson; *Arch. Biochem. Biophys.* **80**, 162 (1959).
9. E. Werle and D. Aures; *Z. physiol. Chem.* **316**, 45 (1959).
10. E. Rosengren; *Acta physiol. Scand.* **49**, 364 (1960).
11. J. A. Oates, L. Gillespie, S. Udenfriend and A. Sjoerdsma; *Science* **131**, 1890 (1960).
12. J. B. Jepson, W. Lovenberg, P. Zaltzman, J. A. Oates, A. Sjoerdsama and S. Udenfriend; *Biochem. J.* **74**, 5P (1960).
13. J. A. Oates and A. Sjoerdsma; *Neurology* **10**, 1076 (1960).
14. W. J. Hartman, R. I. Akawie and W. G. Clark; *J. Biol. Chem.* **216**, 507 (1955).
15. T. L. Sourkes; *Arch. Biochem. Biophys.* **51**, 444 (1954).
16. S. E. Smith; *Brit. J. Pharmacol.* **15**, 319 (1960).
17. S. Udenfriend and Zaltzman-Nirenberg; *J. Pharmacol. Exptl. Therap.* In press.
18. S. Mandeles, R. Koppelman and M. E. Hanke; *J. Biol. Chem.* **209**, 327 (1954).
19. H. F. Schott and W. G. Clark; *J. Biol. Chem.* **196**, 449 (1952).
20. W. Lovenberg, J. D. Barchas, H. Weissbach and S. Udenfriend; *Biochem. et Biophys. Acta*, in press.
21. A. Sjoerdsma, J. A. Oates, P. Zaltzman and S. Udenfriend; *New Eng. J. Med.* **263**, 585 (1960).
22. H. Weissbach, W. Lovenberg and S. Udenfriend; *Biochem. et Biophys. Acta* **50**, 177 (1961).

# SOME ASPECTS OF AMINO ACID DECARBOXYLASE INHIBITION

by S. R. MARDASHEV

Laboratory of Biochemistry of Micro-organisms, Institute of Biological and Medical Chemistry, Academy of Medical Sciences of the U.S.S.R., Moscow

THE effect of inhibitors in two-component enzymes is directed either upon coenzymes or upon apoenzymes or upon both. Even in single-component enzymes some active sites corresponding to coenzymes but firmly " incorporated " into the structure of the enzyme molecule must be present.

Inhibition of pyridoxal enzymes, if this process is not due to destruction of enzyme molecules, may be caused either by a combination of coenzyme or of catalytically active sites of apoenzyme with an inhibitor.

Numerous examples of combination with coenzymes including our data on inhibition of amino acid decarboxylases by penicillamine, cysteine and homocysteine enable one to provide a relatively simple interpretation of the inhibition mechanism of this type.

In 1957 du Vigneaud and collaborators discovered the inhibition of transamination in animal tissues by L-penicillamine.[1] The explanation of the mechanism of this inhibition lies in the formation of the derivative of thiazolidinecarboxylic acid from penicillamine and pyridoxal phosphate which makes it possible to consider penicillamine as a potential inhibitor of any enzyme belonging to the pyridoxal phosphate proteins. This assumption was confirmed in experiments with serinedehydratase[2] and amino acid decarboxylases.[3]

Our experiments in 1959 with DL-penicillamine showed a distinct inhibition of decarboxylation of amino acids by means of microbe preparations.[3] Later, in 1961, Matsuda and Makino observed the inhibition of glutamic decarboxylase in brain by DL-penicillamine.[4] It is possible to assume that not only penicillamine but other mercaptoamino compounds possess an analogous inhibitory action. To check this assumption the action of L-cysteine and DL-homocysteine upon the rate of enzymatic decarboxylation of amino acids has been investigated.

The summary data showing inhibition of decarboxylation activity by DL-penicillamine, L-cysteine and DL-homocysteine are given in Table 1. From the given data we see that penicillamine, cysteine and homocysteine strongly inhibit the enzymatic decarboxylation of amino acids in the concentration of $0.83 \times 10^{-2}$ M (25 $\mu$moles of inhibitor and 8.3 $\mu$moles of amino acid per tube). In some cases the decarboxylation is decreased almost 60 per cent in comparison with the control.

The formation of the catalytically inactive five-member thiazolidine ring from pyridoxal phosphate and inhibitor produces inhibition by penicillamine or cysteine whereas homocysteine cannot form such a five-member cycle.

TABLE 1. INHIBITION OF AMINO ACID DECARBOXYLASE ACTIVITY BY DL-PENICILLAMINE, L-CYSTEINE AND DL-HOMOCYSTEINE
(Inhibition expressed in percentage per 10 min. period decarboxylation, P, phosphate buffer, A, acetate buffer.)

| Decarboxylase | Buffer pH | Penicillamine (μmoles) | | | Cysteine (μmoles) | | | Homocysteine (μmoles) | | |
|---|---|---|---|---|---|---|---|---|---|---|
| | | 0.25 | 2.5 | 25 | 0.25 | 2.5 | 25 | 0.25 | 2.5 | 25 |
| | | Inhibition (%) | | | | | | | | |
| *B. cadaveris* (lysine) | P, 6.0 | 0 | 5.6 | 52.8 | 0 | 11.9 | 54.8 | 4.8 | 23.8 | 28.6 |
| *E. coli* (arginine) | A, 5.6 | 8.4 | 16.7 | 58.4 | 7.0 | 8.0 | 23.0 | 10.0 | 20.0 | 46.0 |
| *S. faecalis* (tyrosine) | A, 4.5 | 0 | 0 | 45.0 | 0 | 5.0 | 20.0 | 0 | 10.0 | 25.0 |
| *Cl. welchii* S.R.12 (glutamic acid) | A, 5.6 | 6.0 | 16.2 | 22.3 | 14.3 | 37.0 | 48.6 | 0 | 8.6 | 57.0 |
| *Mycobacterium* n. sp. (aspartic acid) | A, 5.6 | 1.0 | 3.4 | 15.0 | 0 | 4.1 | 22.6 | 1.4 | 0 | 37.8 |
| *Micrococcus* n. sp. (histidine) | A, 5.6 | 0 | 7.5 | 35.8 | 0 | 0 | 15.6 | 3.5 | 0 | 10.5 |

Evidently, an analogous mechanism of inhibition would lead to condensation of homocysteine with pyridoxal phosphate and form a six-member thiazane ring. We checked the correctness of this assumption chemically by means of the condensation of pyridoxal and homocysteine.

The following structure corresponds to the substance we obtained [2-(3-hydroxy-2-methyl-5-hydromethyl-pyridyl-4-)-1,3-thiazane-4-carboxylic acid]:

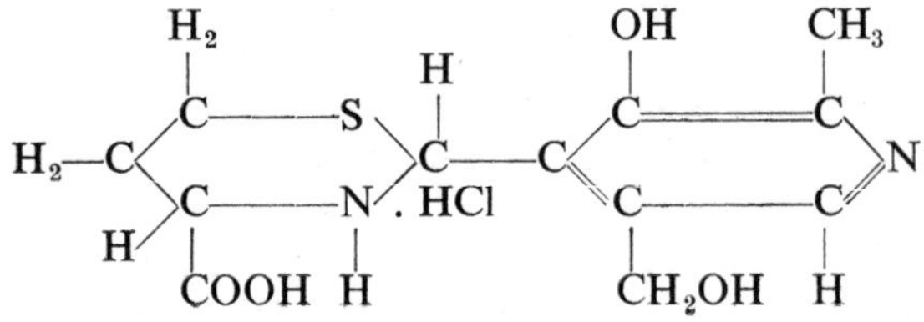

```
           H2                             OH        CH3
           |                 H            |          |
          C---------S        |            C=========C
         /           \       C------C    /           \
  H2---C              \     /        \\ /              N
         \             \   /           C              //
          C-----------N   . HCl         C-----------C
         /|           |                 |           |
        H COOH        H                CH2OH        H
```

The investigation of the absorption spectra in ultraviolet region showed (Fig. 1) that the derivative of thiazanecarboxylic acid which was synthesized by us has a characteristic curve with a maximum of absorption at 330 mμ, completely corresponding to the curve of absorption of the substance formed by a mixture of a solution of pyridoxal phosphate and homocysteine solution.

A further study of the inactivation mechanism caused by homocysteine was conducted by means of experiments which would show the influence of

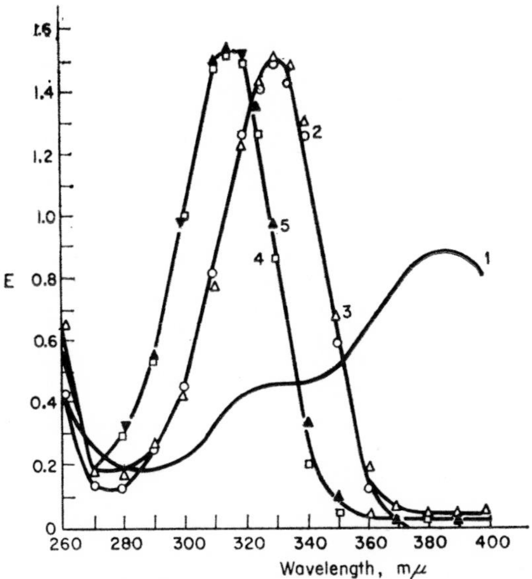


FIG. 1. Ultraviolet absorption spectra in 0.1 M phosphate buffer pH 6.0.
1. PLP (pyridoxalphosphate) 0.20 μmoles/ml.
2. 2-(3-hydroxy-2-methyl-hydroxymethyl-pyridyl-(4)-1,3-thiazane carbonic-4 acid 0.20 μmoles/ml.
3. PLP 0.20 μmoles/ml + HCysH (homocystein) 0.63 μmoles/ml; 2 hr after mixing of solutions.
4. PL.HCl (pyridoxalchloride) 0.20 μmoles/ml.
5. PL.HCl 0.20 μmoler/ml + HCysH 0.63 μmoles/ml; 2 hr after mixing of solutions.

pyridoxal phosphate on amino acid decarboxylases inhibited by homocysteine. From the data obtained it was clear that pyridoxal phosphate has the effect of completely restoring the activity inhibited by homocysteine.

In connection with the data obtained it was of interest to investigate the influence of cysteamine (2-mercaptoethylamine) on amino acid decarboxylases. As is known, cysteamine is a compound possessing a certain protective effect against radiation.

Data on the influence of cysteamine upon the velocity of enzymatic decarboxylation are given in Tables 2 and 3. The obvious conclusion is that cysteamine causes a distinct inhibition of decarboxylation of arginine, histidine and lysine.

To clarify the mechanism of inhibition of amino acid decarboxylases by cysteamine we investigated the possibility of restoring the activity of

TABLE 2. EFFECT OF CYSTEAMINE ON DECARBOXYLATION OF L-ARGININE BY *E. coli* AND L-HISTIDINE BY *Micrococcus* n. sp.
(Acetate buffer, pH 5.6; in a total volume of 3 ml: 15 mg dry acetone powder of microbe and 8 μmoles of amino acid per tube; rate of reaction in μl of $CO_2$).

| Time of reaction (min) | *E. coli* + arginine | | | | *Micrococcus* n. sp. + histidine | | | |
|---|---|---|---|---|---|---|---|---|
| | Cysteamine (μmoles per tube) | | | | | | | |
| | 0 (control) | 0.8 | 8.0 | 24.0 | 0 (control) | 0.8 | 8.0 | 24.0 |
| 10 | 94 | 77 | 58 | 39 | 40 | 33 | 31 | 23 |
| 20 | 134 | 136 | 116 | 79 | 84 | 74 | 68 | 54 |
| 30 | 163 | 156 | 147 | 118 | 102 | — | 101 | 79 |
| 40 | 170 | 168 | 163 | 147 | 146 | 144 | 130 | 106 |
| 50 | 172 | 171 | 165 | 160 | 161 | 158 | 150 | 124 |
| 60 | 172 | 172 | 165 | 168 | 169 | 167 | 167 | 142 |

TABLE 3. EFFECT OF CYSTEAMINE ON DECARBOXYLATION OF L-LYSINE BY *B. cadaveris*
(Phosphate buffer, pH 6.0)

| Time (min) | *B. cadaveris* + lysine | | | |
|---|---|---|---|---|
| | Cysteamine in μmoles per tube | | | |
| | 0 | 0.8 | 8.0 | 24.0 |
| 10 | 102 | 82 | 55 | 42 |
| 20 | 143 | 124 | 96 | 78 |
| 30 | 149 | 139 | 130 | 103 |
| 40 | 151 | 143 | 148 | 128 |
| 50 | 151 | 146 | 154 | 137 |
| 60 | 150 | 148 | 154 | 144 |

decarboxylases by pyridoxal phosphate. These experiments with decarboxylases of arginine and lysine show that pyridoxal phosphate restores the activity inhibited by cysteamine (Table 4).

These results led us to investigate the absorption of light in the ultraviolet region by the compound which was formed as a result of the interaction of pyridoxal phosphate and cysteamine. The curve of absorption of the indicated compound was compared with the curve of pyridoxal phosphate absorption in the ultraviolet region. It was found that the product of condensation of pyridoxal phosphate and of cysteamine has a typical curve of absorption for thiazolidine compounds with a maximum at 330 m$\mu$.

TABLE 4. RESTORATION OF DECARBOXYLASE ACTIVITY *E. coli* AND *B. cadaveris* BY PIRIDOXAL PHOSPHATE (PLP) AFTER 15 MIN INHIBITION BY CYSTEAMINE
(Arginine and lysine 8 $\mu$moles each; cysteamine and PLP 24 $\mu$moles per tube).

| Time (min) | *B. cadaveris* + L-lysine, phosphate buffer, pH 6.0 | | | | *E. coli* + L-arginine, acetate buffer, pH 5.6 | | | |
|---|---|---|---|---|---|---|---|---|
| | Control | | Cysteamine | | Control | | Cysteamine | |
| | without PLP | + PLP | without PLP | + PLP | without PLP | + PLP | without PLP | + PLP |
| 5 | 38 | 44 | 13 | 34 | 25 | 43 | 21 | — |
| 10 | 92 | 97 | 42 | 94 | 99 | 91 | 48 | 112 |
| 15 | 114 | 119 | 60 | 119 | 119 | 119 | 66 | 142 |
| 20 | 135 | 139 | 81 | 139 | 139 | 141 | 84 | 168 |
| 30 | 148 | 152 | 109 | 141 | 150 | 161 | 122 | 181 |
| 40 | 150 | 157 | 117 | 158 | 152 | 168 | 145 | 185 |
| 50 | 150 | 165 | 121 | 160 | 152 | 168 | 160 | 185 |
| 60 | 150 | 165 | 121 | 160 | 152 | 168 | 163 | 185 |

All the data obtained by us[3,6–8] and the data published by other authors[1,2,4,5,9] show that different mercaptoamino compounds inhibit the reactions catalyzed by pyridoxal phosphate enzymes. There is no doubt that inhibition stems from the interaction of inhibitor with pyridoxal phosphate and results in the formation of compounds like semimercaptal and mercaptal and also compounds having thiazolidine and thiazane rings. The effect of inhibition, the absorption spectra in ultraviolet and the restoration of activity by pyridoxal phosphate indicate an analogous mechanism of inhibition of pyridoxal phosphate catalysis by cysteamine, cysteine, penicillamine and homocysteine.

The mercaptoamino compounds (penicillamine, homocysteine, cysteine and cysteamine) in interaction with pyridoxal phosphate depending on the conditions of the reaction and the concentration of the reactive partners may lead via the stage of semimercaptals to the formation of either mercaptals or thiazolidines or thiazanes.

The inhibitory action of mercaptoamino compounds in the reactions catalyzed by pyridoxal phosphate enzymes results from the competition between the amino acid and the mercaptoamino compound for possession of the pyridoxal phosphate.

Pencillamine, cysteamine, cysteine and homocysteine at the concentration of about $0.80 \times 10^{-2}$ M (24–25 $\mu$moles per sample of 3 ml) strongly inhibit the enzymatic decarboxylation of amino acids which in some cases drops 60 per cent in comparison with the control. The use of the middle and lower concentrations gives a much weaker effect and sometimes no effect at all, thus it is impossible to establish any regularity.

It is common knowledge that cysteamine, homocysteine and particularly cysteine are compounds widely distributed in Nature as compared to penicillamine. The data obtained in our laboratory show that cysteine also inhibits the reaction of transamination.[6]

It is highly probable that cysteine, homocysteine and cysteamine can play the role, to a certain extent, of regulators of the velocity of biochemical reactions under normal physiological conditions. This is particularly true of pyridoxal phosphate catalysis.

Inactivation of pyridoxal phosphate enzymes caused by penicillamine, cysteamine, cysteine and homocysteine is a particular instance relating to the significant problem of the regulation of the rates of metabolic processes by compounds containing sulfhydryl and amino groups. In the organism there are many compounds containing carbonyl grouping (aldehyde or ketone) which belong to enzymes, hormones or intermediary products of metabolism and which can enter condensation reactions with homocysteine, cysteine, cysteamine or certain unnatural products containing sulfhydryl and amino groups. The interaction of these compounds, reversible or irreversible, can eliminate them from the reactions of metabolism and thus regulate the rate of metabolism. Thiazolidine compounds which are obtained by means of simple condensation of cysteine with formaldehyde, pyruvic acid, carbohydrates, 3-keto-steroids and a number of other compounds have been described in literature.

It is necessary to note that the sulfhydryl compounds, including cysteine and homocysteine, take part in condensation with compounds containing the carbonyl group producing semimercaptals and mercaptals. These products are either intermediary products in metabolism or fulfil a transport function in the organism.

It is particularly necessary to note that in non-biological systems the rate of condensation of mercaptoamino compounds with aldehydes and the formation of (semi) mercaptals or derivatives of thiazolidine and thiazane depend not only on the nature of the reacting substrates but also on the conditions of the reaction and especially on the pH of the medium. For biological systems the above-mentioned questions as well as the problem of the mechanism of inhibition by mercaptoamino compounds can be elucidated only in some particular cases of pyridoxal phosphate catalysis using individual and homogeneous preparations of enzymes.

Another type of inhibition is determined by chemical interaction between the apoenzyme and inhibitor molecules. Elucidation of mechanisms of such inhibitions in cases when evident destructive alterations are absent presents immense difficulties. Nevertheless studies in this field may give much useful information for understanding the structure of catalytically active sites of enzymes.

In experiments carried out by Dr. L. A. Semina and myself the action of some compounds which may be considered as substrate analogues for glutamate and aspartate decarboxylases was studied. As a source of glutamate decarboxylase dry acetone preparations and water extracts of *Cl. welchii* SR 12 were used; while dry acetone preparations and water–salt extracts of *Mycobacterium* n. sp. were employed as sources of aspartate decarboxylase.

TABLE 5. EFFECT OF α-METHYLGLUTARIC ACID ON GLUTAMIC ACID DECARBOXYLATION
(Acetone powder of *Cl. welchii* SR 12; acetate buffer pH 4.5. Glutamic acid, 10 μmoles; rate of reaction in μl of $CO_2$.)

| Time of reaction (min) | α — Methylglutaric acid (μmoles) | | | |
|---|---|---|---|---|
| | 0 | 10 | 50 | 100 |
| 5 | 83 | 50(40)[a] | 23(72) | 12(86) |
| 10 | 119 | 75(37) | 36(70) | 22(82) |
| 15 | 140 | 88(37) | 40(71) | 24(83) |
| 20 | 165 | 111(33) | 53(68) | 26(84) |
| 25 | 182 | 125(31) | 61(66) | 30(84) |
| 30 | 191 | 144(25) | 72(62) | 40(79) |
| 40 | 206 | 163(21) | 86(58) | 50(76) |
| 50 | 214 | 179(16) | 107(53) | 56(74) |
| 60 | 219 | 192(12) | 118(46) | 68(69) |

[a]Per cent of inhibition in brackets.

The reagents used were of following origin :
L-glutamic acid, Schuchardt; L-aspartic acid, Merck; α-methylglutaric, β-methylglutaric and methylsuccinic acid, Light; β-methylaspartic acid was synthesized in our laboratory by Dr. G. A. Galegov; β-hydroxyglutamic acid, Light; and β-hydroxyaspartic acid was synthezised in laboratory of Prof. A. E. Braunstein. The solution of substrates and inhibitors were neutralized before addition in samples.

In experiments with glutamate decarboxylase the effect of α-methylglutaric, β-methylglutaric, α-methylaspartic and β-hydroxyglutaric acids was studied.

As shown in Table 5, α-methylglutaric acid causes strong inhibition (40 per cent) in concentrations equimolar with respect to those of substrate. Ten-fold increase of the inhibitor concentration increased the inhibition up to 90 per cent. Consequently α-methylglutaric acid may be considered as a potent inhibitor of glutamic acid decarboxylation. Preliminary results of determinations of initial rates of decarboxylation in presence of fixed concentrations of α-methylglutaric acid and varying concentrations of glutamic acid show that in this case the inhibition of combined type (competitive and non-competitive) takes place (Fig. 2).

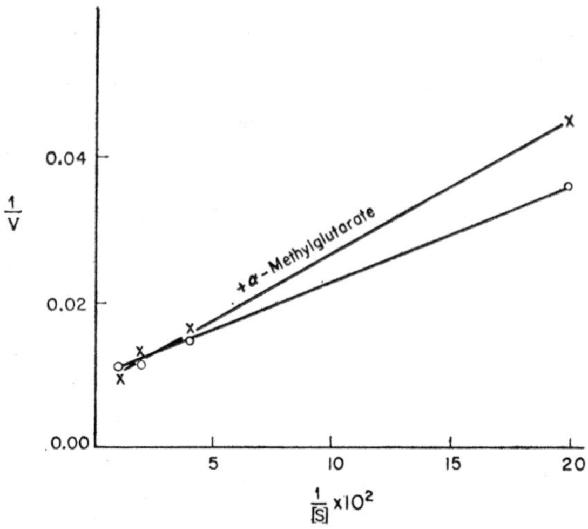


Fig. 2. Inhibition by α-methylglutarate (5 μmoles) of glutamate (5, 25, 50, 75 μmoles) decarboxylation. Reaction velocity expressed in μl $CO_2$ per 5 min. Plotting method by H. Lineweaver and D. Burk.

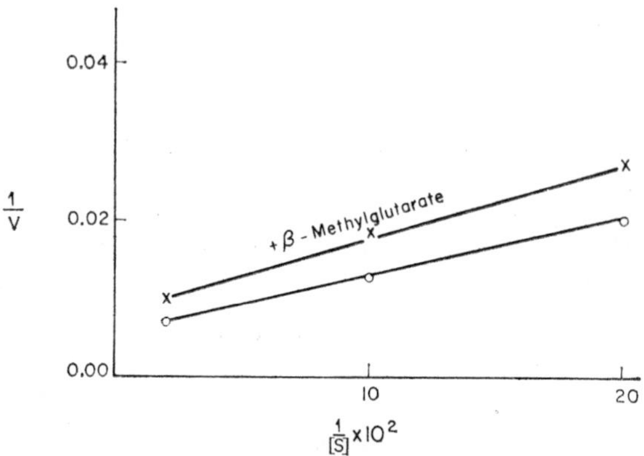


Fig. 3. Inhibition by β-methylglutarate (5 μmoles) of glutamate (5, 10, 50 μmoles) decarboxylation.

β-Methylglutaric acid used in our experiments as a possible inhibitor also had an inhibitory effect upon glutamic acid decarboxylation. But the inhibitory effect of α-methylglutaric acid was approximately three times as high as that of β-methylglutaric acid at the equal concentrations substrate and inhibitor. Preliminary results of determinations of initial rates of decarboxylation in the presence of constant concentration of β-methylglutaric acid and varying concentrations of glutamic acid (Fig. 3) show that in this case the inhibition observed was of non-competitive type.

TABLE 6. EFFECT OF β-METHYLGLUTARIC ACID ON GLUTAMIC ACID DECARBOXYLATION
(Acetone powder of *Cl. Welchii* SR 12, acetate buffer, pH 4.5; glutamic acid 10 μmoles; rate of reaction in μl of $CO_2$.)

| Time (min) | β-Methylglutaric acid (μmoles) | | | |
|---|---|---|---|---|
| | 0 | 10 | 50 | 100 |
| 5 | 72 | 62(14)[a] | 38(47) | 30(58) |
| 10 | 113 | 100(12) | 60(47) | 48(58) |
| 15 | 142 | 122(14) | 73(49) | 62(56) |
| 20 | 165 | 143(13) | 92(44) | 76(54) |
| 25 | 178 | 157(12) | 106(40) | 90(49) |
| 30 | 189 | 170(10) | 117(38) | 102(46) |
| 40 | 204 | 188(8) | 142(30) | 128(37) |
| 50 | 212 | 197(7) | 152(28) | 139(34) |
| 60 | 215 | 199(7) | 165(23) | 155(28) |

[a]Per cent of inhibition in brackets.

TABLE 7. EFFECT OF β-METHYLASPARTATE ON GLUTAMIC ACID DECARBOXYLATION
(Aqueous extract of *Cl. Welchii* SR 12, glutamic acid 5 μmoles, pH 4.5; rate of reaction in μl of $CO_2$.)

| Time (min) | β-Methylaspartate(in μmoles) | | | |
|---|---|---|---|---|
| | 0 | 5 | 25 | 100 |
| 5 | 72 | 71(1)[a] | 57(21) | 48(33) |
| 10 | 100 | 97(3) | 84(16) | 75(25) |
| 15 | 108 | 102(6) | 98(9) | 89(18) |
| 20 | 111 | 108(3) | 105(5) | 95(14) |
| 30 | 112 | 107(5) | 105(6) | 102(9) |

[a]Per cent of inhibition in brackets.

The comparison of inhibitory effect of α-methylglutaric acid (Table 5), β-methylglutaric acid (Table 6) and β-methylaspartic acid (Table 7) gives some information on a possible difference in mechanism of actions of these inhibitors. The strongest inhibitory effect caused by α-methylglutaric acid is probably related to close structural similarity between the inhibitor and substrate. At the same time non-specific inhibition due to the interaction between two carboxyl groups of inhibitor with active sites of apoenzyme molecule takes place. This fact probably accounts for the combined type of inhibition by α-methylglutaric acid and non-competitive inhibition by β-methylglutaric and β-methylaspartic acids. The distance between carboxyl groups of inhibitor is of importance probably because it assures stereochemical correspondence between the inhibitor and active sites of enzyme.

TABLE 8. EFFECT OF METHYLSUCCINIC ACID ON ASPARTIC ACID DECARBOXYLATION
(Aqueous extract of *Mycobacterium* n. sp, acetate buffer, pH 5.6; aspartic acid 5 μmoles, rate of reaction in μl of $CO_2$.)

| Time (min) | Methylsuccinic acid (μmoles) | | | |
|---|---|---|---|---|
| | 0 | 5 | 25 | 100 |
| 5 | 82 | 83 | 75 | 68 |
| 10 | 98 | 103 | 100 | 106 |
| 15 | 102 | 105 | 100 | 108 |
| 20 | 102 | 105 | 100 | 106 |

TABLE 9. EFFECT OF β-METHYLASPARTIC ACID ON ASPARTIC ACID DECARBOXYLATION
(Aqueous extract of *Mycobacterium* n. sp., acetate buffer pH 5.6; aspartic acid, 10 μmoles, rate of reaction in μl of $CO_2$.)

| Time (min) | Methylaspartic acid (in μmoles) | | | |
|---|---|---|---|---|
| | 0 | 10 | 50 | 100 |
| 5 | 80 | 77 | 77 | 72 |
| 10 | 143 | 141 | 141 | 138 |
| 15 | 204 | 202 | 200 | 199 |
| 20 | 214 | 212 | 213 | 222 |

Allo-β-hydroxy-DL-glutamic acid also inhibits the decarboxylation of glutamic acid. The presence of active decarboxylase of hydroxyglutamic acid besides glutamate decarboxylase in *Cl. welchii* SR 12 preparations used in our experiments does not enable us to give unequivocal explanation to the effects observed.

In connection with data obtained it was of interest to study the effect of methylsuccinic acid on enzymatic decarboxylation of aspartic acid. The results obtained are shown in Table 8. They demonstrate the lack of effect of methylsuccinic acid on aspartic acid decarboxylation velocity even in concentrations 5-fold exceeding that of substrate. It was a rather unexpected result as α-methylglutaric acid and β-methylglutaric acids in similar conditions were shown to be strong inhibitors of glutamic acid enzymatic decarboxylation. The study of β-methylaspartic acid effect showed that this

TABLE 10. EFFECT OF β-HYDROXYASPARTIC ACID ON ASPARTIC ACID DECARBOXYLATION
(Aqueous extract of *Mycobacterium* n. sp., acetate buffer pH 5.6, aspartic acid 10 μmoles, rate of reaction in μl of $CO_2$.)

| Time (min) | β-Hydroxyaspartic acid (μmoles) | | | |
|---|---|---|---|---|
| | 0 | 10 | 50 | 100 |
| 5 | 85 | 35(59)[a] | 29(66) | 20(76) |
| 10 | 136 | 68(50) | 48(65) | 32(77) |
| 15 | 204 | 128(37) | 84(59) | 56(73) |
| 20 | 214 | 170(21) | 109(49) | 76(64) |
| 30 | 214 | 209 | 145 | 103 |

[a]Per cent of inhibition in brackets.

TABLE 11. EFFECT OF DIFFERENT CONCENTRATIONS OF ASPARTIC ACID ON THE INHIBITORY EFFECT OF β-HYDROXYASPARTIC ACID
(Aqueous extract of *Mycobacterium* n. sp., acetate buffer pH 5.6, β-hydroxyaspartic acid (β-HAA) 10 μmoles; rate of reaction in μl of $CO_2$.)

| Time (min) | Aspartic acid (μmoles) | | | | | |
|---|---|---|---|---|---|---|
| | 10 | | 50 | | 100 | |
| | β-HAA | | β-HAA | | β-HAA | |
| | − | + | − | + | − | + |
| 5 | 85 | 35(59)[a] | 48 | 23(52) | 48 | 18(62) |
| 10 | 136 | 68(50) | 102 | 55(46) | 97 | 46(53) |
| 15 | 204 | 128(37) | 166 | 109(40) | 155 | 94(39) |
| 20 | 214 | 170(21) | 218 | 149(32) | 200 | 137(31) |

[a]Per cent of inhibition in brackets.

compound in concentration 5-fold exceeding that of substrate did not influence the rate of aspartic acid decarboxylation (Table 9).

Garcia-Hernandes and Kun[11] investigating the inhibition of enzymatic aspartic acid transamination found that hydroxyaspartic acid was a competitive inhibitor of this reaction. Hydroxyaspartic acid was shown to be a potent inhibitor of the reaction; 50 per cent inhibition was reached at equimolar concentrations of the inhibitor and substrate. In connection with these data it seemed interesting to study the effect of α-hydroxyaspartic acid on aspartic acid decarboxylation.

The data summarized in Table 10 demonstrate that in concentration equal to that of substrate β-hydroxyaspartic acid caused more than 50 per cent inhibition. Consequently β-hydroxyaspartic acid may be considered as a potent inhibitor of enzymatic decarboxylation of aspartic acid. The inhibition is probably of competitive type but the attempts to elucidate the mechanism met some difficulties. It was found that a relatively small increase in aspartic acid concentration inhibits the reaction velocity (Table 11).

There are many facts in enzymology concerning deviations of some enzymatic reactions from Michaelis kinetics at high substrate concentrations. At high substrate concentrations the reaction velocity begins to decrease; competitive inhibition caused by the substrate itself is observed. It takes place also in enzymatic decarboxylation of aspartic acid. The most acceptable explanation of the facts observed may be formulated as follows: to form an effective enzyme–substrate complex the substrate molecule has to attach to some chemical groups in the active site of enzyme. At high substrate concentration a part of its molecules is combined with a single chemical group of enzyme which leads to formation of an ineffective enzyme–substrate complex and the reaction velocity decreases. A possibility of another interpretation will be considered somewhat later.

The most difficult point in explanation of data observed is the fact that α-methylglutaric acid is an effective inhibitor of enzymatic glutamic acid decarboxylation while the decarboxylation of aspartic acid is not influenced by methylsuccinic acid.

Braunstein[12] observed that transamination reactions involving α-ketoglutaric acid are strongly inhibited by oxalic acid; complete inhibition of the reaction was noted in the presence of malonic, glutaric and adipinic acids.

Mason[13] notes also significant inhibition of kynurenine transaminase by dicarboxylic acids; $C_6$- and $C_{10}$-dicarboxylic acids being strongest inhibitors, while $C_8$ and $<C_5$-dicarboxylic acids did not cause any inhibitory effect. If all the other conditions of experiments were strictly controlled and constant, the data obtained by these authors may be considered as an indication that two negatively charged (carboxyl in the given case) groups of an inhibitor combine with positively charged groups in the active site of enzyme; these latter are necessary for combination with carboxyl groups of a substrate. This interpretation is not applicable to the phenomena of amino acid decarboxylases inhibition observed in our experiments.

We believe that a suggestion concerning significant importance of secondary and, what is the most probable, tertiary structure of enzyme protein is warranted. It is obvious that for decarboxylation of dicarboxylic amino acids some form of combination between two carboxyl groups and two chemical groups in active site of enzyme is of primary importance. However, the approach to these chemical groups in catalytically active centre is determined by tertiary structure of enzyme molecule. The active site of glutamate decarboxylase is evidently more readily accessible and no strict

TABLE 12. EFFECT OF DIFFERENT DICARBOXYLIC ACID ON GLUTAMIC ACID DECARBOXYLATION
(Per cent of inhibition for 5 and 10 min, glutamic acid, 10$\mu$ moles, inhibitor, 10, 50, 100 $\mu$moles.)

| Inhibitor[a] | 10 $\mu$moles | | 50 $\mu$moles | | 100 $\mu$moles | |
|---|---|---|---|---|---|---|
| | 5 min | 10 min | 5 min | 10 min | 5 min | 10 min |
| Glu | 45 | 39 | 82 | 75 | 93 | 87 |
| $\alpha$-$CH_3$Glu | 40 | 37 | 72 | 70 | 86 | 82 |
| Suc | 14 | 15 | 40 | 37 | 67 | 60 |
| Fum | 19 | 10 | 43 | 34 | 67 | 52 |
| Mal | 8 | 7 | 30 | 25 | 53 | 46 |
| $\beta$-HAsp | 14 | 13 | 44 | 13 | 51 | 38 |
| Malon | 7 | 3 | 22 | 11 | 34 | 30 |
| AcAsp | 2 | 3 | 11 | 10 | 23 | 24 |

[a]Glu, glutaric acid, $\alpha$-$CH_3$Glu, $\alpha$-methylglutaric acid; Suc, succinic acid; Fum, fumaric acid; Mal, maleic acid; Malon, malonic acid; AcAsp, acetylaspartic acid; $\beta$-HAsp, $\beta$-hydroxyaspartic acid.

TABLE 13. EFFECT OF DIFFERENT DICARBOXYLIC ACID ON ASPARTIC ACID DECARBOXYLATION
(Per cent of inhibition for 5 and 10 min, aspartic acid, 10 $\mu$moles, inhibitor, 10, 50, 100 $\mu$moles.)

| Inhibitor | 10 $\mu$moles | | 50 $\mu$moles | | 100 $\mu$moles | |
|---|---|---|---|---|---|---|
| | 5 min | 10 min | 5 min | 10 min | 5 min | 10 min |
| $\beta$-HAsp | 59 | 50 | 66 | 65 | 76 | 77 |
| Malon | 9 | 5 | 23 | 11 | 38 | 23 |
| Suc | 17 | 16 | 32 | 24 | 54 | 48 |
| Mal | 13 | 11 | 29 | 37 | 41 | 46 |
| Fum | 0 | 0 | 4 | 3 | 23 | 12 |
| Glu | 7 | 3 | 7 | 4 | 18 | 12 |
| $\alpha$-$CH_3$Glu | 0 | 1 | 3 | 2 | 7 | 9 |

stereochemical correspondence between substrates and inhibitors is required. That is why not only $\alpha$-methylglutaric acid but also $\beta$-methylglutaric, $\beta$-methylaspartic and $\beta$-hydroxyglutamic acids do not meet considerable spatial hindrance for approaching the active site of catalyst and chemically interacting with it.

The tertiary structure of aspartate decarboxylase apparently imposes stricter requirements upon the substrate and its analogues. The dimensions of the " way of approach " of aspartate towards the active site of catalyst correspond more or less strictly to the size of aspartate molecule. That is why the methylsuccinic acid cannot penetrate towards the catalytically active site and does not possess the inhibitory activity. As the approach to the active site of aspartate decarboxylase is strictly limited stereochemically the increase in aspartic acid concentration may cause an occlusion in the narrow passage through which substrate molecules reach the catalytically active centre of enzyme. As a result, an increase in substrate concentration may cause inhibition of reaction velocity.

Comparison of the inhibitory effect of the different decarboxylic acids (Tables 12 and 13) on decarboxylation does not contradict this point of view.

The above consideration serve to stress the significance of secondary and tertiary protein structures in enzyme catalytyzed reactions.

## REFERENCES

1. V. du Vigneaud, E. J. Kuchinskas and A. Horvath; *Arch. Biochem. Biophys.* **69,** 130 (1957).
2. D. S. Hoare and E. E. Snell; *Proc. Symp. Enzyme Chemistry*, Tokyo and Kyoto, 1957, p. 110, Maruzen, Tokyo (1958).
3. S. R. Mardashev and L. A. Syomina; *Doklady Acad. Nauk S.S.S.R.* **124**, 456 (1959).
4. M. Matsuda and K. Makino; *Biochim. et Biophys. Acta* **48**, 192 (1961).
5. Y. Matsuo; *J. Am. Chem. Soc.* **79**, 2011 (1957).
6. S. R. Mardashev and L. A. Syomina; *Biokhimia* **26**, 31 (1961).
7. S. R. Mardashev and Tien-rhey Tchao; *Doklady Akad. Nauk S.S.S.R.* **133**, 230 (1960).
8. L. A. Syomina and S. R. Mardashev; *Biokhimia* **26**, 1066 (1961).
9. M. V. Buell and R. E. Hansen; *J. Am. Chem. Soc.* **82**, 6042 (1960).
10. S. R. Mardashev; *Uspekhi Biol. Khim.* **1**, 281 (1950).
11. M. Garcia-Hernandez and E. Kun; *Biochim. et Biophys. Acta* **24**, 78 (1957).
12. A. E. Braunstein; *Enzymologia* **7**, 25 (1939).
13. M. Mason; *Federation Proc.* **17**, 271 (1958).

## DISCUSSION

Dr. Fromageot:

The rate of combination of thiol derivatives with pyridoxal being not infinite did you consider an incubation time with such inhibitors before starting assay?

Dr. Mardashev:

In all our experiments the preincubation time with the thiol inhibitors was 15 min. In special experiments with cysteamine we have investigated the influence of preincubation time (15, 30, 60 min) upon the inhibition of histidine decarboxylase. With the increase of the preincubation time the inhibition was increased.

# SOME NOTES ON THE COENZYME ACTIVITY OF PHOSPHOPYRIDOXAL DERIVATIVES FOR THE GLUTAMIC DECARBOXYLASE AND GLUTAMIC ASPARTIC TRANSAMINASE

by K. MAKINO, Y. OOI, M. MATSUDA and T. KURODA

Department of Biochemistry, Jikei University School of Medicine, Shiba, Minatoku, Tokyo, and Wakamoto Pharmaceutical Company, Unanemachi, Setagayaku, Tokyo

MEISTER *et al.* were able to show an equivalent activation of transaminase by either the aldehyde or amino form of the vitamin $B_6$-phosphate. Jenkins and Sizer[1], and Lis *et al.*[2] succeeded in the preparation of pyridoxal phosphate (PLP) and pyridoxamine phosphate forms of glutamic aspartic transaminase (GAT) and demonstrated that the disappearance of enzyme-bound pyridoxal phosphate was associated with the reversible formation of an equivalent amount of ketoglutarate and enzyme-bound pyridoxamine phosphate.

On the other hand, Shukuya and Schwert[3] showed that the addition of glutamate to their purified glutamic decarboxylase, in the pH range in which the enzyme was active, resulted in a dimunition of absorbency at 415 mμ and an increase at 330 mμ, these changes being reversed with time. They imagined that the dimunition of absorption at 415 mμ in the presence of glutamate might result from the disruption of the hydrogen-bonded chelate ring formed between apoenzyme and coenzyme by glutamate, and the chelate ring might be displaced by formation of a Schiff base between substrate and enzyme-bound pyridoxal phosphate. These facts seem to present confirmatory evidence for the concept of Schlenk, Snell, Metzler and Braunstein[4] which assumes the formation of pyridoxylidene azomethine as the active enzyme–substrate complex.

Against this, Gonnard *et al.*[5] have found that acyl hydrazones of PLP act as coenzymes of GAT, dopadecarboxylase and kynureinase like as pyridoxal phosphate, and have stated that acyl hydrazones act as such in these reactions without liberation of PLP because they could not detect the liberated acyl hydrazines in the reaction mixtures.

We have prepared various derivatives of PLP and tested their coenzyme activity. It was found that hydrazone, semicarbazone and isonicotinyl hydrazone (INPP) of PLP can act as coenzyme of brain glutamic decarboxylase while oxime and unexpectedly phenylhydrazone of PLP are inactive as coenzymes. Therefore, we have attempted to determine whether the above coenzyme-active compounds are effective as such or through the liberation of PLP.

TABLE 1

| Derivatives of pyridoxal phosphate | | | Coenzyme activity |
|---|---|---|---|
| 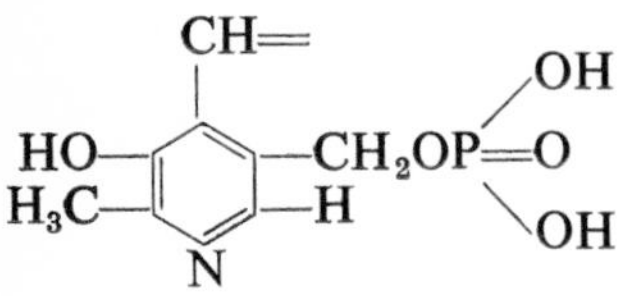 PLP ring: HO—, $H_3C$—, N; CH= at top; —$CH_2OP(=O)(OH)_2$; —H | $=N—NH_2$ | hydrazone | active |
| | $=N—NH—C(=O)—NH_2$ | semi-carbazone | |
| | 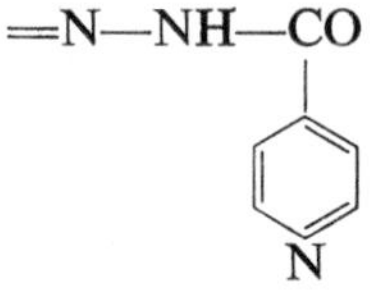 $=N—NH—CO—C_5H_4N$ (pyridine ring) | iso-nicotinyl hydrazone | |
| | $=N—OH$ | oxime | inactive |
| | 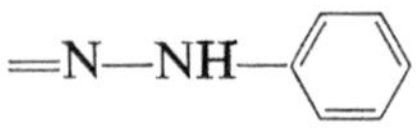 $=N—NH—C_6H_5$ (benzene ring) | phenyl hydrazone | |

TABLE 2. PREPARATION OF GLUTAMIC DECARBOXYLASE FROM MICE BRAIN

Seven grammes of mice brain were homogenized with 70 ml of water and centrifuged at 20,000 × *g* for 30 min. Two millilitres of 0.5 M phosphate buffer (pH 7.2) and 1 ml of 1 M calcium acetate were added to the supernatant solution and the resultant precipitate of calcium phosphate gel was centrifuged off. Ammonium sulphate was added to 15 per cent to the solution, which passed through, followed by centrifugation at 20,000 × *g* for 20 min. To the supernatant solution ammonium sulphate is again added to 35 per cent saturation. The precipitate is dissolved in 12 ml of 0.05 M phosphate buffer (pH 6.2) and dialysed against 1 l. of the same buffer changed three times in the cold.

Specific activity: 192 $CO_2$ $\mu$l/hr per mg protein.

For this experiment, the enzyme used was prepared as follows: 7 g of mouse brain is homogenized with 70 ml of water and centrifuged at 20,000 × *g* for 30 min. Two millilitres of 0.5 M phosphate buffer (pH 7.2) and 1 ml of 1 M calcium acetate are added to the supernatant solution and the resultant precipitate of calcium phosphate gel is centrifuged off. Ammonium sulfate is added to 15 per cent saturation followed by centrifugation at 20,000 × *g* for 20 min. To the supernatant solution ammonium sulfate is again added to 35 per cent saturation. The resultant precipitate is dissolved in 12 ml of

TABLE 3. MEASUREMENT OF GLUTAMIC DECARBOXYLASE

| | |
|---|---|
| Main chamber: | 1 ml of enzyme preparation, 2 ml of phosphate buffer, pH 6.2 and various amounts of PLP derivatives dissolved 0.2 ml of the above buffer. |
| Side Arm (I): | 15 mg of monosodium glutamate in 0.2 ml of water. After the temperature equilibrium for 10 min under 100 per cent nitrogen at 35°C, the content of the side arm (I) is tipped into the main chamber and $CO_2$-evolution is recorded every 10 min. If necessary for checking $CO_2$-retention, 0.2 ml of 3 N $H_2SO_4$ is placed in another $CO_2$-retention, 0.2 ml of 3 N $H_2SO_4$ is placed in another side arm (II). |

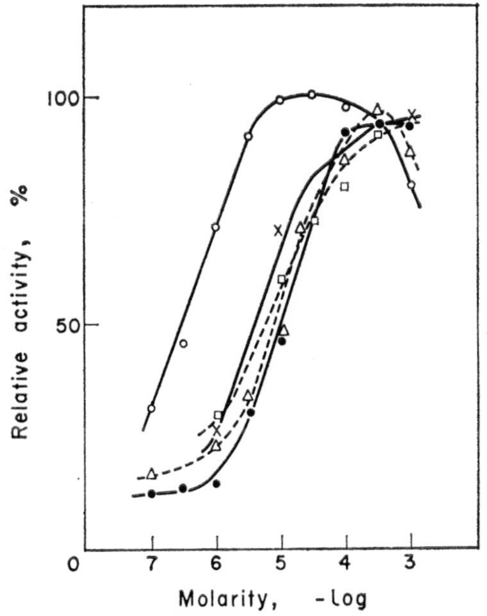


FIG. 1. Relation of relative enzyme activity to molarity.
○——○ PLP.
●——● INPP.
△------△ Semicarbazone of PLP.
×——× Hydrazone of PLP.
□------□ Thiosemicarbazone of PLP.
*The activity of PLP is assigned for 100 per cent.

0.05 M phosphate buffer (pH 6.2) and dialyzed against 1 l. of the same buffer changed three times in the cold. By the above procedure 85–90 per cent of the PLP is removed from the anzyme protein. The enzyme activity is estimated with Warburg's manometer. In the main chamber are placed 1 ml of the enzyme preparation, a solution of each coenzyme dissolved in 0.2 ml of phosphate buffer and 2 ml of phosphate buffer (0.05 M, pH 6.2), and in one side arm 15 mg of monosodium glutamate in 0.2 ml of water, and also, if necessary, in another side arm 0.2 ml of 3 N $H_2SO_4$ (for the estimation of $CO_2$-retention). After temperature equilibrium for 10 min

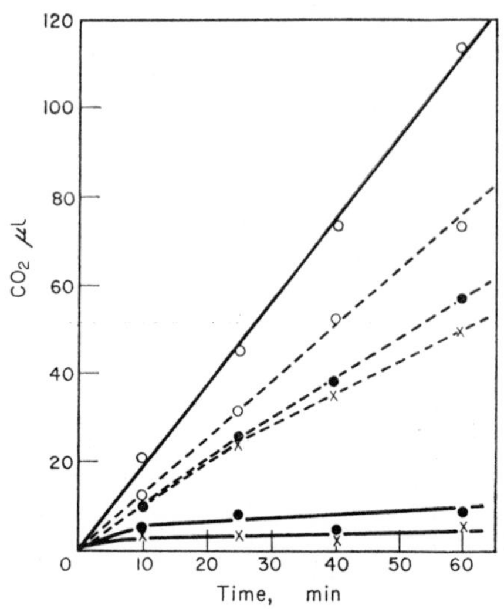


FIG. 2. Inhibition of coenzyme activity with penicillamine.
○——○ PLP 2 × $10^{-5}$ M.
●——● PLP 2 × $10^{-5}$ M + penicillamine $10^{-3}$ M.
×——× PLP 2 × $10^{-5}$ M + penicillamine 2 × $10^{-3}$ M.
○------○ INPP 2 × $10^{-5}$ M.
●------● INPP 2 × $10^{-5}$ M + penicillamine $10^{-3}$ M.
×——× INPP 2 × $10^{-5}$ M + penicillamine 2 × $10^{-3}$ M.

under 100 per cent $N_2$ at 35°C, the solution of monosodium glutamate is tipped into the main chamber and the $CO_2$ evolution is recorded every 10 min for 60 min.

In the case of PLP maximal enzyme activity is produced with 3.3 × $10^{-5}$ M, but above $10^{-4}$ M inhibition of the activity occurs. In the case of INPP the enzyme activity observed by the addition of 3.3 × $10^{-5}$ M corresponds to 65 per cent of the activity of the same concentration of PLP. With 3.3 × $10^{-4}$ M of INPP the same maximal activity as with PLP is attained. $K_m$ of PLP for the apoenzyme is 5.5 × $10^{-7}$, while that of INPP is 1.1 × $10^{-5}$ (Fig. 1).

After the enzyme reaction with the addition of $10^{-3}$ M INPP is finished, the reaction mixture is deproteinized with 20 per cent trichloroacetic acid and centrifuged. The supernatant solution is concentrated under diminished pressure at low temperature to a syrup and applied in a band (8 cm in length) to filter paper No. 50 (Toyo Roshi Company) and developed with a solvent system of n-butanol, acetic acid and water (4 : 1 : 5) or 69 per cent butyric acid (v/v) containing 0.85 per cent NaOH. Compounds are detected by spraying with Gibbs' reagent.[6] If the above coenzyme activity of INPP were due to the liberation of PLP from INPP, the amount of the liberated PLP

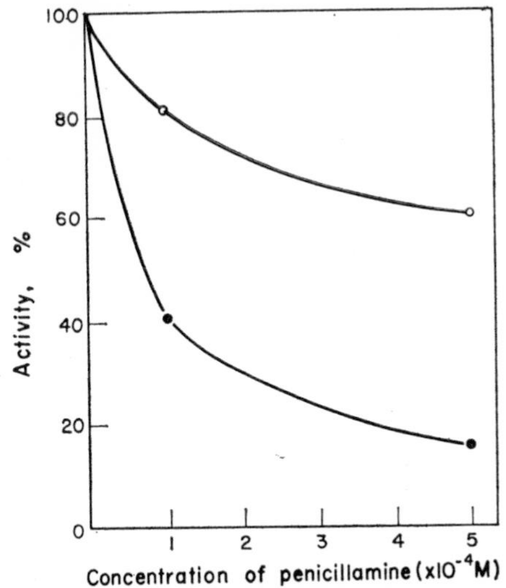


FIG. 3. Inhibition of the enzyme activity by penicillamine after 70 min.
○——○ INPP + penicillamine.
●——● PLP + penicillamine.
The original activity of each coenzyme is assigned for 100 per cent.

might be expected to be enough for the detection by the above paper chromatographic procedure. But no spot other than INPP can be detectable up to 60 min. In case of the addition to the reaction system of INPP purified by paper chromatography, no lag of $CO_2$-evolution is seen whether INPP is preincubated with the apoenzyme for 10 min or not. These facts seem to show that INPP itself acts as the coenzyme of glutamic decarboxylase.

Using DL-penicillamine, which has been considered to inhibit PLP action by forming a thiazolidine derivative, we determined the effect of this inhibitor on enzyme activity with PLP and INPP respectively. For this purpose, $2 \times 10^{-5}$ M of each coenzyme and $10^{-3}$ M penicillamine are put into the main chamber of Warburg flasks and then the apoenzyme solution added. After tipping glutamate from the side arm into the main chamber the $CO_2$ evolution is measured. Though the enzyme activity due to $2 \times 10^{-5}$ M PLP is entirely inhibited by $10^{-3}$ M or $2 \times 10^{-3}$ M DL-penicillamine, the activation due to $2 \times 10^{-5}$ M INPP is inhibited by the addition of $10^{-3}$ M or $2 \times 10^{-3}$ M penicillamine no more than 20 or 30 per cent respectively (Fig. 2).

This fact seems to show that INPP as such can act as a coenzyme of brain glutamic decarboxylase. The slight inhibition by penicillamine found in the experiment with INPP may be due to the effect of DL-penicillamine upon the apoenzyme. This assumption is based on the following analogy found in the

TABLE 4. DERIVATIVES OF PYRIDOXAL PHOSPHATE

| | |
|---|---|
| Thiosemi-carbazide | 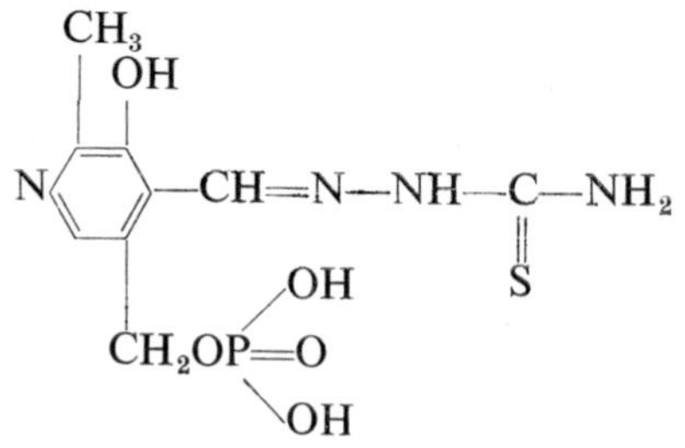 $CH_3$, OH; N(ring)—CH=N—NH—C(=S)—$NH_2$; $CH_2OP(=O)(OH)OH$ |
| Azine | 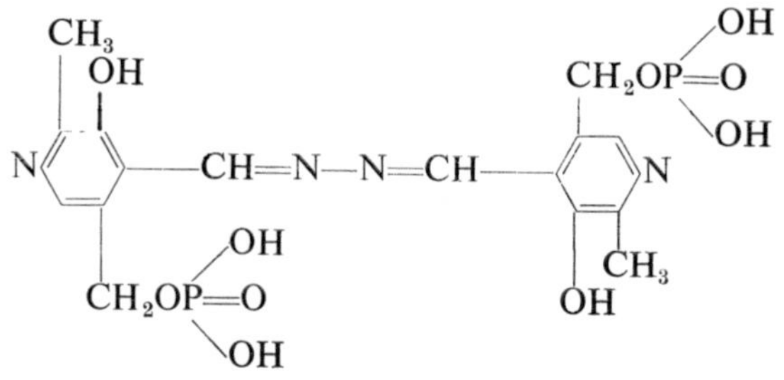 $CH_3$, OH; N(ring)—CH=N—N=CH—(ring)N; $CH_2OP(=O)(OH)OH$; $CH_3$, OH; $CH_2OP(=O)(OH)OH$ |
| Penicill-amine | 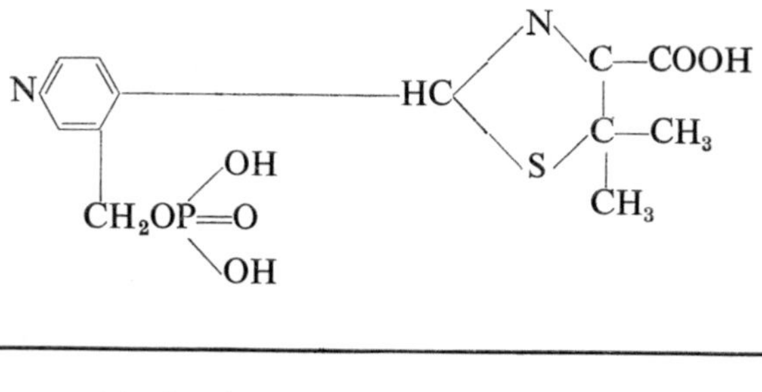 N(ring)—HC<(N, S) ring: N—C—COOH, C—$CH_3$, $CH_3$, S; $CH_2OP(=O)(OH)OH$ |

inhibition experiment with isonicotinyl hydrazide (INAH): the brain glutamic decarboxylase activation by $10^{-5}$ M INPP is inhibited as much as 50 per cent by the addition of $5 \times 10^{-4}$ M INAH indicating that the latter decreases the enzyme activity by affecting the apoenzyme protein.

Even when the coenzymes are preincubated with the apoenzyme, the inhibition of INPP-activity by DL-penicillamine added afterwards is far less than that of PLP : in the experiments using $10^{-5}$ M of each coenzyme, the amount of which is sufficient for the saturation of the apoenzyme in case of PLP, the inhibition of the holoenzyme activity by $5 \times 10^{-4}$ M penicillamine after the 10 min preincubation of the coenzyme with apoenzyme, is 85 per cent in case of PLP and 40 per cent in case of INPP when compared in the reaction time from 30 min to 70 min (Fig. 3).

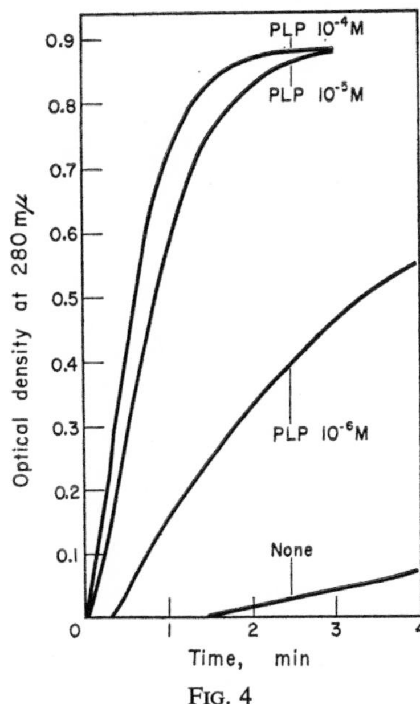


FIG. 4

The possibility that in the above experiment INPP acts at the enzyme surface by liberating PLP, which rapidly recombines with INAH to form INPP, is excluded by the fact that $2 \times 10^{-5}$ M PLP which is preincubated with apoenzyme, when added to a mixture of $2 \times 10^{-5}$ M INAH and $5 \times 10^{-4}$ M penicillamine, loses its coenzyme activity completely indicating that INAH cannot compete with penicillamine in combining with PLP under these experimental conditions.

Phosphopyridoxal hydrazone and semicarbazone, which were mentioned above, took nearly the same attitude as INPP toward the inhibition due to DL-penicillamine.

Then we tested the above compounds and three other PLP derivatives, namely thiosemicarbazone, Bis-phosphopyridoxylidene hydrazine and thiazolidine derivative of DL-penicillamine on their coenzyme activity for GAT.

The enzyme used in this experiment is prepared and purified by the method of Jenkins *et al.*[7] and then PLP is eliminated from it according to the method of Wada and Snell[8]. The full exertion of the reconstructed enzyme activity is attained by the preincubation for 1 hr of PLP with the apoenzyme solution. The enzyme activity is determined according to the method of Cammarata and Cohen[9]. As may be seen from Fig. 4, the coenzyme can be almost completely eliminated from the apoenzyme by the Wada and Snell method. The apoenzyme thus prepared may be saturated by the addition of $3 \times 10^{-5}$ M

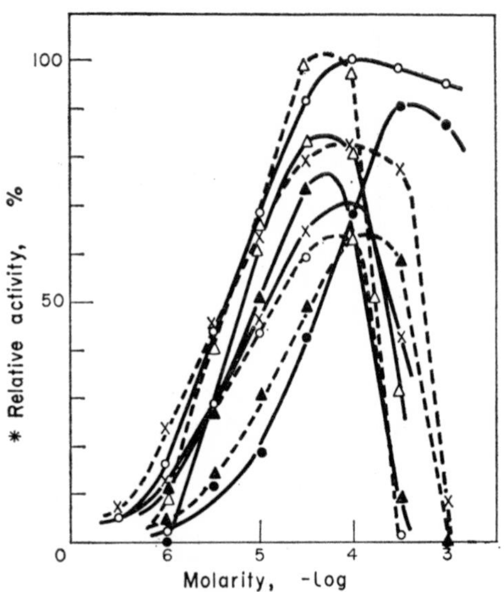


FIG. 5. Relation of relative enzyme activity to molarity of the coenzymes.

○——○ PLP.
△------△ INPP.
×------× Oxime of PLP.
●——● Thiazolidine of PLP.
▲——▲ Semicarbazone of PLP.
▲------▲ Hydrazone of PLP.
×——× Phenylhydrazone of PLP.
△——△ Thenylhydrazone of PLP.
○------○ Azine of PLP.

*The activity of PLP is assigned for 100 per cent.

PLP. The relation of relative GAT activity of various PLP derivatives to the molarities of PLP or PLP derivatives added and expressed in − log is illustrated in Fig. 5, where the activity caused by the addition of $10^{-4}$ M of PLP (final concentration) is assigned for 100 per cent. INPP can activate GAT to the same extent as PLP, the $K_m$ of the former being the same with that of the latter. The thiazolidine derivative of penicillamine shows a considerable coenzyme activity though it has a relatively large $K_m$ value. Oxime and thiosemicarbazone have an activity of 80 per cent of PLP, whereas at concentrations below $10^{-5}$ M the oxime shows the same activity as that of

PLP. Semicarbazone and phenylhydrazone show 70 per cent activity, while hydrazone and bisphosphopyridoxylidene hydrazine 60 per cent. Generally speaking, nearly all the above derivatives of PLP show strong inhibition at their higher concentrations, whereas PLP even at $10^{-3}$ M shows only a slight inhibition. The only compound which still has a considerable activity at the same concentration as PLP, is the penicillamine-thiazolidine derivative.

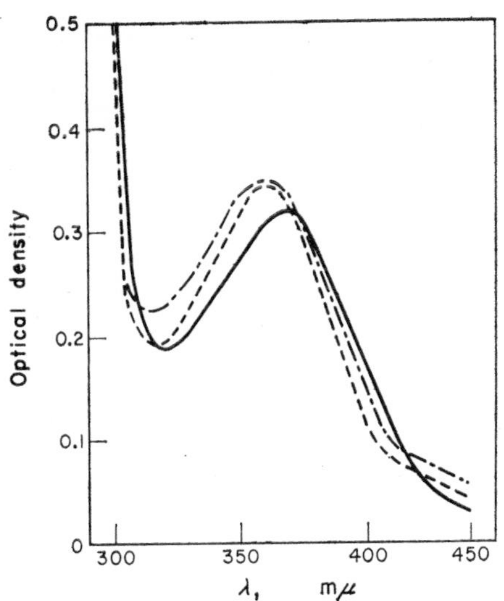


FIG. 6. ---- Holoenzyme -.-.-.- PLP enzyme ——— Oxime-enzyme.

It is interesting to notice that the oxime and phenylhydrazone which were unable to activate glutamic decarboxylase are effective as coenzymes of GAT. If the PLP derivatives as such combine with the apoenzyme of GAT, one may expect that the absorption spectrum of the constructed enzyme may be different from that of the original PLP holoenzyme. Therefore, we prepared PLP-oxime enzyme and compared its absorption spectrum and enzymic activity with those of the reconstructed PLP enzyme. A volume of 0.2 ml of PLP or PLP-oxime solution (final concentration $3.3 \times 10^{-4}$ M) is incubated with 2.8 ml of apoenzyme solution (*ca.* 4.6 mg protein/ml) at 37° for 40 min and then saturated to 70 per cent with ammonium sulfate under cooling. The resulting precipitate, after washing with saturated ammonium sulfate solution, is dissolved in 0.1 M phosphate buffer, pH 8.3 and again saturated to 70 per cent with ammonium sulfate. The resultant precipitate is dissolved in 0.1 M phosphate buffer, pH 8.3 and used as PLP or PLP-oxime enzyme. As the control the original holoenzyme is treated in the same manner except that water is added instead of PLP or PLP-derivative. The reconstructed PLP-enzyme shows the same absorption maximum as that of the original

PLP enzyme, namely at 360 mμ, whereas the oxime-enzyme at 370 mμ as shown in Fig. 6. The specific enzyme activity of the three holoenzymes is all the same as shown in Table 5. Each holoenzyme solution is precipitated by the addition of 50 per cent trichloroacetic acid. The clear filtrate is investigated on its PLP content by adding an excess of phenylhydrazine dissolved in

TABLE 5

| | Protein (mg/ml) | Activity (ΔO.D. 280 mμ/min per ml) | Specific activity | PLP (μmoles/ml) |
|---|---|---|---|---|
| Holoenzyme | 4.90 | 12.1 | 2.5 | 0.025 |
| PLP-enzyme | 4.83 | 12.2 | 2.5 | 0.030 |
| Oxime-enzyme | 4.53 | 11.2 | 2.4 | 0.006 |
| Apoenzyme | 4.60 | 0 | 0 | 0.000 |

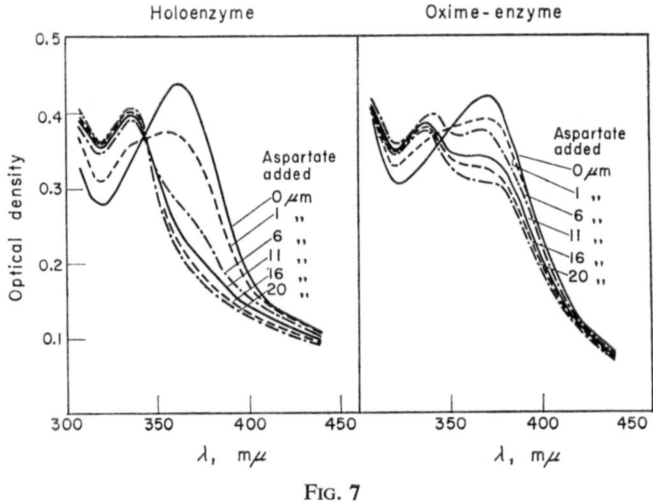


FIG. 7

10 N $H_2SO_4$ (Wada–Snell method) followed by measuring the light absorbency at 410 mμ. The deproteinized filtrate of the PLP-oxime enzyme gives with the above reagent a value as much as one-fifth that of the PLP-enzyme as shown also in Table 5. Then, to 2.6 ml of each holoenzyme solution (4.5 mg protein/ml) which contains 0.087 μM PLP or PLP-oxime is added a solution of aspartate of various concentrations and the change of absorption spectrum is observed. As indicated in Fig. 7, the spectrum of the PLP enzyme is easily

converted to pyridoxamine phosphate–enzyme type by adding aspartate even to 6 μmoles, whereas the course of the spectral change of the oxime-enzyme by the same treatment is fairly different from it. There was seen a considerable resistance towards the descent of the peak at 370 mμ due to the addition of increasing amounts of aspartate.

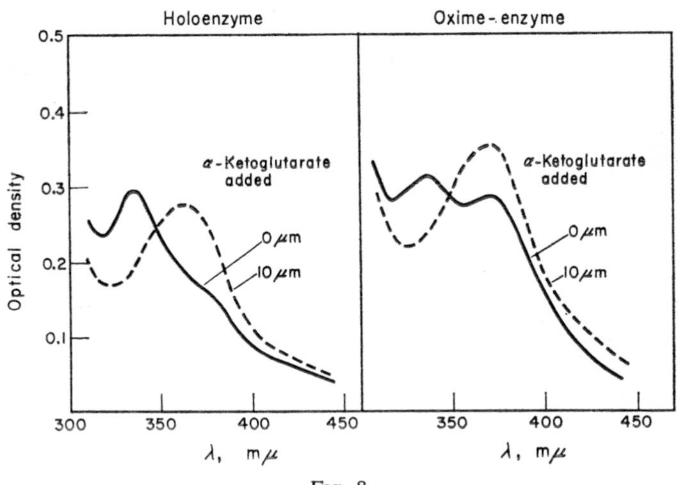


FIG. 8

TABLE 6

| | Activity (△O.D. 280 mμ/min per ml) | μmoles enzyme bound PLP/ml | | |
|---|---|---|---|---|
| | | Before the addition of the substrate | After the addition of the substrate[a] | After the addition of the substrate[b] |
| Holoenzyme | 7.4 | 0.029 | | |
| Oxime-enzyme | 6.8 | 0.0054 | 0.0060 | 0.0056 |

[a]After the addition of 20 μmoles of α-ketoglutarate to the oxime-enzyme which is isolated by ammonium sulphate after preliminary treatment with 20 μmoles aspartate.
[b]After the addition of 20 μmoles of aspartate in the presence of 20 μmoles of α-ketoglutarate.

After adding 20 μmoles of aspartate, both enzymes are precipitated with ammonium sulfate and again dissolved in 0.1 M phosphate buffer (pH 8.3) respectively. When to these solutions giving the same absorption spectra as those seen before adding ammonium sulfate are added 10 μmoles each of α-ketoglutarate, the absorption spectra of both enzyme solutions return to the respective original pattern, that is, presumably of the PLP-enzyme and the corresponding oxime-enzyme as seen in Fig. 8. The mixture is deproteinized and used for measuring PLP according to the method of Wada and Snell. The result is as indicated in Table 6. On the other hand, to 2.6 ml of oxime-enzyme solution (4.5 mg/ml) is added 0.2 ml of α-keto-glutarate containing 20 μmoles under stirring and then 0.2 ml of L-aspartate containing 20 μmoles. The mixture deproteinized and used for measuring PLP. The result of PLP assay is indicated also in Table 6 and shows that the amount of PLP, accordingly the amount of oxime, does not change considerably through these enzymic transformations. In these transformations, the molar ratio of coenzyme to substrates is 1 = 230.

From these facts the possibility that PLP-oxime as such acts as coenzyme of GAT cannot be hastily excluded, though final conclusions cannot be drawn from the results of the present experiment.*

Another experiment which we repeated twice and are still continuing, showed that, whereas the pyridoxamine phosphate enzyme prepared directly from pyridoxamine phosphate and apo-GAT gave no coloration with Wada–Snell's reagent, the above transformed pyridoxamine-type enzyme (prepared from the reconstructed PLP enzyme by the addition of 20 μmoles of aspartate and showing the same absorption spectrum as that of the former) showed clearly visible coloration when the same reagent was added directly to the deproteinized filtrate of the enzyme. This coloration was stronger than that given by the oxime-enzyme. These facts may suggest that the state of the oxime of PLP or pyridoxamine phosphate which are incorporated deeply in GAT-protein is labile, and accordingly may be liable to be decomposed by the above acid treatment yielding PLP-like coloration with Wada–Snell's reagent. Our experimental results showed that the yield in PLP-like coloration remained almost constant in all states of the oxime-enzyme, that is the aspartate, aspartate-α-ketoglutarate treated and the original oxime-enzyme.

Therefore, the coloration of oxime-enzyme might perhaps be artificial. If this is the case, it seems to favour the assumption that oxime as such can act as a co-transaminase, though, at the same time, we are not willing to neglect the fact that there is a sufficient tendency for oxime to be converted into PLP by the addition of a great excess of aspartate.

We used the oxime of PLP in this experiment because the compound as such gives no Wada–Snell reaction (most other derivatives of PLP give the Wada–Snell reaction without previous addition of apoenzyme).

We should like to pay some attention to the unsubstituted carbon-6 next to pyrimidine N (1) besides the C3–C4 area. The pyridine moiety of coenzyme I,

---

*If the enzymic transformations are carried out with such amounts of the purified apotransaminase as the increase in transaminase activity is linear with it, it has been found recently by the use of sodium borohydride reduction method, which will be published elsewhere, that 4-aldehyde of PAL-p is mostly liberated from its oxime.

that is niacinamide, and the thiazol moiety are chemically stable. Through toxopyrimidation of these compounds (namely combining them with the pyrimidine moiety of thiamine (toxopyrimidine) at the nitrogen (1) of pyridine or thiazole as indicated below or incorporating the pyridine into coenzyme I (or II) to make nitrogen (1) quarternay), the carbon-6-nitrogen area of the pyridine nucleus or carbon-2-nitrogen (1) area of thiazol seems to be activated chemically and catalytically (Fig. 9). The toxopyrimidation of pyridine derivatives can be easily estimated by the detection of pyrichrom derivatives in the reaction mixture, which is chemically structurally analogous to thiochrom and strongly fluorescent. Contrary to this, according to our

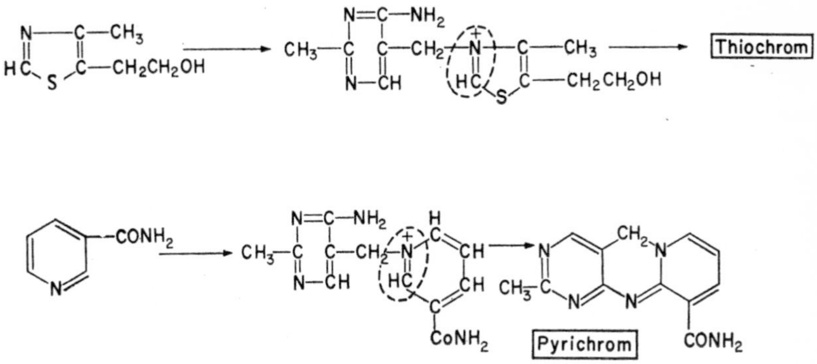

Thiochrom

Pyrichrom

FIG. 9

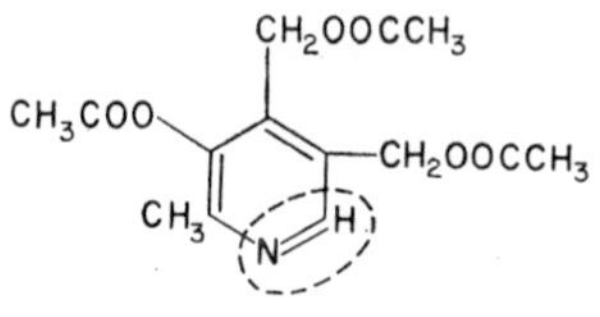

FIG. 10

experiment, pyridoxine, even as the triacetate (Fig. 10), seemed to resist toxopyrimidation. This suggests that the C(6)–N(1) area of pyridoxine is already reactive and perhaps apt to protonize (therefore, toxopyrimidation is difficult).

## ADDENDUM

According to Hayaishi *et al.*[9] though quinolinic acid is enzyme-chemically relatively stable (that is, the conversion of this compound to nicotinic derivative is not easy), it is decarboxylated at C(2) easily to give niacinamide-ribotide when it is combined with ribose phosphate at N(1) of the pyridine

(Fig. 11). Phenolic OH and aldehyde of PLP, or phenolic OH and = N − OH (or = N − NH − R) seem to serve to give a chelating property to PLP and to raise a protonizing tendency at C(2) by producing a Schiff base with the apoenzyme or as such respectively in order to potentiate a catalytical activity at N(1)–C(2) area (Fig. 12).

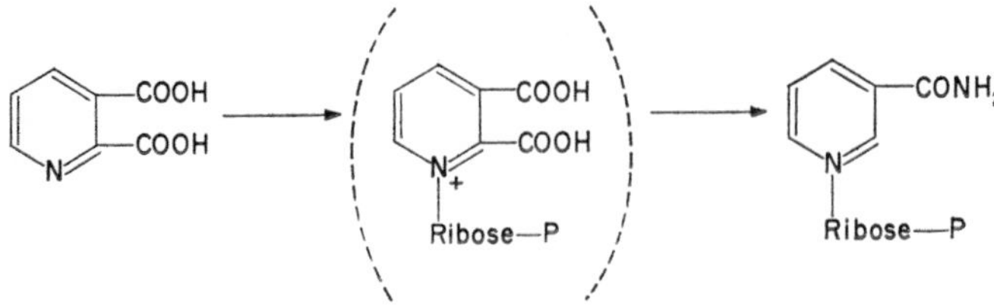

FIG. 11

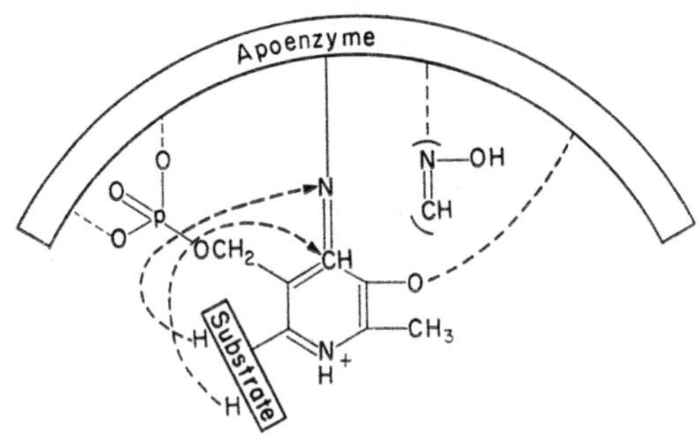


FIG. 12

## REFERENCES

1. W. T. JENKINS and I. W. SIZER; *J. Biol. Chem.* **235**, 620 (1960).
2. H. LIS, P. FASELLA, C. TURANO and P. VECCHINI; *Biochim. et Biophys. Acta* **45**, 529 (1960).
3. R. SHUKUYA and G. SCHWERT; *J. Biol. Chem.* **235**, 1649 (1960).
4. cit. A. E. BRAUNSTEIN; *The Enzymes* (edited by P. D. BOYER, H. LARDY and K. MYRBÄCK), vol. 2, pp. 113–184, 2nd ed., Academic Press, New York (1960).
5. P. GONNARD *et al.*; *Enzymologia* **20**, 231, 237 (1959); *Bull. Soc. Biol.* **43**, 601, 609 (1961).
6. R. J. BLOCK, E. L. DURRUM and G. ZWEIG; *A Manual of Paper Chromatography and Paper Electrophoresis*, p. 299, Academic Press, New York (1955).
7. T. JENKINS, D. A. YPHANTIS and I. W. SIZER; *J. Biol. Chem.* **234**, 51 (1959).
8. H. WADA and E. E. SNELL; *J. Biol. Chem.* **236**, 2089 (1961).
9. O. HAYAISHI; Personal communication.

## DISCUSSION

DR. JENKINS:

Dr. Makino has described the experiment I suggested after Dr. Gonnard's paper; however, I think that the choice of pyridoxal phosphate and its oxime was perhaps confutable for the following reasons:

1. Activation with pyridoxamine phosphate appears open to less objections than the use of pyridoxal phosphate.

2. There are insufficient differences between the spectra of free and bound pyridoxal oxime and the free enzyme. For example, with thiosemicarbazide the binding should be readily observed spectroscopically as should the liberation of thiosemicarbazide.

3. The oxime of pyridoxal phosphate has an atypical stability. This property is utilized by Dr. Makino to validate his assay procedure but it may in some manner not understood invalidate the experiment.

DR. MAKINO:

1. Dr. Jenkins's first comment that activation with pyridoxamine phosphate appears open to less objection than the use of pyridoxal phosphate is not clear to me owing to his too short description.

2. Though the second comment is that differences between the spectra of free (1) and bound pyridoxal oxime (2) and the free enzyme (3) (perhaps PLP enzyme?) are not sufficient, we can discriminate those differences distinctly when close attention is paid. When amino acid is added to each solution, (2) and (3) show characteristic spectral changes respectively, and returned to the original spectra when α-ketoglutarate is added. The use of thiosemicarbazone suggested by Dr. Jenkins is not appropriate for the present purpose because thiosemicarbazone as such gives PLP-like coloration with the Wada–Snell reagent.

3. The third comment is that PLP oxime having atypical stability may in some manner not understood invalidate our experiment. But, according to our opinion, the fact that oxime of PLP is difficult to liberate hydroxylamine is favourable for us, because we have attached importance to the fact that a PLP derivative which gives no appreciable amount of free PLP during enzymic transformation, yet retains a coenzymic action. By pursuing the mechanism of action of such a PLP derivative, one may expect to contribute to the elucidation of the mode of action of PLP itself.

DR. SNELL:

Those of us who have proposed catalytic mechanisms for pyridoxal enzymes that require a free (or potentially free) carbonyl group have of course been interested in the observation of Dr. Makino and Dr. Gonnard and their collaborators which show that certain carbonyl derivatives of pyridoxal phosphate can replace the free coenzyme as an activator of apoenzyme normally dependent upon pyridoxal phosphate. These authors have interpreted their results as indicating that these derivatives function coenzymatically *per se* since they have been unable to show any hydrolysis of the derivatives in the course of the experiment. It should be pointed out that conclusive findings in this field can only be obtained by the use of essentially pure apoenzyme in stoichiometric amount with the activator. All of the results of these authors would be explained if apoenzyme and activator were to interact according to the equation:

$$\text{apoenzyme—NH}_2 + \text{N}\langle\text{ring}\rangle\text{—CH—N—R} \rightarrow \text{enzyme—N}{=}\underset{\text{H}}{\text{C}}\text{—}\langle\text{ring}\rangle\text{N} + \text{H}_2\text{N—R}$$

Only the activator bound at the active site of the enzyme need undergo this reaction; the amount of free carbonyl reagent which would appear, would be stoichiometric with the number of active sites on the protein. In this connection it may be recalled that Meister showed several years ago that purified glutamic–aspartic transaminase binds many times more pyridoxal phosphate than is retained in the holoenzyme following exhaustive dialysis, i.e. only a fraction of the coenzyme bound is bound at active sites. Thus the carbonyl reagent liberated when the hypothetical reactions above occur would be expected to be very small indeed and would certainly escape detection in all of the experiments conducted so far that purport to show that these derivatives of PLP activate directly, without being converted to protein-bound PLP during the course of the reaction.

Dr. Makino's second set of interesting findings, that enzymes activated by a derivative of PLP may be less susceptible to inhibition by carbonyl reagents than when PLP itself is the activator, is likewise susceptible to alternative interpretations that do not exclude a

PLP enzyme as the catalytically active protein. Since such alternative interpretations are wholly speculative, they need not be presented here. These remarks are made only to indicate that further work is required to permit an unequivocal interpretation of these most interesting findings.

Finally, I should like to ask whether any comparison of the rate of reaction of free PLP and of the activating derivative with the inhibitory carbonyl reagents were made.

DR. MAKINO:

1. Dr. Snell's first comment is very important.

The transaminase used by us has been prepared and purified essentially according to the method of Jenkins *et al.* And the content of PLP has been confirmed to be stoichiometric with apoenzyme. The oxime-enzyme prepared by combining PLP oxime with the purified apoenzyme, has been purified by repeated precipitation with ammonium sulfate. In preparing a reconstructed PLP enzyme, the same attention was paid.

We compare by using the Wada–Snell method, the change of PLP amount in oxime-enzymes among enzymic transformations, that is, before treating with substrate, after treating with aspartate and after treating with aspartate followed with $\alpha$-ketoglutarate. The result showed that the yield in PLP-like coloration with the Wada–Snell reagent remained almost constant in every state of enzymic transformation, that is, one-fifth of the PLP holoenzyme. The PLP content is insufficient to interpret the enzymic activity of the oxime-enzyme. (The detection of a small amount of PLP-like coloration in oxime-enzyme may be perhaps not due to the pre-existing PLP, but it may be that the PLP oxime incorporated in enzyme becomes more sensitive to the Wada–Snell reagent than free PLP oxime).

2. The second comment containing phrase " to alternative interpretations that do not exclude a PLP enzyme as the catalytically active protein " is not clear to us.

We have no doubt that PLP enzyme is the natural form of the catalytically active protein.

We only imagine it may be possible to assume some interpretation other than that of Drs. Snell and Braunstein in respect to the function of 4-aldehyde in PLP. For instance, if, though it is only speculative, such formulae as indicated below were assumed for the mode of action of PLP enzyme, the interpretation of the function of 4-aldehyde might be different from that proposed by Drs. Snell and Braunstein. In such a case oxime or isonicotinyl hydrazone might function in the same manner as an aldehyde group.

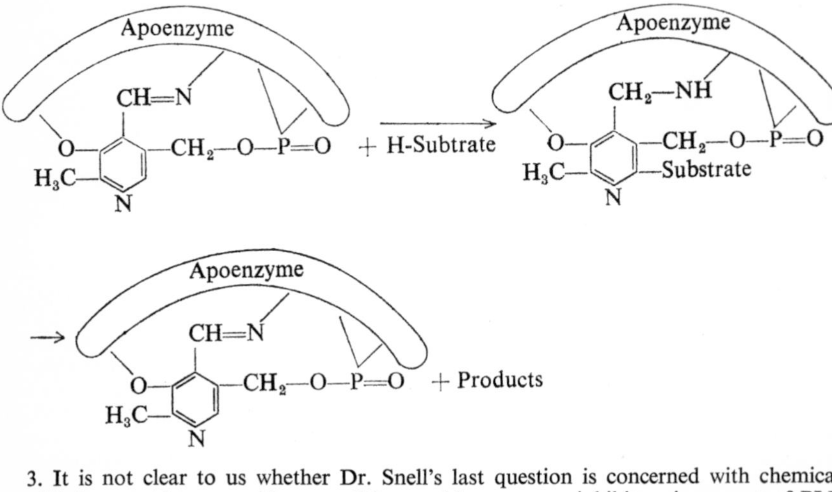

Apoenzyme
CH=N
O
$H_3C$
N
$CH_2$—O—P=O + H-Subtrate → 
Apoenzyme
$CH_2$—NH
O
$H_3C$
N
$CH_2$—O—P=O
—Substrate

→ Apoenzyme
CH=N
O
$H_3C$
N
$CH_2$—O—P=O + Products

3. It is not clear to us whether Dr. Snell's last question is concerned with chemical equilibrium problems or with competition problems among inhibitors in respect of PLP enzymes activity. That we are interested in such a problem can be seen by the paper in *Biochem. Biophys. Res. Comm.* **9**, 250 (1962).

# SUR LES HYDRAZONES DE PHOSPHO-5-PYRIDOXAL, ROLE CO-ENZYMATIQUE ET STABILITÉ

by PIERRE GONNARD

Laboratoire de Chimie Biologique,
Maison Départmentale de Nanterre (Seine)

L'INHIBITION des pyridoxalo-enzymes par l'isoniazide (INH) a été interprétée comme étant due au blocage de la fonction aldéhyde du co-facteur, sous forme d'hydrazone.[1–4]

Les premières expériences que nous avons effectuées dans le but de rechercher la dose limite inhibitrice d'INH vis-à-vis de la dopa-décarboxylase ont mis en évidence, pour les faibles concentrations, non plus une inhibition mais au contraire une activation de l'enzyme. L'activation est plus intense que celle provoquée par l'addition au milieu de phosphate de pyridoxal (la préparation enzymatique n'étant pas spontanément saturée en co-enzyme).[5]

Cette constatation nous a amenés à préparer un certain nombre d'hydrazones de phospho-5'-pyridoxal, à étudier leur comportement vis-à-vis de pyridoxalo-enzymes agissant différemment sur les amino-acides:

| | |
|---|---|
| Desmolasses: | dopa décarboxylase[5–7] glutamo décarboxylase.[8] |
| Transférase: | transaminase glutamique aspartique.[9,10] |
| Hydrolase: | cynuréninase.[11,12] |

Les décarboxylases sont utilisées sous forme d'extraits bruts ou partiellement purifiés; les préparations rénales de dopa-décarboxylase présentent un déficit plus ou moins accentué en co-enzyme, les préparations cérébrales de glutamo-décarboxylase présentent un très important déficit, ce qui constitue une condition favorable pour l'étude des réactivations.

La cynuréninase purifiée est privée de phosphate de pyridoxal.

La transaminase électrophorétiquement pure, préparée selon la méthode de Lis et Fasella[13,14], conserve son co-enzyme; il faut donc l'inhiber, puis, ajouter le phosphate de pyridoxal pour la réactiver, mais, alors que cela est possible avec les extraits bruts, l'enzyme pur est presque insensible à la désoxypyridoxine ou à L'INH.

Dans tous les cas, nous avons obtenu une action co-enzymatique par addition d'hydrazones d'hydrazides de phosphate de pyridoxal, mais à des degrés variables, et dans certains cas avec les hydrazones d'hydrazines.

La *dopa-décarboxylase* est plus active en présence des hydrazones suivantes qu'en présence de phosphate de pyridoxal:

Isonicotylhydrazone et isomères (nicotyl, pycolyl): activité environ 125 par rapport au témoin additionné de phosphate de pyridoxal, considéré à 100.

Benzoylhydrazone: activité environ 125.

Cyanacétylhydrazone: activité environ 200.

Pour la *glutamo-décarboxylase* et la *transaminase*, l'activité en présence des hydrazones cycliques est en moyenne égale à celle obtenue en présence de phosphate de pyridoxal.

La cyanacétylhydrazone entraîne une activation plus forte.

Pour la *cynuréninase*, l'activation est dans tous les cas, y compris celui de la cyanacétylhydrazone, comparable à celle obtenue en présence de phosphate de pyridoxal.

Le cas des combinaisons des iodanilines (*ortho*, *méta* et *para*) avec le phosphate de pyridoxal est particulièrement curieux; on obtient une activation considérable par rapport au témoin, pour la transaminase: plus de 300, et une activation vis-à-vis de la cynuréninase comparable à celle due au phosphate de pyridoxal.

Des hydrazones d'hydrazines ont été étudiées et sont en général actives, sauf vis-à-vis de la cynuréninase.

Il convient de discuter les deux problèmes soulevés par ces résultats:

A. Le mécanisme de l'inhibition provoquée par les hydrazides.

B. Le mécanisme de l'activation provoquée par les hydrazones.

## A. L'INHIBITION PAR LES HYDRAZIDES

L'inhibition de systèmes enzymatiques par les hydrazides et notamment par l'isoniazide (INH) n'est pas due à la formation d'hydrazone par action de l'hydrazide sur le phosphate de pyridoxal. En effet:

(1) De nombreux enzymes non pyridoxaliques sont inhibés par l'INH: phosphatases, lipases, uréase, etc.[15–28]

(2) L'isopropylisoniazide, qui ne possède pas de groupement $—NH_2$ susceptible de se combiner à la fonction aldéhyde du phosphate de pyridoxal, inhibe la dopa-décarboxylase plus activement que l'isoniazide, et à toutes les concentrations (mêmes faibles).[5]

(3) Les quantités d'hydrazide nécessaires pour provoquer une inhibition des pyridoxalo-enzymes sont énormes par rapport à la quantité de phosphate de pyridoxal du milieu; il ne peut s'agir d'une réaction stoechiométrique.

(4) L'isoniazide est un puissant inhibiteur de la pyridoxal-kinase, enzyme responsable de la phosphorylation du pyridoxal en présence d'ATP;[29–31] or, contrairement aux pyridoxalo-enzymes, nous avons constaté qu'il suffisait de très peu d'INH pour obtenir une inhibition. En présence de la

préparation enzymatique d'ATP et de pyridoxal, on obtient, dans les conditions expérimentales choisies, une phosphorylation complète du pyridoxal.

Si le milieu est additionné d'une quantité stoechiométrique d'INH par rapport au pyridoxal, l'inhibition est complète. Mais, si on double la quantité de pyridoxal par rapport à celle de l'INH l'inhibition demeure complète. Si l'on admettait que l'inhibition est due à la formation d'hydrazone, l'excès de pyridoxal devrait être phosphorylé, ce qui serait exprimé en cas de proportion stoechiométrique:

$$n\,\mathrm{PL} + n\,\mathrm{INH} \rightarrow n\,\mathrm{INH} - \mathrm{PL}$$

et en cas d'excès de pyridoxal:

$$2n\,\mathrm{PL} + n\,\mathrm{INH} \rightarrow n\,\mathrm{INH} - \mathrm{PL} + n\,\mathrm{PL}$$

Il faut donc admettre que l'INH agit selon un autre mécanisme pour inhiber la pyridoxal-kinase.

## B. L'ACTIVATION PAR LES HYDRAZONES

Les résultats exposés écartent la possibilité d'inhibition des pyridoxalo-enzymes par blocage du co-enzyme sous forme d'hydrazone. Le fait que les hydrazones étudiées remplacent le phosphate de pyridoxal, étant parfois plus actives que lui vis-à-vis des pyridoxalo-enzymes, soulève le problème de son hydrolyse éventuelle. En effet, on peut concevoir théoriquement que les hydrazones, bien que stables chimiquement, pourraient être hydrolysées par les préparations enzymatiques et libérer progressivement le phosphate de pyridoxal.

La plus grande activité des hydrazones par rapport au phosphate de pyridoxal, constatée dans certains cas, pourrait s'expliquer par une protection du phosphate de pyridoxal combiné, progressivement libéré au cours de la réaction enzymatique.

Nos résultats ne sont pas en faveur de cette hypothèse, tout au moins en ce qui concerne les hydrazones d'hydrazides (les hydrazones d'hydrazines et les bases de Schiff telles que les iodanilides sont encore à l'étude).

(1) Si en cours d'expérience (décarboxylation de la dopa) on ajoute du nouveau phosphate de pyridoxal, il n'y a aucune augmentation de la décarboxylation qui demeure inférieure à celle obtenue en présence d'hydrazone. La conception d'une protection du phosphate de pyridoxal ne peut donc être retenue.

(2) La cinétique de la décarboxylation de l'acide glutamique en présence d'hydrazones est exactement la même que celle obtenue en présence de phosphate de pyridoxal, et se traduit par une droite, lorsque l'apoenzyme est saturé en co-enzyme. Il est difficile, dans ces conditions, d'envisager une hydrolyse même partielle de l'hydrazone. En outre, même si l'hydrolyse était immédiate, il faudrait qu'elle soit aussi totale, car avec le quart ou la moitié même du phosphate de pyridoxal ainsi libéré (correspondant à 5 ou

10 $\mu$g), la décarboxylation serait nettement moins intense, la courbe serait au-dessous de celle obtenue avec 20 $\mu$g.[8] La même activation, sans hydrolyse, a été décrite en présence de diméthyl-hydrazone de phospho-pyridoxal.[33]

(3) Les cinétiques effectuées avec la dopa décarboxylase donnent les mêmes résultats; elles sont cependant moins précises qu'avec la glutamo-décarboxylase. En effet, la réaction s'effectuant en milieu légèrement alcalin, le $CO_2$ n'est pas libéré spontanément; il faut autant de fois 3 flacons de Warburg que de durées étudiées.

(4) La préparation de pyridoxal kinase est tout à fait comparable à celle de glutamo-décarboxylase; or, lorsqu'on met en présence de cette préparation de l'ATP et de l'isonicotylhydrazone de pyridoxal, on ne constate pas de formation de phosphate de pyridoxal quel que soit le temps d'incubation, c'est-à-dire que la séquence suivante n'a pas lieu:

$$\text{INH} - \text{PL} \xrightarrow{\text{hydrolyse}} \text{INH} + \text{PL} \xrightarrow[\text{ATP}]{\text{kinase}} \text{PLP}$$

(5) Nous avons cherché à détecter, par chromatographie, de petites quantités de phosphate de pyridoxal, après incubation de préparations enzymatiques ou d'enzyme pur en présence d'hydrazone, afin de rechercher si l'hydrazone est hydrolysée ou non.

La méthode de chromatographie sur plaque de gel de silice s'est révélée plus sensible que la méthode de chromatographie sur papier. Le phosphate de pyridoxal peut être caractérisé par fluorescence après action de vapeurs d'ammoniac (technique plus sensible que la réaction de GIBBS à la 2,6-dichloroquinone chlorimide). Le solvant le plus sélectif est constitué par n-butanol–acide phosphorique–eau (3 : 1 : 3).

On peut détecter 0,5 $\mu$g de phosphate de pyridoxal en présence de la transaminase glutamique–aspartique pure et 1 $\mu$g en présence de la glutamodécarboxylase, ce qui représente dans les milieux d'expérience moins de 3 $\mu$g pour la transaminase et moins de 6 $\mu$g pour la décarboxylase. Les expériences effectuées avec l'isonicotylhydrazone de phospho-pyridoxal n'ont pas révélé de libération de phosphate de pyridoxal.

(6) Dans les conditions expérimentales choisies, on obtient le même taux de décarboxylation (maximum) de l'acide glutamique en ajoutant au milieu 40 $\mu$g d'isonicotylhydrazone de phospho-pyridoxal ou 20 $\mu$g de phosphate de pyridoxal, l'apo-enzyme est alors saturé. Le phosphate de pyridoxal ajouté au milieu d'incubation est retrouvé par chromatographie.

En admettant une hydrolyse de l'hydrazone libérant du phosphate de pyridoxal qui serait " dissimulé " à la chromatographie, la proportion hydrolysée ne pourrait être que très faible car les taches d'hydrazone avant et après incubation sont apparemment identiques.

En admettant que cette hydrolyse représente 25 pour cent l'hydrazone, cela correspondrait à une libération de 7 $\mu$g de phosphate de pyridoxal, quantité très éloignée de la saturation de l'apo-enzyme, la courbe exprimant la cinétique serait alors très abaissée, ce qui n'est pas le cas.

L'hypothèse d'une libération de phosphate de pyridoxal dissimulé ne peut donc être retenue.

## CONCLUSION

En présence de ces faits il semble permis d'admettre qu'il n'y a pas d'hydrolyse de l'hydrazone qui se comporte comme un co-enzyme aussi actif que le phosphate de pyridoxal.

On peut supposer qu'il s'effectue une réaction initiale entre l'hydrazone et l'enzyme avec libération, consécutive ou immédiate, d'INH et de phosphate de pyridoxal lié à l'enzyme[34] mais il ne s'agit là que d'une hypothèse n'ayant pas reçu de vérification expérimentale.

Dans l'état actuel de la question, l'explication du phénomène reste à trouver.

## BIBLIOGRAPHIE


1. J. Cattanéo-Lacombe et J. C. Senez; *Compt. rend. soc. biol.* **150**, 748 (1956).
2. A. N. Davison; *Biochim. et Biophys. Acta* **19**, 131 (1956).
3. D. S. Moare; *Biochim. et Biophys. Acta* **19**, 141 (1956).
4. J. Mauron et E. Bujard; *Bull. soc. chim. Belge* **65**, 140 (1956).
5. P. Gonnard et J. P. Nguyen Chi; *Bull. soc. chim. biol.* **40**, 485 (1958).
6. P. Gonnard et J. P. Nguyen Chi; *Bull. soc. chim. biol.* **41**, 1455 (1959).
7. P. Gonnard et J. P. Nguyen Chi; *Enzymologia* **20**, 237 (1959).
8. P. Gonnard et S. Fenard; *J. Neurochem.* **9**, 135 (1962).
9. P. Gonnard et C. Nguyen-Philippon; *Enzymologia* **20**, 231 (1959).
10. P. Gonnard et C. Nguyen-Philippon; *Bull. soc. chim. biol.* **43**, 601 (1961).
11. P. Gonnard et N. Boigne; *Enzymologia* **21**, 375 (1960).
12. P. Gonnard et N. Boigne; *Bull. soc. chim. biol.* **43**, 609 (1961).
13. H. Lis; *Biochim. et Biophys. Acta* **28**, 191 (1958).
14. H. Lis et P. M. Fasella; *Biochim. et Biophys. Acta* **33**, 567 (1959).
15. E. A. Zeller et J. Barsky; *Proc. Soc. Exptl. Biol. Med.* **8**, 459 (1952).
16. E. A. Zeller, J. Barsky, J. R. Fouts, F. A. Kircheimer et L. S. Van Orden; *Experientia* **8**, 349 (1952).
17. K. P. Jacobsohn; *Rev. fac. cién. Univ. Lisboa* **2**, 81 (1952–53).
18. M. Yoneda et N. Asano; *Science* **117**, 277 (1953).
19. N. Gutmann, S. Felton et F. M. Huennekens; *Biochim. et Biophys. Acta* **14**, 282 (1954).

19*b*. H. Oberste-Lehn; *Klin. Wochschr.* **32**, 90 (1954).

20. J. Sakai; *Kekkaku* (*Tuberculosis*) **27**, 161 (1954).
21. J. Sakai et F. Ito; *Kekkaku* (*Tuberculosis*) **29**, 237 (1954).
22. D. J. Wort; *Science* **120**, 72 (1954).
23. L. J. Zatman, N. O. Kaplan, S. P. Golowie et M. M. Ciotti; *J. Biol. Chem.* **209**, 453 (1954).
24. N. Jamardo et T. G. A. Griemberg; *Publ. centro invest. fisiol. Argent.* **18**, 51 (1954–55).
25. A. Skelenovsky, V. Delong et P. Rohan; *Acta Univ. Palakianae Olomucensis* **6**, 13 (1955).
26. Z. Vodicka et P. Rohan; *Acta Univ. Palakianae Olomucensis* **6**, 17 (1955).
27. M. Zaruba et P. Rohan; *Acta Univ. Palakianae Olomucensis* **6**, 17 (1955).
28. E. Soru, C. Barber, M. Istrati, M. Paduradu-Dimitrescu et E. Podhorski; *Stu. Cerc. Inframicrobiol. Microbiol. Rom.* **6**, 533 (1955).

29. D. B. MacCormick et E. E. Snell; *Proc. Nat. Accul. Sci. Wash.* **45**, 1371 (1959).
30. D. B. MacCormick, B. M. Guirard et E. E. Snell; *Proc. Soc. Exptl. Biol. Med.* **104**, 454 (1960).
31. B. Bubnick, C. A. Lesson et C. C. Scott; *Toxicol. Appl. Pharmacol.* **2**, 403 (1960).
32. D. B. MacCormick et E. E. Snell; *J. Biol. Chem.* **236**, 2085 (1961).
33. M. A. Medina, H. D. Braymer et J. L. Reeves; *J. Neurochem.* **9**, 307 (1962).
34. I. Jenkins; Communication personnelle.

## DISCUSSION

Dr. Jenkins:

It appears to me that the critical feature of the reaction of pyridoxal apoenzymes with hydrazones of pyridoxal phosphate is not whether pyridoxal phosphate is liberated but whether an amount of the carbonyl reagent is liberated equivalent to the enzyme concentration present.

It is generally acknowledged that very high levels of carbonyl reagent are required to stabilize the enzyme derivatives. Therefore, if these derivatives are formed directly from apoenzyme and hydrazone it seems certain that the carbonyl reagent would be instantaneously liberated to yield the native holoenzyme.

# THE PREDETERMINED SYNTHESIS OF INHIBITORS FOR PYRIDOXALIC ENZYMES

by R. M. Khomutov, M. Ya. Karpeisky and E. S. Severin*

The Institute of Radiation and Physical–Chemical Biology
of the U.S.S.R. Academy of Sciences, Moscow

One of the most effective methods of the structural and mechanical investigation of the action of enzymes is the study of enzyme reactions with specific inhibitors. It is this path that has led to considerable advances in the study of, for example, proteolytic enzymes and esterases. The experimental approach to the elucidation of the structure of the active centre consisted in the selective inactivation of enzymes on interaction with diphosphorates. This allows phosphorylation of the hydroxyl groups of serine and permits the identification of peptide fragments in the active enzyme centre.[1]

The most interesting studies based on this principle are those dealing with the mechanism of inhibition and reactivation of acetylcholine esterase. Not only did these studies establish the formal characteristics of reactivators; they also showed the dependence of their action on the availability and position of the active groups of enzymes. These general considerations have enabled one to formulate and substantiate the criteria underlying an optimum reactivator.[2]

One of the main problems in the domain of enzyme chemistry is thus the preparation of inhibitors with predetermined high specificity. The solution of this problem is connected with a precise description of elementary processes taking place on interaction of active substance with the enzyme. An essential step is the elucidation of such chemical properties of the inhibitor that are responsible for its action, including definite chemical information on the enzyme itself.

For enzymes whose coenzyme is pyridoxal phosphate (PLP) a number of conventional inhibitors is known that act on the aldehyde group of PLP (carbonyl reagents), block the sulphydrile groups of protein (heavy metals, alkylating agents), etc. It is clear that the use of these inhibitors gives only quite general information on the structure and constitution of PLP enzymes.[3]

We have recently succeeded in discovering a new type of PLP inhibitor that become irreversibly bound with the active enzyme centre, namely the derivatives of cycloserine antibiotic, D-aminoisoxazolidone-3. The mechanical

*Translated by A. L. Pumpiansky, Moscow.

investigation of this antibiotic has shown that for the compound of the isoxazolidone-3 series to be biologically active the unsubstituted amino group should be at position-4 and the inner ester of hydroxamic acid must involve a specific grouping. The correlation of these findings and of the fact that many properties of cycloserine and its active analogues resemble those of α-aminomonocarboxylic acids has led us to suggest that the biological activity of cycloserine essentially consists in its action on the processes of nitrogen exchange, particularly on the reactions catalysed by pyridoxal enzymes.[4] It was later shown experimentally that it was this group of enzymes that was the most sensitive to cycloserine.[5,6] The elucida-

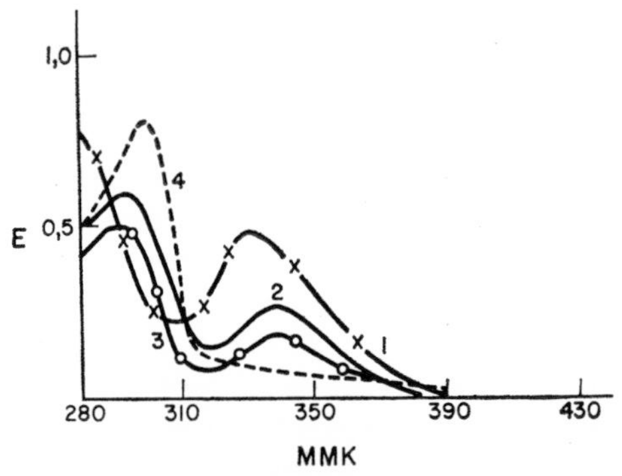


FIG. 1. U.V. spectra of pyridoxalchlorhydrate in the presence of cycloserine and α-aminobutyric acid in alcohol.

1. $1 \times 10^{-4}$ M pyridoxal chlorhydrate + $5 \times 10^{-3}$ M cycloserine.
2. $1 \times 10^{-4}$ M pyridoxal chlorhydrate + $1 \times 10^{-4}$ M cycloserine.
3. $1 \times 10^{-4}$ M pyridoxal chlorhydrate + $1 \times 10^{-4}$ M α-aminobutyric acid.
4. $1 \times 10^{-4}$ M pyridoxal chlorhydrate.

tion of the molecular mechanism of the cycloserine interaction with PLP and its enzymes has enabled us to obtain a detailed description of a new type of inhibitor.

According to current concepts on the mechanism of the action of pyridoxal enzymes[2] the conversions of amino acids start with the formation of pyridohydroxylidene derivatives (Schiff's bases) that further undergo different conversions depending on the specificity of the enzyme. In model systems such Schiff's bases were produced by the interaction of pyridoxal or pyridoxal phosphate with amino acids and amines.

The formation of pyridoxylidene derivatives of amino acids as well as the model reaction of transamination is best of all seen in alcoholic medium.[7] We have shown that cycloserine reacts in alcoholic medium with an equimolar amount of pyridoxal to give, just as do amino acids and amines, an azomethine derivative with $\lambda_{max}$ 340 mμ. The reaction mixture revealed the presence of pyridoxamine thus pointing to the typical reaction of non-enzymatic transamination. Excess cycloserine causes slow spectral change and results in the shift of the maximum at 340 mμ toward shorter wavelengths (see Fig. 1). Amino acids and amines react with pyridoxal or pyridoxal phosphate in aqueous medium as well. In this case, however, azomethine derivative, with maxima at 415 and 270 mμ (pH 7), is formed only with a considerable excess of amino acid.[8] Studying the interaction of cycloserine with pyridoxal and pyridoxal phosphate under similar conditions we have

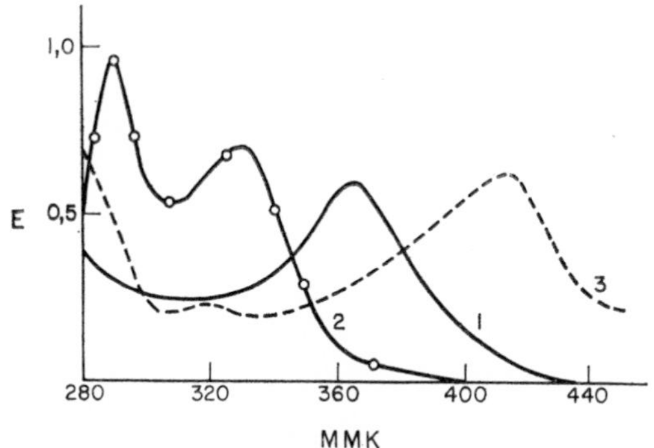


FIG. 2. U.V. spectra of pyridoxal in the presence of cycloserine and valine in water.
1. $1 \times 10^{-4}$ M pyridoxal + $1 \times 10^{-1}$ M cycloserine, pH 7.
2. The same, pH 1.
3. $1 \times 10^{-4}$ M pyridoxal + $5 \times 10^{-1}$ M valine, pH 7.

come across an unexpected and at first sight unaccountable phenomenon: the spectra of the maxima revealed no absorption of imine with hydrogen bonding whatever and a new maximum has appeared at 365 mμ. At pH 1 this spectrum is identical to the one taken in alcohol with excess cycloserine (see Fig. 2).

The analysis of all described u.v. spectra of the compounds of the vitamin $B_6$ group has shown that the appearance of the spectrum and the character of its changes depending on pH allow one to assign the unknown compound to the derivatives of 3-hydroxpyridine and to conclude whether it involves a conjugated or unconjugated system of bonds. With cycloserine a compound is formed that is not an imine but contains a system of conjugated bonds.

The hypsochromic shift in the spectrum (similar to the effect observed in the formation of pyridoxal oxime) and the above evidence permit us to suggest for the reaction product the structure of a substituted pyridoxal derivative.

The spectral study of different O-substituted pyridoxal oximes has shown that these compounds exhibit a hypsochromic shift somewhat smaller than the unsubstituted oximes and reveal in neutral medium a maximum at 365 mμ that is shifted in alkaline medium to 357 mμ and in acid medium to 328 m$\mu$. Hence one has a complete analogy with the spectrum of the cycloserine–pyridoxal reaction product (see Fig. 3).

The reaction of cycloserine with pyridoxal or pyridoxal phosphate is thus anomalous and gives rise to substituted pyridoxal or pyridoxal phosphate oxime.

Indeed, a pyridoxylidene derivative of cycloserine dimer, 3, 6-di(pyridoxylidene aminohydroxymethyl)-diketopiperazine was isolated from the reaction mixture. The formation of such a derivative might have been accounted

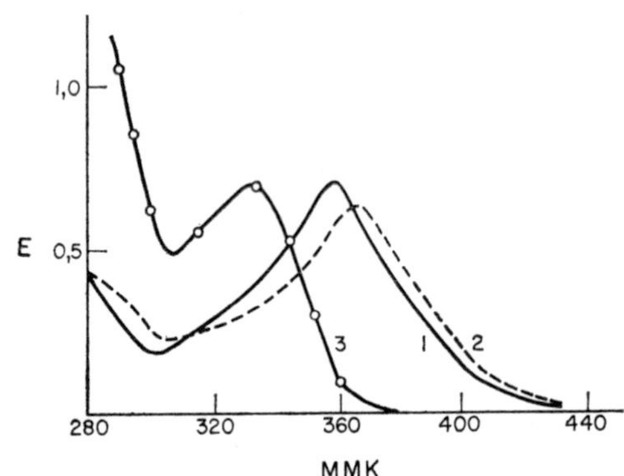


FIG. 3. U.V. spectra of pyridoxal in the presence of $\beta$-amino hydzoxyalanine.
1. pH 7.
2. The same, 0H 7.
3. The same, pH 1.

for by direct reaction of pyridoxal with the corresponding diketopiperazine readily produced from cycloserine in aqueous solution at pH 7. It proved, however, that under the experimental conditions this reaction is practically of no importance because its rate is negligibly slow when the concentration of diketopiperazine corresponds to the percentage of the cycloserine decomposed.

As the cycloserine molecule has no free amino group capable of producing oximes and the formation of diketopiperazine oxime cannot be explained in terms of the known chemical properties of cycloserine as an ester of hydroxamic acid it becomes evident that we are confronted with the action of specific, formerly unknown properties of cycloserine that make it different from amino acids and esters of hydroxamic acids and are directly connected with its biological activity.

The investigation of the chemistry of cycloserine, of the compounds of the isoxazolidone-3-series and the acyclic analogues of this antibiotic has shown that under certain conditions cycloserine and some of its derivatives may exhibit acylating properties. It is these properties that make cycloserine unstable in aqueous solutions and in neutral and acidic media.

At pH 1, when the carbonyl group of cycloserine is not enolized and the amino group is protonated the acylating properties of the molecule are clear cut, leading to a fast hydrolytic decomposition of the antibiotic into β-aminohydroxy-α-alanine. It might be expected that the increase in the absolute values of pH would decrease the acylating capacity of cycloserine. This proved to be the case. In aqueous neutral solutions cycloserine was more stable. In alkaline solutions, where it is present as an anion of the enolic form cycloserine practically remained unaffected.

The stability of enolic forms of isoxazolidone-3 is in accordance with the complete absence of any acylating properties in 3-alkoxyisoxazolidine-3 synthesized by us.[1,3]

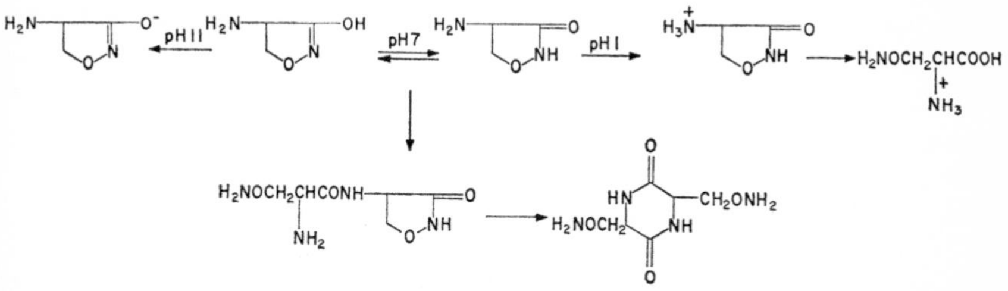

pH 11 pH 7 pH 1 $\rightarrow H_2NOCH_2CH(\overset{+}{N}H_3)COOH$

$H_2NOCH_2CH(NH_2)CONH$– → $H_2NOCH_2$ … $CH_2ONH_2$

SCHEME 1

On the other hand it was found that the stability of the isoxazolidone cycle is dependent on the electrophilicity of the substituent at position-4. In full compliance with the above considerations is our cycloserine acylation reaction of amino acids and peptides in aqueous solution. We have thus found that the specific properties of cycloserine depend on its capacity to act under certain conditions as an acylating agent thus leading to the cleavage of the cycle and the liberation of an aminohydroxy group in the reaction product.

In terms of these considerations we suggest the following mechanism of the reaction of cycloserine with pyridoxal and pyridoxal phosphate:[9]

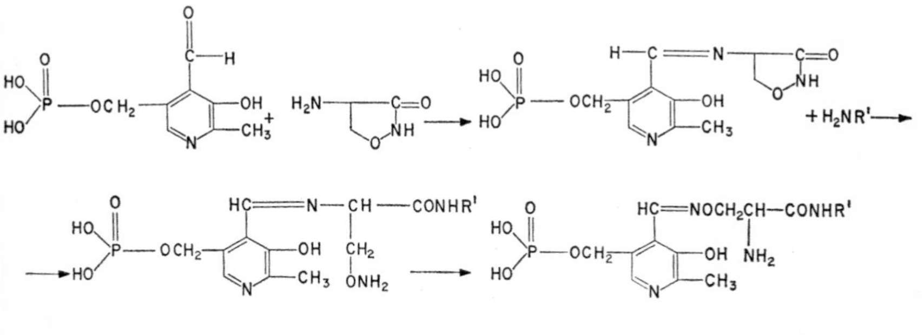

$+ H_2NR' \rightarrow$

$HC{=}N{-}CH(CH_2ONH_2){-}CONHR'$ → $HC{=}NOCH_2CH(NH_2){-}CONHR'$

SCHEME 2

The first step involves the formation of the azomethine derivative that exists in alcohol mainly as enol whereas in the aqueous medium the non-enolized form seems to predominate. Therefore in aqueous solutions the second step, that is the acylation of the amine component with a suitable $pK_a$ value by the pyridohydroxylidene derivative, proceeds extremely readily as does the subsequent rearrangement of imine into oxime. The reaction ultimately gives rise to the substituted amide of $\beta$-aminohydroxy-$\alpha$-alanine. When cycloserine is involved itself as an amine component, this amide undergoes rearrangement into diketopiperazine oxime.

The formation of the azomethine derivative at the first stage of the reaction is substantiated by the correspondence between the formation rate of the oxime spectrum in the reaction of pyridoxal phosphate with 4-N-methyl-cycloserine and its decomposition rate in the absence of pyridoxal.

The above considerations allow us to explain the mechanism of the inhibition of pyridoxal enzymes by cycloserine in terms of molecular mechanism. It is to be expected that cycloserine, similarly to amino acid, becomes initially fixed to the cationic group of the active enzyme centre and forms with its coenzyme an azomethine derivative. This stage may involve a competitive displacement of cycloserine from the active enzyme centre both by keto and amino substrates as well as the reactivation of enzyme. As far as their sensitivity to cycloserine in this phase is concerned, pyridoxalic enzymes should be divided into two groups. The most sensitive are those enzymes whose substrates have a configuration closely similar to that of cycloserine. The azomethine derivative of cycloserine and of its coenzyme acylates one of the reactive groups of the active enzyme centre, markedly affecting thereby the structure of the latter and making its normal functioning practically impossible. Acylation results in the cleavage of the isoxazolidone cycle and liberation of an aminohydroxy group. This may lead to the rearrangement of the imine into the substituted oxime of the coenzyme and hence at the same time result in the screening of the aldehyde group of pyridoxal phosphate. In this case one may observe the conversion of the imine spectrum of the enzyme to that of an oxime.

It is believed that on treating the inhibited enzyme with keto substrate one would observe a reoximation reaction with corresponding spectral changes and not accompanied by the reactivation of the enzyme (see Figs. 4A and 4B).

The above theoretical considerations are in a good agreement with experimental data reported by different authors on cycloserine inhibition of some pyridoxal enzymes.[3,10] Most sensitive to cycloserine are alanine and asparagine transaminase[5] whose substrates are configurationally like cycloserine. The experimental investigation of the interaction of cycloserine and its analogues with high-grade preparations of aspartate–glutamate transaminase has indeed revealed two stages of hindrance with only the first one being reversible.[11] The second stage proceeds rather slowly, is irreversible, and under the action of excess keto substrate practically no reactivation of the enzyme takes place. On the other hand, the enzyme inhibited with such compounds as $\beta$-aminohydroxy-$\alpha$-alanine is readily reactivated under similar conditions.[12]

During the investigation of the action of cysloserine we have shown that in order to display inhibiting properties the molecule must involve a free

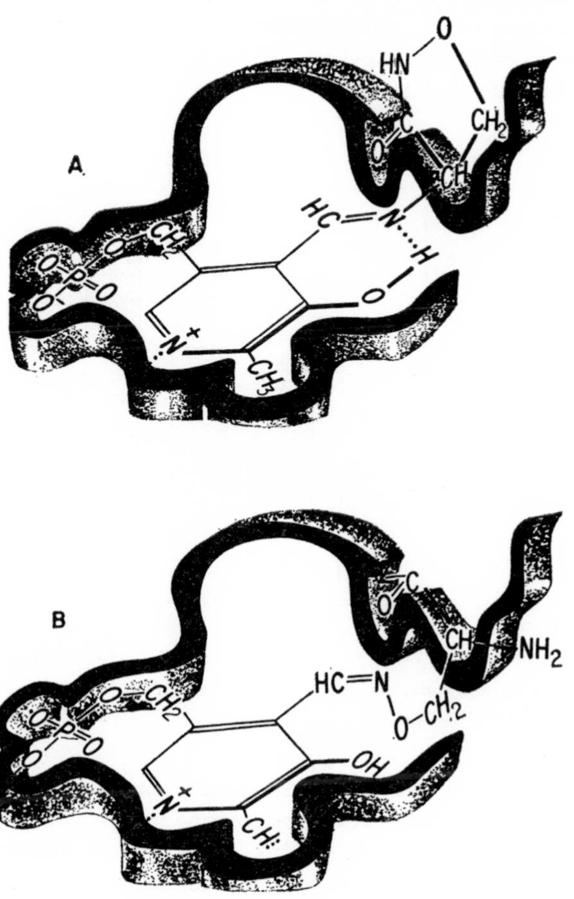


FIG. 4. The formation of the complex cycloserine enzyme.
A. The first stage. B. The second stage.

amino group and a specific grouping of the cyclic ester of hydroxamic acid. The above regularities were then applied to elementary processes and shown to be as follows: through its amino group cycloserine becomes bound to the coenzyme of pyridoxalic enzymes to form an extremely reactive pyridoxylidene derivative that plays a decisive role in subsequent conversions of this antibiotic. The specificity of the cyclic ester grouping of hydroxamic acid lies in its displaying acylating properties that become more pronounced on the interaction of the antibiotic with the enzyme due to the formation of pyridohydroxylidene derivatives.

Starting from the above considerations we have synthesized a number of compounds related to this antibiotic that retained to some extent the properties of cycloserine as an inhibitor of pyridoxalic enzymes. Thus, 4-aminohydroxy-isoxazolidone-3 proved to be a rather strong inhibitor of glutamate–aspartate transaminase.[13]

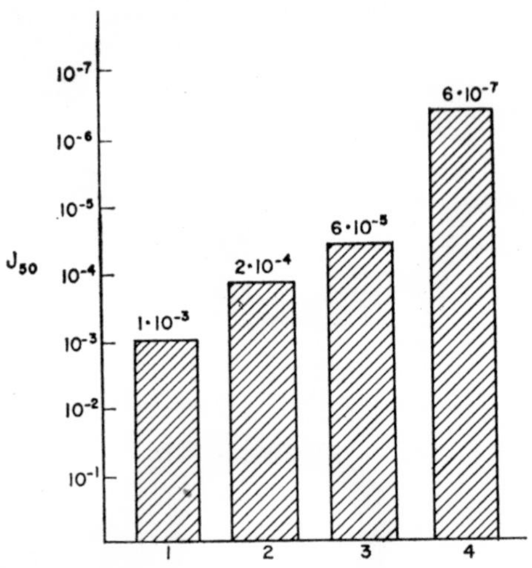


FIG. 5. Comparative power of glutamate–aspartate transaminase inhibitors.
1. Cyclotreonine. 2. Cycloserine.
3. Cyclocanaline. 4. Aminohydroxyisoxazolidone-3.

We have synthesized this compound in the hope of obtaining a structure that would enhance the tendency of cycloserine to bond with PLP enzymes. 4-Aminohydroxyisoxazolidone-3 differs from cycloserine in having at position-4 an amino hydroxy rather than an amino group. This group, $H_2NO$, readily reacts with aldehydes and ketones to form an oxime. Thus the synthesized compound retains the main chemical properties of the antibiotic but, at the same time, has a greater bonding capacity with PLP enzymes involving pyridoxal phosphate aldehyde as their coenzyme.

Another compound that retains the main structural and chemical characteristics of cycloserine is homocycloserine-4-aminotetrahydroxazine-1,2-OH-3.[14]

Homocycloserine contains an amino group and a cyclic ester grouping of hydroxamic acid, just as does cycloserine. It may therefore be regarded as a peculiar cycloserine homologue in which the ester grouping of hydroxamic acid forms part of a sextet. It might be that this accounts for its activity as an inhibitor of transaminoazoglutamate–aspartate and rather high lability under the experimental conditions.

It has thus proved possible in terms of the suggested molecular mechanism of the inhibiting action of cycloserine to prepare specific inhibitors of pyridoxalic enzymes whose character may be predicted on theoretical assumptions.

## REFERENCES


1. F. Sorm; *Proc. Vth Int. Cong. Biochem.*, Plenary Sessions, Moscow, 1962.
2. I. P. Wilson; *Federation Proc.* **18**, 752 (1959).
3. A. E. Braunstein; *The Enzymes* (edited by P. D. Boyer, H. Lardy and K. Myrbäck), vol. 2, p. 112, Academic Press, New York (1960).
4. N. K. Kochetkov, R. M. Khomutov, M. Ya. Karpeisky, E. I. Budovsky and E. S. Severin; *Doklady Akad. Nauk S.S.S.R.* **126**, 1132 (1959).
5. N. N. Azarkh, A. E. Braunstein *et al.*; *Biokhimiya* **25**, 954 (1960).
6. E. D. Vishepan *et al.*; *Bull. eksp. biol. med.* **47**, 52 (1959); **52**, 76 (1961).
7. Y. Matsue; *J. Am. Chem. Soc.* **79**, 2016 (1957).
8. D. E. Metzbr; *J. Am. Chem. Soc.* **79**, 485 (1957).
9. R. M. Khomutov, M. Ya. Karpeisky, E. S. Severin and N. B. Gnuchev; *Doklady Akad. Nauk S.S.S.R.* **140**, 492 (1961).
10. A. E. Braunstein *et al.*; *Biokhimiya* **26**, 882 (1961).
11. R. M. Khomutov, M. Ya. Karpeisky *et al.*; *Proc. Vth Int. Cong. Biochem.*, Theses of Reports, Academy of Sciences of the U.S.S.R., Moscow, 1961.
12. M. Ya. Karpeisky, R. M. Khomutov *et al.*; This volume, pp. 323–32.
13. R. M. Khomutov, M. Ya. Karpeisky and E. S. Severin; *Izvest. Akad. Nauk S.S.S.R.* In press.
14. E. S. Severin, R. M. Khomutov and M. Ya. Karpeisky; *Izvest. Akad. Nauk S.S.S.R.* In press.

# THE INVESTIGATION OF THE INTERACTION OF CYCLOSERINE AND RELATED COMPOUNDS WITH ASPARTATE–GLUTAMATE TRANSAMINASE

by M. Ya. Karpeisky, R. M. Khomutov, E. S. Severin and Yu. N. Breusov*

The Institute of Radiation and Physical–Chemical Biology of the U.S.S.R. Academy of Sciences, Moscow

We have been recently investigating the interaction of the antituberculosis antibiotic, cycloserine, and of some of its derivatives with enzymes of nitrogen exchange involving pyridoxal phosphate as coenzyme (PLP enzymes).[1–3] Studying the cycloserine reaction with PLP in aqueous solution we have found it to proceed according to the following scheme :

$$\text{PyrCHO} + \text{H}_2\text{N}\text{-}\underset{\text{(cycloserine ring: C=O, NH, O)}}{\text{C}_3\text{H}_3\text{O}_2\text{N}} \rightarrow \text{PyrCH}=\text{N}\text{-}(\text{ring: C=O, NN, O}) + \text{H}_2\text{NR}' \rightarrow$$

$$\rightarrow \text{PyrCH}=\text{NCHCONHR}'(\text{CH}_2\text{ONH}_2) \rightarrow \text{PyrCH}=\text{NOCH}_2\text{CHCONHR}'(\text{NH}_2)$$

The results obtained led us to suggest a hypothesis of the mechanism of cycloserine inhibition of PLP enzymes that can be briefly stated as follows. Similarly to amino acid, cycloserine becomes fixed to the cationic group of the active enzyme centre and forms an azomethine derivative with its coenzyme thus enhancing the acylating capacity of cycloserine.

This derivative then acylates one of the active functional groups. This irreversibly affects the structure of the active centre and the normal functioning of the enzyme becomes impossible.

This report deals with the experimental substantiation of the above hypothesis obtained on studying the reaction of cycloserine and its related compounds with a high-grade (above 95 per cent) preparation of aspartate–glutamate transaminase.

At the first stage of the study it proved useful to compare the inhibiting

*Translated by A. L. Pumpiansky, Moscow.

action of cycloserine on aspartate–glutamate transaminase with that of compounds whose molecule involves some structural characteristics of cycloserine and its conversion products (see Table 1).

TABLE 1. INHIBITING CAPACITY OF VARIOUS DERIVATIVES OF HYDROXYLAMINE AND ISOXAZOLIDONE-3 IN RESPECT TO ASPARTATE–GLUTAMATE TRANSAMINASE

| No. | Inhibitor | | $I_{50}$ at 5 min of preincubation | |
|---|---|---|---|---|
| | | | pH 5.8 | pH 8.3 |
| 1. | Hydroxylamine | $HONH_2$ | $1.5\times10^{-6}$ | $9\times10^{-5}$ |
| 2. | O-methylhydroxylamine | $CH_3ONH_2$ | $1\times10^{-6}$ | $5\times10^{-4}$ |
| 3. | β-Aminohydroxyalanine | $H_2NOCH_2CH(NH_2)COOH$ | $4\times10^{-3}$ | $2\times10^{-5}$ |
| 4. | Di(aminohydroxymethyl) diketopiperazine | 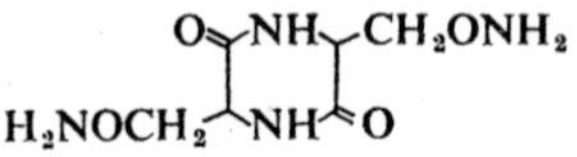 | $5\times10^{-6}$ | $3.3\times10^{-5}$ |
| 5. | α-Aminobutyrolactone | 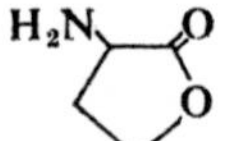 | $\geqslant5\times10^{-3}$ | $\geqslant5\times10^{-3}$ |
| 6. | Cycloserine | 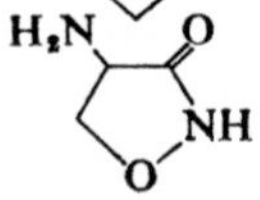 | $1.5\times10^{-4}$ | $1.2\times10^{-3}$ |
| 7. | Isoxazolidone-3 | 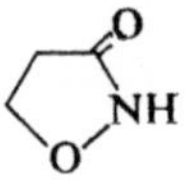 | $3\times10^{-4}$ | $5\times10^{-3}$ |
| 8. | N-Methylcycloserine | 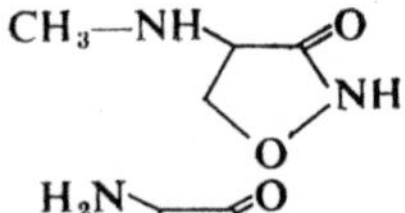 | $5\times10^{-3}$ | $5\times10^{-3}$ |
| 9. | Cyclotreonine | 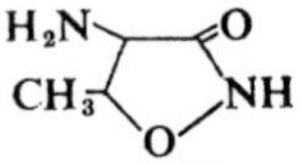 | $1\times10^{-3}$ inhib. by 43% | $1\times10^{-3}$ inhib. by 15% |
| 10. | Cyclocanaline | 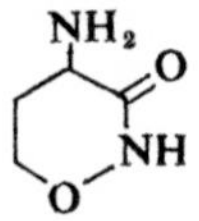 | $6.5\times10^{-5}$ | $5.5\times10^{-4}$ |
| 11. | 4-Aminohydroxyisoxazolidone-3 | 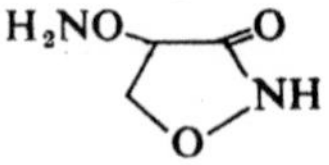 | $6\times10^{-7}$ | $5\times10^{-6}$ |

To find out the role of the amino group of cycloserine in the inhibiting action of this compound we have synthesized deamino-cycloserine (isoxazolidone-3) and 4-N-methylcycloserine. Though the molecule of both compounds contained a cyclic ester grouping of hydroxamine acid they did not show any marked inhibiting action on the enzyme. Certain inhibiting properties of isoxazolidone-3 at the initial stage of the reaction seem to be accounted for by its decomposition under the experimental conditions to form an O-substituted hydroxylamine that is bonded with the coenzyme. As these compounds are unable to form with the aldehyde group of the coenzyme an azomethine bond, it might be thought that the formation of such a bond in the case of cycloserine is one of the essential conditions for it to become fixed into the active enzyme centre. The lack of any inhibiting properties in $\alpha$-aminobutyrolactone whose molecule involves a favourable combination of a planar five-membered lactone structure with an $\alpha$-amino group allows us to suggest that the cyclic ester grouping of hydroxamic acid is responsible not only for the acylating properties but also for the fixing of cycloserine on the cationic group of the active enzyme centre.

In spite of the fact that $\alpha$-aminobutyrolactone exhibits pronounced acylating properties and, having a free amino group, is capable of bonding with the aldehyde group of pyridoxal, it does not inhibit PLP enzymes, for the absence in the molecule of acid groups does not permit $\alpha$-aminobutyrolactone to form a bond with the active enzyme centre.

A number of compounds listed in Table 1, derivatives of O-substituted hydroxylamine, readily react with carbonyl compounds and, as expected, their action on the enzyme resembles that of hydroxylamine alone.[4] The investigation of these compounds as inhibitors was based on the fact that $\beta$-aminohydroxyalanine and di(aminohydroxymethyl)-diketopiperazine are products of cycloserine conversion in aqueous medium. This had to be borne in mind when studying the mechanism of the cycloserine reaction with aspartate–glutamate transaminase. The analysis of data obtained allows the conclusion that the cycloserine molecule involves a successful combination of the amino group in the $\alpha$-position and the cyclic ester grouping of hydroxamic acid that has a flat configuration, so it can become fixed onto the cationic centre of the enzyme and form a bond with the aldehyde group of the enzyme. An important confirmation of the validity of this conclusion is to be found in the fact that 4-aminohydroxyisoxaholidone-3 and cyclocanaline exceed cycloserine as inhibitors of aspartate–glutamate transaminase by several orders of magnitude. We have synthesized the above compounds on the assumption that it was necessary, on the one hand, to increase the ability of cycloserine to react with its coenzyme and on the other hand, to weaken the cycle, part of which consists of the ester grouping of hydroxamic acid.

To elucidate the mechanism of reactions taking place after the introduction of cycloserine into the active enzyme centre it was necessary to investigate and compare the interaction of cycloserine and some O-substituted hydroxylamines with aspartate–glutamate transaminase (methoxylamine having been chosen as such a derivative).

On studying the dependence of the inhibiting action of cycloserine and $CH_3ONH_2$ on the time of preincubation it was found that the hindering of enzymatic activity due to cycloserine increases with time, reaching a constant level after about an hour, whereas the inhibiting activity of O-methylhydroxylamine is practically independent of the time of preincubation (see Table 2). O-methylhydroxylamine being a pronounced carbonyl reagent, the substituted oxime of the enzyme is formed rather readily even at low concentrations.

TABLE 2. DEPENDENCE OF THE INHIBITING CAPACITY ($I_{50}$) ON THE TIME OF PREINCUBATION

| | $I_{50}$ | | | | | |
|---|---|---|---|---|---|---|
| | Preincubation at pH 5.8 during | | | Preincubation at pH 8.3 during | | |
| | 5 min | 30 min | 1 hr | 5 min | 30 min | 1 hr |
| O-Methylhydroxylamine | $2.5\times10^{-6}$ | $2.1\times10^{-6}$ | $2.0\times10^{-6}$ | $8.6\times10^{-4}$ | $7.5\times10^{-4}$ | $6.6\times10^{-4}$ |
| Cycloserine (not purified) | $10\times10^{-5}$ | $6.5\times10^{-5}$ | $5.0\times10^{-5}$ | $7.5\times10^{-4}$ | $3.5\times10^{-4}$ | $2.8\times10^{-4}$ |
| d, 1-Cycloserine (immediately after purification) | $3.3\times10^{-4}$ | $1.6\times10^{-4}$ | $1.2\times10^{-4}$ | $3.5\times10^{-3}$ | $1.5\times10^{-3}$ | $1.2\times10^{-3}$ |

This development during the inhibition effected by cycloserine points in the first place to the involved character of the cycloserine–enzyme interaction.

It is to be noted that when the experiments are conducted with commercial samples of cycloserine or previously prepared aqueous solutions it is not possible to find any marked difference between the action of cycloserine and O-methylhydroxylamine. This is accounted for by the lability of cycloserine that can, even when dry, be converted to di(aminohydroxymethyl)diketopiperazine and $\beta$-aminohydroxyalanine that are inhibitors of aspartate–glutamate transaminase.

Of considerable importance to the understanding of the molecular mechanism of the cycloserine inhibition of aspartate–glutamate transaminase is the spectral study of the enzyme–inhibitor complex together with the estimation of the enzymatic activity.

An unambiguous proof of the irreversibility of inhibition would in this case constitute a serious substantiation of the formation of a covalent bond due to the reaction between the functional group of the active enzyme centre and cycloserine.

It was to be expected that cycloserine would be bound with the pyridoxylidene form of the enzyme, because for cycloserine to exhibit inhibiting properties it is very necessary that an azomethine bond should be formed between the amino group of cycloserine and the aldehyde group of PLP enzymes. On similar assumptions cycloserine was deemed not to react with the amino form of the enzyme. The spectral evidence on the two

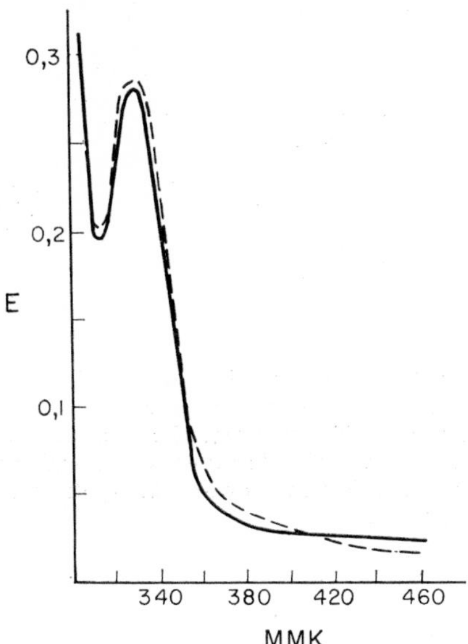


FIG. 1. Interaction of cycloserine with pyridoxamic form of aspartate–glutamate transaminase.

Solid line, the enzyme spectrum; Dotted line, the spectrum of the enzyme at $10^{-2}$ M cycloserine. Protein content: 2 mg/ml, pH 6.4.

enzymatic forms after treatment with cycloserine has indeed shown that the spectrum of the amino form was practically unaffected, with the enzyme fully retaining its activity (see Fig. 1).

Treatment of the pyridoxylidene form of aspartate–glutamate transaminase with a large excess of cycloserine leaves less than 15 per cent activity of the starting enzyme. The absorption maxima, characteristic of the pyridoxylidene form of the enzyme (430 m$\mu$ at pH 4.5, 362 m$\mu$ at pH 8.2) disappear and a new characteristic maximum appears at 335 m$\mu$ with its position practically independent of pH. Besides this a small maximum or a shoulder appears at 380 m$\mu$ (see Fig. 2).

The maximum at 380 m$\mu$ is characteristic of oximes of PLP enzymes[5,6] and is also formed on the interaction of aspartate–glutamate transaminase and O-methylhydroxylamine, $\beta$-aminohydroxyalanine and di(aminohydroxymethyl)diketopiperazine (see Figs. 3 and 4). The presence of this maximum in the spectrum of the cycloserine inhibited enzyme may be explained both

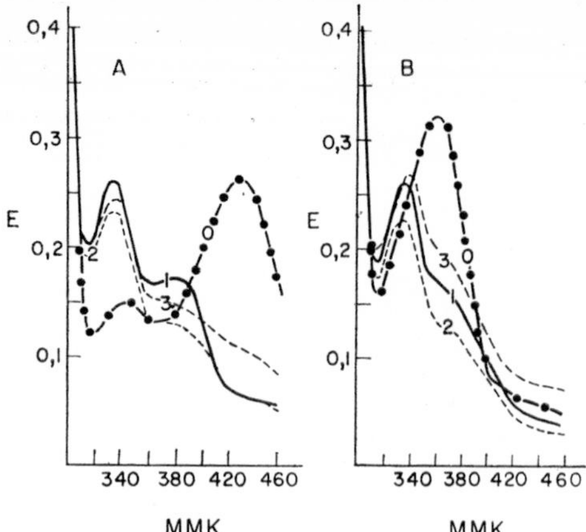


FIG. 2. Interaction of cycloserine with pyridoxylidene form of aspartate–glutamate transaminase, preincubation at pH 6.4.

0. The enzyme spectrum. 1. The spectrum of the enzyme with $10^{-2}$ M cycloserine. 2. The spectrum of the enzyme after being passed through Sephadex gel. 3. The spectrum of the enzyme after interaction with α-ketoglutaric acid.

A, at pH 4.5; B, at pH 8.2.

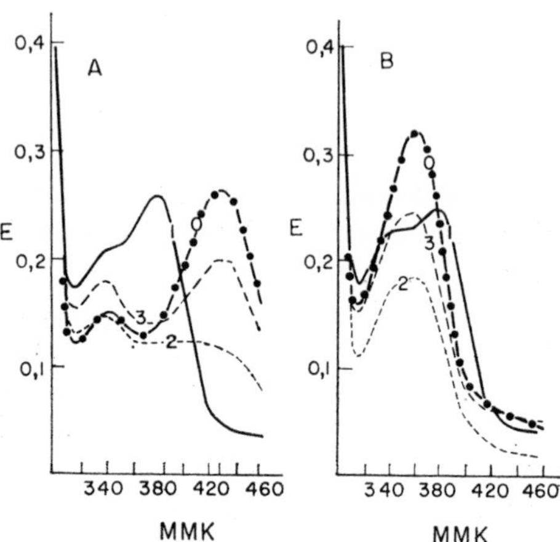


FIG. 3. Interaction of aspartate–glutamate transaminase with O-methylhydroxylamine.

0. The enzyme spectrum. 1. The spectrum of the enzyme with $10^{-2}$ M $CH_3ONH_2$. 2. The spectrum of the enzyme after being passed through Sephadex gel. 3. The spectrum of the enzyme after interaction with α-ketoglutaric acid.

A, at pH 4.5; B, at pH 8.2.

as due to the enzyme being acted upon by di(aminohydroxymethyl)diketopiperazine or β-aminohydroxyalanine formed during the reaction and by the reaction of cycloserine with the enzyme, similar to its reaction with pyridoxal phosphate.

An important step in the course of the investigation was the attempted isolation from the reaction mixture of the enzyme–inhibitor interaction

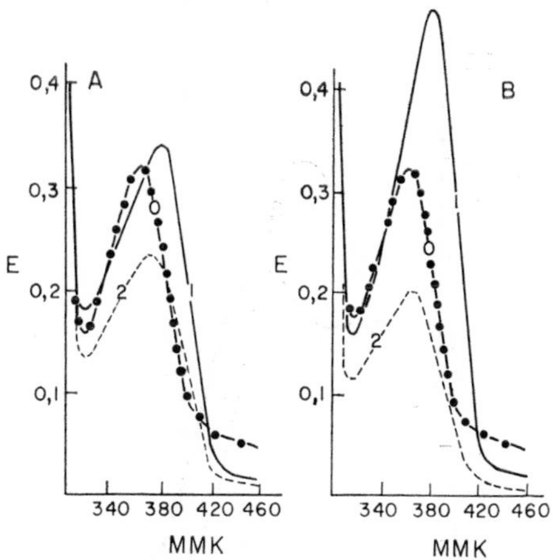


FIG. 4. Interaction of aspartate–glutamate transaminase with β-aminohydroxyalanine (A), and di(aminohydroxymethyl)diketopiperazine (B), at pH 8.2.
0. The enzyme spectrum. 1. The spectrum of the enzyme with $10^{-2}$ M inhibitor. 2. The spectrum of the enzyme after being passed through Sephadex gel.

product, i.e. the enzyme–inhibitor complex, and its structural assignment. To this end we have made use of the ability of Sephadex gel to separate low molecular compounds from high molecular ones.

Indeed, on passing the enzyme treated with cycloserine through a column with Sephadex G-25 it proved possible to isolate cycloserine and to obtain protein with a single absorption maximum at 335 mμ, the protein retaining less than 20 per cent of the starting enzymatic activity (see Fig. 2).

A similar treatment of the enzyme inhibited by a compound with a free aminohydroxy group (Figs. 3 and 4) leads to the disappearance of the maximum at 380 mμ and almost complete reappearance of the spectrum of the starting enzyme. This is accounted for by the fact that the process of the separation of excess aminohydroxy compound is necessarily accompanied by the hydrolysis of the O-substituted oxime of the enzyme. Along with this, one observes an incomplete recovery of the original values of maxima (only by 70 per cent), coinciding with the partial reactivation (also about 70 per cent), apparently due to the splitting off from the apoenzyme of relatively loosely bound pyridoxal phosphate oxime.

These data support the suggestion that the maximum at 380 mμ arising in the enzyme spectrum under the action of cycloserine is to be assigned to the interaction of aminohydroxy compounds cycloserine degradation products with aspartate–glutarate transaminase (see Fig. 2).

As is known, the spectral maximum at 330 mμ for the PLP enzymes is characteristic of the pyridoxamine or aldimine enzymic forms.[7]

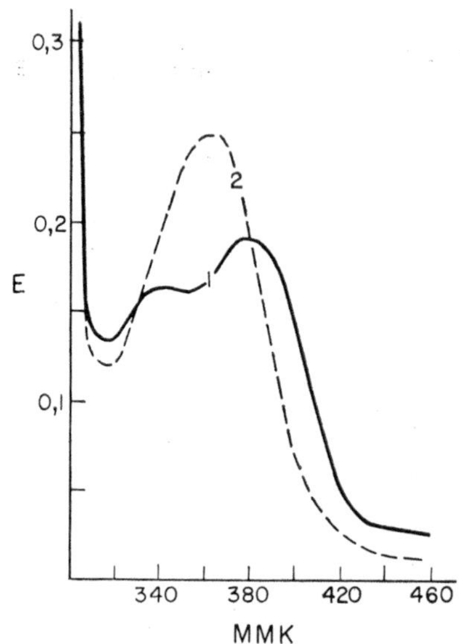


FIG. 5. Interaction of aspartate–glutamate transaminase with cycloserine at pH 4.5 (1) and 9.2 (2). Preincubation during 4 hr, protein content 2 mg/ml, cycloserine $10^{-2}$ M.

If the action of cycloserine on aspartate–glutamate transaminase results in the pyridoxamine form of the enzyme one would have expected the reappearance of the pyridoxylidine spectrum and possibly of the activity under the action of the ketosubstrate. However, the action on the enzyme–inhibitor complex of α-ketoglutaric acid did not affect the spectrum and neither did it lead to reactivation (see Fig. 2).

This allows us to conclude that either cycloserine or its conversion products are closely bound with the coenzyme, or cycloserine is covalently bonded with one of the functional groups of the anchor site of the substrate.

The investigation of the cycloserine interaction with the pyridoxylidene form of aspartate–glutamate transaminase at different pH has shown that prolonged preincubation at pH lower than 5 mainly gives rise to a product with spectral maximum at 380 mμ due to rapid decomposition of cycloserine under these conditions and the formation of aminohydroxy compounds.

On the other hand, at pH higher than 9 the enzyme spectrum is not affected and the activity is almost completely retained.

This is accounted for by cycloserine being present under given conditions as a salt of enolic form unable to acylate (see Fig. 5).

The results of the above work suggest that cycloserine and related compounds, being powerful inhibitors of PLP enzymes, would lead to valuable information on the configuration and chemical structure of the active site of enzymes.

## REFERENCES


1. R. M. Khomutov, M. Ya. Karpeisky and E. S. Severin; *Biokhimia* **26**, 772 (1961).
2. R. M. Khomutov, M. Ya. Karpeisky, E. S. Severin and N. V. Gnuchev; *Doklady Akad. Nauk S.S.S.R.* **140**, 492 (1961).
3. R. M. Khomutov, M. Ya. Karpeisky *et al.*; *Proc. Vth Int. Cong. Biochem.*, Theses, Academy of Sciences of the U.S.S.R., Moscow, 1961.
4. O. L. Polyanovsky and Yu. M. Torchinsky; *Doklady Akad. Nauk S.S.S.R.* **141**, 488 (1961).
5. Y. Matsuo and D. M. Greenberg; *J. Biol. Chem.* **230**, 561 (1958).
6. R. Shukuya and G. W. Schwert; *J. Biol. Chem.* **235**, 1653 (1960).
7. W. T. Jenkins; *Federation Proc.* **20**, 978 (1961).


## DISCUSSION

Dr. Jencks:

The nitrogen atom of hydroxylamine and its derivatives has a very high affinity for the carbonyl group, the reason for which is not understood. The addition of the hydroxylamine nitrogen atom of cycloserine to pyridoxal phosphate, followed by loss of water, would give an intermediate which is activated for attack at the amine carbonyl group and thus would be a reasonable intermediate for the acylation reactions.

This intermediate is similar to the presumed intermediate in morpholine-catalyzed transaldimination.

# PRELIMINARY REPORT ON THE PRESENCE IN HUMAN URINE OF SUBSTANCES INFLUENCING PYRIDOXAL PHOSPHATE-DEPENDENT ENZYMES

by L. MUSAJO, C. A. BENASSI, E. LONGO and G. ALLEGRI

Padova Istituto di Chimica Farmaceutica
dell'Università e II Gruppo di ricerca
" Chimica delle sostanze naturali " del
Consiglio Nazionale delle Ricerche

FOR many years we have been interested in the urinary excretion of tryptophan metabolites by man. As it is well known the degradation steps of this amino acid by the so-called " via kynurenine " are influenced by enzymes requiring pyridoxal-5-phosphate (PLP). Researches on xanthurenic acid, one of these metabolites, originated, in fact, the study of the relationships between vitamin $B_6$ deficiency and tryptophan metabolism.

Having considered our collected data we have been led to investigate the possible presence, in human urine, of substances interfering with pyridoxal phosphate-dependent enzymes.

The preliminary results reported here point to the correctness of our assumption.

It has been found that crude and partially purified extracts, obtained under suitable experimental conditions from the urine of several individuals, influence the activity of tyrosine decarboxylase, kynurenine transaminase and kynureninase, three pyridoxal-5-phosphate-dependent enzymes.

## EXPERIMENTAL

(1) Rat kidney kynurenine apotransaminase was partially purified as described by Mason[1].

All assays were made in a total volume of 1.5 ml containing 0.8 ml enzyme preparation (1.03 mg of protein N/ml), 0.15 ml of 0.006 M $\alpha$-ketoglutarate; 0.15 ml of 0.0004 M pyridoxal phosphate; 0.2 ml of 0.0035 M L-kynurenine and 0.05 M potassium phosphate buffer pH 7.4.

Enzyme activity was measured spectrophotometrically by the change in absorbency at 333 m$\mu$ ($\Delta^{333}$) resulting from the formation of kynurenic acid during a 30-min incubation period at 37°C.

(2) Rat liver kynureninase was a crude enzyme preparation prepared according to Wiss[2].

The assays were performed as follows: 1.0 ml enzyme solution in N/1 potassium phosphate buffer pH 7.4; 1.0 ml of 0.0046 M L-kynurenine in the same buffer and 0.1 ml of 4 × $10^{-7}$ M pyridoxal phosphate.

Enzyme activity was measured fluorometrically by an Aminco spectro fluorometer at w.l. optimal for the activation and emission of anthranilic acid fluorescence (respectively 310 and 410 mμ) during a 30–60 min incubation period at 37°C.

(3) Tyrosine apodecarboxylase was obtained from cells of *Streptococcus faecalis* R 8043 according to Umbreit *et al.*[3], with some modifications to obtain a better growth of the micro-organism.

The procedure was the following: each vessel of the Warburg apparatus contained: in the side arm 0.5 ml of a suspension of 0.03 M L-tyrosine in 0.5 M acetate buffer pH 5.5; in the main compartment 1.5 ml of the same acetate buffer, 0.5 ml of a suspension of cells (8 mg/ml water), 0.1 ml of 2.5 × $10^{-7}$ M pyridoxal phosphate and water to give final volume of 3 ml. The $CO_2$ evolution was measured, after 10-min preincubation, every 5 min over a 30-min period at 28°C.

(4) Urines of several individuals, aged 23–45 years and fed on a normal diet and who had not been given drugs or other substances unrelated with food, were adjusted to pH 1 with mineral acid, heated on a boiling-water bath and extracted with solvents in a liquid–liquid apparatus.

The solvent was then removed from the extract *in vacuo* under nitrogen. A preliminary study was made of the conditions optimal for the hydrolysis and extraction of the material under examination. The crude extraction residues thereby obtained were assayed with the above-mentioned enzyme systems.

This note reports the preliminary results of attempts to isolate the active agent. By means of silica gel column chromatography it was possible to fractionate the crude syrupy residues, in three portions: fraction I, fraction II, fraction III, active on the chosen enzyme systems.

(5) For the assay of the activity on kynurenine transaminase and kynureninase crude or partially purified residues were disolved in 0.05 M phosphate buffer pH 7.4; if necessary the pH was adjusted with the addition of 0.1 N NaOH. For the assay of their activity on tyrosine decarboxylase the residues were dissolved in 0.5 M acetate buffer pH 5.5.

## RESULTS

### *Effects of the Crude Urinary Extracts*

Crude extracts from urines of ten men and ten women, all in good health and fed on a normal diet, were examined. Each group values are largely fluctuating but inhibition, referred to the residue of 1 ml urine added to the above described volumes of reaction mixture, is always present and it is varying from 18 to 55 per cent when assayed on kynurenine transaminase, from 37 to 53 per cent with kynureninase and from 7 to 37 per cent with tyrosine decarboxylase.

*Effects of Partially Purified Residues*

Fraction I activates all three enzymes even though male urine contains the active agent in a larger amount. Fraction II, on the contrary, inhibits all three enzymes. Fraction III is even more markedly an inhibiting agent than fraction II.

All assayed residues from different urines show the presence of the same fractions.

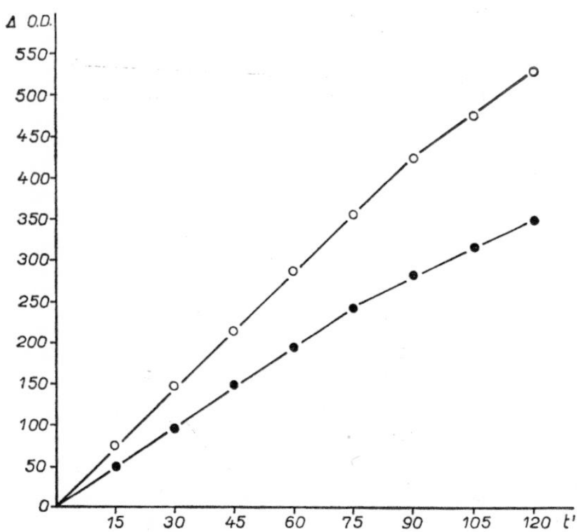


FIG. 1A. Relationship of velocity of kynurenine transaminase activity to time. Without ○—○ and with ●—● inhibitor of the fraction III present in 3 ml urine. The inhibitor was dissolved in phosphate buffer, pH 7.4.
Activity is defined under " Experimental ".

*Mode of Action of the Inhibitor Present in Fraction III*

Fraction III was studied more extensively in order to establish the type of inhibition on the three enzymes. The following data obtained with " fraction III " from the urine of one of the many examined subjects are reported, as an example.

Standard Lineweaver and Burk plots[4] of the reciprocals of the initial reaction velocities against reciprocals of the coenzyme concentration in the presence and absence of fraction III are reported for the same enzymes in Figs. 1B, 2B and 3B. The corresponding experimental data used to calculate initial velocities are given in Figs. 1A, 2A and 3A.

Since the degree of inhibition decreased as the pyridoxal phosphate concentration increased the inhibition by fraction III seems to be competitive with the coenzyme (Figs. 1B, 2B, 3B and 1C, 3C).

In all the above experiments inhibitor and coenzyme were added simultaneously. The order of addition of the inhibitor and of the coenzyme markedly affects the extent of inhibition.

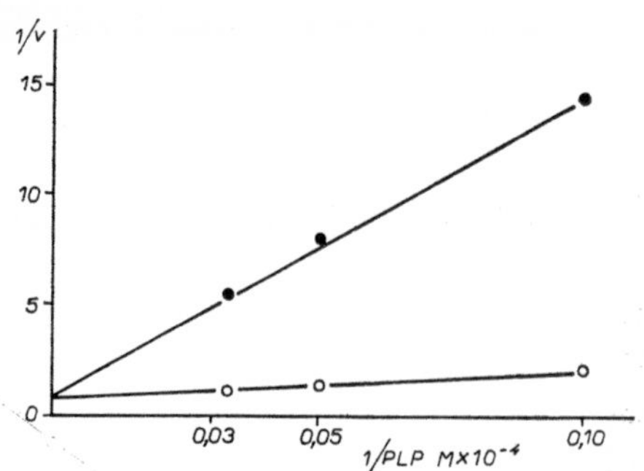


FIG. 1B. Relationship of the reciprocal of kynurenine transaminase reaction velocity ($v$) to the reciprocal of coenzyme concentration, without ○—○ and with ●—● the urinary inhibitor of the fraction III present in 3 ml urine. The inhibitor was dissolved in phosphate buffer, pH 7.4.

($v$) is defined under " Experimental ".

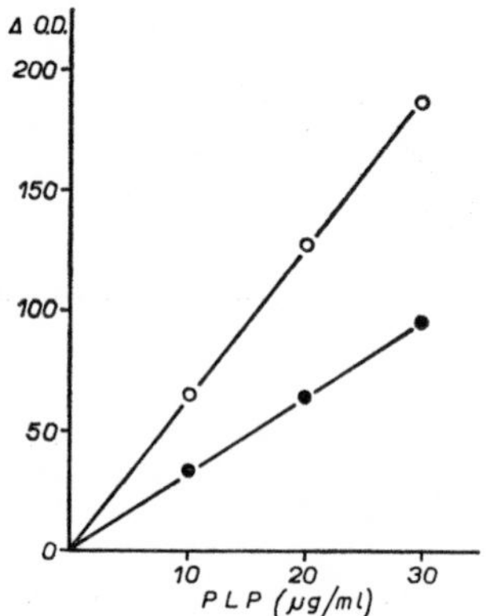


FIG. 1C. The effect of the pyridoxal phosphate (PLP) concentration on the kynurenine transaminase activity without ○—○ and with ●—● inhibitor of the fraction III present in 3 ml urine. The inhibitor was dissolved in phosphate buffer, pH 7.4.

Activity is defined under " Experimental ".

When fraction III is incubated for 15 min with a given amount of apoenzyme, before the addition of the coenzyme, the inhibition is the maximal obtainable with the amount of inhibitor used and is not reversed by the subsequent addition of excess PLP.

When the inhibitor is added immediately before the coenzyme the inhibition is slightly less and can be partially reversed by large amounts of PLP.

Inhibition becomes negligible when fraction III is added to the holoenzyme, i.e. after the addition of amounts of PLP sufficient to saturate the apoenzyme.

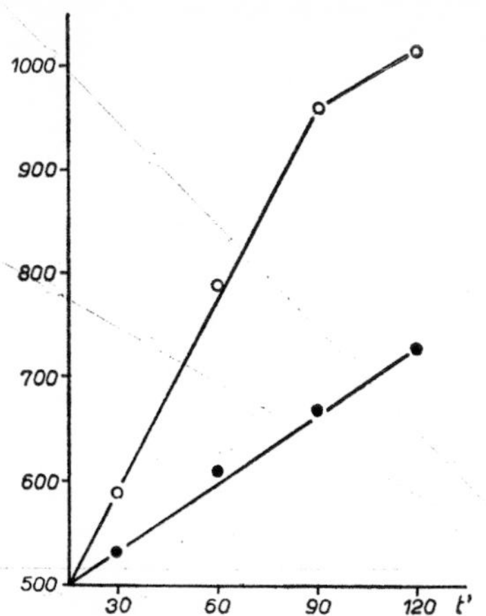


FIG. 2A. Relationship of velocity of kynureninase action to time. Without ○—○ and with ●—● inhibitor of fraction III present in 0.75 ml urine. The inhibitor was dissolved in M/15 phosphate buffer, pH 7.35.

Activity is defined as fluorescence intensity reported as arbitrary units.

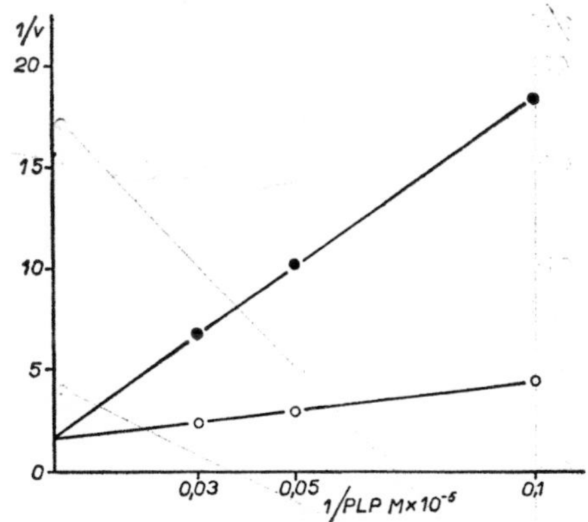


FIG. 2B. Relationship of the reciprocal of kynureninase reaction velocity ($v$) to the reciprocal of coenzyme concentration, without ○—○ and with ●—● inhibitor of fraction III present in 0.75 ml urine. The inhibitor was dissolved in M/15 phosphate buffer, pH 7.35.

($v$) is defined as fluorescence intensity.

The effect of dialysis, according to the procedure used by Mason and Gullekson[5], has been studied on kynurenine transaminase preparations initially inhibited by means of added fraction III. The results show that the inhibition produced by the extract not only is not removed after 24 hr of

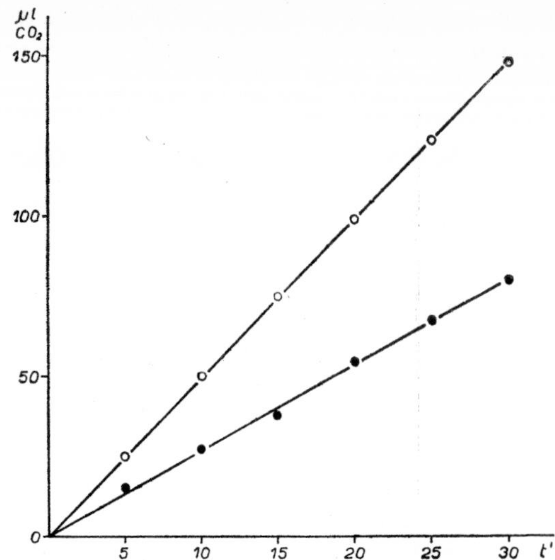


FIG. 3A. Relationship of velocity of tyrosine apodecarboxylase activity to time. ($v$) is defined as μl $CO_2$ developed without ○—○ and with ●—● inhibitor of the fraction III present in 2 ml urine.

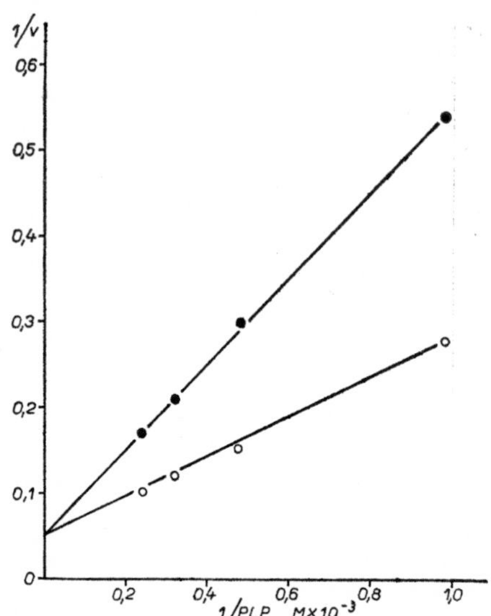


FIG. 3B. Relationship of the reciprocal of tyrosine apodecarboxylase reaction velocity ($v$) to the reciprocal of coenzyme concentration, without ○—○ and with ●—● the urinary inhibitor of fraction III present in 2 ml urine. The inhibitor was dissolved in acetate buffer, pH 5.5.

($v$) is defined as μl $CO_2$ developed at 30 min.

dialysis but rather is significantly increased, unlike the behaviour reported by Mason and Gullekson[5] for the kynurenine transaminase–estrogen complex, for which dialysis relieves largely the activity to control levels even after 8 hr.

All the above results may suggest that the urinary inhibitor present in fraction III forms rather stable complexes with the enzyme.

Similar behavior is shown by the crude extracts and by fraction II.

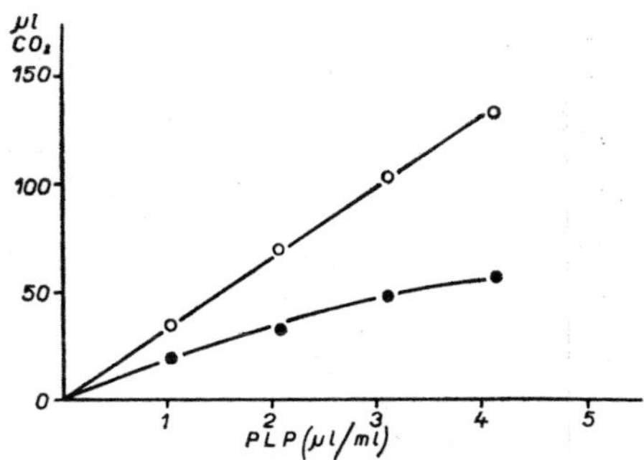


FIG. 3C. Effect of the pyridoxal phosphate (PLP) concentration on the tyrosine apodecarboxylase activity, without ○—○ and with ●—● inhibitor of fraction III present in 2 ml urine. The inhibitor was dissolved in acetate buffer, pH 5.5.
The activity is defined as μl $CO_2$ developed at 30 min. The assays were carried out as usual except for the variation of coenzyme concentration.

## DISCUSSION

The data so far obtained suggest that the inhibiting activity of the urinary extracts, both crude or partially purified, seems not to be due to any substance similar to those studied by Mason[6], Mason and Gullekson[5,7] and by Scardi *et al.*[8,9]

Mason studied the action of a variety of mono- and di-carboxylic acids on kynurenine transaminase.[6] Mason and Gullekson[5,7] found that estradiol disulfate, diethylstilbestrol disulfate and estrone sulfate even at extremely low concentration inhibit kynurenine transaminase and muscle phosphorylase while their unconjugated parent compounds were inert even in saturated solutions.

Scardi *et al.*[8] observed a similar effect of estrogens on glutamic–oxalacetic transaminase and Scardi *et al.*[9] demonstrated that phosphoric esters of estradiol and diethylstilbestrol compete with pyridoxal phosphate and are more effective inhibitors than the corresponding sulfate derivatives for kynurenine and aspartate apotransaminase.

The inhibiting activity observed by us is not ascribable to carboxylic acids, the inhibition of which, according to Mason[6], was relieved by dialysis and resulted from competition of the acids with kynurenine for the enzyme. Similarly this action can not be attributed to estrogen esters because, in the experimental conditions of hydrolysis and extraction employed by us, hydrolysis of estrogen sulfates occurs, as demonstrated by Lieberman and Dobriner[10].

Furthermore, chromatographic analysis of crude and partially purified residues confirmed the absence of estrogen sulfate esters which, when added, show spots clearly separated, for $R_F$ and chromatic reactions, from the zones supporting the inhibitory agents. Moreover the inhibitory properties

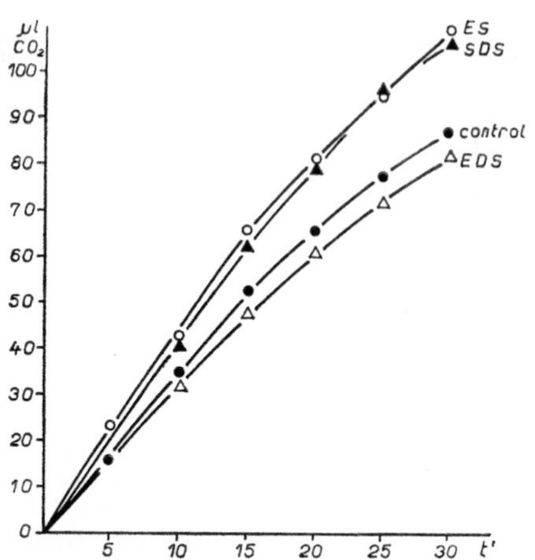


FIG. 4. Effect of estrogen sulfates on tyrosine decarboxylase.
○—○ ES, estrone sulfate ($M \times 10^{-3}$).
▲—▲ SDS, diethylstilbestrol disulfate ($M \times 10^{-3}$).
△—△ EDS, estradiol disulfate ($M \times 10^{-3}$).
Activity was assayed as described under "Experimental". The estrogens were dissolved in acetate buffer, pH 5.5.

of crude residues are preserved or increased after hydrolysis, while, in our parallel experiments, sulfate esters of estradiol, estrone and diethylstilbestrol completely lose their inhibitory effects on the enzyme systems.

As reported in Fig. 4, these estrogen esters show on tyrosine decarboxylase a behavior different from the one they display on other pyridoxal-requiring enzymes. Estrogen esters are in fact slightly activating or without effect on the latter enzyme while our crude or partially purified extracts give complete inhibition.

When non pyridoxal phosphate-dependent enzymes, as flavin enzymes, are assayed no activity is detectable.

In conclusion these experiments show that inhibition by crude urinary extracts and by fractions II and III involves competition with pyridoxal-5-phosphate for kynurenine transaminase, kynureninase and tyrosine decarboxylase apoenzymes.

Our goal is, of course, the isolation of the active agents in pure form.

*Acknowledgment*—Our thanks are due to Dr. P. Fasella and Dr. C. Turano, Institute of Biological Chemistry of the University of Rome, for many valuable discussions.

## SUMMARY

Normal human urine contains agents active on the following pyridoxal-5-phosphate-dependent enzyme systems : kynurenine transaminase, kynureninase and tyrosine decarboxylase.

Evidence is given for the presence of one activating and of two inhibiting fractions.

The nature of the inhibitory effects involves competition between pyridoxal phosphate and the agents present in the urine for the assayed apoenzymes.

Work is in progress for the isolation of these active substances.

## REFERENCES

1. M. Mason; *J. Biol. Chem.* **227**, 61 (1957).
2. O. Wiss; *Z. Physiol. Chem.* **303**, 232 (1956).
3. W. W. Umbreit, W. D. Bellamy and I. C. Gunsalus; *Arch. Biochem.* **7**, 185 (1945).
4. H. Lineweaver and D. Burk; *J. Am. Chem. Soc.* **56**, 658 (1934).
5. M. Mason and E. Gullekson; *J. Biol. Chem.* **235**, 1312 (1960).
6. M. Mason; *J. Biol. Chem.* **234**, 2770 (1959).
7. M. Mason and E. Gullekson; *J. Am. Chem. Soc.* **81**, 1517 (1959).
8. V. Scardi, S. Magno and E. Scarano; *Boll. soc. ital. biol. sper.* **36**, 1719 (1960).
9. V. Scardi, M. Iaccarino and E. Scarano; *Biochem. J.* **83**, 413 (1962).
10. S. Lieberman and K. Dobriner; *Recent Progr. Hormone Research* **3**, 71 (1948).

# INHIBITION *IN VIVO* ET *IN VITRO* DE CERTAINS ENZYMES À PYRIDOXAL PHOSPHATE (PLP) PAR L'HYDRAZIDE DE L'ACIDE ISONICOTINIQUE (INH)* ET PAR LA CYCLOSERINE (CS)

by FRANCESCO CEDRANGOLO

Institut de Chimie Biologique, Université de Naples,
rue Constantinople, 16, Naples—Italie

EN 1952 dans une série de recherches[1–4] sur la possibilité de réduire les effets toxiques de l'hydrazide de l'acide isonicotinique (INH) j'observai que l'ac. glutamique est en mesure de neutraliser complètement l'effet convulsivant, de même que l'effet mortel de l'INH. Dans des recherches successives nous avons démontré, mes collaborateurs et moi,[5–7] que ce même acide est aussi capable de prévenir et de soigner les lésions hépatiques produites par l'administration prolongée du médicament. Toutefois certains troubles toxiques aux dépens du système nerveux périphérique, n'étaient pas éliminés après l'administration de l'acide glutamique alors qu'ils pouvaient être rapidement supprimés par l'administration de vit. $B_6$.[8,9]

Je concluai donc en 1957 (Ref. 10, voir aussi Ref. 11), dans le même sens de ce que j'avais déjà indiqué en 1954[12] que l'INH exerce sa toxicité par un double mécanisme: d'une part, par la scission enzymatique de la molécule de l'INH,[13] libération de $NH_3$ responsable de la toxicité aigüe et des lésions hépatiques (au moins d'une partie de ces lésions); d'autre part, action anti-$B_6$ de la molécule entière de l'INH, responsable surtout du syndrome névritique.

Cette action anti-$B_6$ de l'INH a été confirmée par de nombreuses recherches qui ont mis en évidence une action inhibitrice de cette dernière substance à l'égard de divers enzymes à pyridoxalphosphate.[14–20]

En 1957[21] on a remarqué que la cyclosérine (4-amino-3-isoxazolidone), qui est un antibiotique ayant une forte action antituberculaire, exerce également un effet inhibiteur évident sur de nombreux systèmes enzymatiques

*Les abréviations suivantes sont employées dans le présent travail: INH = hydrazide de l'ac. isoniconicotinique; CS = cyclosérine; GPT = glutamique–pyruvique transaminase; GOT = glutamique–oxaloacétique transaminase; GD = glutamique décarboxylase; PLP = pyridoxal phosphate; PL = pyridoxal; PMP = pyridoxaminophosphate; GABA = ac. $\gamma$-aminobutirique.

$B_6$-dépendants. Beaucoup d'autres recherches se sont succédées surtout grâce à Braunstein et à son Ecole[22–26]; ces recherches ont aussi établi que la D-cyclosérine (naturelle) aussi bien que la L-cyclosérine (synthétique) sont douées de cette activité inhibitrice. Le mécanisme par lequel ces deux isomères exercent l'inhibition serait double: d'une part formation d'un composé stable avec la pyridoxal phosphate, inactif du point de vue enzymatique, de l'autre action de compétition à l'égard de quelques substrats.[24–30]

En partant de toutes ces observations sur l'INH comme sur la CS j'ai entrepris en 1959 avec mes collaborateurs une série de recherches en vue d'étudier l'effet de ces substances sur quelques systèmes enzymatiques $B_6$-dépendants: glutamique–pyruvique transaminase, glutamique–oxalo-acétique transaminase, glutamique décarboxylase. L'action des ces deux médicaments a été étudiée aussi bien *in vivo* que *in vitro: in vivo* on a déterminé l'activité des enzymes cités plus haut dans des homogénats de tissus d'animaux auxquels on avait injecté l'INH et la CS; *in vitro* on a évalué l'action inhibitrice des deux substances ajoutées à des homogénats de tissus.

Les résultats obtenus dans cette série de recherches démontrent avant tout que l'INH de même que la CS agissent *in vivo* et *in vitro* comme des inhibiteurs des trois enzymes (GPT, GOT, GD); les résultats, en outre, mettent en lumière un phénomène tout à fait nouveau, c'est-à-dire que les doses des deux inhibiteurs nécessaires pour obtenir une certaine inhibition de la GPT et de la GOT hépatique *in vitro* sont bien supérieures à celles qui produisent *in vivo* une inhibition de la même importance. Ce phénomène ne se manifeste pas pour la GD du cerveau.

Nous avons enfin énoncé des considérations générales sur les résultats obtenus surtout en ce qui concerne ce dernier phénomène.

## RÉSULTATS

### 1. *Recherches sur la GPT hépatique de Rat*

(*a*) *Action de l'INH.* Dans le Tableau 1 on a indiqué les résultats relatifs à l'action inhibitrice, sur la transamination entre la L-alanine et l'ac. α-cétoglutarique, exercée par l'INH ajoutée *in vitro* à un homogénat de foie de rat.

Du Tableau 1 il résulte que l'INH est capable d'inhiber la GPT hépatique de rat dans la proportion du 10,5 pour cent, du 44,5 pour cent et du 89,5 pour cent respectivement pour des concentrations de l'inhibiteur de l'ordre de $10^{-3}$, $10^{-2}$ et $10^{-1}$ M.

Dans le Tableau 2 sont indiqués les résultats des expériences dans lesquelles l'INH a été administrée aux rats par voie intramusculaire et où l'on a dosé la GPT dans des homogénats de foie.

Les résultats obtenus démontrent: 500 mg de INH par kg de poids corporel, injectés par voie intramusculaire, sont en mesure de produire une inhibition de la transaminase en moyenne de 75 pour cent quand l'activité de cet enzyme est mesurée une heure après l'administration de l'inhibiteur;[33] après ce laps de temps on sait que l'on atteint des concentrations élevées du médicament dans le sang et dans les tissus.[34]

TABLEAU 1. ACTION DE L'INH *in vitro* SUR LA GPT DU FOIE DE RAT (ALIOTO[31])

| Concentration INH | Pyruvate extraformé ($\mu$moles /g tissu frais) | Inhibition (%) |
|---|---|---|
| — | 1050 | — |
| $10^{-3}$ M | 940 | 10,5 |
| $10^{-2}$ M | 580 | 44,5 |
| $10^{-1}$ M | 110 | 89,5 |

Le mélange d'incubation est aussi composé: homogénat de foie de rat 1 pour cent: 0,25 ml; 0,2 M alanine: 0,5 ml; 0,1 M $\alpha$-cétoglutarique: 0,2 ml; volume final: 2 ml, avec tampon de phosphate M /15 à pH 7,4. Incubation 10 min à 37°. Le dosage de l'activité transaminasique a été effectué suivant la méthode de Salvatore *et al.*[32]

TABLEAU 2. ACTION DE l'INH *in vivo* SUR LA GPT HÉPATIQUE DE RAT (ALIOTO[33])

| Quantité de l'INH administrée (mg /kg) | Pyruvate extraformé ($\mu$moles /g tissu frais) | Inhibition (%) |
|---|---|---|
| — | 1050 | — |
| 500 | 262 | 75 |
| 500 | 273 | 74 |
| 500 | 268 | 74,5 |

Les expériences ont été effectuées en utilisant comme source enzymatique des homogénats de foie de rats traités par l'INH par voie intramusculaire et sacrifiés une heure après. Pour les autres procédés expérimentaux, v. Tableau 1.

Dans Fig. 1 on compare les concentrations de INH capables de déterminer dans les expériences *in vivo* et dans celles *in vitro* une inhibition de 75 pour cent de la GPT hépatique de rat.

Il résulte de façon évidente que les doses de INH actives *in vivo* sont extrêmement plus petites que les doses actives *in vitro*.

Pour cette figure comme pour les autres, les données sont calculées sur la base des valeurs reportées sur les tableaux relatifs.*

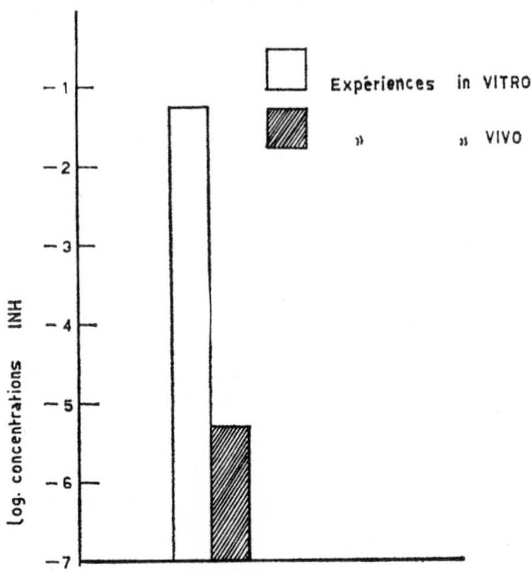


Fig. 1. Concentrations de l'INH (exprimées en logarithmes décimaux) capables de provoquer *in vivo* et *in vitro* une inhibition de la GPT hépatique de rat égale à 75 pour cent.

Les concentrations de l'INH présentes dans le mélange d'incubation dans les expériences *in vivo* ont été calculées en admettant une distribution uniforme de l'inhibiteur dans l'organisme des animaux (Manthei *et al.*[34]).

(*b*) *Action de la CS.* Des expériences analogues à celles que nous avons décrites en (*a*) ont été effectuées dans le but d'examiner l'action de la CS sur la GPT hépatique de rat.

Dans le Tableau 3 sont indiqués les résultats des expériences exécutées en ajoutant la CS à des homogénats de foie de rat.

Dans ce tableau on remarque que l'inhibition croît avec l'augmentation de la concentration de l'inhibiteur: du 11 au 69 pour cent pour des concentrations finales de CS variant de $10^{-5}$ à $10^{-3}$ M.

Des expériences *in vivo*, analogues à celles effectuées avec l'INH, ont été faites pour la CS et sont reproduites dans le Tableau 4.

D'après ce tableau on remarque que l'administration de 20 mg de CS/kg ne détermine aucune inhibition de la GPT hépatique deux heures après l'administration du médicament : ce laps de temps est celui qui permet d'atteindre des concentrations élevées dans le sang du médicament (Alioto,

*Les ordonnées de la Fig. 1 et des suivantes expriment les concentrations en mole/1. de mélange d'incubation.

données inédites). Avec des concentrations croissant jusqu'à 125 mg de CS/kg l'inhibition augmente jusqu'à atteindre le 75 pour cent. En augmentant ultérieurement la quantité de l'inhibiteur (250 et 500 mg/kg) l'inhibition reste à peu près constante.

TABLEAU 3. ACTION DE LA CYCLOSÉRINE DEXTROGYRE *in vitro*, SUR LA GPT HÉPATIQUE DE RAT (ALIOTO[36])

| Concentration CS | Pyruvate extraformé ($\mu$moles/g tissu frais) | Inhibition (%) |
|---|---|---|
| — | 1055 | — |
| $10^{-3}$ M | 325 | 69,1 |
| $10^{-4}$ M | 770 | 27 |
| $10^{-5}$ M | 933 | 11,5 |

Pour les procédés expérimentaux v. Tableau 1.

TABLEAU 4. ACTION DE LA CYCLOSÉRINE DEXTROGYRE *in vivo* SUR LA GPT HÉPATIQUE DE RAT (ALIOTO[36])

| Quantité de CS injectée (mg/kg) | Pyruvate extraformé ($\mu$moles/g tissu frais) | Inhibition (%) |
|---|---|---|
| — | 1055 | — |
| 500 | 264 | 74,9 |
| 250 | 260 | 75,3 |
| 125 | 270 | 74,4 |
| 50 | 581 | 44,9 |
| 20 | 1070 | 0 |

Les expériences ont été exécutées en utilisant comme source enzymatique des homogénats de foie de rats traités par la CS par voie intramusculaire et supprimés deux heures après l'inoculation de l'inhibiteur. Pour les autres procédés expérimentaux v. Tableau 1.

Dans la Fig. 2 sont reportées les concentrations de CS capables de provoquer dans les expériences *in vivo* et dans celles *in vitro* une inhibition de la GPT hépatique du 75 pour cent. Dans cette figure apparaît de façon évidente le phénomène déjà observé pour l'INH, c'est-à-dire la " dissociation " entre les

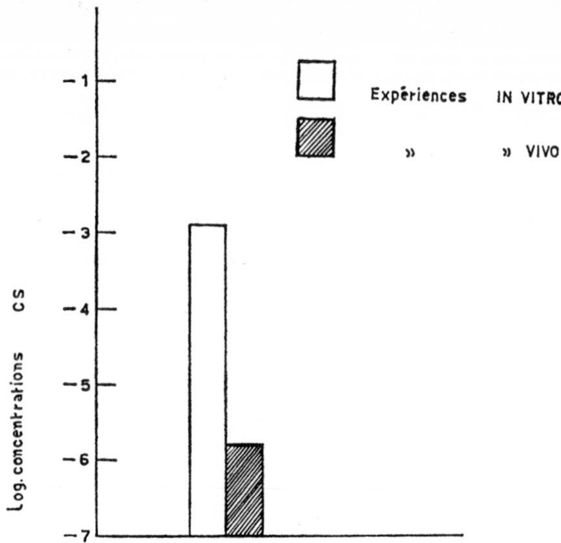


Fig. 2. Concentrations de CS (exprimées en logarithmes décimaux) capables de provoquer *in vivo* et *in vitro* une inhibition de la GPT hépatique de rat égale à 75 pour cent.

Les concentrations de CS présentes dans le mélange d'incubation dans les expériences *in vivo* ont été calculées en admettant une distribution uniforme de l'inhibiteur dans l'organisme des animaux.

Tableau 5. Action de l'INH *in vitro* sur la GOT Hépatique de Rat (Alioto[37])

| Concentration INH | Oxaloacétate extraformé (µmoles/g tissu frais) | Inhibition (%) |
|---|---|---|
| — | 947 | — |
| $10^{-1}$ M | 329 | 65,2 |
| $10^{-2}$ M | 713 | 24,7 |
| $10^{-3}$ M | 939 | 0,8 |

Les procédés expérimentaux sont ceux que l'on a indiqués dans le Tableau 1: au lieu de l'alanine on a employé l'acide aspartique 0,2 M. L'oxaloacétate a été dosé comme pyruvate (décarboxylation en présence de citrate d'aniline, v. Salvatore[32]).

doses de CS capables de provoquer *in vivo* et *in vitro* une inhibition de la même importance. Dans ce cas aussi les doses actives *in vivo* sont bien inférieures à celles qui produisent *in vitro* la même inhibition.

TABLEAU 6. ACTION DE l'INH *in vivo* SUR LA GOT HÉPATIQUE DE RAT (ALIOTO[37])

| Quantité de l'INH administrée (mg/kg) | Oxaloacétate extraformé ($\mu$moles/g tissu frais) | Inhibition (%) |
|---|---|---|
| — | 990 | — |
| 500 | 613 | 38 |
| 500 | 603 | 39 |
| 500 | 565 | 43 |

Pour les procédés expérimentaux v. Tableau 2. Pour le dosage de la GOT v. Tableau 5.

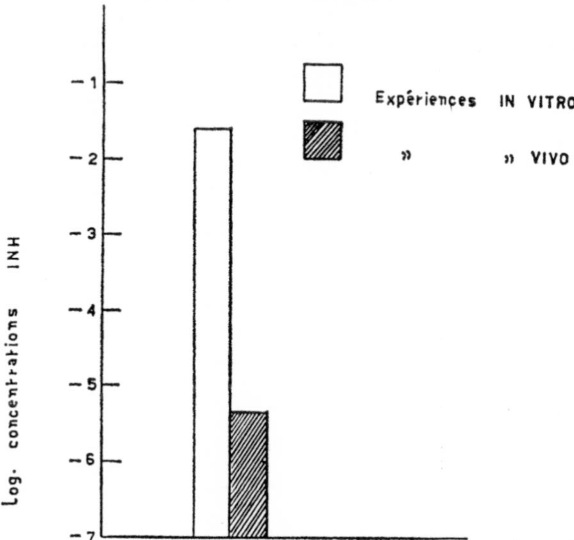


FIG. 3. Concentrations de l'INH (exprimées en logarithmes décimaux) capables de provoquer *in vivo* et *in vitro* une inhibition de la GPT hépatique de rat égale à 40 pour cent.

Les concentrations de l'INH présentes dans le mélange d'incubation dans les expériences *in vivo* ont été calculées en admettant une distribution uniforme de l'inhibiteur dans l'organisme des animaux (Manthei *et al.*[34]).

## 2. *Recherches sur la GOT Hépatique de Rat*

(*a*) *Action de l'INH.* Dans le Tableau 5 sont indiquées les valeurs de l'inhibition de la GOT en présence de INH *in vitro*.

L'inhibition croît avec l'augmentation de la concentration de l'INH atteignant des valeurs de 65 pour cent pour des concentrations égales à $10^{-1}$ M.

Dans des expériences *in vivo* aussi on a observé l'action inhibitrice de l'INH sur la GOT hépatique. L'inhibition est du 40 pour cent environ une heure après l'administration de 500 mg/kg de INH (voir Tableau 6).

TABLEAU 7. ACTION DE LA CYCLOSÉRINE DEXTROGYRE *in vitro* SUR LA GOT HÉPATIQUE DE RAT (ALIOTO[37])

| Concentration CS | Oxaloacétate extraformé ($\mu$moles/g tissu frais) | Inhibition (%) |
|---|---|---|
| — | 1010 | — |
| $10^{-3}$ M | 74 | 27,3 |
| $10^{-4}$ M | 920 | 8,9 |
| $10^{-5}$ M | 1010 | 0 |

Pour les procédés expérimentaux v. Tableau 5.

TABLEAU 8. ACTION DE LA CYCLOSÉRINE DEXTROGYRE *in vivo* SUR LA GOT HÉPATIQUE DE RAT (ALIOTO[37])

| Quantité de CS administrée (mg/kg) | Oxaloacètate extraformé ($\mu$moles/g tissu frais) | Inhibition (%) |
|---|---|---|
| — | 1010 | — |
| 500 | 1031 | 0 |
| 1000 | 801 | 20,6 |
| 1500 | 722 | 28,5 |
| 2000 | 566 | 43,9 |

Pour les procédés expérimentaux v. Tableau 4. Pour le dosage de la GOT v. Tableau 5.

Dans la Fig. 3 on compare les concentrations de INH nécessaires pour provoquer dans les expériences *in vivo* et dans celles *in vitro* une inhibition de la GOT hépatique de rat du 40 pour cent.

Ici aussi il résulte clairement que les doses de INH actives *in vivo* sont nettement plus petites que les doses actives *in vitro*.

(*b*) *Action de la CS*. L'action exercée *in vitro* par la CS sur la GOT hépatique de rat apparaît dans les résultats reportés sur le Tableau 7. Dans le Tableau 7 il apparaît que l'inhibition atteint des valeurs du 27 pour cent pour des concentrations de CS égales à $10^{-1}$ M. On n'a pas employé de concentrations supérieures à cause des interférences qui se vérifient dans le dosage du pyruvate en présence de fortes concentrations de CS (Alioto, données inédites).

Dans le Tableau 8 sont présentés les résultats relatifs à l'action de la CS *in vivo* sur la GOT hépatique du rat. Dans ce tableau on remarque que

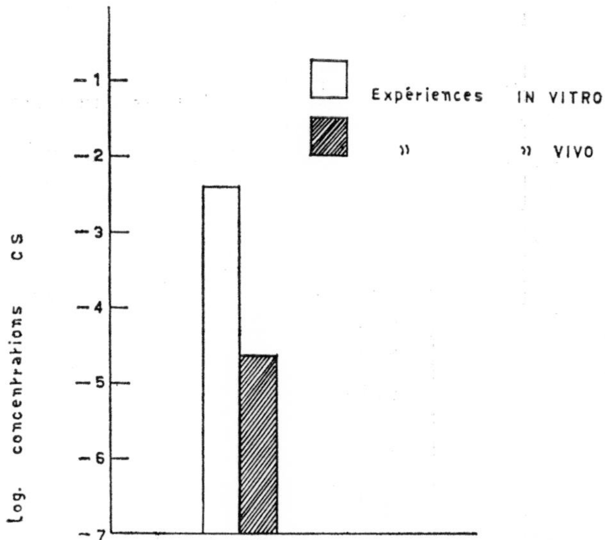


FIG. 4. Concentrations de CS (exprimées en logarithmes décimaux) capables de provoquer *in vivo* et *in vitro* une inhibition de la GOT hépatique de rat égale à 40 pour cent.

Les concentrations de la CS présentes dans le mélange d'incubation dans les expériences *in vivo* ont été calculées en admettant une distribution uniforme de l'inhibiteur dans l'organisme des animaux.

l'inhibition atteint des valeurs du 44 pour cent pour des quantités de CS égales à 2 g/kg de poids corporel.

Dans ce cas aussi, si l'on calcule les quantités de CS capables *in vivo* et *in vitro* de provoquer une inhibition de la GOT de la même importance, l'on observe que les concentrations de CS actives *in vitro* sont beaucoup plus élevées que celles actives *in vivo*. Dans la Fig. 4 on compare les concentrations de CS nécessaires pour provoquer dans les expériences *in vivo* et dans celles *in vitro* une inhibition de la GOT hépatique de rat du 40 pour cent.

### 3. *Recherches sur la GD Cérébrale de Rat*

(*a*) *Action de l'INH.* Dans le Tableau 9 on montre l'action inhibitrice de l'INH *in vitro* sur la GD du cerveau de rat. L'inhibition augmente avec l'augmentation de la concentration de l'inhibiteur et atteint des valeurs du 100 pour cent pour des concentrations de INH de l'ordre de $4 \times 10^{-4}$. Pour des concentrations de $2 \times 10^{-4}$ M l'inhibition est égale au 77 pour cent.

Dans le Tableau 10 sont présentés les résultats des expériences exécutées *in vivo*. Il résulte que l'inhibition est de 67 pour cent et de 77 pour cent pour des quantités de INH égales respectivement à 250 et 500 mg/kg.

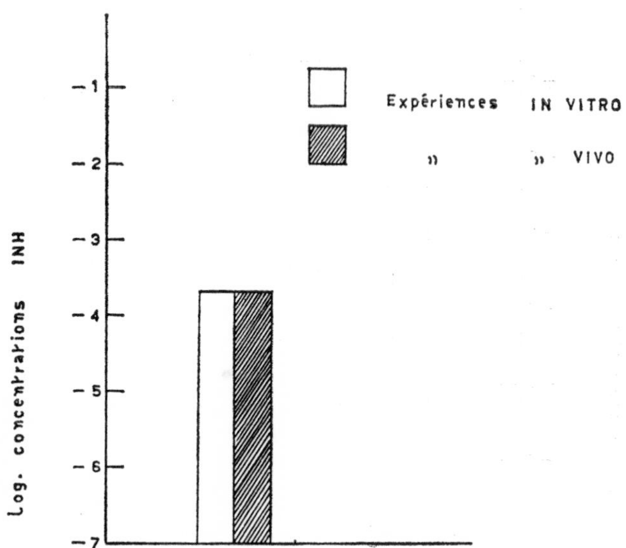


Fig. 5. Concentrations de l'INH (exprimées en logarithmes décimaux) capables de provoquer *in vivo* et *in vitro* une inhibition de la GD cérébrale égale à 75 pour cent. Les concentrations de l'INH dans le système nerveux ont été calculées sur la base des résultats de Manthei *et al.*[34]

Dans la Fig. 5 on compare les concentrations de INH capables de provoquer *in vivo* et *in vitro* une inhibition du 77 pour cent de la GD cérébrale de rat.

Ces résultats montrent que dans le cas de la GD cérébrale il n'y a aucune différence entre les doses de INH capables *in vivo* et *in vitro* de provoquer une inhibition de la même importance.

(*b*) *Action de la CS.* Dans le Tableau 11 on remarque que l'inhibition de la GD croît avec l'augmentation de la concentration de CS ajoutée *in vitro*. Celle-ci atteint des valeurs du 100 pour cent pour des concentrations de CS de $10^{-2}$ M.

Les essais sur la GD cérébrale de rat, exécutés après l'administration *in vivo* de CS en doses graduées, révélaient une inhibition de l'activité enzymatique qui atteignait des valeurs du 66 pour cent pour des quantités de CS égales à 500 mg/kg (voir Tableau 12).

Dans le cas de la CS l'observation des données nous porte à constater également l'absence du phénomène de la dissociation entre les doses actives *in vivo* et *in vitro*. Dans la Fig. 6 sont reportées les concentrations de CS capables de provoquer *in vivo* et *in vitro* une inhibition de la GD cérébrale de 75 pour cent environ.

TABLEAU 9. ACTION DE l'INH *in vitro* SUR LA GD DU CERVEAU DE RAT (DELLA PIETRA *et al.*[38])

| Concentration INH | Ac. glutamique décarboxylé ($\mu$g/340 mg de cerveau) | Inhibition (%) |
|---|---|---|
| — | 403 | — |
| $8 \times 10^{-4}$ M | 0 | 100 |
| $4 \times 10^{-4}$ M | 0 | 100 |
| $2 \times$ M$0^{-4}$ M | 90 | 77 |

Le mélange d'incubation est ainsi composé: homogénat de cerveau dans du tampon de phosphate potassique 0,05 M, pH 6, égal à 340 mg de cerveau; 0,1 M NaF: 0,1 ml; ac.glutamique 31 $\mu$moles; vol.final 3,1 ml. L'activité enzymatique a été mesurée en appliquant la technique usuelle à l'appareil de Warburg.

TABLEAU 10. ACTION DE l'INH *in vivo* SUR LA GD DU CERVEAU DE RAT (DELLA PIETRA *et al.*[38])

| Quantité de INH administrée (mg/kg) | Ac. glutamique décarboxylé ($\mu$g/340 mg de cerveau) | Inhibition (%) |
|---|---|---|
| — | 448 | — |
| 500 | 101 | 77 |
| 250 | 148 | 67 |

Les animaux ont été tués 80 min après l'injection de INH par voie intramusculaire. Pour les autres procédés expérimentaux v. Tableau 9.

Dans le but de rendre plus évidentes l'existence et l'importance du phénomène de la dissociation, dans le Tableau 13 sont indiqués les rapports entre les concentrations *in vivo* et celles *in vitro* des deux inhibiteurs. Il résulte du tableau que le rapport oscille entre un maximum de 11100 (dans le cas de l'inhibition de la GPT par l'INH) et un minimum de 1 (dans le cas de l'inhibition de la GD par l'INH et par la CS).

## DISCUSSION

Les résultats que nous avons exposés jusqu'à présent démontrent:

(1) Que l'INH aussi bien que la CS sont en mesure d'inhiber *in vitro* la GPT et la GOT du foie de rat et la GD du cerveau du même animal: le degré d'inhibition varie selon la variation des concentrations des deux inhibiteurs.

TABLEAU 11. ACTION DE LA CYCLOSÉRINE DEXTROGYRE *in vitro* SUR LA GD CÉRÉBRALE DE RAT (DELLA PIETRA *et al.*[39]).

| Concentration CS | Ac. glutamique décarboxylé ($\mu$g/340 mg de cerveau) | Inhibition (%) |
|---|---|---|
| — | 404 | — |
| $10^{-2}$ M | 0 | 100 |
| $10^{-3}$ M | 59 | 85 |
| $5 \times 10^{-4}$ M | 186 | 53 |
| $3,2 \times 10^{-4}$ M | 285 | 29 |
| $10^{-4}$ M | 397 | 2 |

Pour les procédés expérimentaux v. Tableau 9.

TABLEAU 12. ACTION DE LA CYCLOSÉRINE DEXTROGYRE *in vivo* SUR LA GD DU CERVEAU DE RAT (DELLA PIETRA *et al.*[39])

| Quantité de CS administrée (mg/kg) | Ac. glutamique décarboxylé ($\mu$g/340 mg de cerveau) | Inhibition (%) |
|---|---|---|
| — | 401 | — |
| 500 | 133 | 66 |
| 350 | 240 | 40 |
| 200 | 364 | 9 |
| 100 | 385 | 3 |

Les animaux ont été tués deux heures après l'administration intramusculaire de la CS. Pour les autres procédés expérimentaux v. Tableau 9.

(2) Que l'INH aussi bien que la CS administrées *in vivo* sont en mesure d'inhiber les mêmes activités enzymatiques dans les organes cités ci-dessus.

Il nous semble ici opportun de faire remarquer que dans les travaux scientifiques précédents on n'a pas décrit d'expériences d'inhibition par la CS *in vivo*.

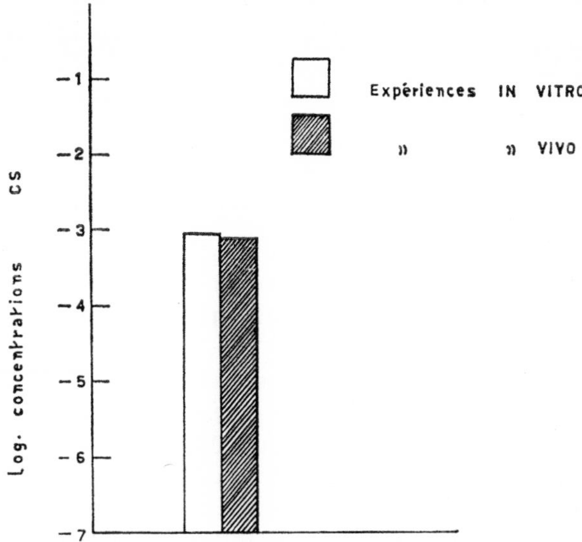


FIG. 6. Concentrations de CS (exprimées en logarithmes décimaux) capables de provoquer *in vivo* et *in vitro* une inhibition de la GD cérébrale de rat égale à 75 pour cent.

Les concentrations de CS présentes dans le mélange d'incubation dans les expériences *in vivo* ont été calculées en admettant une distribution uniforme de l'inhibiteur dans l'organisme des animaux.

TABLEAU 13. RAPPORTS ENTRE LES CONCENTRATIONS *in vitro* ET CELLES *in vivo* DES DEUX INHIBITEURS (ÉLABORÉS D'APRÈS LES DONNÉES DES TABLEAUX 1–12).

| Inhibiteur | Concentrations *in vitro*/concentrations *in vivo* | | |
|---|---|---|---|
| | GPT (inhibition 75%) | GOT (inhibition 40%) | GD (inhibition 75%) |
| INH | 11,100 | 6000 | 1 |
| CS | 866 | 181 | 1,1 |

Il est très intéressant de faire ensuite une comparaison entre les doses de l'inhibiteur actives *in vivo* et les doses actives *in vitro*. Au cours de l'inhibition exercée par l'INH de même que par la CS sur la GPT et sur la GOT, il résulte en effet que les doses actives *in vivo* sont beaucoup plus faibles que les doses actives *in vitro*. Il résulte, d'après les figures, que la comparaison est toujours établie sur la base d'une même inhibition: 75 pour cent pour la GPT, 40 pour cent pour la GOT. Au cours des expériences effectuées sur la GD, il semble au contraire que pour une même inhibition (75 pour cent) les doses de l'inhibiteur (INH ou CS) actives *in vitro* sont pratiquement égales à celles actives *in vivo*.

Il semble donc évident que dans le cas de l'inhibition de la GOT et de la GPT il se produit un phénomène que nous pouvons appeler phénomène de " dissociation ", c'est-à-dire dissociation entre les doses de l'inhibiteur actives *in vitro* et celles actives *in vivo*. Ce phénomène ne semble pas se manifester au contraire dans le cas de l'inhibition exercée par l'INH et par la CS sur la GD.

En ce qui concerne l'importance de la dissociation nous pouvons dire qu'elle est diverse et qu'elle varie selon l'inhibiteur et selon le système enzymatique: pour le même enzyme elle est toujours plus grande dans le cas où l'inhibiteur est l'INH, pour l'INH comme pour la CS toujours plus grande dans le cas où l'enzyme est la GPT.*

Bien que cela sorte du sujet que nous sommes chargés de traiter, il me semble opportun de souligner ici une observation expérimentale, que je considère d'un grand intérêt. Il résulte du Tableau 10 que l'INH, administré *in vivo* dans la dose de 250 mg/kg, inhibe la GD cérébrale dans la mesure du 67 pour cent; d'après le Tableau 12 il résulte aussi que la CS dans les doses de 500 mg/kg inhibe la GD cérébrale dans la mesure du 66 pour cent. On a donc pratiquement la même valeur d'inhibition de la GD cérébrale dans le premier comme dans le second cas. Or, puisqu'en administrant l'INH à la concentration indiquée ci-dessus, on observe certainement chez les rats de fortes convulsions, tandis que celles-ci ne se manifestent pas quand on administre la CS dans la dose citée plus haut, il nous semble qu'il faut conclure que la cause des symptômes convulsifs ne réside pas dans l'inhibition de la GD et par conséquent dans la diminution des valeurs du GABA dans le cerveau.

Précédemment divers auteurs[16,40,41] étaient arrivés à ces mêmes conclusions

*En réalité la comparaison est faite entre l'INH dont l'activité inhibitrice est mesurée une heure après l'administration et la CS dont l'activité inhibitrice a été étudiée au contraire deux heures après l'administration. Pour obtenir des données sûrement comparables, on aurait dû créer les mêmes conditions, c'est-à-dire utiliser les données obtenues après un intervalle de temps identique dans les deux cas. Ou mieux encore: on aurait dû construire des courbes sur les abscisses desquelles on aurait indiqué les périodes de temps aprés lesquelles étaient effectuées les mesures d'activité, et sur les ordonnées les pourcentages d'inhibition. On aurait obtenu vraisemblablement pour l'INH aussi bien que pour la CS des courbes en forme de cloche, dont on aurait utilisé pour les rapports reportés dans le Tableau 13 la valeur de l'inhibition maximum.

Toutefois pour confirmer la validité des rapports que nous avons établis, on doit souligner que les données inédites d'Alioto en ce qui concerne la CS, et les données de Manthei *et al.*[34] et de Crema et Baroli[35] pour l'INH, démontreraient que les temps choisis pour nos expériences sont ceux pour lesquels se vérifie une plus grande concentration de ces inhibiteurs dans le sang et dans les tissus et, donc, vraisemblablement aussi la plus grande inhibition des enzymes.

sur la base d'expériences effectuées avec divers types d'hydrazides, de nombreux convulsivants et des antivitamines $B_6$. Dans ces expériences ces auteurs ne constataient pas un rapport direct entre l'inhibition de la GD cérébrale et les phénomènes convulsifs (voir aussi Williams et Bain[42]). Contre l'opinion que la diminution du taux de GABA est l'unique responsable des convulsions par l'INH, voyez aussi Williams[43], Purpura[44] et Curtis et Watkins[45].

Et, arrivé à ce point, je m'arrête préférant, comme l'on dit, m'en tenir aux faits: en réalité l'interprétation des phénomènes que nous avons observés, surtout du phénomène de la dissociation entre les doses actives *in vivo* et celles actives *in vitro*, est très difficile, peut-être impossible actuellement. Il est évident aussi que l'interprétation d'une donnée expérimentale est déterminée par le moment historique dans lequel cette donnée a été obtenue (voir de Broglie[46]). Et le moment actuel n'est pas mûr pour apporter une explication satisfaisante et vraisemblable du phénomène de la " dissociation ".

Il est évident que l'on peut faire aujourd'hui aussi autant d'hypothèses que l'on veut. Mais, comme l'a justement observé le fameux astronome anglais Sir James Jeans[47], quand elle n'est pas corroborée par l'expérience, une hypothèse, qui par la suite se révélera juste, ne vaut pas plus qu'une hypothèse erronée.

De toutes façons je pense qu'il est opportun d'indiquer quelques faits expérimentaux, que nous pourrons, ou, peut-être même, devrons, mettre en discussion, tous ou seulement quelques uns, quand on voudra essayer de donner une interprétation sur des bases chimiques et enzymatiques du phénomène observé, et tenter aussi d'expliquer pourquoi le phénomène est présent dans le cas de l'inhibition de la GPT et de la GOT et non pas dans le cas de l'inhibition de la GD.

Il est possible aussi que dans la discussion qui, je le souhaite, va suivre ici, l'on réussisse à tracer une ligne générale d'interprétation.

Les faits expérimentaux que j'ai indiqués sont essentiellement les suivants:

(1) Le fait que la GOT et la GPT, pour lesquelles se vérifie le phénomène de la dissociation, ont pour coenzyme soit le PLP soit la PMP, là où la GD, pour laquelle on ne constate pas ce phénomène, a pour coenzyme seulement le PLP.[48]

(2) Que l'isonicotinilhydrazone du PL est un puissant inhibiteur de la PL-kinase, c'est-à-dire de l'enzyme qui phosphorylise le PL.[49,50]

(3) Que les hydrazones formés par interréaction entre le groupe formilique du PLP et le groupe hydrazinique de l'INH abandonnent rapidement l'organisme par l'urine.[42]

Enfin je dois vous rappeler que le phénomène de la " dissociation " que nous avons découvert, semble être un phénomène très étendu et d'une portée, si l'on peut dire, générale. En effet, au dernier Congrès International de Biochimie qui s'est tenu au mois d'Août 1961 à Moscou, nous avons rapporté que ce phénomène est aussi présent dans le cas de l'inhibition de la réaction de Ratner et Pappas par l'ac. méthylaspartique.[51] Mon collaborateur, le docteur Cittadini[52], a remarqué aussi ce même phénomène en étudiant *in vitro* et *in vivo* l'action de la L-lysine sur l'arginase.

Un champ fertile et nouveau s'ouvre donc à l'expérimentation et aux capacités de synthèse intellectuelle du Biochimiste, qui, toutefois, devra toujours considérer que le résultat obtenu *in vitro* ne donne pas dans tous les cas une idée exacte de ce qui se produit *in vivo.*

*In vivo* un phénomène est toujours la résultante d'une série de réactions là où *in vitro* ces dernières sont pour ainsi dire anatomisées, se mettant en évidence, tantôt l'une tantôt l'autre, mais jamais ces réactions dans leur ensemble. Sur ces différentes façons de réagir de la cellule vivante et de l'organisme vivant à l'égard de ce que nous montre l'expérience *in vitro*, nous avons été ceux qui, plus que les autres peut-être, avons mis au point cette question et avons essayé de corriger depuis longtemps, déjà en 1941,[53,54] une mentalité qui malheureusement aujourd'hui, après 20 ans environ, semble encore dangereusement répandue.

Les recherches actuelles, qui ont mis en évidence le phénomène de la "dissociation" entre les doses de deux inhibiteurs enzymatiques actives *in vivo* et celles actives *in vitro*, sont donc encore une preuve et une démonstration à l'appui de ces idées et de cette conclusion.

## RÉSUMÉ

Après quelques considérations préliminaires l'auteur passe en revue les recherches effectuées dans son Laboratoire sur l'action de l'hydrazide de l'acide isonicotinique (INH) et de la cyclosérine (CS) sur certains enzymes à pyridoxal phosphate (PLP).

Les résultats démontrent:

(1) L'alanine-α-cétoglutarique transaminase (GPT), l'acide aspartique-α-cétoglutarique transaminase du foie de rat et la glutamique décarboxylase (GD) du cerveau de rat sont inhibées *in vitro* par l'INH et la CS.

(2) L'inhibition des ces mêmes enzymes a été observée *in vivo* (rats) après injection intramusculaire de INH et CS.

(3) Les doses des deux chémiothérapiques qui sont capables de provoquer une inhibition de la GPT et GOT dans des expériences *in vivo* et dans celles *in vitro* sont très différentes: pour obtenir la même inhibition les quantités de INH et de CS qui sont nécessaires *in vitro* sont beaucoup plus grandes que celles nécessaires *in vivo.*

(4) Au contraire ce phénomène de " dissociation " (dissociation entre les doses de l'inhibiteur actives *in vivo* et celles actives *in vitro*) ne se manifeste pas dans le cas de l'inhibition de la GD.

Dans le but d'expliquer les résultats reportés, quelques hypothèses sont présentées.

## BIBLIOGRAPHIE

1. F. CEDRANGOLO, A. GIOIA et R. BAGNULO; *Boll. soc. ital. biol. sper.* **29**, 34 (1953).
2. F. CEDRANGOLO, A. GIOIA et R. BAGNULO; *Boll. soc. ital. sper.* **29**, 37 (1953).
3. F. CEDRANGOLO, A. GIOIA et R. BAGNULO; *Boll. soc. ital. biol. sper.* **29**, 39 (1953).
4. F. CEDRANGOLO, A. GIOIA et R. BAGNULO; *Enzymologia* **16**, 41 (1953).
5. P. JANNELLA, E. SCALA et L. ZARRILLI; *Boll. soc. ital. biol. sper.* **31**, 1604 (1955); *Biochim. Appl.* **3**, 280 (1956).
6. G. DELLA PIETRA, E. ROGLIANI, C. ROGLIANI et P. JANNELLA; *Biochim. Appl.* **4**, 257 (1957).
7. V. GRAMAZIO et B. POZZO BALBI; *Annali Medici di Sondalo* **5** (1957); R. PIAZZA et U. DE BELLIS; *Biochim. Appl.* **5**, 347 (1958).
8. G. ZBINDEN et A. STUDER; *Experientia* **12**, 442 (1956).
9. F. CEDRANGOLO; *Biochim. Appl.* **3**, 247 (1956).
10. F. CEDRANGOLO; *Enzymologia* **18**, 366 (1957).
11. F. CEDRANGOLO; *Ann. pharm. franc.* **17**, 368 (1959).
12. F. CEDRANGOLO; *Biochim. Appl.* **1**, 1 (1954).
13. G. PORCELLATI et P. PREZIOSI; *Enzymologia* **17**, 47 (1954).
14. K. F. KILLAM; Ph.D. Thesis, University of Illinois, Chicago, Illinois, cit. in 42.
15. K. F. KILLAM; *J. Pharmacol. Exptl. Therap.* **119**, 263 (1957).
16. K. F. KILLAM et J. A. BAIN; *J. Pharmacol. Exptl. Therap.* **119**, 255 (1957).
17. J. P. BIEHL et R. W. VILTER; *Proc. Soc. Exptl. Biol. Med.* **85**, 389 (1954).
18. R. G. WIEGAND; *J. Am. Chem. Soc.* **78**, 5307 (1956).
19. A. N. DAVISON; *Biochim. et Biophys. Acta* **19**, 131 (1956).
20. A. E. BRAUNSTEIN; *Advances in Enzymol.* **19**, 335 (1957).
21. T. AOKI *et al.*; *Keikkaku* **32**, 544 (1957).
22. E. D. VYSHEPAN, K. I. IVANOVA et A. M. CHERNUKH; *Byull. Eksp. Biol. Med.* **47**, 52 (1959).
23. R. M. AZARKH, A. E. BRAUNSTEIN et T. S. PASKHINA; *Biokhimia* **25**, 954 (1960).
24. N. N. BEROZOVSKAYA; *Biokhimia* **25**, 106 (1960).
25. A. E. BRAUNSTEIN; *Proc. Vth Int. Cong. Biochem.*, Moscow, 1961, Symposium No. 4, Preprint No. 1 Pergamon Press, sous presse.
26. A. E. BRAUNSTEIN, R. M. AZARKH et SYUI TIN-SEN; *Biokhimia* **26**, 882 (1961).
27. R. M. KHOMUTOV, M. YA KARPEISKII, E. S. SEVERIN et N. V. GNUCHEV; *Doklady Akad. Nauk. S.S.S.R.* **140**, 2 (1961).
28. N. K. KOCHETOV, R. M. KHOMUTOV, M. YA KARPEISKII, E. I. BUDOVSKII et E. S. SEVERIN; *Doklady Akad. Nauk. S.S.S.R.* **126**, 1132 (1959).
29. R. M. KHOMUTOV, M. YA KARPEISKII et E. S. SEVERIN; *Biokhimia* **26**, 772 (1961).
30. O. L. POLYANOVSKII et YU M. TORCHINSKII; *Doklady Akad. Nauk. S.S.S.R.* **141**, (1961).
31. M. R. ALIOTO; *Giorn. biochim.* **8**, 357 (1959).
32. F. SALVATORE, V. BOCCHINI, M. R. ALIOTO et D. CITTADINI; *Biochim. Appl.* **6**, 130 (1959).
33. M. R. ALIOTO; *Biochim. Appl.* **8**, 239 (1961).
34. R. W. MANTHEI, L. J. ROTH, W. R. BARCLAY et R. H. EBERT; *Arch. intern. pharmacodynamie* **98**, 183 (1954).
35. A. CREMA et F. BAROLI; *Arch. sci. farmacol.* **5**, 56 (1955).
36. M. R. ALIOTO; *Biochim. Appl.* **9**, 238, (1962).
37. M. R. ALIOTO; *Biochim. Appl.* **9**, 333, (1962).
38. G. DELLA PIETRA, G. ILLIANO et F. DE LORENZO; *Biochim. Appl.* **10,** sous presse (1963).
39. G. DELLA PIETRA, F. DE LORENZO et G. ILLIANO; *Biochim. Appl.* **10**, sous presse (1963).
40. C. F. BAXTER et E. ROBERTS; *Proc. Soc. Exptl. Biol. Med.* **104**, 426 (1960).
41. F. ROSEN, J. MILHOLLAND et C. A. NICHOL; *Symposium on Inhibition in the Nervous System and γ-Aminobutyric Acid* (edited by E. ROBERTS), p. 338, Pergamon Press, New York (1960).
42. H. L. WILLIAMS et J. A. BAIN; *Intern. Rev. Neurobiol.* **3**, 319 (1961).
43. H. L. WILLIAMS; *J. Pharmacol. Exptl. Therap.* **122**, 83 (1958).

44. D. P. Purpura; *Symposium on Inhibition in the Nervous System and γ-Aminobutyric Acid* (edited by E. Roberts), p. 495, Pergamon Press, New York (1960).
45. D. R. Curtis et J. C. Watkins; *Symposium on Inhibition in the Nervous System and γ-Aminobutyric Acid* (edited by E. Roberts), p. 424, Pergamon Press, New York (1960).
46. L. De Broglie; *Materia e Luce*, Bompiani ed., Milano (1940).
47. G. Amaldi et L. Fermi; *Alchimia del Tempo Nostro*, p. 3, Hoepli ed., Milano (1936).
48. A. Meister; *Biochemistry of Amino Acids*, p. 207, Academic Press, New York (1957).
49. D. B. McCormick et E. E. Snell; *Proc. Natl. Acad. Sci. U.S.* **45**, 1371 (1959).
50. E. E. Snell; *Proc. Vth Int. Cong. Biochem.*, Moscow, 1961, Symposium No. 4, Preprint No. 187, Pergamon Press, sous presse.
51. F. Cedrangolo, G. Della Pietra et F. De Lorenzo; *Communication Vth Int. Cong. Biochem.*, Moscow, 1961; *Biochim. Appl.* **8**, 211 (1961).
52. A. Scala, C. Pietropaolo et D. Cittadini; *Boll. soc. ital. biol. sper.* **38**, sous presse (1962).
53. F. Cedrangolo et G. Carandante; *Boll. soc. ital. biol. sper.* **16**, 442 (1941); **17**, 208 (1942); *Arch. sci. biol.* **28**, 1 e 216 (1942).
54. F. Cedrangolo; La posizione dell'Enzimologia nella Biologia e nella Medicina d'oggi. *Rapport au Symposium International* " *Enzimi in Medicina* ", Ed. Instituto Sieroterapico Milanese, Torino p. 12 (1957).

## DISCUSSION

Dr. Gonnard :

Le pouvoir inhibiteur de l'isoniazide, plus accentué *in vivo* qu' *in vitro* vis-à-vis des pyridoxalo-enzymes, pourrait être attribué, dans le premier cas, à une action sur un autre système enzymatique, absent dans les préparations étudiées *in vitro*. La pyridoxal-kinase, par exemple, est très sensible à l'action de l'isoniazide, son inhibition entraînant secondairement une diminution de l'activité des pyridoxalo-enzymes par carence en co-facteur.

Dr. Cedrangolo :

Je suis parfaitement d'accord avec vous car, comme je l'ai déjá dit dans mon rapport, le plus grand pouvoir d'inhibition *in vivo* de l'INH peut etre dû à la formation de l'isonicotynilhydrazone du phosphate de pyridoxal qui, selon Snell, est un fort inhibiteur de la pyridoxalkinase.

# THE IDENTITY OF CYSTEINE DESULFHYDRASE WITH CYSTATHIONASE AND MECHANISM OF CYSTEINE-CYSTINE DESULFHYDRATION

by D. CAVALLINI, B. MONDOVÌ and C. DE MARCO

Institutes of Biological Chemistry of the Universities of Modena and Rome, Italy

EXTRACTION and purification of cysteine desulfhydrase* has been attempted many times.[1-7] It has been frequently observed that in the course of the purification of the enzyme, cystathionase† activity was not removed[3,5-7] and the possible identity of the desulfhydrase with cystathionase has thus occasionally been claimed. Nevertheless the purification of cysteine desulfhydrase has never been extended so far as to obtain a homogeneous product.

Cystathionase on the other hand has been highly purified from rat liver[8] and bacterial source.[9] The enzyme prepared from rat liver has been also crystallized[8] and has been found to desulfhydrate cysteine.[10]

As a consequence of the above findings the problem arises whether cysteine desulfhydrase and cystathionase are two different enzymes, each one having also the activity of the other, or one single enzyme provided with both the activities. To establish this point we have analyzed the chromatographic and electrophoretic patterns of a rat liver extract under various conditions in order to establish whether or not with different experimental procedures the two enzymes behave similarly. We believe this procedure more appropriate than that of the determination of the activity ratio with specific substrates in the course of the purification, because, as will be seen later, the enzyme seems heterogeneous and the substrate for the desulfhydrase activity is not cysteine as it is generally accepted to be.

## EXPERIMENTAL

The most relevant experimental data are reported in the legend of the figures and of the tables. The details of the procedures used will be found in the quoted papers of our group and in those which are in the press.

*E.C. 4.4.1.1., L-cysteine hydrogensulfide-lyase deaminating.

†E.C. 4.2.1.15., L-homoserine hydro-lyase deaminating.

## RESULTS

### *Identity of Cysteine Desulfhydrase with Cystathionase*

Figures 1 to 4 show that under various chromatographic and electrophoretic conditions the two activities are indistinguishable. The results

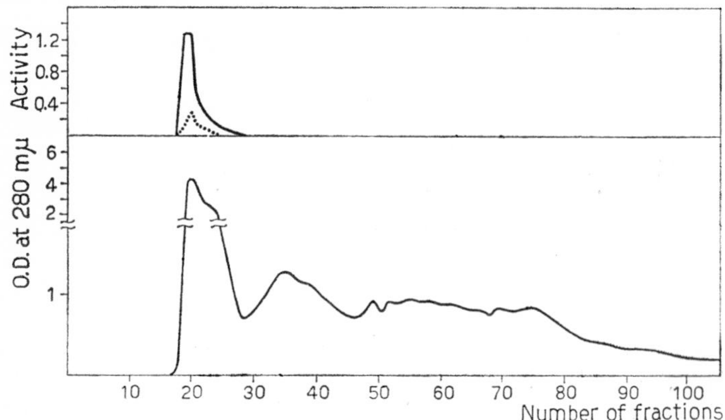


FIG. 1. Chromatography of rat liver extract on DEAE–cellulose column with a potassium phosphate pH 7.2 gradient from 0.01 to 0.3 M.

Activity in arbitrary units: full line, cystathionase; dotted line, cysteine desulfhydrase. See Ref. 11 for details.

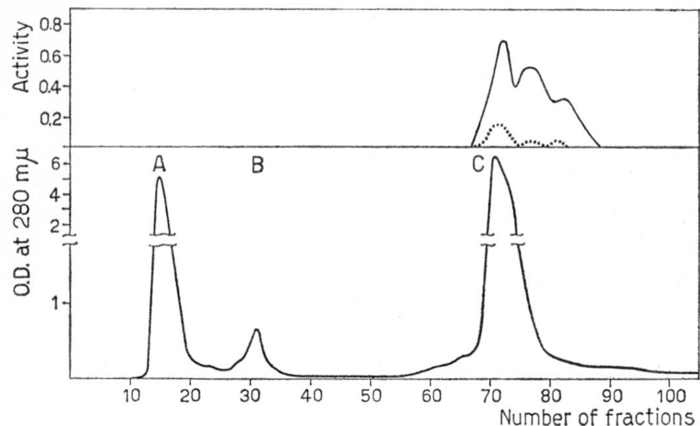


FIG. 2. Chromatography of rat liver extract on CM–cellulose column with a potassium phosphate gradient from 0.01 M pH 5.6 to 0.05 M pH 8.5. Activity in arbitrary units: full line, cystathionase; dotted line, cysteine desulfhydrase. See Ref. 11 for details.

illustrated in the figures have been repeated many times with the same conclusions. Electrophoresis has been performed also at pH 6.8 with the same results, although at this pH both the activities were depressed owing to a partial inactivation of the enzyme during the electrophoretic course.

TABLE 1. ACTIVITY OF CYSTATHIONASE COMPONENTS ON VARIOUS SUBSTRATES

Values in μmoles of keto acids released after 2 hr of incubation with the listed substrates under identical experimental conditions (see Ref. 11 for details).

| | | Cystathionase | |
|---|---|---|---|
| | | Component I | Component II |
| DL-homoserine | 20 μmoles | 0.40 | 1.06 |
| DL-cystathionine | 20 μmoles | 0.55 | 0.93 |
| L-Djenkolic acid | 20 μmoles | 0.13 | 0.47 |
| L-Cystine | 10 μmoles | 0.05 | 0.24 |
| L-Cysteine | 20 μmoles | 0.03 | 0.03 |

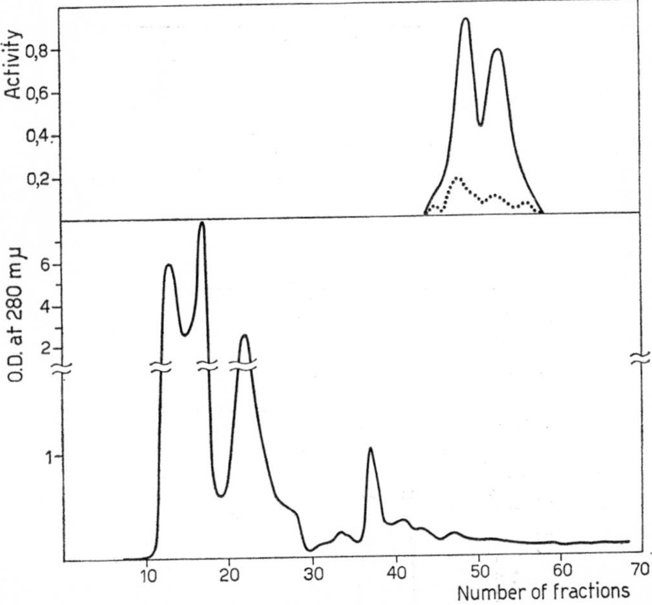


FIG. 3. Chromatography of rat liver extract on CM–cellulose column with a composite potassium phosphate gradient.[12] The eluting buffer was produced with a Varigrad mixing device (Technicon chromatography Corp.). Six chambers of the varigrad were charged in the order with potassium phosphate buffer of the following molarity and pH:

(1) 0.01 M, pH 6.5; (2) 0.01 M, pH 7.3; (3) 0.01 M, pH 8.5;
(4) 0.03 M, pH 8.5; (5) 0.05 M, pH 8.5; (6) 0.05 M, pH 8.5.

Activity in arbitrary units: full line, cystathionase; dotted line, cysteine desulfhydrase.

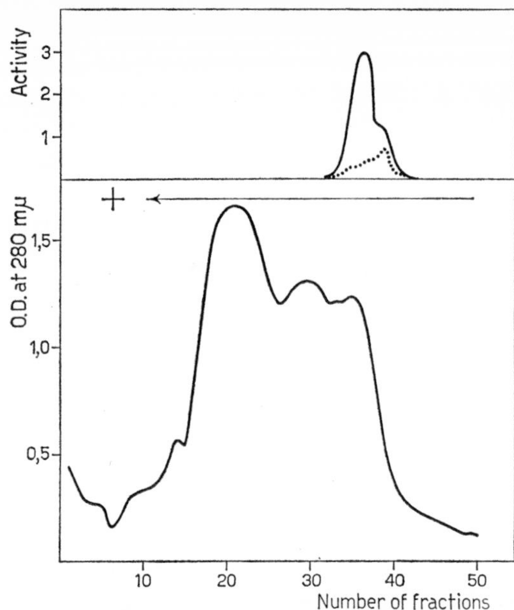


FIG. 4. Column electrophoresis of rat liver extract. Potassium phosphate buffer pH 7.4, 0.01 M. Electrophoresis conditions: borohydrure treated cellulose column 65.1 × 3.8 cm; 800 V; 40 mA; 15 hr.

Activity in arbitrary units: full line, cystathionase; dotted line, cysteine desulfhydrase.

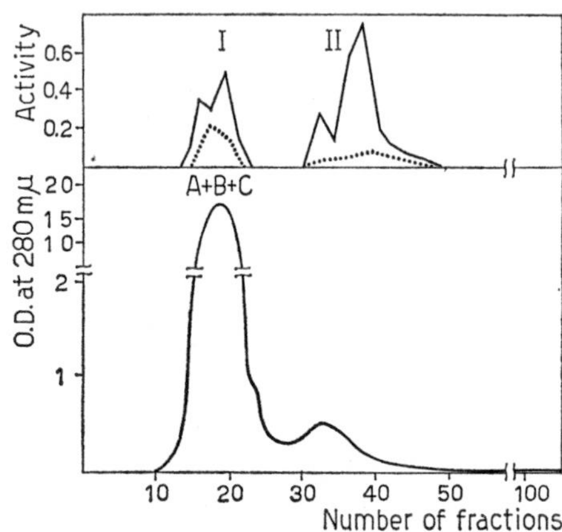


FIG. 5. Chromatography of rat liver extract on CM–cellulose with a potassium phosphate gradient pH 8.5 from 0.01 M to 0.05 M.

Activity in arbitrary units: full line, cystathionase; dotted line, cysteinedesulfhydrase.

By using an alkaline potassium phosphate gradient of concentration we have succeeded in obtaining the separation of the enzyme in two components (Fig. 5). We do not know at present whether the two components are two isoenzymes or whether the separation is the result of a polymerization process. Heterogeneity of cystathionase has actually been observed by Matsuo and Greenberg[8] by sedimentation analysis of their crystalline enzyme. As far as our problem is concerned, both the components decompose the same substrates although the activity ratio with different substrates is different for the two components. As it is seen in Table 1 the highest activity is towards homoserine and cystathionine and therefore the two enzymes have to be regarded as two components of the same enzyme, namely cystathionase. These findings thus demonstrate that a specific enzyme for the desulfhydration of cysteine is lacking in the rat liver and that this reaction is catalysed by cystathionase.

### *Cystine as the Substrate for Cystathionase*

Our group has presented evidence that cystine is cleaved by cystathionase and by a pyridoxal model simulating cystathionase activity, without being previously reduced into cysteine.[13–15] The products of the cleavage of cystine by the enzyme and by the pyridoxal model are : pyruvate, ammonia, and a compound which has been presumed to be the persulfide analogue of cysteine, named thiocysteine. The intermediate production of thiocysteine has been recognized by the occurrence in the reacting mixture of reactions peculiar for polysulfides, like the transulfuration of sulfinates[16] and the cleavage by cyanide.[17] It was also inferred by the appearance of free sulfur, and by the production of ammonia and pyruvate, which are indicative of an $\alpha$, $\beta$-elimination process. Any attempt to isolate thiocysteine from the incubates or to prepare it in the pure form have failed owing to the lability of the compound in water solution.[13]

More recently this type of cleavage of cystine has been confirmed by Flavin[9], using purified cystathionase of bacterial origin. Thiocysteine in this case has been trapped by the addition of iodoacetate and detected by paper electrophoresis in the form of the mixed cysteine–thioglycolic acid disulfide.

Enzymic and model experiments thus indicate that cystine may be easily cleaved by an $\alpha$, $\beta$-elimination reaction according to the formulation :

$$\begin{array}{ll} CH_2\text{—}SS\text{—}CH_2 & \\ | \qquad\qquad | & \\ CH\text{—}NH_2\ CH\text{—}NH_2 & \\ | \qquad\qquad | & \\ COOH \quad COOH & \end{array} \rightarrow \begin{array}{c} CH_2\text{—}SSH \\ | \\ CH\text{—}NH_2 \\ | \\ COOH \\ \text{thiocysteine} \end{array} + \begin{array}{l} CH_3 \\ | \\ CO + NH_3 \\ | \\ COOH \\ \phantom{x} \end{array}$$

If one considers the poor solubility of cystine at the pH prevailing in most of the enzymic incubates, the prompt oxidation of cysteine into cystine by oxygen and a number of other oxidants, the possibility of the oxidation of cysteine by thiol–disulfide exchange,[18] and finally that cysteine, like many other aminothiols, is an inhibitor of cystathionase and pyridoxal enzymes in general[19–22] the easy cleavage of cystine by cystathionase opens the problem of the real substrate for this enzyme. In other words it is possible that cystine and not cysteine is the substrate for cystathionase.

TABLE 2. COMPARATIVE CLEAVAGE OF CYSTINE AND CYSTEINE BY CYSTATHIONASE

Incubation under $N_2$ at 38°, pH 7.4. Values in $\mu$moles or $\mu$atoms of products from 20 $\mu$moles cysteine or 10 $\mu$moles cystine after 6 hr incubation. Enzyme preparation, 50 mg acetone dried rat liver extract, PLP 10 $\mu$g, total vol. 3 ml potassium phosphate buffer 0.1 M (see Ref. 11 for details).

| | Pyruvate | $NH_3$ | $H_2S$ | S |
|---|---|---|---|---|
| Cystine | 4.5 | 9.1 | 1.5 | 5.3 |
| Cysteine | 2.6 | 9.0 | 9.2 | 0.0 |

The products of the cleavage of cystine and cysteine incubated with a partially purified cystathionase under the same conditions are shown in Table 2. It is seen that cystine, although it is very poorly soluble, is cleaved at least as extensively as cysteine. A relevant difference between the two substrates is found in the form of the inorganic sulfur produced, which apparently would indicate that a different enzymic process is operative with the two substrates. With cystine as substrate the main inorganic sulfur product is elementary sulfur while in the case of cysteine it is $H_2S$. Nevertheless this discrepancy may be reconciled if one considers the possibility that cystine is the real substrate also when cysteine is added to the enzyme, while the excess of cysteine is used to reduce elementary sulfur to $H_2S$:

$$2\ \mathrm{R{-}SH} + \mathrm{S} \rightarrow \mathrm{R{-}SS{-}R} + \mathrm{H_2S}$$

In this case a certain amount of cystine is necessary in order to permit the reaction with cystathionase while the cystine used is regenerated by the oxidation of cysteine with sulfur. Since thiocysteine is the precursor of elementary sulfur, and in any case the oxidation of cysteine by elementary sulfur passes through the stage of a polysulfide,[23] we may ascribe to thiocysteine the role of the producer of cystine and $H_2S$ by reacting with cysteine:

$$\mathrm{R{-}SSH} + \mathrm{R{-}SH} \rightarrow \mathrm{R{-}SS{-}R} + \mathrm{H_2S}$$

Thus a cyclic reaction may be envisaged which may account for the indirect desulfhydration of cysteine, provided that a certain amount of cystine is present to function as substrate for cystathionase.

$CH_2$–SH | CH–$NH_2$ | COOH

$CH_2$–SSH | CH–$NH_2$ | COOH

$CH_3$ | CO + $NH_3$ | COOH

spontaneous

cystathionase

$H_2S$

$CH_2$–SS–$CH_2$ | CH–$NH_2$ CH–$NH_2$ | COOH COOH

According to the scheme reported above, two types of enzymic reactions, one for the cleavage of cystine and one for the cleavage of cysteine, need not to be postulated. It is evident that when cystine is the substrate, thiocysteine is produced which, being unstable,[13] decomposes into sulfur and cysteine or into cystine and a polysulfide, which in turn at neutral pH is decomposed into sulfur and $H_2S$ :

$$R\text{—}SSH \rightarrow R\text{—}SH + S$$

$$2\ R\text{—}SSH \rightarrow R\text{—}SS\text{—}R + H_2S_2 \rightarrow H_2S + S$$

This is in accordance with the results listed in Table 2 where a large amount of sulfur and a small amount of $H_2S$ are produced by cystine. When cysteine is the substrate, the presence in the system of a certain amount of cystine to be used as substrate for the enzyme is necessary. In this case the excess of cysteine permits the production of $H_2S$ and the regeneration of cystine.

In order to establish experimentally the validity of the above postulation we have tried to demonstrate the inability of purified cystathionase to cleave cysteine in such a condition that cystine was certainly absent in the incubates. However, we have found it difficult to realize this experiment because cystine may be present in the incubates not only by the oxidation of cysteine but also through a thiol–disulfide exchange of cysteine with the proteins of the enzymic system,[18] or it may be present as an impurity in the substrate or in the enzyme system. We have therefore performed the experiments in the presence of agents capable of reducing any trace of cystine and to keep it in the reduced state in the course of the reaction. Other experiments have been performed in the presence of agents capable of avoiding the regeneration of cystine, once it has been cleaved into thiocysteine. Table 3 illustrates this point.

It is evident that mercaptoethanol leaves almost unmodified the cleavage of homoserine while it strongly depresses the cleavage of cystine by cystathionase. Since the enzyme is not modified by the addition of mercaptoethanol, as is indicated by the experiments with homoserine, this result may be explained only if one takes into account a reaction of mercaptoethanol with the substrate. The only plausible reaction of mercaptoethanol with

TABLE 3. EFFECT OF CERTAIN AGENTS ON THE CLEAVAGE OF CYSTEINE AND HOMOSERINE BY CYSTATHIONASE

Incubation under $N_2$ at 38°, pH 7.4. Values in $\mu$moles of products from 20 $\mu$moles of substrates after 6 hr of incubation. Enzyme preparation, 50 mg of acetone-dried rat liver extract; PLP 10 $\mu$g; total vol. 3 ml; potassium phosphate buffer 0.1 M (see Ref. 24 for details).

| Substrate | Addition | Products | | |
|---|---|---|---|---|
| | | Keto acids | $NH_3$ | $H_2S$ |
| L-Cysteine | — | 3.0 | 8.8 | 9.1 |
| L-Cysteine | Et-SH 1 mmole | 0.4 | 1.1 | 1.0 |
| L-Cysteine | hypo 1 mmole | 0.4 | 2.7 | 0.7 |
| DL-Homoserine | — | 3.6 | 8.7 | — |
| DL-Homoserine | Et-SH 1 mmole | 3.1 | 7.5 | — |
| DL-Homoserine | hypo 1 mmole | 2.2 | 6.7 | — |

Et-SH = mercaptoethanol; hypo = hypotaurine.

cysteine is that of keeping it in the reduced state and eventually reducing any trace of cystine which may be accidentally present in the incubate :[25]

$$R—SS—R + 2\ R'—SH \rightarrow 2\ R—SH + R'—SS—R'$$

The same effect is produced by the addition of a sulfinate like hypotaurine. The inhibitory effect in this case has to be ascribed to the ability of a sulfinate to act as a sulfur acceptor in the transulfuration reaction with organic and inorganic polysulfides :[16,26]

$$R—SSH + R—SO_2H \rightarrow R—SH + R—SO_2SH$$

By reacting with thiocysteine or any other polysulfide which may have been produced from cystine, accidentally present in the incubate, hypotaurine stops the cycle by preventing the regeneration of cystine. The results presented above are therefore consistent with the proposed indispensable role of cystine for the desulfhydration of cysteine by cystathionase.

### *Model Experiments*

It is known that cystine is extensively cleaved by pyridoxal at a temperature of 38° in the presence of catalytic amounts of copper ions.[15] This reaction mimics the cleavage of cystine operated by cystathionase and has been carefully studied in order to disclose the mechanism of the breakdown of cystine by pyridoxal catalysts in general. We have now observed that cystine is also cleaved by pyridoxal phosphate even at room temperature and without the presence of added metal ions, provided the reactants are at a suitable concentration.

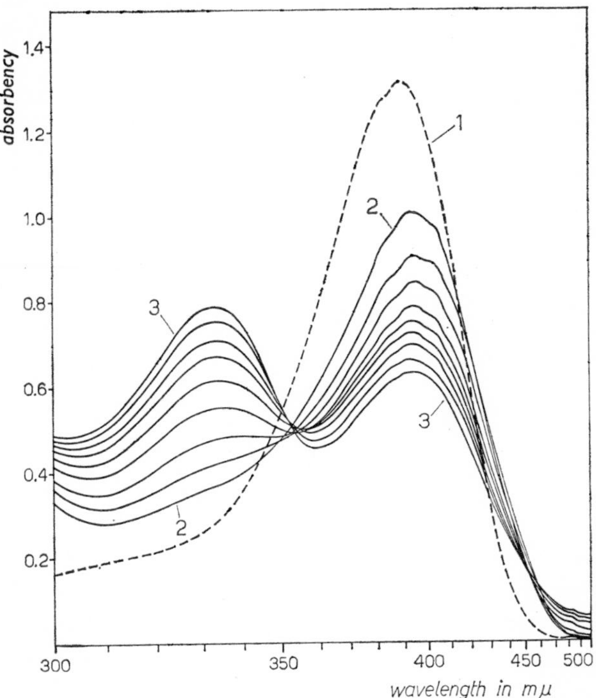


FIG. 6. Absorption spectrum curves of a solution of pyridoxal phosphate ($10^{-3}$ M) and cystine ($10^{-3}$ M) in sodium phosphate buffer 0.5 M pH 8.5. The spectra were obtained with a Beckman DK 2 recording spectrophotometer. Light path 0.2 mm; scanning time 2 min; temp. 20–24°. Curve 1: pyridoxal phosphate without the addition of cystine; curve 2: as soon as possible after the addition of cystine; remaining curves up to 3: at 15 min intervals after the addition of cysteine.

When equimolar amounts of cystine and pyridoxal at a final concentration of $10^{-3}$ M for both compounds are dissolved in 0.5 M phosphate buffer pH 8.5, and the absorbency between 300 and 500 mμ is registered at intervals of time in a cuvette of 2 mm light path, the picture seen in Fig. 6 is obtained. The following changes are apparent :

(1) The 390 mμ peak of pyridoxal phosphate is shifted by 5–10 mμ towards longer wavelengths and its extinction decreases with time.

(2) A new peak appears at 330 mμ which increases with time, paralleling the decrease of the 390 mμ peak.

(3) The solution becomes turbid owing to the production of elementary sulfur, as it is also indicated by the increased absorbency in the range of 500 m$\mu$.

Control experiments are reported in Fig. 7. This figure indicates that under the same conditions, valine, used as a representative of a non-sulfur

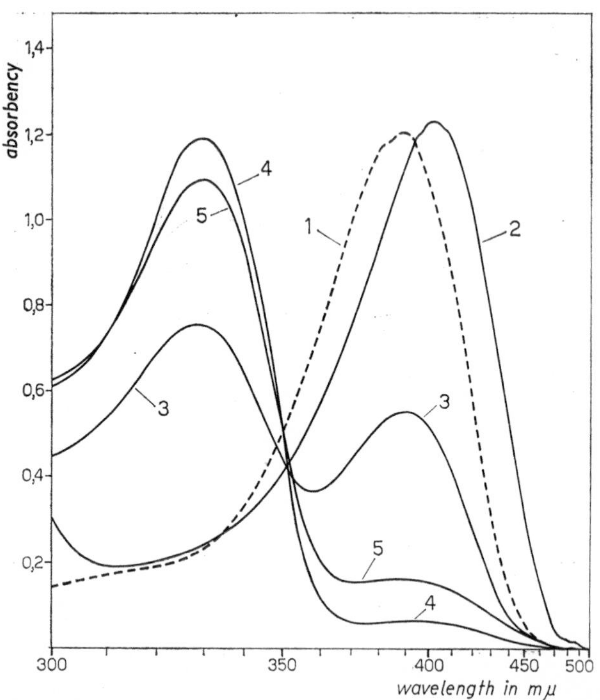


FIG. 7. Absorption spectrum curves of pyridoxal phosphate with cysteine and valine. The same conditions as in Fig. 6. Curve 1: pyridoxal phosphate ($10^{-3}$ M) without any addition; Curve 2: with the addition of valine ($2 \times 10^{-3}$ M); Curve 3: with the addition of cysteine ($2 \times 10^{-3}$ M) as soon as added; Curve 4: the same as in curve 3, 30 min after the addition of cysteine; Curve 5: the same as in curve 3, 2 hr after the addition of cysteine.

amino acid, produces the curve of a typical Schiff base as shown by the shift of the pyridoxal phosphate peak to 410 m$\mu$, which is stable for long time. Cysteine on the other hand abolishes the peak at 390 m$\mu$ and produces a large 330 m$\mu$ peak. This behaviour of cysteine, which has been observed by previous workers,[27] is usually interpreted by the production of a thiazolidine between cysteine and pyridoxal phosphate. Since the thiazolidine is in equilibrium with its components and since we have performed the experiments in the presence of air, the slow reappearance of the 390 m$\mu$ peak and the simultaneous slow decrease of the 330 m$\mu$ peak are due to the partial oxidation of cysteine to cystine in the second part of the observation period.

In the light of the above findings we may now reasonably explain the changes observed in Fig. 6: (1) when cystine is added to pyridoxal phosphate a Schiff base is initially produced as indicated by the prompt shift of the 390 mμ peak towards longer wavelengths; (2) in this form cystine is unstable and is broken down into thiocysteine, ammonia and pyruvate; (3) thiocysteine decomposes into cysteine and elementary sulfur as indicated by the production of turbidity; (4) cysteine then reacts with pyridoxal phosphate producing the thiazolidine responsible for the 330 mμ peak.

TABLE 4. COMPOUNDS PRODUCED AFTER THE INCUBATION OF CYSTINE AND CYSTEINE WITH PYRIDOXAL PHOSPHATE UNDER VARIOUS CONDITIONS

Pyridoxal phosphate 2 μmoles; cystine 2 μmoles; cysteine 4 μmoles; sodium phosphate buffer 0.5 M, pH 8.5; total volume 2 ml. Values in μmoles or μatoms of products after 2 hr of incubation at 20–24°.

| | Addition | Pyruvate | $NH_3$ | S | $H_2S$ |
|---|---|---|---|---|---|
| Cystine | — | 0.67 | 0.73 | 0.1 | 0 |
| Cystine | 0.2 μmoles $CuSO_4$ | 1.06 | 1.21 | 1.5 | 0 |
| Cystine | 4 μmoles iodacetate | 1.16 | 1.07 | 0.31 | 0 |
| Cysteine | — | 0 | 0 | 0 | 0 |
| Cysteine | 0.2 μmoles $CuSO_4$ | 0.30 | 0.77 | 1.1 | 0 |

The appearance of the 330 mμ peak and the decline of that at 390 mμ thus represent the documentation that cystine has been extensively broken-down to the point that cysteine is produced in the absence of any reducing agent. On the contrary, cysteine when added to pyridoxal phosphate is not cleaved under the same conditions used for cystine, it produces a thiazolidine ring which is in equilibrium with its reactants. The changes observed in Fig. 7 when cysteine is added to pyridoxal phosphate may be actually interpreted on the basis of a partial oxidation of cysteine with a consecutive decrease of the thiazolidine.

The data collected in Table 4 indicate that the above interpretation is essentially correct. After 2 hr of incubation with pyridoxal phosphate, products of decomposition are detected only in the case of cystine. The ratio of the amount of the products is very close to 1 mole of ammonia and 1 atom of sulfur for any mole of pyruvate produced. The data presented are thus consistent with the assumption that cystine has been cleaved by pyridoxal phosphate through an $\alpha$, $\beta$-elimination reaction to pyruvate, ammonia and thiocysteine and that the model system operates in a fashion very similar to the enzymic process.

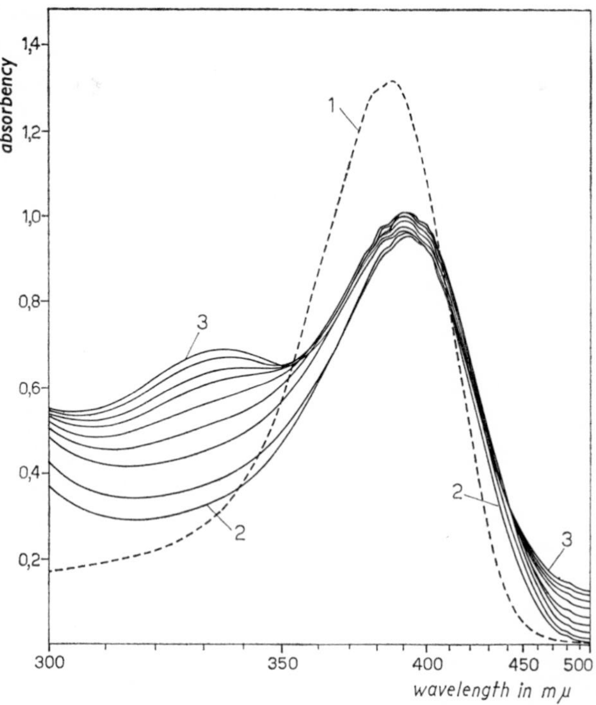


FIG. 8. Absorption spectrum curves of pyridoxal phosphate ($10^{-3}$ M) and cystine ($10^{-3}$ M) in sodium phosphate buffer 0.5 M pH 8.5 in the presence of $10^{-4}$ M $CuSO_4$. The same conditions as in Fig. 6. Curve 1: pyridoxal phosphate; Curves 2 to 3 at 15 min of intervals after the addition of cystine (curve 2 as soon as possible after the addition).

The addition of Cu ions is not necessary for the breakdown of cystine as, was the case with the pyridoxal model.[15] Nevertheless the addition of catalytic amounts of $CuSO_4$ accelerates the decomposition of cystine while it allows also the decomposition of cysteine. However, the effect of copper in this case seems to be that of a catalyst for the reoxidation of cysteine to cystine more than that of a chelate-forming agent. This is shown in Fig. 8 where the spectrophotometric pattern of the mixture of pyridoxal phosphate with cystine in the presence of Cu ions is followed with time. Although the cleavage of cystine is more extensive than in the absence of Cu ions as indicated in

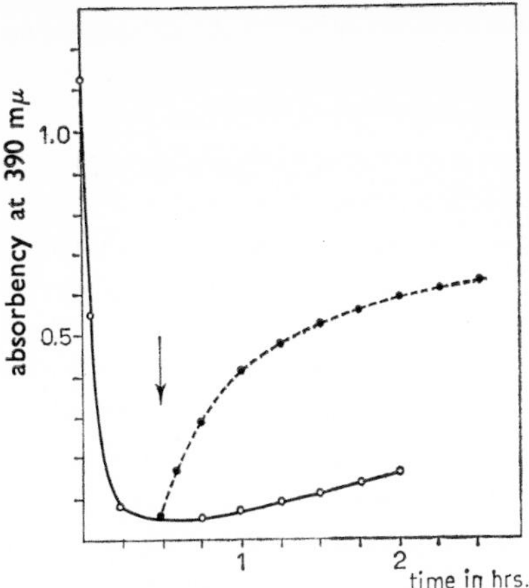


FIG. 9. Variation of the absorbency at 390 mμ as a function of time after the addition of cysteine ($2 \times 10^{-3}$ M) to pyridoxal phosphate ($10^{-3}$ M) in the presence (dotted line) and in the absence (full line) of Cu ions. At the arrow, $CuSO_4$ ($10^{-4}$ M) was added. Experimental conditions as in Fig. 6.

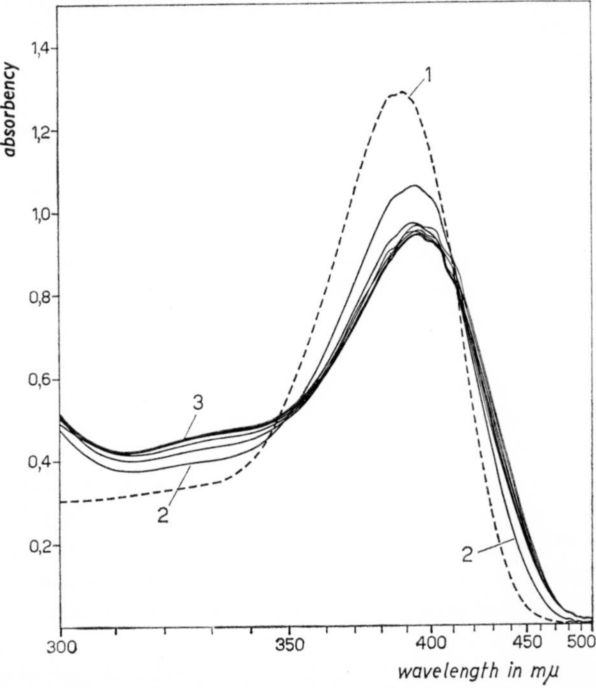


FIG. 10. Absorption spectrum curves of pyridoxal phosphate ($10^{-3}$ M) and cystine ($10^{-3}$ M) in sodium phosphate buffer 0.5 M pH 8.5 in the presence of sodium mono-iodacetate ($2 \times 10^{-3}$ M). The same conditions as in Fig. 6. Curve 1: pyridoxal phosphate; Curves 2 to 3, at 15 min of intervals after the addition of cystine (curve 2 as soon as possible after the addition).

Table 4, Fig. 8 indicates that the amount of cysteine present is lower. This is suggested by the relatively lower absorption at 330 mμ and higher at 390 mμ than in the absence of copper. The presence of copper seems to have hastened the reoxidation of cysteine to cystine with the consequence that less pyridoxal phosphate is trapped in the thiazolidine form. Figure 9 indeed shows that cysteine when bound to pyridoxal phosphate in the thiazolidine form is oxidized in the presence of copper ions. The analysis of the decomposition products reported in Table 4 for cysteine indicates that cysteine, if allowed to be oxidized by copper ions, is also cleaved by pyridoxal phosphate.

The interpretation that the accelerating effect of copper ions is that of an oxidizing agent for cysteine more than that of a chelating agent is supported by the results obtained in the experiments performed in the presence of monoiodacetate. Figure 10 shows that in the presence of iodacetate less thiazolidine is produced than in its absence owing to the reaction of the alkylating agent with cysteine or thiocysteine. Nevertheless as it is seen in Table 4 the decomposition of cystine is more extensive than in the absence of iodacetate. The lower production of sulfur may be due to reaction of iodacetate with thiocysteine as indicated by Flavin[9] in the case of the enzymic experiments. Thus it seems that the elimination of cysteine either by its faster reoxidation into cystine by copper ions or by trapping with iodacetate speeds the cleavage of cystine. This may possibly be due to the fact that, when cysteine is present in the incubates in low amounts, a higher amount of pyridoxal phosphate is available for reacting with cystine.

## DISCUSSION

It is always a hard task to establish at what point one can safely say that two reactions are catalyzed by the same enzyme. There is always the possibility that a procedure not yet experienced may accomplish the separation of two activities which has been unsuccessfully attempted by previous means. We believe, however, that the evidence presented in this paper makes very remote the possibility that cysteine desulfhydrase and cystathionase are not identical enzymes.

Obviously this conclusion leads to the consequences that the name, cysteine desulfhydrase, as applied to a specific enzyme in the rat liver, has to be rejected, and that cystathionase among the many reactions which it is known to catalyse takes also the care of the desulfhydration of cysteine. According to Flavin[9] this conclusion has to be extended also to the system present in *E. coli*.

Enzymic and model systems suggest that cystine and not cysteine is the compound cleaved by cystathionase. The products detected when cystine is cleaved enzymically or by the model are consonant with an $\alpha$, $\beta$-elimination reaction. The product of this reaction should be thiocysteine. This compound however, has not been isolated and its presence has been inferred by the detection of reactions indicative of the production of a polysulfide, like the transulfuration of sulfinates to thiosulfonates, the reaction with cyanide to produce thiocyanate, and the decomposition into elementary sulfur. The intermediate formation of thiocysteine permits us to understand the cleavage of cysteine through a cyclic reaction where cystine is the real substrate for cystathionase. Evidence is obtained indicating that this cycle is operative in the enzymic system we have studied. In the intact cell, however, both the oxidation of cysteine to cystine and the reduction of thiocysteine or sulfur into $H_2S$ may be of course performed also by other means.

## REFERENCES

1. C. Fromageot, E. Wookey and P. Chaix; *Enzymologia* **9**, 198 (1940).
2. C. V. Smythe; *J. Biol. Chem.* **142**, 387 (1942).
3. F. Binkley; *J. Biol. Chem.* **186**, 287 (1950).
4. M. Suda, T. Saigo and K. Ichihara; *Med. J. Osaka Univ.* **5**, 127 (1954).
5. F. Chatagner, J. Labousse, O. Trautman and B. Jolles-Bergeret; *Compt. rend.* **253**, 742 (1961).
6. E. V. Goryachenkova; *Biochimiia* (Engl. edit.) **26**, 480 (1961).
7. J. Brüggeman and M. Waldschmidt; *Biochem. Z.* **335**, 408 (1962).
8. Y. Matsuo and D. M. Greenberg; *J. Biol. Chem.* **230**, 545 (1958).
9. M. Flavin; *J. Biol. Chem.* **237**, 768 (1962).
10. Y. Matsuo and D. M. Greenberg; *J. Biol. Chem.* **234**, 516 (1959).
11. D. Cavallini, B. Mondovì, C. De Marco and A. Scioscia-Santoro; *Enzymologia* **24**, 253 (1962).
12. In the press.
13. D. Cavallini, C. De Marco, B. Mondovì and B. G. Mori; *Enzymologia* **22**, 161 (1960).
14. B. Mondovì and C. De Marco; *Enzymologia* **23**, 156 (1961).
15. D. Cavallini, C. De Marco and B. Mondovì; *Arch. Biochem. Biophys.* **87**, 281 (1960).
16. C. De Marco, M. Coletta and D. Cavallini; *Arch. Biochem. Biophys.* **93**, 179 (1961).
17. J. W. Hylin and J. L. Wood; *J. Biol. Chem.* **234**, 2141 (1959).
18. E. Jensen; *Science* **130**, 1319 (1959).
19. Y. Matsuo; *J. Am. Chem. Soc.* **79**, 2011 (1957).
20. V. Du Vigneaud, E. J. Kuchinskas and A. Hovarth; *Arch. Biochem. Biophys.* **69**, 130 (1957).
21. S. R. Mardashev and Chao Ti'eng-rei; *Doklady Akad. Nauk S.S.S.R.* (Engl. Ed.) **133**, 147 (1961).
22. C. De Marco, B. Mondovì and D. Cavallini; *Biochem. Pharmacol.* **2**, 509 (1962).
23. W. A. Pryor; *Mechanisms of Sulfur Reactions*, p. 156, McGraw-Hill, New York (1962).
24. D. Cavallini, B. Mondovì, C. De Marco and A. Scioscia-Santoro; *Arch. Biochem. Biophys.* **96**, 456 (1962).
25. E. S. G. Barron; *Advances in Enzymol.* **11**, 201 (1951).
26. C. De Marco, M. Coletta and D. Cavallini; *Experientia* **18**, 117 (1962).
27. M. V. Buell and R. E. Hansen; *J. Am. Chem. Soc.* **82**, 6042 (1960).

## DISCUSSION

Dr. Flavin:

I have one technical question. We have found that it is rather difficult to get protein to stick on carboxymethyl cellulose at high pH. Even at pH 6.5 a single enzyme may partially wash through with the solvent front and partially be eluted in a second peak. I wonder whether you had re-run the two different cystathionase fractions to see whether each appear again exclusively at its original position?

I would also like to emphasize our agreement with Dr. Cavallini about the specificity of cystathionine cleavage enzymes toward cystine. I don't know whether anyone still believes that cysteine is directly decomposed by liver cystathionase. With a *Neurospora* enzyme resembling the latter in many respects, cysteine can be shown not to be a substrate simply by anaerobic incubation with Fieser solution. Homocysteine is not decomposed even under aerobic conditions. *E. coli* contains a cystathionine cleavage enzyme of opposite polarity. It has been shown that mutants having this enzyme also have a reduced " cysteine desulphydrase " content.

DR. CAVALLINI:

We have not re-chromatographed the two components of cystathionase. However, the separation in two components is apparent also in the chromatograms of rat liver extract eluted with a less alkaline buffer as seen in the figures I have shown.

F. CHATAGNER:

As additional evidence for the identity of cysteine desulfurase (or desulfhydrase) and cystathionase-homoserine desaminase crystallized by Matsuo and Greenberg I shall indicate some other results. We observed (F. Chatagner and O. Trautmann, *Nature* **194**, 1281, 1962) that in the liver of rats killed 4 hr after a single injection of DL-homoserine, according to the method employed by Knox *et al.* in studies of induction of tryptophan pyrrolase and other enzymes, the levels of desulfuration of cysteine by the non-particulate fraction and of deamination of homoserine are significantly increased; similar findings were obtained after injection of L-methionine while L-alanine and DL-tryptophane were ineffective. These results strongly suggest that desulfuration (or desulfhydration) of cysteine and deamination of homoserine are catalyzed by a single enzyme which is an adaptive one.

DR. CAVALLINI

This information represents a valuable support, obtained by a biological method, on the identity of the two enzymes we have obtained by more traditional procedures.

Other questions by Drs. Fromageot, Chapeville and Snell have not been submitted in written form.

# MICROBIAL TRANS-SULFURATION AND THE MECHANISMS OF SOME PYRIDOXAL PHOSPHATE POTENTIATED ELIMINATION AND REPLACEMENT REACTIONS

by MARTIN FLAVIN

Enzyme Section, National Heart Institute,
Bethesda, Maryland, U.S.A.

" TRANS-SULFURATION " is a term which has been applied to the biological transfer of sulfur between the 3- and 4-carbon amino acids, cysteine and homocysteine. This process is mediated by a series of enzymatic elimination and replacement reactions of which most, though perhaps not all, are potentiated by pyridoxal-P. Before describing some recent studies relating to the mechanisms of these reactions, it may be well to review the current status of microbial trans-sulfuration.

## TRANS-SULFURATION IN *NEUROSPORA*

The requirement for methionine in the diets of animals reflects their ability to carry out trans-sulfuration only in the direction homocysteine → cysteine.[1] This transformation has been shown to be mediated by two separable, pyridoxal-P dependent liver enzymes.[2,3] The first catalyzes replacement of the $\beta$-hydroxyl group of serine by SH of homocysteine (Eq. 1), and the second catalyzes $\gamma$-elimination* from the resultant unsymmetrical thioether,

$$\mathrm{HOOCCH(NH_2)CH_2OH + HSCH_2CH_2CH(NH_2)COOH \rightarrow H_2O + HOOCCH(NH_2)CH_2SCH_2CH_2CH(NH_2)COOH} \quad (1)$$

$\beta$-replacement

cystathionine, forming cysteine, $\alpha$-ketobutyrate, and ammonia (Eq. 2). The enzymes also rapidly catalyze dehydration of, respectively, serine and homoserine.

$$\mathrm{Cystathionine + H_2O \rightarrow HOOCCH(NH_2)CH_2SH + NH_3 + CH_3CH_2COCOOH} \quad (2)$$

$\gamma$-elimination

*The term " $\gamma$-elimination " is used here, not in the usual chemical sense of a 1, 3-elimination, but only to indicate that the electronegative leaving group is on the fourth carbon of the amino acid.

Until recently, microbial trans-sulfuration has been formulated chiefly in terms of analogy to liver, and of patterns of nutritional requirement and metabolite accumulation in methionine-requiring mutants of *Neurospora crassa*,[4,5] to which this discussion will mostly be confined. The first organic sulfur compound formed in this case is presumably cysteine,[6] though as yet its formation from serine and sulfide has not been shown in *Neurospora*, nor has a gene been identified for such a reaction. The transfer of sulfur from cysteine to homocysteine (Eq. 3 and 4), the reverse of the process

$$HOOCCH(NH_2)CH_2CH_2OH + HSCH_2CH(NH_2)COOH \rightarrow H_2O + \\ + \text{cystathionine} \quad (3)$$

γ-replacement

$$\text{Cystathionine} + H_2O \rightarrow HOOCCH(NH_2)CH_2CH_2SH + NH_3 + \\ + CH_3COCOOH \quad (4)$$

β-elimination

occurring in liver, is supported by the identification of four different genetic loci.[5] Mutants at any of three of these (me-3, me-5, me-7), each of which is on a different chromosome, will grow when provided with methionine, homocysteine or L-cystathionine, but not with cysteine (block in reaction 3). In one case (me-5) they have been shown to accumulate small amounts of homoserine and threonine.[7] The participation of homoserine is also supported by the fact that mutants blocked in its synthesis require methionine as well as threonine.[8] Mutants at the me-2 locus grow when provided with methionine or homocysteine, but not L-cystathionine (block in reaction 4), which they accumulate in large amounts.[4]

Some evidence has indicated that *Neurospora* may also contain the two enzymes studied in liver,[4,9] though trans-sulfuration is probably not reversible in all micro-organisms. However, no *Neurospora* mutants are known for this reverse pathway, which is not essential for laboratory growth on minimal medium, though it might confer a selective advantage in nature.

These results have suggested a schematic pathway (Fig. 1) in which the reversible transfer of sulfur between cysteine and homocysteine is mediated by four different, irreversible reactions (Eq. 1–4), presumably catalyzed by four different enzymes. Several early observations have stimulated speculation as to the number of enzyme components which might be involved in the hypothetical process described in Fig. 1. These deserve brief mention because the number of enzymes involved is still, in fact, uncertain. Catalysis of several of the reactions by a single enzyme, or modified forms thereof, might have unusual implications for metabolic control, and would have some bearing on the reaction mechanisms.

One such observation was a report that an me-7 mutant, blocked, by nutritional criteria, in cystathionine synthesis from cysteine, lacked also the homologous, non-essential elimination reaction from cystathionine to cysteine.[9] The implication that two enzymes might catalyze homologous pairs of eliminations and replacements is indicated by the dashed line in Fig. 1.

A second observation was the discovery of an unlinked supressor mutation capable of partial restoration of prototrophy when present in mutants from

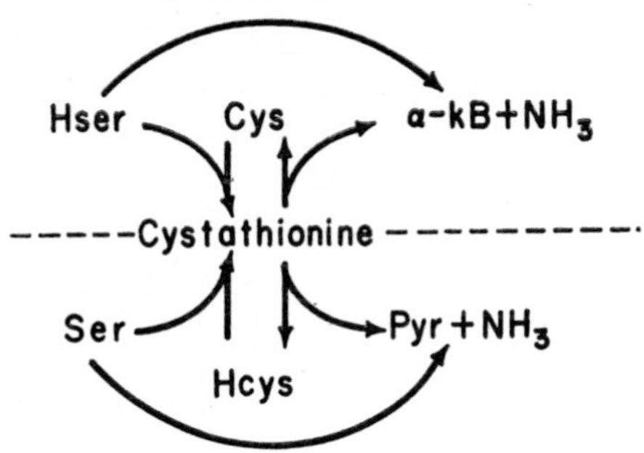


FIG. 1.

either locus me-2 or me-7,[10] but not me-5.[9] There are probably many possible explanations, one of which might be a structural alteration in an unidentified enzyme allowing it to catalyze homoserine (or X-homoserine) + $S^{2-} \rightarrow$ homocysteine. However, this observation has also led to a suggestion that a single enzyme might catalyze non-homologous $\beta$-elimination and $\gamma$-replacement.[11] In this case the enzyme would presumably resemble hemoglobin in being composed of multiple unlike subunits.

## REACTIONS AND ENZYME COMPONENTS

With this introduction, we would like to describe some enzymatic studies of trans-sulfuration in *Neurospora* from the standpoint, first, of the existence of the reactions shown in Eqs. (1) to (4), and of the enzyme components involved in their catalysis. The reactions of $\beta$- or $\gamma$-elimination may be investigated by measuring the proportions either of cysteine and homocysteine, or of pyruvate and $\alpha$-ketobutyrate, liberated from cystathionine, and we have routinely determined the proportions of the $\alpha$-keto acids. These can be accurately determined in mixtures by a procedure based on their differing $K_m$ and $V_{\max}$ values in the reaction with lactic dehydrogenase.[12] A sulfhydryl trapping reagent must be present in the reaction mixture, since both mercaptan products, after air oxidation to disulfides (which is especially difficult to avoid with cysteine), become substrates for a cystathionine cleavage enzyme and in turn liberate $\alpha$-keto acid.[13]

If iodoacetate is employed as the sulfhydryl trap, suitable extracts of wild-type *Neurospora* liberate variable but roughly comparable proportions of the two keto acids from cystathionine. The enzymatic activity can be separated into two fairly well resolved peaks by salt and DEAE fractionation (steps 2 and 4b as described for purification of "$\gamma$-enzyme"[13]), which respectively catalyze about 90 per cent $\beta$- or $\gamma$-elimination.

The $\beta$-enzyme has as yet been little studied. It probably decomposes L-serine, but not L-homoserine. Its ability to decompose cysteine or homocystine is uncertain; it is inhibited by aromatic disulfides, as well as by *p*-chromomercuriphenylsulfonate and by N-ethylmaleimide.[12] If the iodoacetate in the reaction mixture is replaced by N-ethylmaleimide, or if $\beta$-enzyme is preincubated with the latter, and excess inhibitor removed by dialysis, a small residual $\gamma$-activity remains, which could be attributed to contamination with the $\gamma$-enzyme.

The $\gamma$-enzyme has been purified 400-fold,[13] and has been used in the studies which will be described below. It appears truly to catalyze a heterogeneous decomposition of cystathionine. In the presence of N-ethylmaleimide the enzyme liberates about 3 per cent of homocysteine, at all stages of purification (as will be seen, the apparent liberation of 10 per cent of pyruvate is misleading). The proportion of $\beta$-elimination is higher in the presence of iodoacetate, even with the most purified fractions isolated from a type of extract in which $\beta$-enzyme seems to be essentially absent.[13] The characteristic leakiness of me-2 mutants, which lack $\beta$-enzyme,[9] is therefore not surprising. We have now confirmed the absence of $\beta$-enzyme from me-2.[12] Our previous error was due to mis-typing of the me-2 mutant used at that time. We have not, however, been able to confirm the absence of $\gamma$-enzyme from me-7 (K79, 4894).[14]

Certain ambiguities concerning the separate identities of $\beta$- and $\gamma$-enzymes[14] might be mentioned now since, perhaps fortuitously, it is so far in me-7 mutants that they have been observed. These can be illustrated by an enzyme fraction from K79 which catalyzes 93 per cent $\beta$-elimination in the presence of iodoacetate and 92 per cent $\gamma$-elimination in the presence of N-ethylmaleimide, the rates of total keto acid formation being not much different under the two conditions. Apparent transformation of $\beta$- $\rightarrow$ $\gamma$-enzyme has also been observed after storage of the former. It has not been possible, by incubating spontaneously present $\gamma$-enzyme with mercaptans, to observe any significant increase in the per cent of $\beta$-elimination. Interpretations which rest on rates of reaction in the presence of N-ethylmaleimide must be guarded, because this reagent has many diverse effects on cystathionine cleavage (see below). But the possibility must be considered that $\beta$-enzyme is susceptible to transformation at least into a, if not into the, $\gamma$-enzyme.

As yet little is known about the two replacement reactions (Eqs. 1 and 3). Beta-replacement can readily be demonstrated in extracts of wild type, by the incorporation into cystathionine of serine-$C^{14}$ or homocysteine-$S^{35}$.[15]

Requirements have not been established, except for the cosubstrate. The presence of this reaction in me-2 mutant extracts suggests that β-elimination and β-replacement are not catalyzed by the same enzyme.[15] However, the reaction does seem to be catalyzed by highly purified (step 4b) γ-enzyme preparations.[15] We have not detected it in *E. coli* W extracts, but its absence is not certain, because we have also been unable to repeat, with wild type, the synthesis by γ-replacement which has been reported (see below).[15] *E. coli* extracts appear also to catalyze pure β-elimination from cystathionine,[15] in confirmation of previous reports.[16] This β-elimination is not affected by N-ethylmaleimide or aromatic disulfides.[15]

It has not, until now, been possible to show any incorporation of homoserine-$C^{14}$ or cysteine-$S^{35}$ into cystathionine with cell-free preparations of *Neurospora*. Recently, Rowbury has briefly reported the occurrence of this γ-replacement reaction with enzyme preparations from an *E. coli* mutant.[17] This interesting report indicates that at least two enzymes are involved, the first catalyzing the formation of an unidentified intermediate from homoserine and succinate, which in the presence of the second enzyme reacts with cysteine to form cystathionine.[18] The report indicates that pyridoxal-P may not be a cofactor for the latter reaction.[17]

## PYRIDOXAL-P AND γ-REPLACEMENT REACTIONS

These preliminary results prompt a mention of some questions connected with the role of pyridoxal-P in γ-replacement reactions. Thermodynamically, formation of a thioether from an alcohol and a mercaptan is strongly exergonic.[19] Figures 2 and 3 illustrate, in terms of cystathionine synthesis and cleavage, the chemical plausibility of pyridoxal-P catalysis of γ-replacement. The reaction is considered to occur by coupled elimination and addition. Figure 2 shows some alternative mechanisms for γ-elimination from cystathionine, the relevant portion being I → II → VI → VII. Synthesis of cystathionine by γ-replacement (Fig. 3, VI → XI) involves a parallel elimination from homoserine (Fig. 3, VI → VIII), followed by an exact reversal (Fig. 3, VIII → XI) of the above steps in Fig. 2. If an enzyme catalyzing γ-elimination from cystathionine were found able also to dehydrate homoserine, nothing would apparently be lacking to prevent the same enzyme from synthesizing cystathionine. This is in fact what has been reported for liver cystathionine cleavage enzyme.[20] We have confirmed that this enzyme (sent to us by Dr. D. M. Greenberg) can incorporate labeled homoserine and labeled cysteine into a compound chromatographically similar to cystathionine.[15] The synthetic reaction is very slow, though cysteine markedly inhibits homoserine dehydrase activity.[20]

The logical expectation that microbial trans-sulfuration would be mediated by a comparable enzyme, so modified as to favor the synthetic reaction,

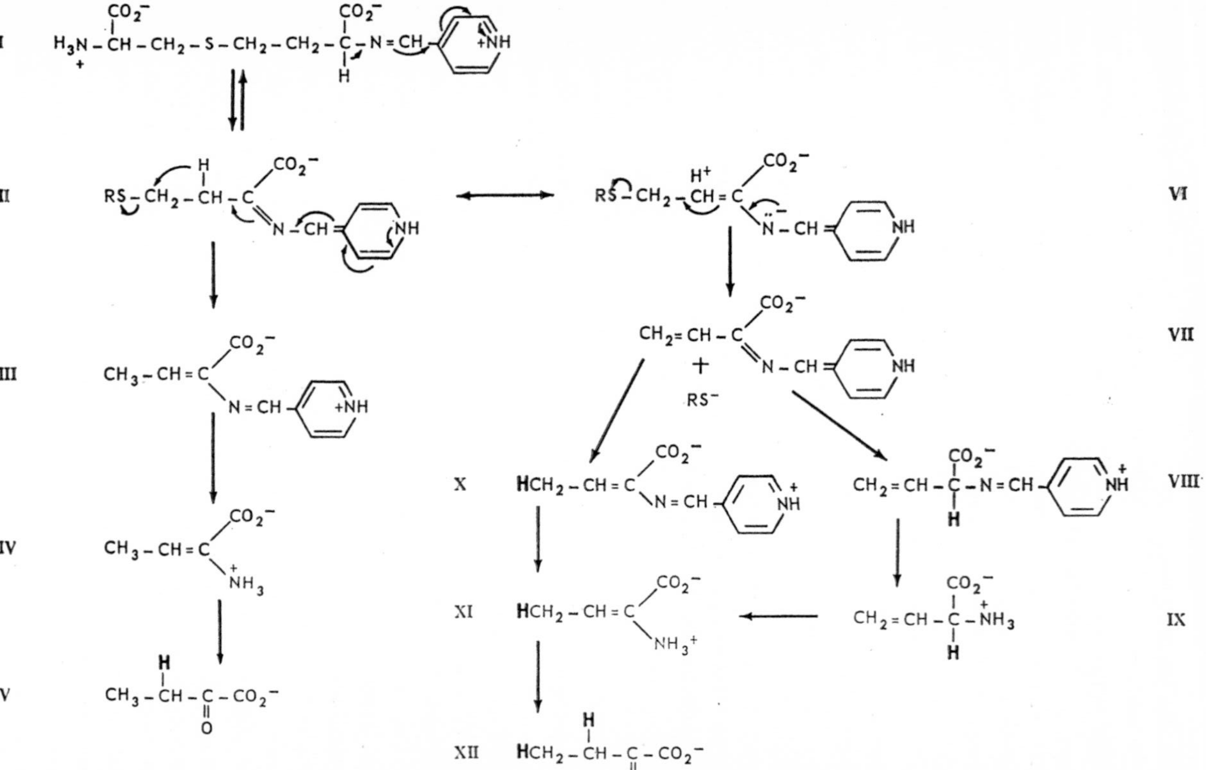


FIG. 2. Cystathionine cleavage by $\gamma$-elimination. Hydrogen residues originating in the solvent are shown in bold print. Pyridoxal-P substituents have been omitted for convenience.

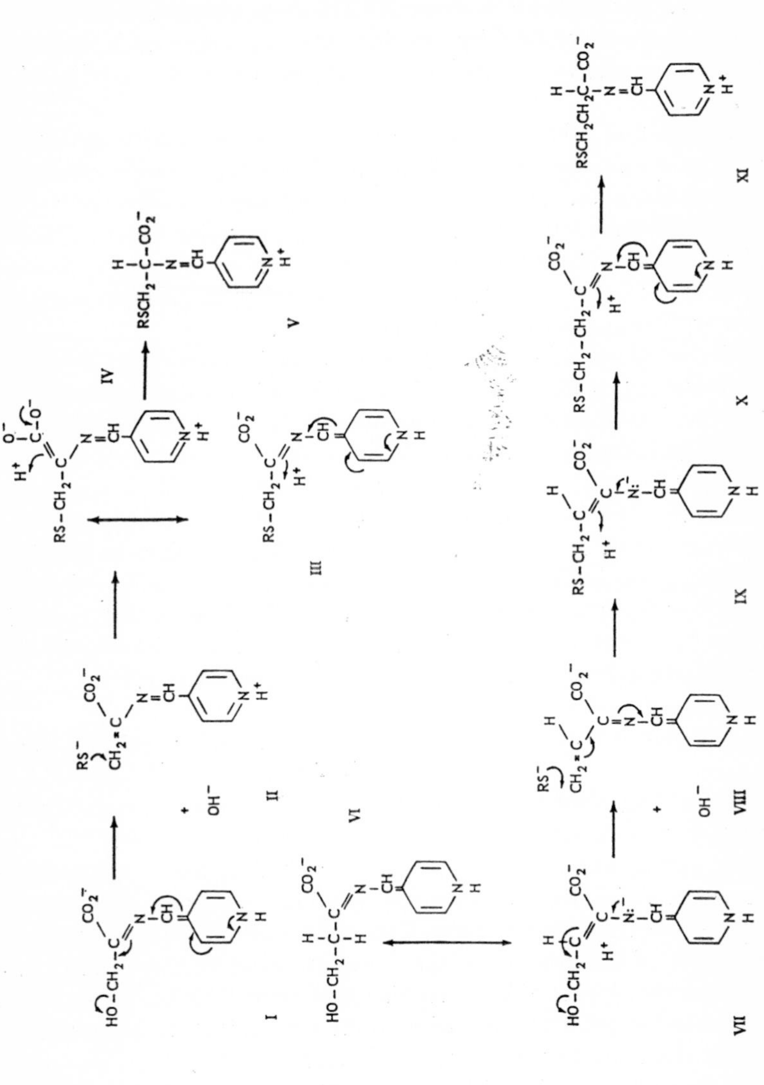

FIG. 3. Cystathionine synthesis by $\beta$- or $\gamma$-replacement.

seems to be incorrect. Like the liver enzyme, γ-enzyme from *Neurospora* specifically dehydrates L-homoserine,[12,13] though relatively very slowly. We have not been able to detect any synthesis of, or exchange of cysteine into, cystathionine by this enzyme,[15] under the same conditions used for the liver enzyme. The presence in *Neurospora* of three genetic loci affecting the formation of cystathionine from cysteine[5] has long suggested it might be a complicated process; the suggestion finds substance in the results of Rowbury with *E. coli*.[17,18]

It is curious that, with the single exception mentioned above, pyridoxal-P enzymes have not been reported, to our knowledge, which catalyze γ-replacement reactions. The absence of such enzymes is emphasized by cases of enzymatic β-replacement (Fig. 3, I → V), such as serine hydroxyl replacement by $H_2S$,[6] or $CH_3SH$,[21] where analogous reactions of homoserine would be useful to the cell if they occurred, and would yield products for which enzymes are known which catalyze γ-elimination.[13,22]

One factor which might account for more facile catalysis of β- than of γ-replacement by pyridoxal-P would be participation of the carboxyl group in resonance stabilization of an intermediate in the former case (Fig. 3, IV). A recent example of similar potentiation of an enzymatic reaction by an intermediary carboxylate dianion is in the Michael addition of ammonia to mesaconate.[23] The carboxyl group could not have a comparable role in γ-replacement (Fig. 3, VI → XI). On the other hand it might be mentioned that similar activation energies have been observed for β- and γ-*elimination* reactions by the same enzyme (see below). The implication that β-addition might not be an exact reversal of β-elimination may be of interest from the standpoint of catalysis of both reactions by the same enzyme.[3,24]

## COUPLED γ-ELIMINATION AND β-ADDITION IN THREONINE SYNTHESIS

The preceeding comments on the problem of γ-replacement catalysis by pyridoxal-P may be clarified by reference to a *Neurospora* enzyme which catalyzes γ-elimination but β-addition, a disarticulated " replacement ". This enzyme, which has been purified 500-fold,[25] catalyzes elimination of orthophosphate from the phosphate ester of homoserine, coupled to effective isomerization of the primary to the secondary alcohol, threonine (Fig. 4). Another relevant aspect of the threonine synthetase reaction is the question it poses as to the point of bifurcation in the mechanisms of the pyridoxal-P dependent reactions by which homoserine (or cystathionine) yields α-keto-butyrate, but P-homoserine yields threonine; and as to the respective roles of enzyme, coenzyme and substrate phosphate at this bifurcation point.

This reaction proceeds to completion without evident dissociation of any intermediates from the enzyme; no overall reversibility could be shown with threonine-$C^{14}$ (ref. 12). The mechanism has been studied so far mainly

BB

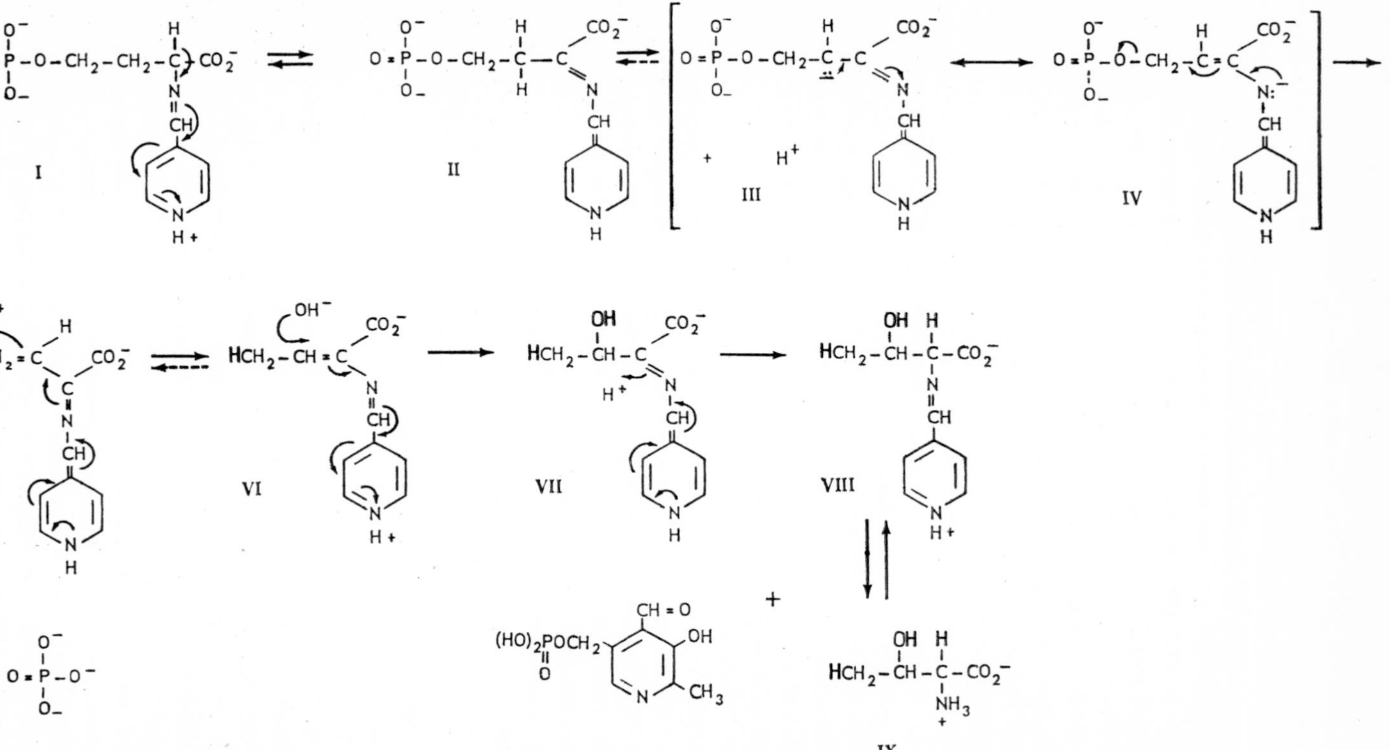


FIG. 4. Threonine synthesis by coupled $\gamma$-elimination and $\beta$-addition. Hydrogen and oxygen originating in the solvent are shown in bold print.

by allowing the reaction to proceed in oxygen-[26] or hydrogen-labeled[27] solvent, and determining the isotope distribution in the reaction products. As might have been predicted from the lack of metal ion requirement,[28] no solvent oxygen was incorporated into phosphate; about 0.8 atom was found in threonine. This eliminated mechanisms involving intermediary formation of O–P-threonine or N–P-threonine,[26] whose attractiveness lay in providing a role for phosphate to block the consumation of the elimination to $\alpha$-ketobutyrate. Some further evidence against an atypical hydrolytic cleavage of O–P-threonine was that purified enzyme did not decompose this substrate, although other experiments are still needed to rule out enzyme-bound O–P-threonine. The results indicated that phosphate was formed by non-hydrolytic elimination with C–O cleavage.

The first experiments with hydrogen-labeled water were complicated by unusually marked discrimination against tritium.[27] Conditions were first established for threonine degradation such that its five carbon-bound hydrogens did not exchange with solvent. The $\alpha$-hydrogen was isolated as glyoxylate, the $\beta + 3\gamma$-hydrogens as acetaldehyde, and the $\gamma$-hydrogens alone as acetate.[12,27,29] Newly formed threonine was found to have acquired 0.1 atom of solvent hydrogen in the $\alpha$-, none in the $\beta$-, and 0.02 in the $\gamma$-position. The amounts were constant through the time course of the reaction, and purified enzyme catalyzed negligible exchange into threonine *per se*. In contrast, the enzymatic exchange of solvent tritium into residual un-utilized P-homoserine was much larger than the incorporation into threonine; it increased with time, and reached a value greater than one atom of solvent hydrogen per mole of substrate.

Since substrate and product contain the same number of non-exchangeable hydrogen atoms, the low tritium content of threonine in the face of tritiation of both substrate and solvent indicated that there was selection against tritium in the reaction. To circumvent isotope selection, the reaction was carried out in pure $D_2O$. The rate was 15 per cent of that in water, and threonine now acquired exactly 2 atoms of solvent deuterium, one in the $\alpha$- and one in the $\gamma$-position.

In Fig. 4 these results are incorporated into a scheme for the course of the reaction, in which oxygen and hydrogen atoms originating in the solvent are shown in bold print. The reversible tautomerization of the Schiff base (Fig. 4, I $\leftrightarrows$ II) between pyridoxal-P and P-homoserine will incorporate solvent hydrogen into the $\alpha$-position of the latter. The extent of incorporation of solvent tritium will not be limited by relative rates of addition of tritium ions and protons, and will increase with time as isotope equilibrium is approached. If the elimination of phosphate is unconcerted, as it has been depicted (Fig. 4, II $\rightarrow$ V), solvent hydrogen may be incorporated into the $\beta$-position of P-homoserine as well as into the $\alpha$-position (Fig. 4, IV $\rightarrow$ I). However, the observed incorporation of more than one atom of solvent hydrogen could also be due for discrimination against I tritiated only in the $\alpha$-position. The reaction would be stereospecific for one of the two $\beta$-hydrogens, and would not introduce isotope into this position in threonine.[30]

The results now permit a choice between two general mechanisms which have been proposed, on the basis of model reactions, for elimination of $\gamma$-substituents (Fig. 2). In one (Fig. 2, I $\rightarrow$ II $\rightarrow$ VI $\rightarrow$ VII), elimination is potentiated by withdrawal of four electrons toward the pyridine ring[31,32] in the second (Fig. 2, I $\rightarrow$ III), by a hydride shift driven by the push of electrons out of the quinoid ring, and the electronegativity of the $\gamma$-substituent.[31] These mechanisms can also formally be regarded as overcoming the insulation of the $\gamma$-substituent from the coenzyme by rendering the intervening $\beta$-carbon respectively relatively electropositive or negative. The hydride shift will not introduce solvent hydrogen (bold print) into the $\gamma$-position of the product (Fig. 2, V), and therefore cannot be correct.

It is in the next step, the protonation of the $\gamma$-carbon to yield the Schiff base of aminocrotonate (Fig. 4, V $\rightarrow$ VI), that the rate of addition of tritium ions must be only 2 per cent (and that of deuterium ions at least 15 per cent) of that of protons. This result provides evidence against the possibility that labeling of threonine $\gamma$-hydrogen might be due to an exchange (Fig. 4, VI $\leftrightarrows$ V). This exchange cannot be ruled out solely because only one solvent deuterium is introduced. A terminal methyl group has no potential asymmetry as such,[30] but might undergo exchange of only one of its three hydrogens while its rotation was prevented by uninterrupted binding to an enzyme. But it seems unlikely that one atom of deuterium would be introduced, and yet so little tritium, in an exchange reaction where there would be a choice between hydrogen isotopes in both cases. The high discrimination against tritium might suggest that a proton is transferred by the enzyme from $\beta$- to $\gamma$-carbon without allowing its equilibration with water, were it not for the deuterium results. It will be interesting to compare the tritium isotope effect in a consumated $\gamma$-elimination (Fig. 2).

Formation of threonine from the Schiff base of aminocrotonate (Fig. 4, VI $\rightarrow$ IX) is entirely comparable to $\beta$-addition to the aminoacrylate analog (Fig. 3, II $\rightarrow$ V).

Threonine synthetase appears to represent the only reported case of effective " replacement " of a $\gamma$-substituent potentiated by pyridoxal-P, and it is interesting that in this case the new substituent is introduced at the $\beta$- rather than the $\gamma$-position. If, in this light, we consider the rather ineffective and physiologically useless $\gamma$-replacement catalyzed by liver cystathionase, the question arises whether the product of this reaction might not actually be $\beta$-methyllanthionine, rather than cystathionine.

The proposed mechanism does not confer any role on coenzyme, or substrate phosphate, in influencing the course of the reactions : P-homoserine $\rightarrow$ threonine; homoserine $\rightarrow$ $\alpha$-ketobutyrate. Two possible points of divergence are shown in Fig. 2 : in VII $\rightarrow$ IX the $\alpha$- rather than the $\gamma$-carbon is protonated, leading to free vinylglycine as an intermediate; in X $\rightarrow$ XII the sequence of addition of 2 moles of water is reversed. Either way leaves open a question, which we have thought was not meaningless, of a needless expenditure of phosphate bond energy in threonine biosynthesis. While such energy may be expended in the phosphorylation of coenzymes, merely to make them more soluble in their aqueous environment or to give them electrostatic handles for attachment to enzymes, this largesse does not seem to be extended to substrates which are formed or consumed in large amounts. In this context, the expenditure of ATP in threonine biosynthesis can at present be understood only as a means for shifting the equilibrium in favor of the accumulation of a protein building block.

## PROPERTIES OF A *NEUROSPORA* CYSTATHIONINE CLEAVAGE ENZYME

We can now return to trans-sulfuration, and mention a few properties of a highly purified *Neurospora* " $\gamma$-enzyme " which has been used to study the mechanisms both of a $\gamma$-elimination, from cystathionine, and a $\beta$-elimination, from cystine.

The enzyme was isolated from me-2 mutants, using an extraction procedure, and an assay, both of which inactivate " $\beta$-enzyme ".[13] The assay involved incorporation of an aromatic disulfide into the reaction mixture with cystathionine, and measurement of the rate of formation of colored aromatic mercaptan instantaneously liberated by spontaneous reaction with cysteine or homocysteine. The mixed elimination from L-cystathionine, and the question of the separate identity of $\beta$- and $\gamma$-enzyme, have been mentioned above.

Cystathionine was shown to liberate equal amounts of total keto acid and mercaptan in incubations with aromatic disulfide;[13] in incubations with iodoacetate equal amounts of total keto acid, ammonia and inorganic iodide were formed.[12] But difficulties were encountered in trying to show that the pyruvate and $\alpha$-ketobutyrate were balanced by the expected amounts of homocysteine and cysteine. Trapping of the latter with labeled iodoacetate, followed by separation of the two S-carboxymethyl derivatives, was unsatisfactory.[33] On substituting radioactive N-ethylmaleimide, about 3 per cent of the cystathionine was found to have undergone $\beta$-elimination, as judged by the equal amounts of pyruvate and NEM adduct of homocysteine. But only half as much $\alpha$-ketobutyrate as cysteine adduct was present.[12] Further investigation of this discrepancy will be described later.

The $\gamma$-enzyme was found to decompose a number of other substrates besides cystathionine, among them : lanthionine, L-djenkolic acid, L-homoserine, L-cystine and L-homocystine. All of the reactions required pyridoxal-P. In contrast to threonine synthetase,[25] pyridoxal-P could not be replaced by pyridoxamine-P, and its ability to reactivate apoenzyme was not inhibited by prior incubation of the latter with deoxypridoxine-P.[12] Except for hydroxy-amino acid substrates, the enzyme catalyzed $\beta$-elimination with the same or greater facility than $\gamma$-elimination, cystine reacting faster than homocystine, lanthionine as fast as cystathionine. Constancy of $K_m$ and relative $V_{max}$ values for the substrates over a 400-fold purification indicated that a single enzyme was involved, as did the non-additivity of rates of reaction of pairs of substrates. Thus when L-cystine (low $K_m$ and $V_{max}$) was incubated together with cystathionine, the total reaction rate was reduced exactly to that of the former alone.[13] L-Homoserine and L-serine (which is not a substrate) were found to competitively inhibit the decomposition of cystine and cystathionine; $K_i$ values were the same for each against the two substrates, and for homoserine $K_i = K_m$.[34] These results provide evidence against the participation of more than one enzyme, or of multiple unlike subunits.

Preliminary evidence has been mentioned that $\gamma$-enzyme may also catalyze synthesis of cystathionine by $\beta$-replacement, as well as its cleavage by $\gamma$-elimination (i.e. can perform both of the reactions catalyzed by separable liver enzymes). These two reactions would involve bonds between pyridoxal-P and the amino groups at different ends of cystathionine, which brings to mind the possibility that $\gamma$-enzyme might contain two pyridoxal-P residues in its active center. Although nothing has suggested that this is so,[13] it is noteworthy that all the compounds so far definitely shown to be decomposed by the enzyme are " double ended " amino acids, except for L-homoserine.[13] Kinetic studies indicate that only one equivalent of homoserine is bound to the enzyme when it acts as an inhibitor,[34] but binding of two equivalents has not been ruled out when it serves as a substrate.

## THE MECHANISM OF A $\beta$-ELIMINATION

The facility of *Neurospora* $\gamma$-enzyme in catalyzing $\beta$- as well as $\gamma$-elimination can be illustrated first by some studies of the mechanism of a $\beta$-elimination. This topic, and the following one, could perhaps better be coupled under the heading of anomalous reactions of " sulfhydryl " reagents.

Cavallini *et al.*[35] first discovered that pyridoxal could decompose cystine non-enzymatically, and followed with a remarkably successful guess that the same reaction might be catalyzed by liver cystathionine cleavage enzyme.[36] By following a quite different experimental path, we have independently been led towards conclusions similar to theirs,[13] and have been able to obtain proof that the nature of the reaction was a $\beta$-disulfide elimination (Eq. 5), by trapping and identifying a stable derivative of a reactive intermediate.

$$HOOCCH(NH_2)CH_2SSCH_2CH(NH_2)COOH + H_2O \rightarrow CH_3COCOOH + \\ + NH_3 + HSSCH_2CH(NH_2)COOH \qquad (5)$$

Our attention was directed to the problem when we found that the $\gamma$-enzyme specifically decomposed the L- (and meso-) forms of cystine and homocystine. Meso-cystine reacted three times faster than L-cystine; we have not been able to see any explanation of this in terms of potentially greater conformational resemblance to cystathionine. In preliminary determinations, the energy of activation was found to be the same (17,000 cal/mole) for the reactions of meso-cystine and L-cystathionine, but appeared to be 4000 calories higher for L-cystine.[34] The corresponding mercaptans did not react, and partially inhibited the decomposition of disulfides.[13,37] Indeed, the existence of the " cysteine desulfhydrase " reaction is now in question, as many reports of it can be reconciled with the true substrate being a catalytic amount of disulfide.[13,38] In liver, there appears to be no enzyme other than cystathionase catalyzing $\beta$-elimination from cystine (or " cysteine ").[39,40]

A clear understanding of the nature of the reaction was hampered by the fact that the final products which could be identified reflected a variety of secondary, spontaneous reactions of sulfur compounds which occurred under different experimental conditions.[13] Unequivocal resolution of the problem resulted from the fortuitous observation of a puzzling effect of iodoacetate on the decomposition of L-cystine.

When iodoacetate was added to reaction mixtures, liberation of pyruvate and ammonia was unimpeded, but sulfur could not be acounted for in the reaction products as elemental sulfur, sulfide or mercaptan.[13] Inorganic iodide was also liberated in amounts equimolar with pyruvate. The explanation was found when it was observed that there was no decrease in total disulfide throughout the incubation. When the reaction mixture was examined by paper electrophoresis, after liberation of one equivalent of pyruvate, no cystine remained, and the only sulfur compound present was identified as the mixed disulfide of mercaptoacetic acid and cysteine. These results are consistent with coupling of the enzymatic reaction (Eq. 5) with the plausible spontaneous reaction shown in Eq. (6), in which the unstable, hypothetical alkyl hydrogen disulfide displaces iodide from iodoacetate to form a mixed

$$\mathrm{HOOCCH(NH_2)CH_2SSH + ICH_2COOH \rightarrow I^- + H^+ + \\ + HOOCCH(NH_2)CH_2SSCH_2COOH} \quad (6)$$

disulfide, in much the same fashion as mercaptans react to form thioethers. In fact we have not been able to think of any other interpretation of the results. Preliminary investigation of the rate of reaction of intermediary alkyl hydrogen disulfide with iodoacetate suggests that it is comparable to cysteine in nucleophilic character.[13]

If incubations are continued after the cystine has been entirely consumed, there is a further but much slower liberation of pyruvate and iodide in equimolar amounts, accompanied by the appearance of some mercaptoacetic disulfide.[13] This may be attributed to spontaneous dismutation of, or, more likely, slow enzymatic attack on, the mixed disulfide, followed by further reaction with iodoacetate (Eq. 7).

$$HOOCCH_2SSH + ICH_2COOH \rightarrow I^- + H^+ + \\ + HOOCCH_2SSCH_2COOH \quad (7)$$

It is unprofitable to list disproven mechanisms which might have been, but never were, proposed. But in case some should think $\beta$-disulfide elimination so plausible that experiment was unecessary, we might mention, as an example, one close variant ruled out by these results. It might have been attractive to formulate the first step as liberation of cysteine by a disulfide interchange between cystine and a reactive cysteine of the enzyme.[41] Pyridoxal-P mediated $\beta$-elimination would then have yielded pyruvate, ammonia and enzyme hydrogen disulfide. Enzyme-SSH might also, at least in part, have transferred elemental sulfur to still nearby cysteine. Any such mechanism, in which cysteine and elemental sulfur are formed first, and condense to alkyl hydrogen disulfide afterward, is ruled out, because iodoacetate would trap cysteine as soon as it was formed. The same objection would apply to a mechanism involving liberation of elemental sulfur in the first step, with intermediary formation of lanthionine. The latter is decomposed faster than cystine by the enzyme.[13] These possibilities could not otherwise be ruled out, even if it were possible to isolate the alkyl hydrogen disulfide as such, or if there were a specific assay for it.

## THE MECHANISM OF A $\gamma$-ELIMINATION

Three alternate mechanisms for $\gamma$-elimination from cystathionine (Fig. 2) have already been discussed. Two of them are differentiable by studies with isotopic hydrogen, which have not yet been done for this reaction. The third (Fig. 2, VI $\rightarrow$ IX $\rightarrow$ XI $\rightarrow$ XII) would not introduce a unique pattern of solvent hydrogen into the product, but could be tested if there were a way of detecting free vinylglycine (Fig. 2, IX). This compound has not been prepared, and is expected to be very unstable, decomposing in water by IX $\rightarrow$ XI $\rightarrow$ XII.

As mentioned above, when radioactive N-ethylmaleimide (NEM) was used to trap the mercaptans formed from cystathionine by $\gamma$-enzyme, in an attempt to get the complete stoichiometry, the small amount of pyruvate formed was equal to the NEM-homocysteine adduct, but the amount of $\alpha$-ketobutyrate was only half that of NEM-cysteine.[12] In these experiments, cysteine and homocysteine were determined by measuring total radioactivity in their NEM-adducts after these had been separated by paper chromatography.[33] Keto acids were measured in separate aliquots of the reaction mixture, and unreacted cystathionine by quantitative ninhydrin after elution from chromatograms. Influenced by earlier results with labeled iodoacetate,[33] we first thought the discrepancy might lie in an apparent excess of cysteine, due to a reaction with more than one equivalent of NEM. But the disappearance of cystathionine was found to parallel the increase in NEM-cysteine, indicating that the discrepancy was due to a deficiency of α-ketobutyrate.

A new radioactive spot was next observed in the chromatograms.[12] The unknown appeared radiographically homogeneous after it had been separated from the overlapping N-ethylmaleamic acid which first obscured its presence. In companion incubations, α-ketobutyrate itself did not give rise to the unknown, nor did it disappear, by lactic dehydrogenase assay. No unknown was formed on incubating enzyme and NEM-$C^{14}$ with homocysteine thiolactone, pyruvate, cysteine or lanthionine. In the last case pyruvate and NEM-cysteine were formed in equal amounts. DL-Homoserine-2-$C^{14}$, however, did give rise to the same unknown when incubated with enzyme and unlabeled NEM.

The quantitative yield of NEM-cysteine indicated that there was no sulfur in the unknown. It was acidic by ion exchange and electrophoresis, and stable to mild acid or alkaline hydrolysis.[12] Assuming 1 mole of NEM per mole of unknown, the amount of it recovered varied from 45 to 85 per cent of the amount of missing α-ketobutyrate. The ratio of unknown to α-ketobutyrate formed did not change with reaction time, but increased markedly at higher pH (from pH 7.3 to 7.9 the ratio increased 4-fold).

NEM has been reported to slowly acylate the more basic of the two amino groups of cystine (p$K$ about 8) under conditions somewhat similar to those used above.[42] We have confirmed that the new ninhydrin-reactive component contains the elements both of cystine-$S^{35}$ and of NEM-$C^{14}$, and have found that cystathionine and lanthionine react in a parallel manner.[12] Very little of the N-(N-ethylmaleyl)-cystathionine appeared in radiograms from enzyme incubations. It seemed unlikely that this compound could have been the source of the unknown. However, we isolated it from the non-enzymatic reaction of NEM-$C^{14}$ and cystathionine, and incubated it with enxyme, in place of cystathionine + NEM-$C^{14}$. Negligible α-keto acid, and no detectable unknown, was formed.

These results indicated that NEM was trapping an unstable precursor of α-ketobutyrate in the enzymatic γ-elimination from cystathionine or homoserine, but did not react with any comparable intermediate in β-elimination by the same enzyme. The reaction schemes so far considered indicate two candidates for such an unstable precursor. If it were α-aminocrotonate (Fig. 2, IV or XI), one would expect α-aminocrylate formed in β-elimination to show similar reactivity. The remaining possibility is vinylglycine (Fig. 2, IX). The preceeding results on the acylation of amino groups by NEM suggest the possible structure for the unknown shown in Fig. 5. Effective acylation of vinylglycine would require that it have an unusually basic amino group. Since α-ketobutyrate and mercaptan are formed in parallel amounts throughout incubations without NEM,[13] no precursor of the former can have a very appreciable lifetime (it is possible that such a precursor would be decomposed only during the deproteinization necessary before α-ketobutyrate determination). On these grounds a p$K$ below 8 would seem to be required in the unstable intermediate trapped by NEM. In this respect also the allylamine, vinylglycine, would be a better candidate than the vinylamine, aminocrotonate. It seems not unlikely that some other unrecognized potentiating factor would also have to be involved in the reaction.

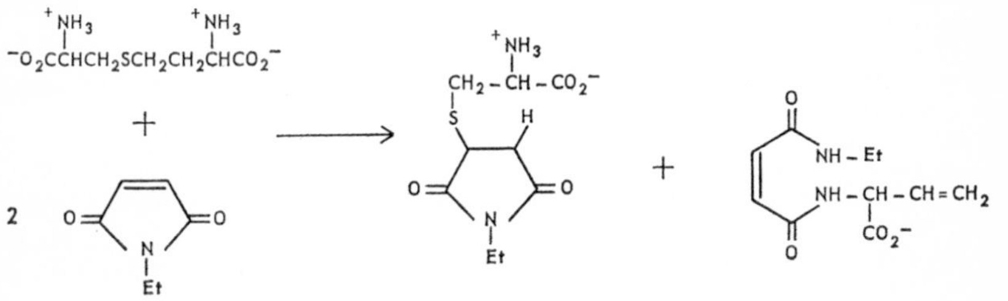

$$^{-}O_2C\underset{|}{\overset{+NH_3}{C}}HCH_2SCH_2CH_2\underset{|}{\overset{+NH_3}{C}}HCO_2^{-} + 2\,\text{(N-ethylmaleimide)} \longrightarrow \text{(S-substituted N-ethylsuccinimide, } CH_2-CH(NH_3^+)-CO_2^-\text{)} + \text{(maleamide: } NH-Et,\ NH-CH(CO_2^-)-CH=CH_2\text{)}$$

FIG. 5.

While these results point to some sort of reaction between NEM and vinylglycine, there is no evidence, at the time of writing, for the specific structure for the unknown shown in Fig. 5. Strong alkaline or acid hydrolysis of the unknown yields complex mixtures, from which nothing has been identified but N-ethylmaleamic acid. Catalytic hydrogenation converts the unknown into a new, radiographically homogeneous compound, but so far neither succinate nor α-aminobutyrate has been identified in its acid hydrolysis products.

## REFERENCES

1. V. DU VIGNEAUD; *A Trail of Research*, Cornell University Press, New York (1952).
2. Y. MATSUO and D. M. GREENBERG; *J. Biol. Chem.* **230**, 545 (1958).
3. A. S. M. SELIM and D. M. GREENBERG; *J. Biol. Chem.* **234**, 1474 (1959).
4. N. H. HOROWITZ; *J. Biol. Chem.* **171**, 255 (1947).
5. N. E. MURRAY; *Heredity* **15**, 199 (1960).
6. K. SCHLOSSMAN and F. LYNEN; *Biochem. Z.* **328**, 591 (1957).
7. M. FLING and N. H. HOROWITZ; *J. Biol. Chem.* **190**, 277 (1951).
8. H. J. TEAS, N. H. HOROWITZ and M. FLING; *J. Biol. Chem.* **172**, 651 (1948).
9. G. A. FISCHER; *Biochim. et Biophys. Acta* **25**, 50 (1957).
10. N. GILES; *Cold Spring Harbour Symposium* **16**, 283 (1951).
11. N. H. HOROWITZ; *Cold Spring Harbour Symposium* **16**, 313 (1951).
12. M. FLAVIN and C. SLAUGHTER; Unpublished results.
13. M. FLAVIN; *J. Biol. Chem.* **237**, 768 (1962).
14. M. FLAVIN and C. SLAUGHTER; *Federation Proc.* **21**, 245 (1962).
15. C. DELAVIER-KLUTCHKO and M. FLAVIN; Unpublished results.
16. S. WIJESUNDERA and D. D. WOODS; *J. Gen. Microbiol.* **9**, III (1953).
17. R. J. ROWBURY; *Biochem. J.* **81**, 42P (1961).
18. R. J. ROWBURY; *Biochem. J.* **82**, 24P (1962).

19. G. L. Cantoni; *Comparative Biochemistry* (edited by M. Florkin and H. S. Mason), vol. I, p. 220, Academic Press, New York (1960).
20. Y. Matsuo and D. M. Greenberg; *J. Biol. Chem.* **234**, 516 (1959).
21. E. C. Wolff, S. Black and P. F. Downey; *J. Am. Chem. Soc.* **78**, 5958 (1956).
22. K. Ohigashi, A. Tsunetoshi and K. Ichihara; *Med. J. Osaka Univ.* **2**, 111 (1951); *C. A.* **46**, 6678 (1952).
23. L. L. Ingraham; *Biochemical Mechanisms*, p. 51, John Wiley, New York (1962).
24. F. Chapeville and P. Fromageot; *Biochim. et Biophys. Acta* **49**, 328 (1961).
25. M. Flavin and C. Slaughter; *J. Biol. Chem.* **235**, 1103 (1960).
26. M. Flavin and T. Kono; *J. Biol. Chem.* **235**, 1109 (1960).
27. M. Flavin and C. Slaughter; *J. Biol. Chem.* **235**, 1112 (1960).
28. M. Cohn; *J. Cell. Comp. Physiol.* **54**, Suppl. 1, 17 (1959).
29. M. Flavin and C. Slaughter; *Federation Proc.* **19**, 48 (1960).
30. H. Hirschmann; *J. Biol. Chem.* **235**, 2762 (1960).
31. D. E. Metzler, M. Ikawa and E. E. Snell; *J. Am. Chem. Soc.* **76**, 648 (1954).
32. A. E. Braunstein; *The Enzymes* (edited by P. D. Boyer, H. Lardy and K. Myrbäck), vol. II, p. 113, Academic Press, New York (1960).
33. M. Flavin; *Anal. Biochem.* In press.
34. A. Segal and M. Flavin; Unpublished results.
35. D. Cavallini, C. De Marco and B. Mondovi; *Arch. Biochem. Biophys.* **87**, 281 (1960).
36. D. Cavallini, C. De Marco, B. Mondovi and B. G. Mori; *Enzymologia* **22**, 161 (1960).
37. M. Flavin and C. Slaughter; *Federation Proc.* **20**, 230 (1961).
38. B. Mondovi and C. De Marco; *Enzymologia* **23**, 156 (1961).
39. E. V. Goraychenkova; *Biokhimiya* **26**, 541 (1961).
40. D. Cavallini, B. Mondovi, C. De Marco and A. Scioscia-Santoro; *Enzymologia* **24**, 235 (1962).
41. A. Pihl and R. Lange; *J. Biol. Chem.* **237**, 1356 (1962).
42. D. G. Smyth, A. Nagamatsu and J. S. Fruton; *J. Am. Chem. Soc.* **82**, 4600 (1960).

# LES ENZYMES À PYRIDOXAL DANS LA SYNTHÈSE DE LA TAURINE À PARTIR DU SULFATE

by F. CHAPEVILLE and P. FROMAGEOT

Section Autonome de Chimie Biologique du Départment de Biologie, Centre d'Etudes Nucléaires de Saclay—Gif-sur-Yvette (France)

PARMI les réactions dont la catalyse implique le phosphate de pyridoxal se trouvent celles qui conduisent à la synthèse de la liaison S—C à partir de soufre minéral. Pendant sa période de développement embryonnaire, l'oiseau possède l'aptitude à synthétiser de façon extrêmement intense de telles liaisons S—C. Ce métabolisme conduit à la biosynthèse de la taurine, dont l'œuf renferme à la veille de son éclosion 40 à 50 mg. Machlin *et al.*[1] ont montré les premiers que l'origine de cette taurine était particulière. En effet, après introduction dans un oeuf embryonné de sulfate $S^{35}$ ces auteurs pouvaient isoler de la taurine $S^{35}$. Il en résultait que l'œuf embryonné est capable de créer une liaison S—C à partir du soufre minéral et oxydé.

TABLEAU 1. RADIOACTIVITÉ DE L'ACIDE CYSTÉIQUE ET DE LA TAURINE DE L'EMBRYON ET DU SAC VITELLIN + VITELLUS APRÈS INTRODUCTION DANS LE VITELLUS DE SULFATE $S^{35}$ OU DE SULFITE $S^{35}$ *in vivo*. Temps: 20 min

| Radioactivité introduite $1,8 \times 10^6$ ipm | Embryon | | Sac vitellin + vitellus | |
|---|---|---|---|---|
| | Acide cystéique | Taurine | Acide cystéique | Taurine |
| $S^{35}O_4Na_2$ 2 mg | 0 | 200 | 150 | 370 |
| $S^{35}O_3Na_2$ 2 mg | 1900 | 16 320 | 162 000 | 52 000 |

L'étude de ce phénomène montre tout d'abord que le sulfite est beaucoup mieux utilisé que le sulfate pour la synthèse de la taurine (Tableau 1).

D'autres expériences[2] ont montré que l'oeuf embryonné est capable de réduire le sulfate en sulfite et que le sulfite est le précurseur immédiat de l'acide cystéique ultérieurement décarboxylé en taurine (Fig. 1). Le squelette carboné et aminé de l'acide cystéique est fourni par la L-cystéine.[3] La synthèse de l'acide cystéique correspond à une substitution du soufre du groupe thiol de la cystéine par celui du sulfite, (Fig. 2), selon la réaction:

$$SO_3H_2 + HS{-}CH_2{-}\underset{\displaystyle NH_2}{\underset{|}{CH}}{-}COOH \longrightarrow HO_3S{-}CH_2{-}\underset{\displaystyle NH_2}{\underset{|}{CH}}{-}COOH + H_2S$$

Cette réaction est irréversible et est catalysée par un enzyme, que nous avons appelé cystéinelyase. Cet enzyme possède du phosphate de pyridoxal comme coenzyme[4] (Fig. 3).

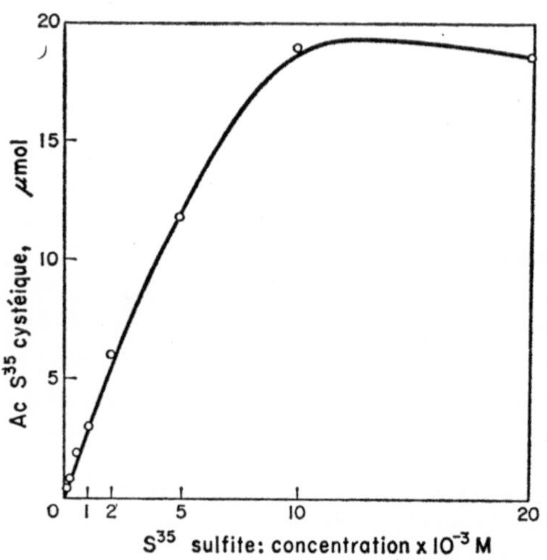


FIG. 2. Influence de la concentration en sulfite sur la synthèse d'acide cystéique. Cystéine: 25 μmoles, tampon Tris 0,2 M pH 8, préparation enzymatique: 40 mg, volume final: 5 ml. Incubation 2 hr à 38° sous azote.[5]

La cystéinelyase, outre la fixation du sulfite sur le carbone $\beta$ de la cystéine, catalyse aussi l'échange entre le soufre du groupe thiol de la cystéine et celui du sulfure minéral:[4]

$$H_2^*S + HS{-}CH_2{-}\underset{\displaystyle NH_2}{\underset{|}{CH}}{-}COOH \rightleftharpoons H_2S + H^*S{-}CH_2{-}\underset{\displaystyle NH_2}{\underset{|}{CH}}{-}COOH$$

Le Tableau 2 montre que cette réaction, comme la synthèse d'acide cystéique, est bien catalysée par le même enzyme.

En l'absence de soufre minéral (sulfure ou sulfite), la cystéinelyase transforme la cystéine d'une part en lanthionine, d'autre part en acide pyrovique,

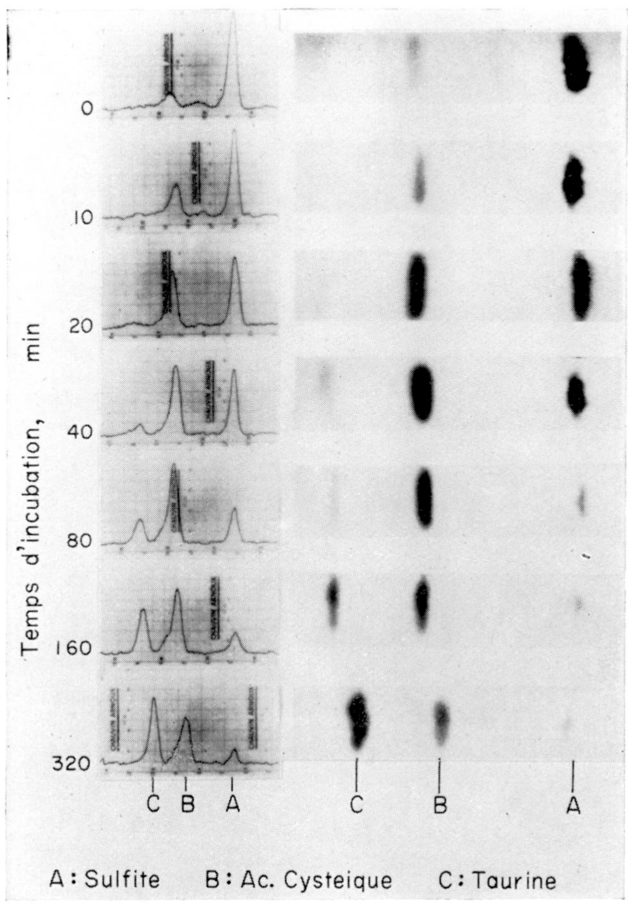


FIG. 1. Autoradiographie et enregistrement de la radioactivité d'électrophorèses d'extraits bruts de sac vitellin + vitellus incubés pendant des temps variables avec du $S^{35}O_3Na_2$.

A. Sulfite oxydé en sulfate par $H_2O_2$.

B. Acide cystéique.

C. Taurine.

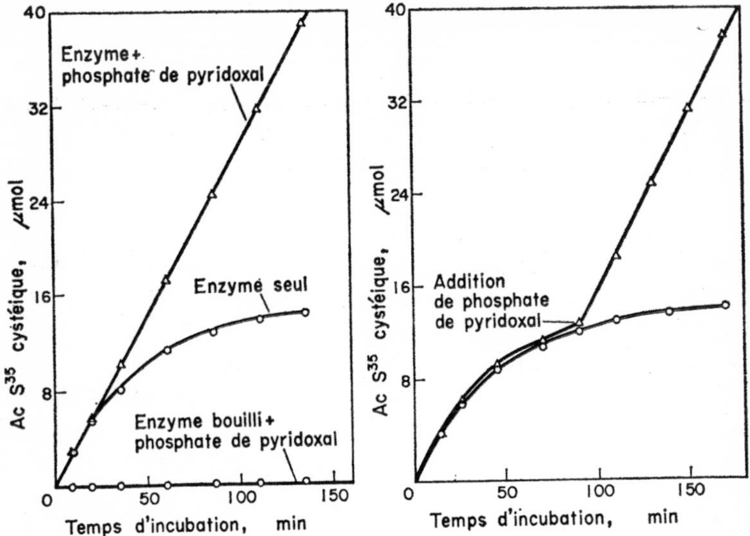


FIG. 3. Influence du phosphate de pyridoxal sur la formation de l'acide cystéique. Cystéine, $2{,}10^{-2}$ M; sulfite $S^{35}$, $2{,}10^{-2}$ M; tampon Tris, 0,2 M pH 8,5; phosphate de pyridoxal, 0 ou $1{,}10^{-5}$ M; préparation enzymatique 10 mg. Volume final, 10 ml. Incubation à l'air à 37°.

TABLEAU 2. RAPPORT DES ACTIVITÉS DES DIFFÉRENTES FRACTIONS OBTENUES AU COURS DE LA PURIFICATION DE L'ENZYME DU SAC VITELLIN

Incubation sous azote pendant 1 hr à 37° dans les conditions optimales de pH pour chaque réaction: tampon Tris, 5 ml; préparation enzymatique, 6 unités environ; cystéine, $1{,}10^{-2}$ M; sulfite $S^{35}$ ou sulfure $S^{35}$, $1{,}10^{-2}$ M.

| | Activité enzymatique spécifique | Rapport des activités $\frac{\text{Cystéine}+\text{sulfite } S^{35} \rightarrow \text{ac. cystéique } S^{35} + H_2S}{\text{Cystéine} + H_2S^{35} \rightleftarrows \text{cystéine } S^{35} + H_2S}$ |
|---|---|---|
| I. Préparation S + V brute | 0,51 | 0,82 |
| II. Préparation (P.E.E.) | 1,47 | 0,87 |
| III. Préparation (P.E.A.) | 4,42 | 0,86 |
| IV. Préparation (P.E.S.) | 11,03 | 0,89 |
| V. P.E.S. après chauffage (1 h à 55°) | 3,15 | 0,87 |

ammoniaque et sulfure. Ces réactions sont cependant lentes par rapport aux précédentes et correspondent aux transformations:

$$\underset{\displaystyle HN_2}{\text{COOH—CH}}\text{—CH}_2\text{—SH} + \text{HS—CH}_2\text{—}\underset{\displaystyle NH_2}{\text{CH}}\text{—COOH} \longrightarrow \text{COOH—}\underset{\displaystyle NH_2}{\text{CH}}\text{—CH}_2\text{—S—CH}_2\text{—}\underset{\displaystyle NH_2}{\text{CH}}\text{—COOH} + H_2S$$

$$\text{HS—CH}_2\text{—}\underset{\displaystyle NH_2}{\text{CH}}\text{—COOH} \longrightarrow H_2S + CH_3\text{—COOH} + NH_3$$

On remarquera ici que la désulfhydration de la cystéine par la cystéinelyase est une désulfhydration directe, sans transamination préalable. La spécificité de la cystéinelyase à l'égard de la cystéine est stricte. Tous les dérivés de la cystéine essayés ne font l'objet d'aucune transformation. Les réactions décrites apparaissent comme la conséquence d'un seul phénomène, l'activation du carbone $\beta$ de la cystéine par la cystéinelyase. Cette activation se manifeste

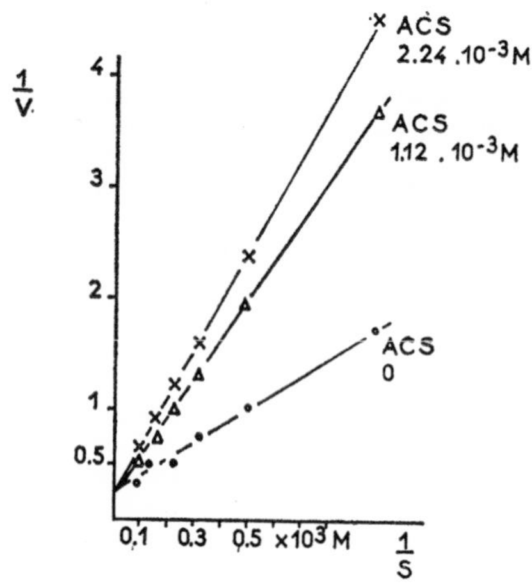


FIG. 4. Influence de l'acide cystéinesulfinique sur la décarboxylation de l'acide cystéique. On mesure la quantité de taurine $S^{35}$ formée à partir d'acide cystéique $S^{35}$. Préparation enzymatique correspondant à 200 mg de foie d'embryon; phosphate de pyridoxal, $1{,}10^{-4}$ M. Tampon phosphate, 0,4 M, pH 7,7. Volume final 2 ml. Incubation à 37° pendant 2 hr sous azote.

par la labilisation de la liaison S—C de la cystéine, qui entraîne soit la substitution du soufre par un atome de soufre porteur d'un doublet libre, soit le détachement du soufre et formation d'acide pyruvique et d'ammoniaque. Parmi les réactions décrites, seule la synthèse d'acide cystéique présente une importance physiologique dans la chaîne des réactions qui conduisent du sulfate à la taurine. L'acide cystéique ainsi formé est décarboxylé en taurine par une décarboxylase qui possède du phosphate de pyridoxal comme coenzyme.[6] Cette décarboxylase est spécifique de l'acide cystéique et est inhibée par l'acide cystéinesulfinique (Fig. 4). L'acide cystéinesulfinique n'est pas lui-même décarboxylé et se comporte comme un inhibiteur compétitif. On doit remarquer que la synthèse de l'acide cystéique à partir de cystéine et de sulfite, conduit à une libération d'hydrogène sulfuré. Le devenir de cet hydrogène sulfuré a été examiné: les résultats obtenus montrent que cet hydrogène sulfuré est utilisé pour la re-synthèse de la cystéine; le squelette carboné et aminé provient soit de la sérine soit de la phosphosérine, (Tableau 3), selon les réactions:

$$S + HO{-}CH_2{-}\underset{\displaystyle NH_2}{\underset{|}{CH}}{-}COOH \longrightarrow HS{-}CH_2{-}\underset{\displaystyle NH_2}{\underset{|}{CH}}{-}COOH + H_2O \qquad (A)$$

$$S + H_2O_3P{-}O{-}CH_2{-}\underset{\displaystyle NH_2}{\underset{|}{CH}}{-}COOH \longrightarrow HS{-}CH_2{-}\underset{\displaystyle NH_2}{\underset{|}{CH}}{-}COOH + H_3PO_4 \qquad (B)$$

TABLEAU 3. FORMATION DE CYSTÉINE À PARTIR DE SÉRINE OU DE PHOSPHOSÉRINE ET D'HYDROGÈNE SULFURE

Les substances introduites sont dissoutes dans du tampon Tris 0,1 M, pH 8,95. Volume total 190 µl. Résultats exprimés en mµmoles de cystéine formée pour 100 µl d'une solution de protéines dont la densité optique à 280 mµ est de 1.

| | Composition du milieu (µmoles) | | | | |
|---|---|---|---|---|---|
| DL-Sérine $C^{14}$ | 0,5 | — | 4 | 4 | — |
| DL-Phosphosérine | — | 4 | — | — | 4 |
| Sulfure de sodium | 1 | 4[a] | 8 | 4 | 4[a] |
| Phosphate de pyridoxal | 0,03 | — | 0,03 | — | — |
| Tampon Tris 0,1 M, pH 9 µl | 45 | 60 | 45 | 60 | 60 |
| Extrait de foie µl | 100 | 100 | — | — | — |
| Extrait de sac vitellin non purifié µl | | | 100 | — | — |
| Extrait de sac vitellin purifié µl | | | | 100 | 100 |
| Cystéine $C^{14}$ ou $S^{35}$: mµmoles | 26 | 0 | 85 | 0 | 600 |

[a] $S^{35}Na_2$.

La réaction A est catalysée par la sérinesulfhydrase et la réaction B par un enzyme distinct de cette sérinesulfhydrase, qu'on peut appeler par analogie phosphosérinesulfhydrase. En effet, la sérine n'est pas un substrat pour la phosphosérinesulfhydrase, ni la phosphosérine pour la sérinesulfhydrase. En outre, la phosphosérinesulfhydrase peut utiliser le sulfite pour former l'acide cystéique. Cette dernière réaction est cependant négligeable par rapport à celle que la cystéinelyase catalyse. Cette observation et le fait que la phosphosérinesulfhydrase se trouve présente dans le même organe (sac vitellin) que la cystéinelyase, posent la question de l'identité entre ces deux enzymes. Les données actuelles semblent indiquer qu'il s'agit d'enzymes distincts. En effet, au cours de la purification de la cystéinelyase, l'activité spécifique des diverses fractions à l'égard de la fixation du sulfure sur la cystéine ou la phosphosérine varie de 11/1 à 26/1. L'ensemble de ces résultats peut être décrit par le schéma suivant.

$SO_4^{=}$ → $SO_3^{=}$ — CYSTÉINE — $H_3PO_4$

PP PP

AC. CYSTÉIQUE — $H_2S$ — PHOSPHOSÉRINE

SÉRINE

PP

$CO_2$ — TAURINE

Il apparaît ainsi qu'au cours de la synthèse de la taurine à partir du sulfate, la cystéine est constamment renouvelée puisqu'elle est synthétisée à partir de sérine ou de phosphosérine, et de sulfure.

Au cours du fonctionnement d'un tel système, seul l'hydrogène sulfuré n'est pas consommé et se comporte comme un facteur de type catalytique nécessaire à la fixation du sulfite sur le carbone $\beta$ des chaînes tricarbonées et aminées impliquées.

Dans l'œuf embryonné d'oiseau, il existe ainsi des enzymes catalysant les réactions suivantes:

I. $SO_3H_2 + HS{-}CH_2{-}CH(NH_2){-}COOH \longrightarrow HO_3S{-}CH_2{-}CH(NH_2){-}COOH + H_2$

II. $H_2^*S + HS{-}CH_2{-}CH(NH_2){-}COOH \longrightarrow H^*S{-}CH_2{-}CH(NH_2){-}COOH + H_2S$

III. $H_2S + HO{-}CH_2{-}CH(NH_2){-}COOH \longrightarrow HS{-}CH_2{-}CH(NH_2){-}COOH + H_2O$

IV. $H_2S + H_2PO_3{-}O{-}CH_2{-}CH(NH_2){-}COOH \longrightarrow HS{-}CH_2{-}CH(NH_2){-}COOH + H_3$

V. $HO_3S{-}CH_2{-}CH(NH_2){-}COOH \longrightarrow HO_3S{-}CH_2{-}CH_2{-}NH_2 + CO_2$

La cystéinelyase, qui catalyse les réactions I et II, contient du phosphate de pyridoxal comme coenzyme. Il a été démontré par Schlossmann et Lynen[7] que la réaction III implique aussi du phosphate de pyridoxal. On signalera ici que la sérinesulfhydrase catalyse aussi la réaction II. La participation du phosphate de pyridoxal à l'activité de la phosphosérinesulfhydrase (réaction IV) n'a pas été démontrée. Cependant du fait de l'analogie entre la réaction IV et les réactions précédentes, et du fait que les réactions I à IV ont été reproduites, non enzymatiquement, en présence de pyridoxal ou de phosphate de pyridoxal[8] et d'un métal, on peut conclure à la très probable participation du phosphate de pyridoxal à l'activité de la phosphosérinesulfhydrase. Toutes ces réactions I à IV se présentent ainsi comme des $\beta$-substitutions catalysées par le phosphate de pyridoxal. Aussi est-il très probable que ces transformations résultent du même mécanisme d'action du pyridoxal, mécanisme qui a été décrit par Braunstein[9] et par Snell.[10] Ce mécanisme fait intervenir une base de Schiff entre l'acide aminé et le groupe formyl du pyridoxal. En l'absence d'enzyme, mais en présence d'union métallique, la base de Schiff forme avec cet ion métallique un chélate qui subit des réarrangements électroniques conduisant à la $\beta$-élimination ou à la $\beta$-substitution. On a fait participer à ces réarrangements le noyau aromatique du pyridoxal et son azote pyridinique. Toutefois il a été possible, en utilisant le pyruvate[11] à la place du pyridoxal et des ions cuivre, de reproduire ces mêmes réactions.

Du point de vue biologique, il est intéressant de noter que les enzymes impliqués dans la réduction du sulfate en sulfite, la cystéinelyase et la phosphosérinesulfhydrase, sont localisées exclusivement dans les cellules de l'endoderme du sac vitellin.[12] Ils apparaissent dans les premières heures du développement de l'embryon. La question qui se pose est de savoir si l'apparition de ces enzymes dans les cellules de l'endoderme est synchrone. Ce point n'a pas été éclairci, mais par analogie avec les systèmes bactériens ($\beta$-galactosidase et galactoside-transacetylase)[13] on peut supposer que ces enzymes du sac vitellin sont sous le contrôle d'un même gène opérateur. Tous ces enzymes disparaissent complètement après l'éclosion et la résorption du sac vitellin et du vitellus. Que les enzymes qui font l'objet de cette discussion existent exclusivement dans des cellules se développant au contact du vitellus est un fait qui pourrait indiquer un rôle actif des substances présentes dans le vitellus dans l'expression des gènes correspondants. La constatation que l'enzyme impliqué dans la réduction du sulfate, la cystéinelyase et la phosphosérinesulfhydrase interviennent successivement dans le même cycle métabolique, est un argument en faveur des considérations discutées ci-dessus.

## BIBLIOGRAPHIE

1. J. L. Machlin, P. B. Pearson and C. A. Denton; *J. Biol. Chem.* **212**, 469 (1955).
2. F. Chapeville and P. Fromageot; *Compt. rend.* **244**, 388 (1957).

3. F. CHAPEVILLE and P. FROMAGEOT; *Biochim. et Biophys. Acta* **26**, 538 (1957).
4. F. CHAPEVILLE and P. FROMAGEOT; *Biochim. et Biophys. Acta* **49**, 328 (1961).
5. F. CHAPEVILLE and P. FROMAGEOT; *Bull. soc. chim. biol.* **42**, 877 (1960).
6. G. SIMONNET, F. CHAPEVILLE and P. FROMAGEOT; *Bull. soc. chim. biol.* **42**, 891 (1960).
7. K. SCHLOSSMANN and F. LYNEN; *Biochem. Z.* **328**, 591 (1957).
8. O. RATSISALOVANINA, F. CHAPEVILLE and P. FROMAGEOT; *Biochim. et Biophys. Acta* **49**, 322 (1961).
9. A. E. BRAUNSTEIN; *The Enzymes* (édité par P. D. BOYER, H. LARDY et K. MYRBÄCK), vol. 2, p. 113, Academic Press, New York (1960).
10. E. E. SNELL; *Vitamins and Hormones* **16**, 77 (1958).
11. P. FROMAGEOT, U. R. RODERICK and J. POUZAT; A paraître.
12. F. CHAPEVILLE and L. KHAU VAN KIEM; *Ann. Histochim.* **6**, 313 (1961)
13. F. JACOB and J. MONOD; *J. Mol. Biol.* **3**, 318 (1961).

## DISCUSSION

DR. SNELL:

In the model reactions with pyridoxal studies by Longenecker and myself, phosphoserine was converted to pyruvate and ammonia much more rapidly than was serine itself. This would lead us to predict that cysteine formation from phosphoserine in Dr. Fromageot's enzymatic experiments should be much more rapid than its formation from free serine? Was any such effect observed?

DR. FROMAGEOT:

To compare rates of formation, the catalyst concentration should be comparable. In the case of model experiment, this can be done easily and in the presence of pyridoxal phosphate and a metal or in the presence of pyruvate and copper, the rate of cysteine formation from $H_2S$ and phosphoserine is greater than from $H_2S$ and serine. In enzymatic experiment, using crude homogenates from the yolk sack the same observation is made and the ratio of both rate is about 5. This means either that phosphoserine sulfhydrase is five times more active than serinesulfhydrase, or that the concentration of phosphoserine is five times greater than that of serinesulfhydrase.

DR. CHAPEVILLE:

As Dr. Fromageot pointed out, several enzymes involved in taurine synthesis from mineral sulfate are present only in the endodermal cells of the chick yolk sac. The others such as cysteic acid decarboxylase and serine sulfhydrase are found also in the embryo itself. It would be interesting to look for the yolk sac enzymes in embryos of different zoological groups (ovo and ovo-viviparous) and find out at which stage of evolution they appeared and at which they disappeared.

The serine sulfhydrase is also an interesting enzyme. We regret that Dr. Lynen is not present at this meeting. He would certainly comment its physiological role. It seems very likely that in micro-organisms and probably in plants it is responsible for cysteine synthesis from mineral sulfide which comes from sulfate. However, the serine sulfhydrase is also present in mammals which do not reduce mineral sulfate. The question arises, does this enzyme have any physiological role in mammals or should it be classified among the so-called vestigial enzymes?

# CLEAVAGE OF CYSTAMINE BY DIAMINEOXIDASE

by Carlo De Marco

Institute of Biological Chemistry, University of Rome, and
Centro Studi di Enzimologia del CNR, Rome (Italy)

Diamineoxidase (DAO), prepared either from hog kidney or from pea seedlings, is able to oxidize, among other diamines, cystamine also.[1–3]

The oxidative deamination of cystamine by DAO is indeed of particular interest because this enzyme is so far the only system which is able to metabolize cystamine *in vitro*.

It is in effect well known that cystamine is degraded *in vivo* to hypotaurine,[4] taurine,[5,6] and sulfate,[7] but the enzymic pathways involved in these oxidations have not yet been completely clarified.[8,9]

The oxidation of cystamine by DAO was demonstrated first by measurements of oxygen uptake, which showed that cystamine was as good a substrate for the enzyme as cadaverine or putrescine. However, a striking difference was noted between cystamine and the other two typical substrates.

Figure 1 shows that while with cadaverine as a substrate the oxygen uptake is close to the theoretical one, i.e. 0.5 mole per mole substrate, with cystamine a higher oxygen consumption is invariably found, more than twice the expected amount for a typical oxidative deamination. The same behaviour was found with both the pig kidney or pea seedlings enzymes.

On the other hand, the analytical data obtained on the deproteinized reaction mixture at the end of the oxygen uptake, were indicative of a typical oxidative deamination of cystamine, resulting in the formation of the corresponding aminoaldehyde.[1] Table 1 shows that 1 mole of ammonia was produced per mole of cystamine, and that no other oxidation products, like hypotaurine, taurine or sulfate, were present in the supernatant of the deproteinized incubation mixture. However, an unexpected result was the large decrease in the amount of disulfide groups. We will return to this question later.

Since it has been reported that the products of oxidation of cadaverine and putrescine could be recovered as the cyclized internal Schiff bases instead of their free aminoaldehyde derivatives,[10,11] it was assumed that the aminoaldehyde resulting from oxidation of cystamine also could give rise to the corresponding cyclic compound.

To test this hypothesis, diamineoxidase prepared from pea seedlings was incubated with cystamine in the presence of *o*-aminobenzaldehyde. *o*-Aminobenzaldehyde (OABA) has the property of combining spontaneously

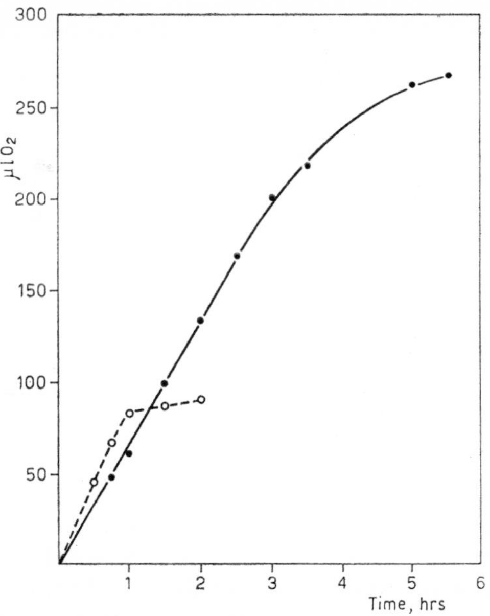


FIG. 1. Oxidation of cadaverine and cystamine by diamineoxidase. Incubation was performed at 38°C in Warburg vessels containing 0.2 g pig kidney acetone powder in 2 ml phosphate buffer 0.1 M, pH 7.4; substrates 10 $\mu$moles; water to 3 ml, 0.2 ml 25 per cent NaOH in the center well. Gas phase: air. Full line: cystamine. Dotted line: cadaverine (see Ref. 1).

TABLE 1. ANALYSIS OF A DEPROTEINIZED REACTION MIXTURE OF PIG KIDNEY DAO INCUBATED FOR 6 HR AT 38°C WITH 10 $\mu$MOLES OF CYSTAMINE

| | Theory | Found |
|---|---|---|
| $O_2$ uptake ($\mu$moles) | 5 | 12 |
| $NH_3$ ($\mu$moles) | 10 | 9.6 |
| Cystamine ($\mu$moles) | 0 | 0 |
| Taurine ($\mu$moles) | ? | 0 |
| Hypotaurine ($\mu$moles) | ? | 0 |
| —SS-groups (%) | 100 | 21 |
| Sulfate ($\mu$moles) | 0 | 0 |
| $H_2S$ ($\mu$moles) | 0 | 0 |

and specifically with cyclized aldimine compounds yielding yellow or orange derivatives.[10–12] The incubation of DAO with cystamine in the presence of OABA resulted in the production of a golden yellow colour. Furthermore, the total oxygen uptake was depressed to the theoretical value of 0.5 mole per mole substrate. These results were a strong indication of the production of a cyclic aldimine also in the case of cystamine, and accordingly it has been possible to isolate this compound.

This was achieved as follows. To a large quantity of an incubation mixture containing cystamine and OABA, picric acid was added and the picrate of the dihydroquinazolinium compound resulting from the reaction of OABA with the cyclized aldimine, was precipitated. A few milligrams of red-coloured crystals were then obtained, and their microanalysis showed a very good agreement with the calculated values.[13]

It was thus established that the product of oxidation of cystamine by DAO is the cyclized aminoaldehyde, for which we proposed the name cystaldmine:

$$\begin{matrix} CH_2-S-S-CH_2 \\ | \qquad\qquad | \\ CH_2NH_2 \quad CH_2NH_2 \end{matrix} \xrightarrow[-NH_3]{+\frac{1}{2}O_2} \begin{matrix} CH_2-S-S-CH_2 \\ | \qquad\qquad | \\ CH_2NH_2 \quad CHO \end{matrix} \longrightarrow \begin{matrix} S-S \\ CH_2 \quad CH_2 \\ | \qquad | \\ CH_2 \quad CH \\ N \end{matrix}$$

Cystamine Cystaldimine

These results demonstrated therefore that DAO acts on cystamine in the same way as on the other diamines, giving rise to the same products : ammonia and the corresponding aminoaldehyde in a cyclized form. However, the higher oxygen uptake shown by cystamine, suggested a particular unstability of cystaldimine, and the possibility of further spontaneous or enzymic modifications, of the latter compound.

This has been verified by the observation that labile sulfur was produced during cystamine oxidation in presence of DAO. The labile sulfur was detected by the cyanolysis reaction,[19] which was positive either in the TCA supernatant and in the precipitate, and increased as the reaction proceeded.

As shown in the Table 1, not all the sulfur was recovered in the supernatant of the deproteinized incubation mixture. In addition to the cyanolysis reaction in the precipitate, it has been possible to demonstrate, by detection of increasing amounts of sulfate in the oxidized TCA precipitate,[2] or by using radioactive cystamine, that about half of the cystamine sulfur was bound to the enzyme proteins (Table 2).

In order to exclude that unoxidized cystamine as such was bound to the enzyme proteins, control experiments have been made incubating $S^{35}$-cystamine with DAO in the presence of 5 $\mu$moles of INH, which completely inhibits the reaction. As shown in Table 2, in this case practically no radioactivity was found in the precipitate. Attempts to elute the sulfur from the precipitate by the use of boiling alcohol, pyridine or carbon sulfide, have been unsuccessful. After all these treatments the amount of radioactivity in the precipitate remained constant, and also the values of the cyanolysis reaction.

By treatment of the precipitate with an excess of cysteine,[14] it was possible to recover about 30 per cent of the protein-bound sulfur as hydrogen sulfide. It has also been possible to exclude that the sulfur present in the precipitate was still bound to the carbon chain of cystamine, because after oxidation of the precipitate, no taurine was detected by paper or column chromatography.

TABLE 2. PROTEIN-BOUND SULFUR AFTER INCUBATION FOR 6 HR AT 38°C OF PIG KIDNEY DAO WITH 10$\mu$MOLES OF CYSTAMINE

| | DAO | DAO + INH |
|---|---|---|
| $S^{35}$ cystamine added (counts/min) | 14,000 | 14,000 |
| $S^{35}$ found in the TCA ppt. (counts/min) | 6,931 | 545 |

These results suggest the presence in the TCA precipitate of an unidentified form of inorganic sulfur, insoluble in the usual organic solvents, and firmly bound to the enzyme proteins.

The further degradation of cystaldimine was also suggested by the demonstration of transulfuration reactions, coupled to cystamine oxidation.[15,16] If cystamine and DAO are incubated in the presence of

$$\begin{matrix} CH_2-SO_2H \\ | \\ CH_2NH_2 \end{matrix} \longrightarrow \begin{matrix} CH_2-SO_2-SH \\ | \\ CH_2NH_2 \end{matrix}$$

Hypotaurine → Thiotaurine

$$\begin{matrix} CH_2-SO_2H \\ | \\ CHNH_2 \\ | \\ COOH \end{matrix} \longrightarrow \begin{matrix} CH_2-SO_2-SH \\ | \\ CHNH_2 \\ | \\ COOH \end{matrix}$$

Cysteinesulfinic acid → Alaninethiosulfonic acid

hypotaurine or cysteinesulfinic acid, the corresponding thiosulfonates are produced, namely thiotaurine[17] and alaninethiosulfonic acid.[18] These compounds have been estimated by the cyanolysis reaction,[19] and using radioactive cystamine it has also been possible to demonstrate that there is some correlation between the sulfur linked to the enzyme proteins and the labile sulfur involved in the transulfuration reactions. In other words, when transulfuration takes place as demonstrated by the production of thiosulfonates, a corresponding lesser amount of sulfur is recovered in the

TABLE 3. EFFECT OF TRANSULFURATION COUPLED TO CYSTAMINE OXIDATION, ON THE PROTEIN BOUND SULFUR

10 μmoles of $S^{35}$-cystamine (=40,000 counts/min) incubated for 6 hr at 38°C with DAO. CSA = cysteinesulfinic acid. HYP = hypotaurine.

| Sulfinate added | Thiosulfonate as μmoles KSCN | Per cent of radioactivity | |
|---|---|---|---|
| | | In the supernatant | In the ppt. |
| None | 0.50 | 28 | 72 |
| CSA (20 μmoles) | 1.03 | 37 | 64 |
| HYP (20 μmoles) | 1.39 | 40 | 59 |

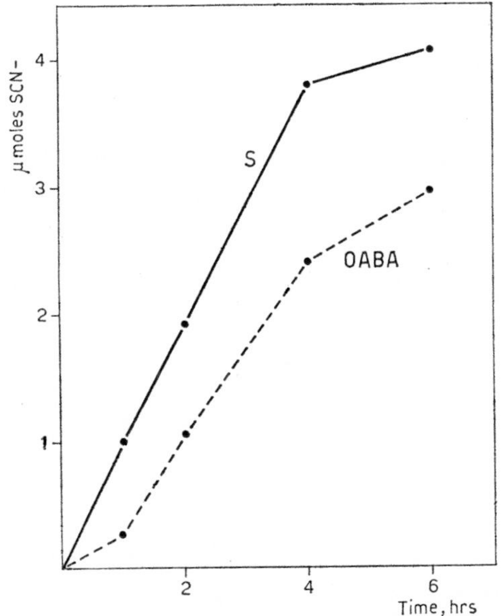


FIG. 2. Effect of *o*-aminobenzaldehyde on the protein-bound sulfur. Incubation mixture: 0.2 g acetone powder obtained from pig kidney homogenate heated at 60°C for 10 min; phosphate buffer 0.1 M pH 7.4, 2 ml. Cystamine 10 μmoles. *o*-aminobenzaldehyde 12 μmoles. Water to 3 ml.

Cyanolysis reaction was performed on the TCA precipitate, washed with 5 per cent TCA and dissolved in 1 N $NH_3$. The values are reported as μmoles of KSCN formed from 10 μmoles of substrate. S = standard system; OABA = standard system added with *o*-aminobenzaldehyde.

protein precipitate. Experiments have been then performed in presence of OABA, and it was found that the amount of sulfur detectable in the protein precipitate by the cyanolisis reaction was greatly reduced. At the same time a little increase of the labile sulfur in the supernatant was observed. This can be explained assuming that cystaldimine is almost in part responsible for the cyanolysis in the supernatant, while the cyanolysis in the precipitate is imputable to a product of degradation of cystaldimine, whose formation is avoided when cystaldimine is trapped by OABA.

These results suggest that cystaldimine is the direct source of the sulfur released during incubation.

The release of sulfur from cystaldimine can be explained on the assumption that cystaldimine is split either spontaneously or enzymically into the persulfide analogue of cysteamine, that we called thiocysteamine, and a two-carbon fragment, according to the following scheme:



Cystaldimine Thiocysteamine

The compounds with the general formula R—S—SH are unstable and liberate sulfur very easily,[20] and moreover spontaneously transulfurate suitable acceptors.[21,22] Thus thiocysteamine might well fulfil the role of an intermediate in the side reactions occurring during cystamine oxidation.

Owing to the unstability of thiocysteamine, isolation or synthesis of this compound has been so far unsuccessful. Therefore attempts have been made for obtaining indirect proofs of its formation in incubation mixtures.

Cystamine has been incubated with DAO in the presence of monoiodacetic acid (MIA) or N-ethyl-malcinimide (NEM), with the aim of isolating their addition products with thiocysteamine. By a similar procedure, recently Flavin[23] has been able to show that thiocysteine was formed from cystine by the action of cystathionase.

We expected to find carboxymethylthiocysteamine in our reaction mixture, but in fact using paper chromatography this compound has not yet been found.

However, the very presence of MIA modifies to some extent the behaviour of the reaction : the oxygen uptake is depressed and tends to approach the theoretical value; the amount of sulfur bound to the proteins and correspondingly the coupled transulfuration reactions are decreased.

The results of these experiments which were performed using radioactive cystamine, are summarized in Table 4. However by paper chromatography the presence of carboxymethylcysteamine in the deproteinized incubation mixture, was proved. This finding indicates the release of free cysteamine in the incubation medium.

Analogous results have been obtained with NEM: depressed oxygen uptake, decrease of transulfuration and protein-bound sulfur. Also in this case the addition product of cysteamine with NEM has been detected by paper chromatography, and by the red colour developed in TCA supernatant when brought to alkaline pH.

TABLE 4. EFFECT OF MONOIODACETIC ACID ON THE PROTEIN-BOUND SULFUR AND ON TRANSULFURATION REACTIONS

10 μmoles of $S^{35}$-cystamine (=40,000 counts/min) incubated with DAO for 6 hr at 38°C.

| Addition | Counts/min in the TCA ppt. |
|---|---|
| None | 28,751 |
| MIA (50 μmoles) | 17,000 |

| Addition | μmoles of thiotaurine |
|---|---|
| HYP (20 μmoles) | 0.95 |
| HYP (20 μmoles) +MIA (50 μmoles) | 0.32 |

The failure of the sulfur to be released in the incubation medium, could be explained on the basis that thiocysteamine was trapped by NEM or MIA.

At any rate, the presence of free cysteamine and sulfur indicates a splitting of cystaldimine, and therefore we have looked for the possible two-carbon compounds originating from the remaining half molecule. Deproteinized incubation mixtures have been analysed for glycolic, glyossilic and oxalic acid,[24] with negative results.

It was also demonstrated that during cystamine oxidation no carbon dioxide was formed. It has been possible to detect only a small amount of glycolaldehyde (or glyoxal) as 2,4-dinitrophenylosazone. This was identified spectrophotometrically and quantitatively determined by the method of Neuberg and Strauss.[25]

In spite of the very poor amount of glycolaldehyde found (a few micrograms from 10 μmoles of cystamine), the production of this compound is in agreement with the splitting of cystaldimine according to the above reported scheme.

Further indications on the postulated mechanism of breakdown of cystaldimine, were obtained from experiments on the action of DAO on lanthionamine, another sulfur-containing diamine, which was previously shown to be a good substrate for DAO.[1]

With lanthionamine too, an extra oxygen uptake was observed, indicating that in this case also the product of oxidation is undergoing further degradation.

It is reasonable to admit that just as for cadaverine, putrescine and cystamine, the aminoaldehyde resulting from lanthionamine forms a cyclized compound, which differs from cystaldimine by the presence of only a single atom of sulfur.

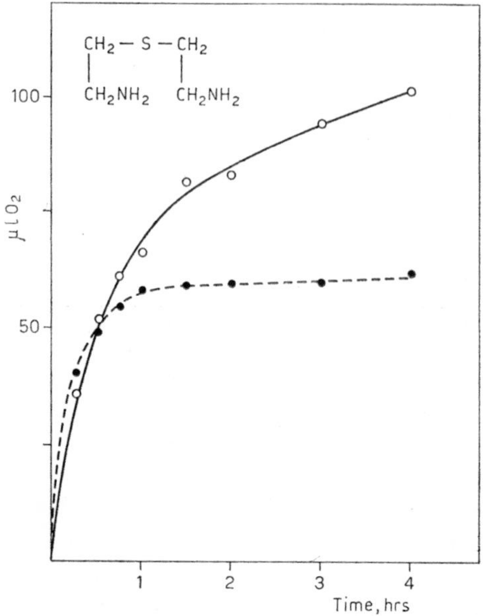


FIG. 3. Oxidation of lanthionamine by pea seedlings diamineoxidase.

Enzyme preparation 20 mg. Substrates 5 $\mu$moles. Final volume 3 ml. Final pH 5.6. Temperature, 25°C.

Dotted line: cadaverine. Full line: lanthionamine. (See Ref. 1.)

Cystaldimine

In these experiments with lanthionamine a very small amount of sulfur was found to be bound to the enzyme proteins, and coupled transulfuration reactions were practically absent (Tables 5 and 6).

However, free cysteamine is released during the oxidation of lanthionamine, as it is indicated by the formation of carboxymethylcysteamine when oxidation is allowed to occur in presence of MIA (Fig. 4). Beyond this, glycololdehyde is produced from lanthionamine, although to a minor extent.

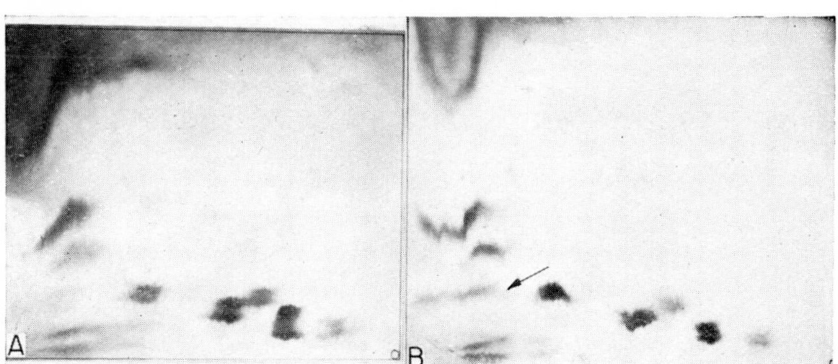


FIG. 4. Paper chromatography of the TCA supernatant of pig kidney diamine-oxidase after 6 hr of incubation at 38°C with lanthionamine (A) or with lanthion-amine and monoiodacetic acid (B). Enzyme preparation 20 mg. Water 6 ml. pH adjusted to 7.4. Substrates 20 μmoles. Monoiodacetic acid 100 μmoles. After incubation 0.6 ml 100 per cent TCA were added and 0.6 ml of the supernatant were spotted on the paper.

Solvents: phenol (from the right to the left), collidine–lutidine (from the bottom to the top). Carboxymethylcysteamine is indicated by the arrow.

From the results reported above, it should be concluded that DAO acts on cystamine in the same way as on other diamines.

The different behaviour of these compounds must be due to the different stability of the oxidation products.

Cystaldimine is an unstable compound, probably because of the presence of both an aldimine and a disulfide bond. Certainly a splitting of the sulfur–carbon bond takes place in the case of cystamine, as well as in the case of lanthionamine.

TABLE 5. PROTEIN-BOUND SULFUR, DETECTED BY CYANOLYSIS IN THE TCA PPT., AND REPORTED AS μMOLES OF KSCN FORMED FROM 10 μMOLES OF SUBSTRATE.
The values of zero time have been substracted.

| Time of incubation (hr) | Cystamine | Lanthionamine |
|---|---|---|
| 2 | 2.7 | 0.1 |
| 4 | 3.2 | 0.27 |
| 6 | 4.1 | 0.27 |

TABLE 6. TRANSULFURATION COUPLED TO CYSTAMINE AND LANTHIONAMINE OXIDATION
μmoles of KSCN formed by cyanolysis in the TCA supernatant; 10 μmoles of substrate incubated with DAO for 6 hr at 38°C. Sulfinate added = 20 μmoles.

| Substrate | μmoles KSCN | Substrate | μmoles KSCN |
|---|---|---|---|
| Cystamine | 0.54 | Lanthionamine | 0.28 |
| Cystamine + CSA | 1.04 | Lanthionamine + CSA | 0.20 |
| Cystamine + HYP | 1.38 | Lanthionamine + HYP | 0.40 |

For lanthionamine, the results obtained indicate a β-substitution of cysteamine. As far as cystamine is concerned, the analogous reaction might produce thiocysteamine.

Even if this compound has not yet been unequivocally identified, the results reported above and the consideration that the release of labile sulfur

$$\begin{matrix} & S & \\ CH_2 & & CH_2 \\ | & & | \\ CH_2 & N & CH \end{matrix} \longrightarrow \begin{matrix} CH_2-SH \\ | \\ CH_2NH_2 \end{matrix} + C_2$$

Cysteamine

$$\begin{matrix} & S-S & \\ CH_2 & & CH_2 \\ | & & | \\ CH_2 & N & CH \end{matrix} \longrightarrow \begin{matrix} CH_2-S-SH \\ | \\ CH_2-NH_2 \end{matrix} + C_2$$

Thiocysteamine

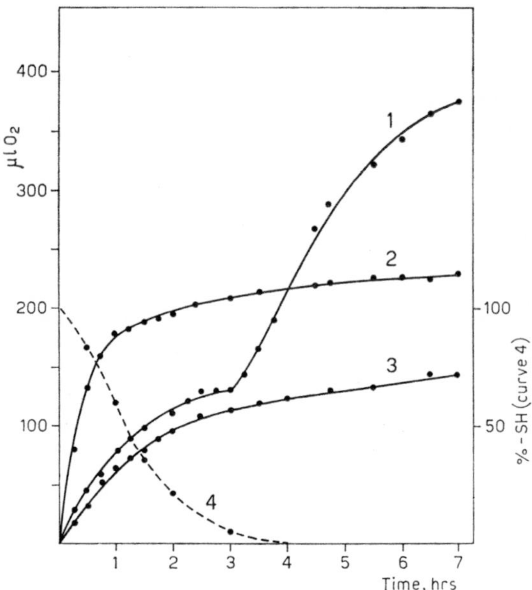


Fig. 5. Oxidation of cysteamine by pig kidney diamineoxidase, at pH 7.4. Temp. 38°C.

1. 20 μmoles cysteamine.
2. 10 μmoles cystamine.
3. 20 μmoles cysteamine + 5 μmoles isoniazid.
4. Disappearance of —SH groups in an incubate like that of curve 1 (ordinates at the right). (See Ref. 26.)

is a specific property of cystamine, strongly suggest that thiocysteamine is produced in our incubation mixtures. On the basis of these results, we may put cystamine among the natural substrates for DAO,

In the course of studies on the effect of DAO on the corresponding monoamine, cysteamine, an interesting observation has been made, which is pertinent to the possible PLP content of DAO.

Unlike cystamine, cysteamine is not oxidized in the presence of DAO, but instead acts as a powerful inhibitor.[26]

In the experimental conditions used, cystamine causes a transient inhibition of DAO activity. This is due to the fact that cysteamine is non-enzymically oxidized to cystamine; until it is completely oxidized, DAO activity is prevented : then the inhibitor is spontaneously transformed into a substrate for the enzyme. These observations are of some interest, because they could be indicative of the presence of PLP in DAO.

It has been demonstrated in fact, that cysteamine also, when linked to PLP in a thiazolidine ring, is spontaneously oxidized to cystamine, so liberating PLP again.[27]

This observation is certainly not a proof of the presence of PLP in DAO. The inhibition caused by cysteamine could be due in fact to its property of being a carbonyl reagent, and cysteamine might be thus enumerated among the other carbonyl reagents, powerful inhibitors of DAO. Contrary to these well known inhibitors, however, cysteamine shows the peculiar characteristic of giving rise to a transient inhibition.

## REFERENCES


1. D. Cavallini, C. De Marco and B. Mondovì; *Experimentia* **12**, 377 (1956).
2. D. Cavallini, C. De Marco and B. Mondovì; *Boll. soc. ital. biol. sper.* **32**, 1145 (1956).
3. D. Cavallini, C. De Marco and B. Mondovì; *Biochim. et Biophys. Acta* **24**, 353 (1957).
4. D. Cavallini, B. Mondovì and C. De Marco; *Ricerca Sci.* **24**, 2649 (1954).
5. D. Cavallini, B. Mondovì and C. De Marco; *Giorn. Biochim.* **2**, 13 (1953).
6. L. Eldjarn; *J. Biol. Chem.* **206**, 483 (1954).
7. L. Eldjarn; *Scand. J. Clin. & Lab. Invest.* supl. 6, **13** (1954).
8. B. Mondovì, C. De Marco, L. Tentori and D. Cavallini; *Boll. soc. ital. biol. sper.* **37**, 1695 (1961).
9. D. Cavallini, C. De Marco and B. Mondovì; *Enzymologia* **23**, 101 (1961).
10. P. J. G. Mann and W. Smithies; *Biochem. J.* **61**, 89 (1955).
11. K. Hasse and H. Maisack; *Biochem. Z.* **327**, 296 (1955).
12. H. J. Vogel and B. D. Davis; *J. Am. Chem. Soc.* **74**, 109 (1952).
13. D. Cavallini, C. De Marco and B. Mondovì; *Biochim. et Biophys. Acta* **24**, 353 (1957).
14. C. V. Smythe; *J. Biol. Chem.* **142**, 387 (1942).
15. C. De Marco, M. Coletta and B. Mondovì; *Giorn. Biochim.* **9**, 75 (1960).
16. C. De Marco; *Giorn. Biochim.* **10**, 197 (1961).
17. D. Cavallini, C. De Marco and B. Mondovì; *Bull. soc. chim. biol.* **40**, 1711 (1958).
18. C. De Marco, M. Coletta, B. Mondovì and D. Cavallini; *Giorn. Biochim.* **9**, 1 (1960).
19. B. Sorbo; *Biochim. et Biophys. Acta* **24**, 324 (1957).

20. H. Böhme and G. Zinner; *Ann. Chem. Liebigs* **585**, 142 (1954).
21. C. De Marco, M. Coletta and D. Cavallini; *Arch. Biochem. Biophys.* **93**, 17 (1961).
22. C. De Marco, M. Coletta and D. Cavallini; *Experientia* **18**, 117 (1962).
23. M. Flavin; *J. Biol. Chem.* **237**, 786 (1962).
24. F. Deigl; *Spot Tests in Organic Analysis*, Elsevier (1960).
25. C. Neuberger and E. Strauss; *Arch. Biochem. Biophys.* **7**, 211 (1945).
26. C. De Marco, B. Mondovì and D. Cavallini; *Biochem. Pharmacol.* **11**, 509 (1962
27. C. De Marco and D. Bognolo; *Arch. Biochem. Biophys.* **98**, 562 (1962).

## DISCUSSION

Dr. Kapeller-Adler:

Have you tried the action of diamine oxidase on mixtures of cystamine and histamine and of cystamine and cadaverine, and, if so, were the enzymatic effects of a competitiv or of an additive nature?

Dr. De Marco:

This has been done with pea seedlings (see Ref. 1) and using cadaverine and cystamin together as substrates. The oxygen consumption curves showed that the enzymatic effect were of a competitive nature.

# THE PURIFICATION OF HOG KIDNEY DIAMINE OXIDASE

by BRUNO MONDOVÌ, GIUSEPPE ROTILIO, M. TERESA COSTA

Institute of Biological Chemistry, University of Rome
and Department of Enzymology of CNR, Rome, Italy

IN SPITE of a great number of studies on pig kidney diamine oxidase, the enzyme is not yet adequately known mainly because of the difficulty in obtaining large quantities of highly purified preparations.

We were particularly interested in purifying DO* in order to investigate cystamine methabolism.[1] Other more general and still unanswered interesting questions about the enzyme were its relations with the pea seedlings DO and histaminase and the nature of its prosthetic groups.

The sensitivity of animal DO to carbonyl reagents suggests that this enzyme contains a functional aldehyde or ketone group.[2]

Davison[3], Goryachenkova[4,5], Kapeller-Adler[6] and others[7,8], have provided evidence that both FAD and pyridoxal phosphate are the coenzymes of DO.

Werle and Hartung[9] have demonstrated that plant and animal DO are inhibited by sodium diethyldithiocarbamate, salicylaldoxime, dithizone and 8-hydroxyquinoline: these results suggest that the enzyme contains also a heavy-metal essential for its activity.

Recently Mann[10–12] has obtained a highly purified preparation of pea seedlings DO, and has demonstrated that the prosthetic group of the enzyme is a copper complex of a carbonyl compound which undergoes reduction and oxidation during the catalytic activity.

Yamada and Yasunobu[13,14] have shown that crystalline plasma amine oxidase can be represented as protein $(Cu^{2+})_4$-(pyridoxal phosphate)$_2$. No flavins were detected.

The question whether diamine oxidase and histaminase are identical has not yet been solved : Goryachencova[15] and Zeller[16,17] believe that they are the same enzyme; Kapeller-Adler on the other hand has purified histaminase and demonstrated that it was inactive on cadaverine, the typical substrate of DO.[18]

---

*The following abbreviations will be used in this paper:
DO, diamine oxidase; FAD, flavin-adenine-dinucleotide; TRIS, tris(hydroxymethyl)-aminomethane; DDC, diethyldithiocarbamate; DEAE, cellulose, diethylaminoethyl-cellulose; EDTA, ethylenediaminetetra-acetic acid.

Pig kidney DO was previously purified by many authors[19-25]; Uspenkaia and Goryachenkova[24], and Mondovì[25] have obtained the most highly purified preparations.

In the present work an enzyme preparation has been obtained which has a greater purity, is stable for several days and is active both with cadaverine and histamine.

The preliminary purification procedure of DO as described by Tabor[22] has been modified, mainly because we observed a great loss of enzyme activity in the preparation of the acetone powder.

The present procedure is simpler and gives a better yield and a higher specific activity than that previously described by us.[25]

## MATERIALS AND METHODS

### *Materials*

Cadaverine chloride was obtained from Light and Co., Ltd., or Fluka Chemische Fabrik; TRIS and 2-mercaptoethanol from the Fluka Chemische Fabrik; histamine dihydrochloride, DL-lysine, EDTA, sodium borohydrure and sodium dithionite from Merck; cysteamine from Bracco Ind. Chim.; cystamine was obtained from cysteamine by oxidation according to Nathan and Bogert[26]; sodium diethyldithiocarbamate from the Judex Special Reagent; pyridoxal-5-phosphate from Hoffman La Roche and Co., Ltd.; DEAE cellulose from Servall; cellulose powder ashless from Whatman (W. and R. Bolston Ltd.).

### *Enzyme Assay*

The enzyme assay was followed by the $O_2$ uptake in a conventional Warburg apparatus at 38°. Air was used as gas.

One hundred micromoles of substrate were dissolved in 0.1 ml of water and placed in the side arm; the main compartment contained the enzyme, 1 ml of 0.3 M potassium phosphate buffer pH 7.4; 100 $\mu$g of cathalase; 100 $\mu$moles of ethanol; 10 $\mu$g of pyridoxal-5-phosphate; water to 3 ml. The center well contained 0.2 ml of 30 per cent NaOH.

Proteins were determined by the biuret procedure of Goa[27] or by the spectrophotometric method of Adams[28].

Spectrophotometric measurement were made with a Beckman DK 2 recording spectrophotometer.

A unit of enzyme activity was taken as 1 $\mu$l of $O_2$ consumed during 1 hr under the experimental conditions described above. The specific activity was expressed in terms of the enzyme units per mg of protein.

During the purification, the presence of DO was revealed qualitatively by a simple procedure: test tubes, containing 0.3–0.6 ml of the sample with 0.5 ml of 0.15 M potassium phosphate buffer pH 7.4 and 0.05 ml of a 5 per cent oxyhaemoglobin solution with 50 $\mu$moles of cadaverine as substrate, were incubated for 3 hr at 38°. When the enzyme was present the solution turned from red to light brown due to the formation of oxidation products of haemoglobin by hydrogen peroxide produced by the action of DO on the substrate.

## PURIFICATION OF ENZYME

*Crude Enzyme Extract*

Five hundred grammes of frozen hog kidney were homogenized in 600 ml water for 5 min by a waring blendor. (Fraction (1), Table 1.)

TABLE 1. PURIFICATION OF HOG KIDNEY DIAMINE OXIDASE

| Fraction | Total protein (mg) | Total activity (units) | Specific activity (units/mg) | Yield (%) | Purification (fold) |
|---|---|---|---|---|---|
| 1. Crude homogenate | 71,500 | 37,900 | 0.53 | 100 | 1 |
| 2. Supernatant from homogenate heated to 60° for 10 min | 7700 | 25,250 | 3.28 | 67 | 6.2 |
| 3. Ammonium sulfate (33–60%) | 2100 | 23,300 | 11.1 | 61 | 21 |
| 4. Column electrophoresis | 52 | 6240 | 120 | 16 | 226 |
| 5. Column chromatography on DEAE cellulose | 2.6 | 2160 | 830 | 6 | 1570 |

*The data refer to four electrophoretic columns, corresponding to one preparation of crude homogenate.

*Controlled Heat Denaturation*

The crude homogenate was placed into a beaker and stirred in a water bath at 60° for 10 min, the beaker was then transferred to an ice bath and quickly cooled to about 20°. The cooled homogenate was centrifuged for 1 hr at 6000 $\times g$ and the precipitate discarded. (Fraction (2), Table 1.)

*Ammonium Sulfate Fractionation*

All the subsequent operations were performed at 0°.

Solid ammonium sulfate was added to the heated extract to reach 33 per cent saturation.[29] The mixture was left with continuous stirring for at least 30 min and the precipitate was centrifuged off at 6000*g* for 20 min. The supernatant was brought to 60 per cent ammonium sulfate saturation.

The precipitate, suspended in 10 ml 0.01 M potassium phosphate buffer pH 6.9, was dialyzed at 5° against this buffer for three days (changing the buffer every 12 hr) to remove ammonium sulfate and to equilibrate the protein solution with the buffer to be used for electrophoresis. At the end of the dialysis the volume of the dialyzed solution was about 50 ml.

At this stage the enzyme could be stored for several weeks without appreciable loss of activity at − 20°. (Fraction (3), Table 1.)

*Zone Electrophoresis with Cellulose Powder*

All the subsequent operations were performed at 4°.

The apparatus used and the procedure followed were those described by Porath[30]. The cellulose was pre-treated with borohydrure according to Porath[31].

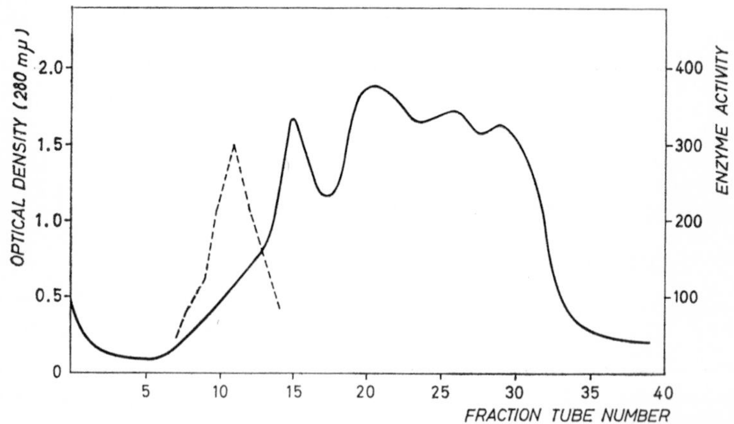


FIG. 1. Elution pattern obtained by column electrophoresis. The enzyme activity (dotted line) is expressed as microlitres of oxygen uptake per mg of protein per hr. Each fraction contains 10 ml of eluant.

Twelve millilitres, containing about 0.5 g of proteins of the solution obtained from the previous step, were applied to the top of a 65 × 3.8 cellulose electrophoretic column; the top of the column was connected to the cathode, the bottom to the anode.

The electrophoretic run was made in 0.01 M potassium phosphate buffer pH 6.9 for 22 hr, with 30 mA and a potential of 800V.

After the run the column was eluted and 10-ml fractions were collected and tested with the haemoglobin method with 0.5 ml of each. The enzyme activity of active fractions was determined in the Warburg apparatus. Only the fractions with a specific activity higher than 110 were collected and directly lyofilized without removing the phosphate salt.

At this step the enzyme was stable for about a month without appreciable loss of activity at —20°.

Figure 1 shows the elution pattern obtained by this method. (Fraction (4), Table 1.) The data refer to four electrophoretic columns, corresponding to one preparation of crude homogenate.

*Column Chromatography on Diethylaminoethyl–Cellulose*

All the subsequent operations were performed at 4°.

The freeze-dried preparations obtained from the previous step (four

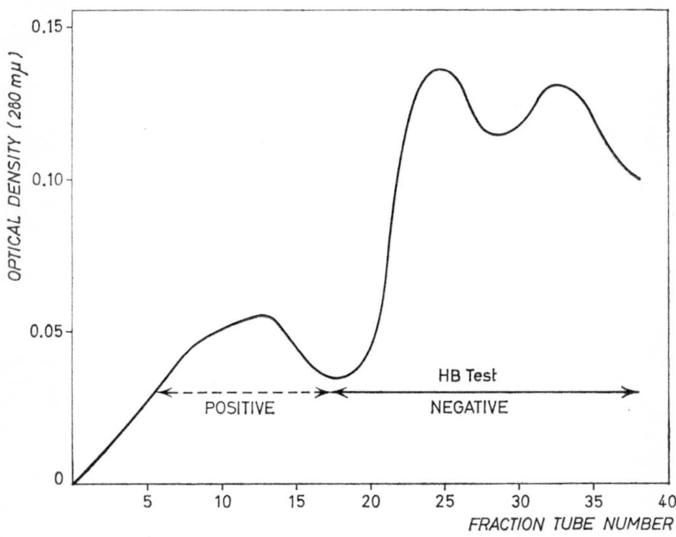


FIG. 2. Elution pattern obtained by column chromatography on DEAE cellulose. Each fraction contained 5 ml of eluant. Hb test as described in the text.

electrophoretic runs) corresponding to about 50 mg of proteins, were dissolved in 4 ml 0.05 M potassium phosphate buffer pH 7.2 and dialyzed against this buffer for 12 hr and placed on a 24 × 2.2 cm column of DEAE–cellulose pre-equilibrated with potassium phosphate buffer 0.05 M pH 7.2.

Chromatography was carried out according to Peterson and Sober[32].

The column was eluted with a concentration gradient obtained by three successive mixing chambers each containing 70 ml of, respectively, 0.05, 0.15 and 0.3 M potassium phosphate buffer pH 7.2 with 5 ml fractions collected by a fractions collector.

The enzyme activity was determined on 0.5 ml of each fraction positive to the haemoglobin test. Figure 2 shows the elution pattern obtained.

All the active fractions were combined and directly lyofilized. The powder so obtained was dissolved in 4 ml of water, dialyzed against 0.1 M potassium phosphate buffer pH 7.4 and, eventually, concentrated again by freeze drying.

At this step the enzyme was stable for at least 5 days with a little loss of activity at −20°.

The solutions generally appeared colorless. Sometimes we have obtained concentrated preparations which presented a very pale yellow color.

## STUDIES ON DIAMINE OXIDASE

To clarify the problem of whether DO and histaminase were the same enzyme and to see if the purified enzyme was also active on cystamine, which we had studied previously[1,33] the $O_2$ uptake during the purification steps using cadaverine, cystamine and histamine as substrates has been studied.

TABLE 2. SPECIFIC ACTIVITY DURING PURIFICATION STEPS OF DIAMINE OXIDASE WITH CADAVERINE, HISTAMINE AND CYSTAMINE AS SUBSTRATE

| Fraction | Substrate | | |
|---|---|---|---|
| | Cadaverine | Cystamine | Histamine |
| 1. Crude homogenate | 0.53 | 0.38 | 0.18 |
| 2. Supernatant from homogenate heated to 60° for 10 min | 3.28 | 3.6 | 0.91 |
| 3. Ammonium sulfate (33–60%) | 11.1 | 9.2 | 2.5 |
| 4. Column electrophoresis | 120.0 | 105.0 | 17.0 |
| 5. Column chromatography on DEAE–cellulose | 830.0 | 445.0 | 134.0 |

As it is clearly shown in Table 2 and Fig. 4, the purified enzyme is also active on the three substrates analysed but, during the purification, the difference between the specific activity on cadaverine and histamine increases and, while the ratio of the specific activity for these two substrates in the homogenate is about 3, it rises with purified enzyme to about 6.

Comparison of the $O_2$ uptake using cadaverine and lysine as substrate (Figs. 3 and 4) shows that after 2 hr the activity is similar both in the presence of crude homogenate (Fig. 3) and of purified enzyme (Fig. 4).

To explain the smaller $O_2$ uptake of cystamine (Table 2, and Fig. 2) when purified enzyme is used instead of crude homogenate, further research is necessary because the oxidation of this substrate is complicated by many products of reaction[1,33] and many enzymes are involved in its methabolism.[33]

It is of interest to note that with the crude homogenate, pyridoxal phosphate has no effect on the oxidation of cadaverine (Fig. 3), while, with the purified

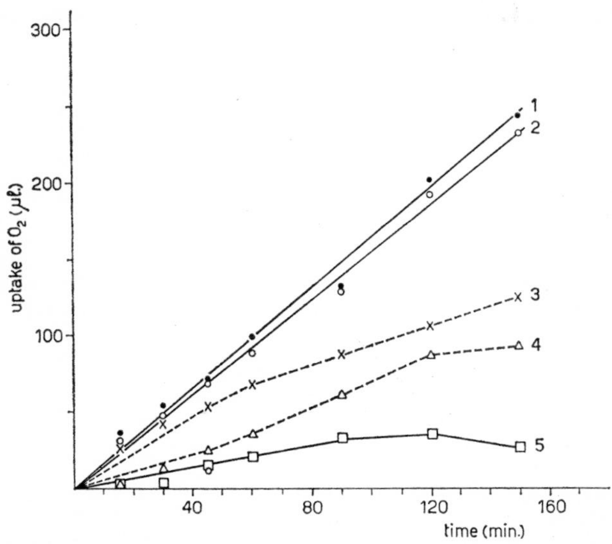


FIG. 3. Oxidation of cadaverine, cystamine and histamine by the "crude homogenate". Each vessel contained 200 mg of proteins, 100 μmoles of substrate, 100 μg of cathalase, 100 μmoles of ethanol, 1 ml of 0.3 M potassium phosphate buffer pH 7.4, water to 3 ml, temp. 38°; gas, air. Pyridoxal phosphate was added in all vessels except in the one corresponding to curve 2. The oxygen uptake of the incubation mixture without the substrate has been subtracted.

Curve 1. Cadaverine (in the presence of pyridoxal phosphate).
Curve 2. Cadaverine (without adding pyridoxal phosphate).
Curve 3. Cystamine.
Curve 4. Histamine.
Curve 5. Lysine.

enzyme, this coenzyme strongly increases the $O_2$ uptake, especially in the first time of incubation (Fig. 4). This effect may be unspecific, but it is in agreement with the hypothesis that pyridoxal phosphate is one of the coenzymes of DO.

Attempts have been made to resolve pyridoxal phosphate from the enzyme. For this purpose, a preparation of DO, at the step after electrophoresis with a specific activity of 45, was dialyzed for 8 days against 0.2 M TRIS buffer pH 8 containing 0.01 M EDTA and 0.003 M 2-mercaptoethanol (changing the buffer every 12 hr). This is the procedure described by Matsuo and Greenberg[34] to split pyridoxal phosphate from cystathionase. As it is shown in Fig. 5 no differences were observed in the activity of dialyzed enzyme in the presence and in the absence of added pyridoxal phosphate. Therefore, if this compound is one of the coenzymes of DO, it must be assumed that it is strongly bound to the protein.

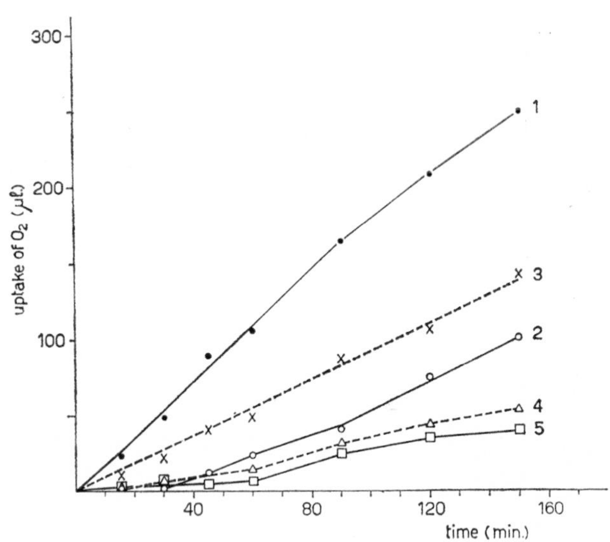


FIG. 4. Oxidation of cadaverine, cystamine and histamine by the purified enzyme (after column chromatography on DEAE cellulose). Each vessel contained 140 μg of proteins. Experimental conditions as in Fig. 3.

Pyridoxal phosphate was added in all vessels except in the one corresponding to curve 2.

Curve 1. Cadaverine (in the presence of pyridoxal phosphate).
Curve 2. Cadaverine (without adding pyridoxal phosphate).
Curve 3. Cystamine.
Curve 4. Histamine.
Curve 5. Lysine.

Diethyldithiocarbamate (0.01 M), employed as described by Mann[10], abolished the $O_2$ uptake (Fig. 5), in agreement with the data of Werle and Hartung[9]. On removal of DDC by dialysis for 24 hr against 0.1 M phosphate buffer pH 7.4, the activity is partially restored and not modified by adding $Cu^{2+}$ (Fig. 5).

These results indicate that the eventual metal present in DO has a higher affinity for the protein than for DDC.

*Spectrophotometric Studies*

As it is clearly shown in Figs. 6, 7 and 8 the spectrophotometric curves of the protein solutions during the purification steps demonstrate a decrease of absorbence in the Soret zone and an increase between 255 and 280 m$\mu$.

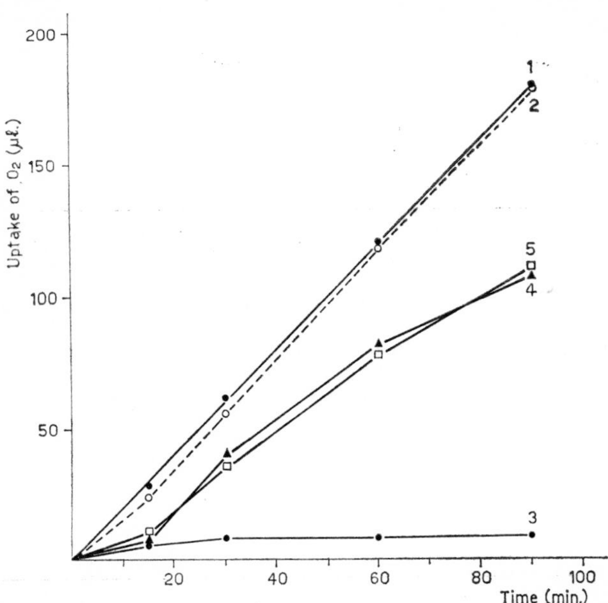


FIG. 5. Oxidation of cadaverine by DO after dialysis against TRIS buffer, as described in the text. Inactivation of DO by diethyldithiocarbamate and reactivation of enzyme activity after removing DDC.

Each vessel contained 2.75 mg of protein of a DO preparation collected after column electrophoresis.

Experimental conditions as in Fig. 3. Pyridoxal phosphate was added in all vessels except in the one corresponding to curve 2.

Curve 1. The DO preparation was dialyzed against TRIS buffer, as described in the text. This incubation was carried out after adding 10 $\mu$g of pyridoxal phosphate.

Curve 2. Same as curve 1, but without adding pyridoxal phosphate.

Curve 3. The DO preparation was dialyzed against 0.01 M DDC in 0.1 M potassium phosphate buffer for 4 hr at 0–5°.

Curve 4. Same as in curve 3, but the DO preparation, after the dialysis against DDC, was dialyzed again in 0.1 M potassium phosphate buffer for 25 hr at 0–5°.

Curve 5. Same as curve 4, after adding of 5 $\mu$moles of $CuCl_2$. With 1–10–20 $\mu$moles of $CuCl_2$ the results were identical.

The purified enzyme shows a broad absorption in the visible spectrum. Difference spectra were determined with purified enzyme comparing an aerobic solution with the same solution maintained anaerobically in the

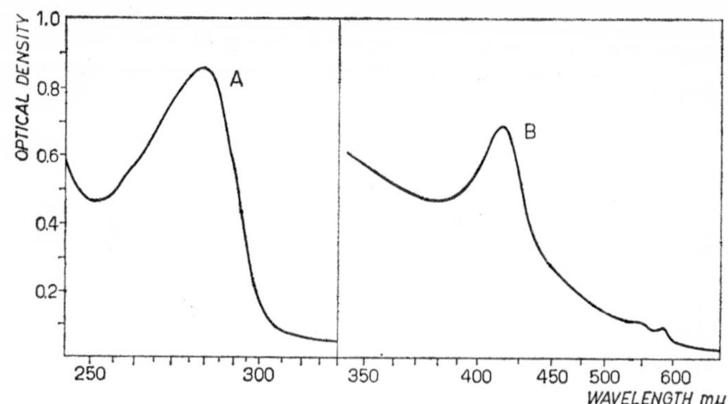


FIG. 6. Light absorption spectrum of a DO preparation obtained at the step (3) in Table 1.

Curve B. Corresponds to a protein concentration of 8.9 mg/ml in 0.1 M potassium phosphate buffer pH 7.4.

Curve A. The same solution diluted 1 : 10 with the buffer.

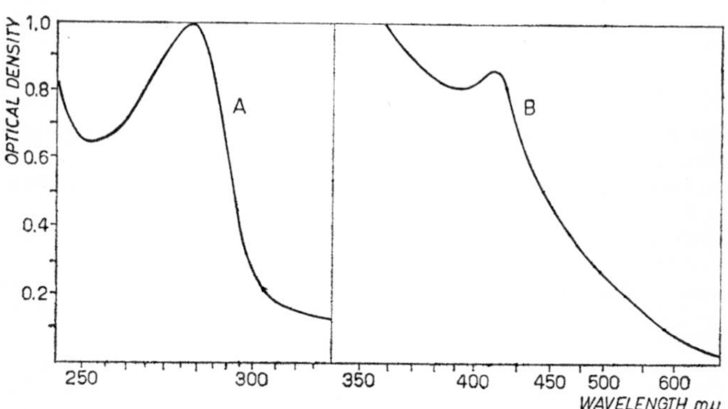


FIG. 7. Light absorption spectrum of a preparation obtained at the step (4) in Table 1.

Curve B. Corresponds to a protein concentration of 9.7 mg/ml in 0.1 M potassium phosphate buffer pH 7.4.

Curve A. The same solution diluted 1 : 10 with the buffer.

presence of cadaverine. The conditions described by Rajagopalan[35], who demonstrated the presence of FAD in the acetaldeyde-oxidase by this method, were used.

Our experiments did not show any spectral change, even when dithionite (as described by Mann[10] for DO extracted from pea seedlings) was employed.

Recently Yamada and Yasubobu[14] have demonstrated that one prosthetic group of plasma amine-oxidase is pyridoxal phosphate, but this was revealed only in the presence of diethyldithiocarbamate; this substance removes copper from the enzyme and spectrum of pyridoxal phosphate appears.

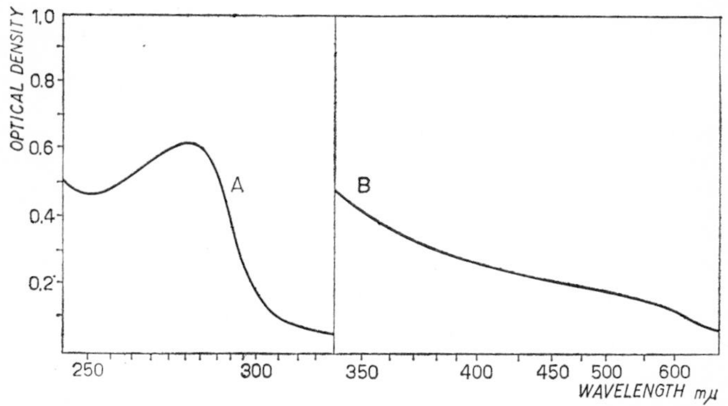


FIG. 8. Light absorption spectrum of a preparation obtained at the step (5) in Table 1.

Curve B. Corresponds to a protein concentration of 5.5 mg/ml in 0.1 M potassium phosphate buffer pH 7.4.

Curve A. The same solution diluted 1 : 10 with the buffer.

In the presence of 0.01 M DDC, a DO solution gives rise to a curve with a band at 442 mμ (Fig. 9).

This peak is stable at pH 7.4 and 4, disappears in 0.1 N NaOH and is restored by adjusting the pH again to 7.4. With 1 mg of borohydrure[34] it is stable and disappears by adding 1 mg of dithionite.

It is improbable that pyridoxal phosphate is responsible for this spectrum because : (*a*) under these conditions the pyridoxal phosphate band appears in another wavelength[14,36]; (*b*) in 0.1 N NaOH the typical spectrum is not present; (*c*) in the presence of borohydrure no change of spectrum was observed.[34]

As it is shown in Fig. 10 the spectrum is similar to that observed with copper DDC complex.[10,37]

Mahler *et al.*[37] have obtained an identical spectrum, with a peak at the same wavelength as the one obtained by us, with purified uricase in the presence of DDC, demonstrating that it was a copperprotein. Other metals ($Ni^{2+}$, $Fe^{2+}$, $Fe^{3+}$, $Zn^{2+}$, $Mn^{2+}$) which give chelates with DDC do not give rise to similar spectra,[37] which can be considered specific for copper.

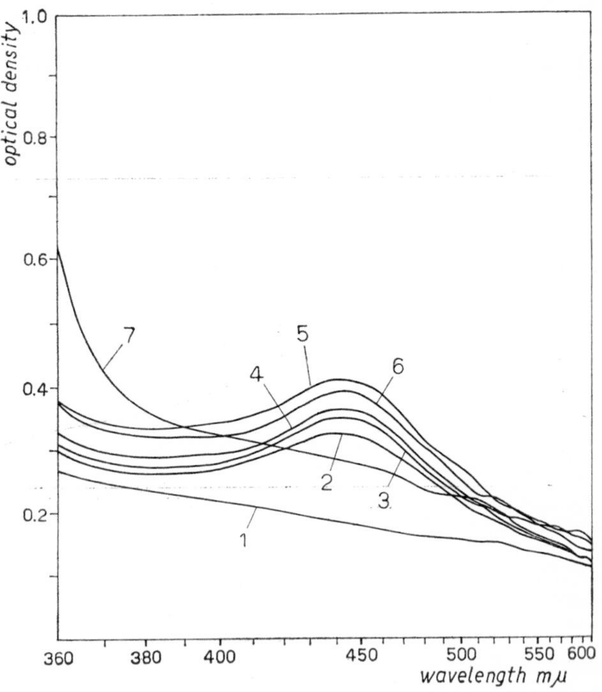


FIG. 9. Light absorption spectrum of purified DO in the presence of 0.01 M diethyldithio carbamate, in 0.1 M potassium phosphate buffer pH 7.4.

Curve 1. Enzyme as such (3.5 mg of protein in 1 ml of buffer).

Curves 2–5. The same solution in the presence of 0.01 M DDC after 1, 5, 20, 60 min.

Curve 6. The same as in curve 5, 1 hr after the addition of 1 mg of sodium borohydrure.

Curve 7. The same as in curve 5, 10 min after the addition of 1 mg of sodium dithionite.

Thus DO extracted from pig kidney might well be a copperprotein, but it is not yet certain whether it is similar to the DO extracted from pea seedlings,[10] and if it contains pyridoxal phosphate.

The presence of pyridoxal phosphate is indeed suggested by the sensitivity of DO to inhibitors as isoniazid, sulfite, cyanide and cysteamine, but the specificity of these substances is not absolute. The activation by pyridoxal phosphate of the purified enzyme, demonstrated in the present work, adds evidence however on the possible role of pyridoxal phosphate as a coenzyme of DO.

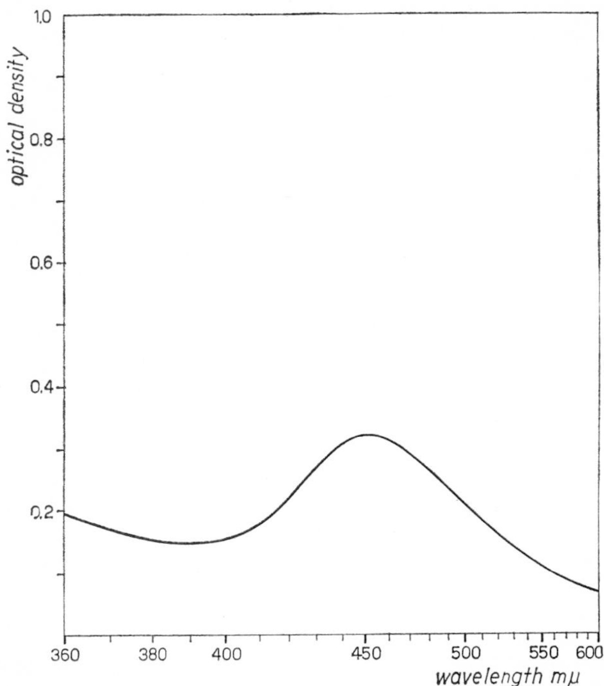


FIG. 10. Light absorption spectrum of 0.01 M diethyldithio carbamate in 0.1 M potassium phosphate buffer pH 7.4, in the presence of 2.3 μg $Cu^{2+}$ per ml (as the chloride).

## REFERENCES


1. D. CAVALLINI, C. DE MARCO and B. MONDOVÌ; *Enzymologia* **23**, 101 (1961).
2. E. A. ZELLER; *Naturwissenschaften* **26**, 578 (1938).
3. A. N. DAVISON; *Biochem. J.* **64**, 546 (1956).
4. E. V. GORYACHENKOVA; *Biokhimiya* **21**, 247 (1956).
5. E. V. GORYACHENKOVA; *Vitaminy Akad. Nauk. Ukr. S.S.R.* **4**, 15 (1959).
6. R. KAPELLER-ADLER; *Biochem. J.* **44**, 70 (1949).
7. E. A. ZELLER, R. STERN and M. WENK; *Helv. Chim. Acta* **23**, 3 (1940).
8. B. SWEDIN; *Acta Med. Scand.* **64**, 209 (1943).
9. E. WERLE and G. HARTUNG; *Biochem. Z.* **328**, 228 (1956).
10. P. J. G. MANN; *Biochem. J.* **79**, 623 (1961).
11. P. J. G. MANN; *Biochem. J.* **59**, 609 (1955).
12. P. J. G. MANN; *Biochem. J.* **76**, 44p (1960).
13. H. YAMADA and K. T. YASUNOBU; *J. Biol. Chem.* **237**, 1511 (1962).
14. H. YAMADA and K. T. YASUNOBU; *Biochem. Biophys. Res. Comm.* **8**, 387 (1962).

15. E. V. GORYACHENKOVA; *Doklady Akad. Nauk. S.S.S.R.* **123,** 898 (1958).
16. E. A. ZELLER; *Advances in Enzymol.* **2,** 93 (1942).
17. E. A. ZELLER; in: *The Enzymes* (edited by J. SUMMER and T. MYRBÄCK), Vol. 2, part 1, p. 544. Academic Press, New York, 1961.
18. R. KAPELLER-ADLER and H. MACFARLANE; *Proc. Biochem. Soc.*, 412th Meeting; *Biochem. J.* **82,** 49p (1962).
19. N. R. STEPHENSON; *J. Biol. Chem.* **149,** 169 (1943).
20. M. LASKOWSKY; *Arch. Biochem.* **6,** 105 (1945).
21. R. KAPELLER-ADLER; *Biochem. J.* **44,** 70 (1949).
22. H. J. TABOR; *J. Biol. Chem.* **188,** 125 (1951).
23. B. SWEDIN; *Acta Physiol. Scand.* **42,** 1 (1958).
24. V. D. USPENSKAIA and E. V. GORYACHENKOVA (with Z. G. MOGILEVSKAIA and V. P. POLIAKOV); *Biokhimiya* (English translation), **23,** 199 (1958).
25. B. MONDOVÌ; *Proc. Vth Int. Cong. Biochem.*, Moscow, 1961, Abstr. Comm., vol. 5, p. 102, 1294.
26. A. H. NATHAN and M. T. BOGERT; *J. Am. Chem. Soc.* **63,** 2361 (1941).
27. J. GOA; *Scand. J. Clin. Invest.* **5,** 218 (1953).
28. E. ADAMS; monograph distributed by Cal. Corp. Biochem. Res., based on data given by WARBURG and CHRISTIAN, *Biochem. Z.* **310,** 384 (1942).
29. S. P. COLOWICK and N. O. KAPLAN; *Methods in Enzymology*, vol. I, p. 76, Academic Press, New York (1955).
30. J. PORATH; *Biochim. et Biophys. Acta* **22,** 151 (1956).
31. J. PORATH and S. HJERTÉN; in: *Methods of Biochemical Analysis*, Vol. 9, p. 193. Ed. by D. GLICK, Interscience Publ., New York and London (1962).
32. E. A. PETERSON and H. A. SOBER; *J. Am. Chem. Soc.* **78,** 751 (1956).
33. D. CAVALLINI, C. DE MARCO and B. MONDOVÌ; *Biochim. et Biophys. Acta* **24,** 353 (1957).
34. Y. MATSUO and D. M. GREENBERG; *J. Biol. Chem.* **234,** 507 (1959).
35. K. V. RAJAGOPALAN, I. FRIDOVICH and P. HANDLER; *J. Biol. Chem.* **237,** 922 (1961).
36. Y. MATSUO and D. M. GREENBERG; *J. Biol. Chem.* **230,** 561 (1958).
37. H. R. MAHLER, G. HÜBSCHER and H. BAUM; *J. Biol. Chem.* **216,** 625 (1955).

## DISCUSSION

DR. KAPELLER-ADLER:

I think that you and I are dealing with two different enzyme systems, i.e. that you have purified diamine oxidase (DO) and I have purified histaminase. In your purification procedure the enzymatic effect on cadaverine increased and that on histamine decreased with progressing purification. Whereas in my purification attempts the initial crude pig kidney extract showed a considerable enzymatic activity on histamine and cadaverine, which was almost alike on both substrates, with progressing purification the enzymatic effect on cadaverine steadily decreased to become nil in the purest chromatographic effluents of DEAE–cellulose columns. Besides, the ratio of the enzymatic effect on histamine in relation to that on cadaverine was in the initial fractionation stages by no means constant, but varied from one purification step to another one.

PROF. MONDOVÌ:

It is possible that our preparation could be identified with diamine oxidase and yours with histaminase, nevertheless the final answer on this much discussed question shall be given when both diamine oxidase and histaminase will be extracted separately and in pure form from the same organ homogenate.

# HISTAMINASE, A PYRIDOXAL PHOSPHATE AND FLAVIN ADENINE DINUCLEOTIDE DEPENDENT ENZYME

by R. Kapeller-Adler

Department of Clinical Chemistry, University of Edinburgh,
Royal Infirmary, Edinburgh, Scotland

## INTRODUCTION

In 1929 Best[1] discovered histaminase and in the following year Best and McHenry[2] further characterized this enzyme and found it to be specific for the destruction of histamine. In 1938 Zeller[3], however, reported that pig's kidney preparations as well as other animal tissue extracts were capable of destroying by oxidative deamination not only histamine but also diamines, such as putrescine, cadaverine and agmatine. Since the enzyme system, described by Best and McHenry, and the other one, described by himself appeared to Zeller to be in many aspects very similar, he concluded that both enzyme systems were identical and substituted the term diamine oxidase (DO) for that of histaminase. Subsequently, not only have the terms histaminase and DO been interchangeably used, but also the substrates histamine, cadaverine and putrescine, despite considerable disagreement in the literature on the question whether or not a single enzyme carried out in different biological media such as animal tissue extracts, plant and microbiological material both types of activity, the original one, first reported by Best, and the other one, described by Zeller.

Since a renewed study of the enzyme histaminase, aiming at the elucidation of the problem of its identity, specificity and mode of action, appeared to be essential, the work to be reported here has been first concerned with the elaboration of a modern technique, adequate to produce in a good yield a stable preparation of pure histaminase.

## PURIFICATION PROCEDURE

The starting material, a saline homogenate of pig's kidney cortices, was fractionally precipitated with ammonium sulphate, then freed from inert protein by thermal denaturation at 60°, and after a short dialysis against borate buffer of pH 8.6, the material precipitated at 0.6 ammonium sulphate saturation, but soluble at 0.2 saturation was subjected to chromatography on DEAE–cellulose, at pH 8.6. A simple elution at a constant pH of 5.5 was then carried out, when the enzyme activity was found to be concentrated in a single, well resolved symmetrical peak, emerging at pH 7.0, with an about 15- to 20-fold increase in specific activity. Histaminase activity was determined by a simple microvolumetric technique,[4] involving a coupled oxidation reaction in which indigodisulphonate is oxidized by the $H_2O_2$, formed during the action of histaminase on histamine, and is expressed in units, one unit representing the amount of histaminase, capable of degrading 0.463 $\mu$g of histamine/hr, corresponding to $6.95 \times 10^{-5}$ $\mu$moles of histamine/min. The specific activity of histaminase is defined as the number of histaminase units/mg of protein. The effluents were then submitted without previous concentration to electrophoresis on cellulose acetate strips, at pH 6.8, using normal human serum as a marker.

Figure 1 represents a typical elution diagram, obtained in these assays. On the basis of the elution pattern this diagram has been divided into three parts : A, B and C. To each of these three sections an electropherogram, typical of the relevant part, has been attached, each of them showing in its upper part a pattern of normal human serum proteins. D in the right upper corner is an electropherogram of the crude enzyme solution before column chromatography.

It can be seen from this diagram that the total enzyme activity emerged from the column as a single, well resolved almost symmetrical peak in section B, shown in the corresponding electropherogram to have moved as a single, distinct band towards the anode, located in the region between the $\alpha_2$- and $\beta$-globulin fractions. The effluents of this section showed a very pale yellow colour, and displayed a distinct greenish yellow fluorescence under ultra-violet light. Part A with a negligible amount of histaminase consisted merely of inert protein, seen in the electropherogram of this section to have moved as a broad diffuse band with some protein remaining at the point of application. Likewise, section C contained very little histaminase activity but comparatively large amounts of protein, depicted in the corresponding electropherogram as a broad diffuse band in the globulin fraction in addition to a distinct band with the mobility of albumin. On comparison of the electropherograms of these three sections with the electropherogram D of a crude histaminase preparation before column chromatography one realises the great resolution power of DEAE–cellulose. In about fifty-five independent chromatographic assays the yield of histaminase activity ranged from 125 to 190 per cent with a recovery of only 30 per cent of the total protein content before chromatography. This indicates that the bulk of histaminase inhibitors must have been retained on the column. For further purification, effluents of various DEAE–cellulose columns, showing highest specific activity and electrophoretically the same degree of purity, were pooled and either rechromatographed on DEAE–cellulose, or precipitated with $(NH_4)_2SO_4$ to 0.6 saturation. A

2000- to 2700- fold purification of histaminase as compared to the crude enzyme preparation could be thus achieved.

Figure 2 shows that on rechromatography on DEAE–cellulose columns the total histaminase activity emerged from the column almost immediately after the commencement of elution as a single, well resolved, symmetrical peak, well separated from a small tail of inert protein. The purified histaminase solutions were concentrated in dialysing tubings with powdered sucrose without any loss of histaminase activity and were used for the study of the behaviour of this enzyme.

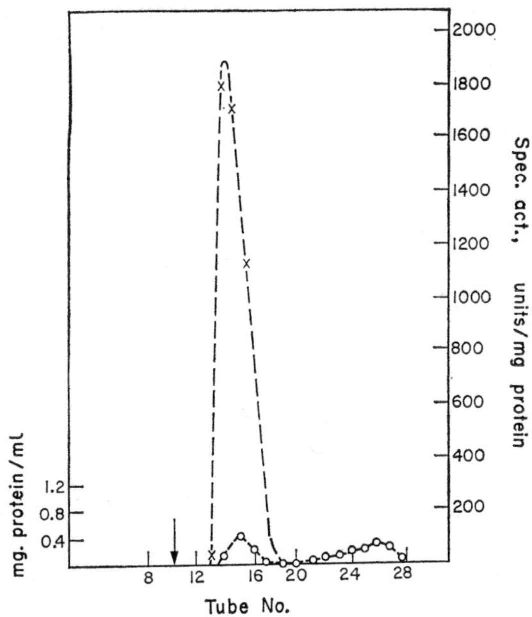


FIG. 2. Elution diagram of a histaminase preparation after rechromatography on a DEAE-cellulose column.

At the arrow elution was started. o——o mg protein/ml. ×——× specific activity of histaminase (units/mg protein).

## PROPERTIES OF PURIFIED HISTAMINASE

### *Electrophoretic mobility*

Purified histaminase solutions were subjected to electrophoresis on cellulose acetate strips over a pH range extending from 4.6 to 8.6, with the ionic strength of the buffer varying between 0.05 and 0.1. Normal human serum was used as a marker.

From Fig. 3 it can be seen that purified histaminase travelled at pH values above 5.2 towards the anode as a single, apparently homogeneous band to be located at pH 6.8 and pH 8.6 in the region between the $\alpha_2$- and $\beta$-globulin fractions of human serum. Whereas at pH 4.6 the enzyme migrated towards the cathode, no migration of histaminase was seen between pH 5.0 and pH 5.15 which would place the isoelectric point between these two pH values.

The fact that varying the amount of enzyme protein, or the ionic strength, or the pH value of the buffer did not reveal more than one component in the resulting ionograms seems to indicate electrophoretical homogeneity of these purified histaminase preparations.

*Stability*

Preparations of pure histaminase were stable at 4° for weeks, and at − 18° to − 20° (deep freeze cabinet) for months with almost no loss of activity. Heating up to 62° did not affect the enzyme.

*Effect of Substrate Concentration*

The optimal substrate concentration for a histaminase content of from 10 to 25 units was 2.72 to 5.44 μmoles of histamine dihydrochloride/10 ml. It should be emphasized that in the presence of superoptimal concentrations of histamine a considerable inhibition of histaminase activity was always observed. The significance of this finding will be discussed later.

*Effect of pH*

The activity of pure histaminase appears to be optimal at pH 6.8 with a rather steep decline above and below this pH value.

*Nature of the Reaction Product of the Histaminase Action on Histamine*

Pure histaminase acts on histamine on incubation at 37°/60 min with the formation of only one reaction product (Fig. 4), apparently imidazole acetaldehyde, which can be oxidized by further incubation at 37°/60 min with either added xanthine oxidase (Fig. 5) or by DPN in the presence of beef liver aldehyde dehydrogenase (Fig. 6), or by heating (50°/5 min) with minute amounts of 0.1 N $KMnO_4$ (Fig. 7) to imidazole acetic acid (ImAA).

This confirms previous findings[5] when by means of paper chromatography and chemical synthesis evidence was obtained that the only product of the histaminase action on histamine is indeed imidazole acetaldehyde.

*Substrate Specificity*

Whereas, as mentioned above, minute amounts of electrophoretically pure histaminase were found to be highly active on histamine as substrate no enzyme effect whatsoever was obtained when putrescine, cadaverine or hexamethylene diamine were used as substrates. This finding along with the observation, made at the early stages of the purification procedure of histaminase, of a missing relative constancy of the enzymic effect on histamine to that on cadaverine, and, finally, the fact that no enzymic activity on putrescine

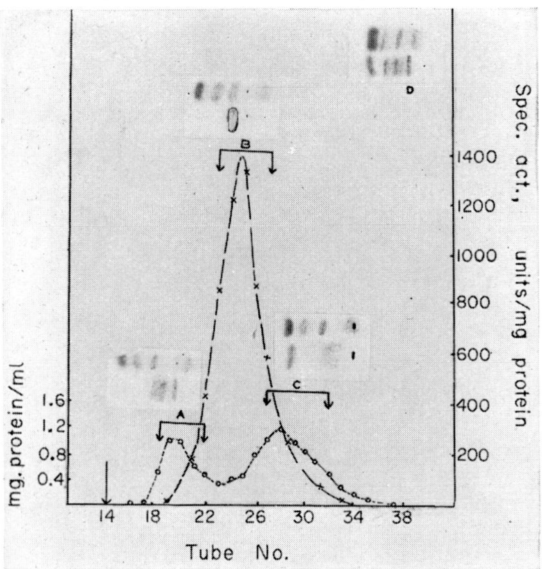


FIG. 1. Elution diagram obtained on chromatography of histaminase on DEAE-cellulose columns.

○——○ protein mg/ml, ×——× specific activity of histaminase (units/mg protein). At the arrow elution was started. Electrophoresis was carried out on cellulose acetate strips with an ionic strength of the phosphate buffer of 0.05, at pH 6.8. A current of 0.6 mA/cm width of strip was used/4 hr. The strips were stained with Ponceau S. Electropherograms above sections A, B and C as well as the electropherogram D show in their upper parts patterns of normal human serum proteins.

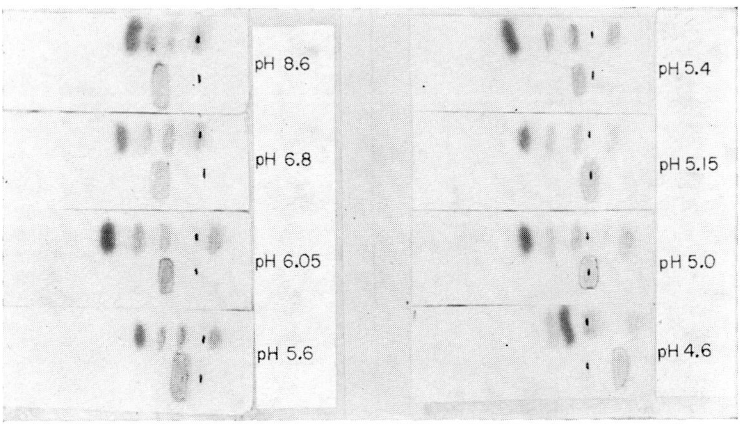


FIG. 3. Electropherograms of pure histaminase obtained on cellulose acetate strips, at pH values ranging from 4.6 to 8.6, with the ionic strength of the buffer solutions varying between 0.05 and 0.1. A current of 0.6 mA/cm width of strip used/4 hr. Strips stained with Ponceau S. Normal human serum used as a marker.

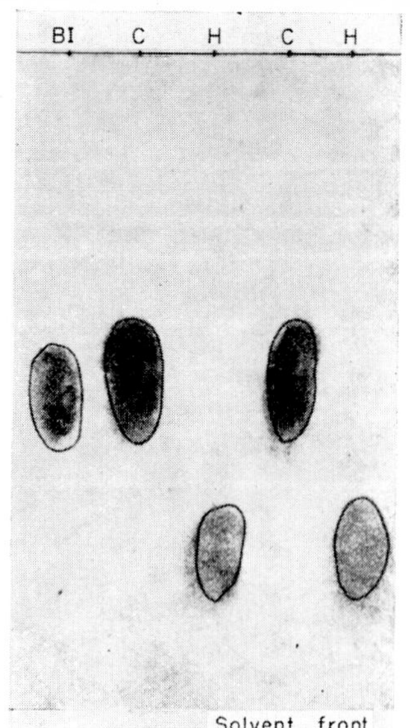


FIG. 4. Paper chromatogram of the histaminase–histamine reaction product.
C. Control, histaminase–histamine reaction mixture without incubation.
H. The same mixture after incubation showing the histaminase–histamine metabolite " H ".
Bl. Authentic histamine.

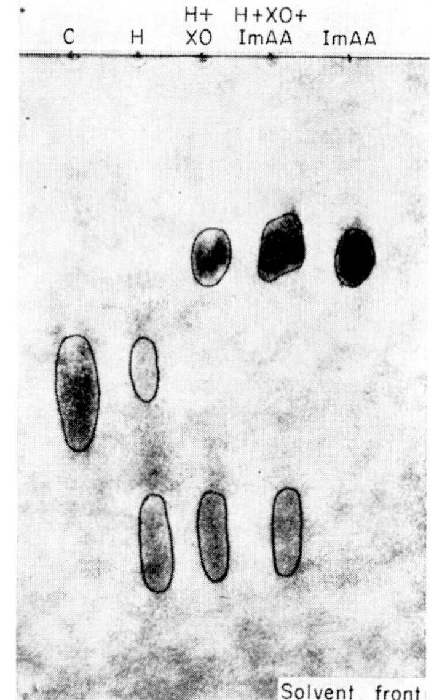


FIG. 5. Paper chromatogram of products obtained from coupled histaminase–histamine–xanthine oxidase system.
C. Control, histaminase–histamine reaction mixture without incubation.
H. The same mixture after incubation (spot with the large $R^*$, metabolite " H "; spot with the smaller $R^*$, unchanged histamine).
ImAA = authentic imidazole acetic acid.
XO = xanthine oxidase.

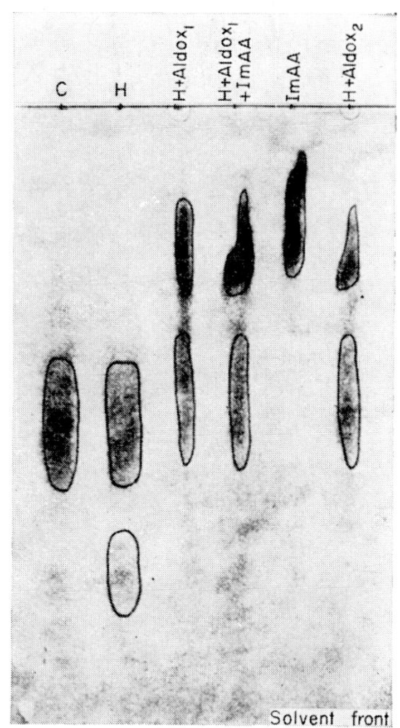


FIG. 6. Paper chromatogram of products obtained from the coupled histaminase–histamine–DPN–aldehyde oxidase system.

C. Control, histaminase–histamine reaction mixture without incubation.

H. The same mixture after incubation (spot with larger $R^*$, metabolite " H "; spot with smaller $R^*$, unchanged histamine).

Aldox$_1$ = aldehyde oxidase, pH 7.0.

Aldox$_2$ = aldehyde oxidase, pH 8.5.

ImAA = authentic imidazole acetic acid.

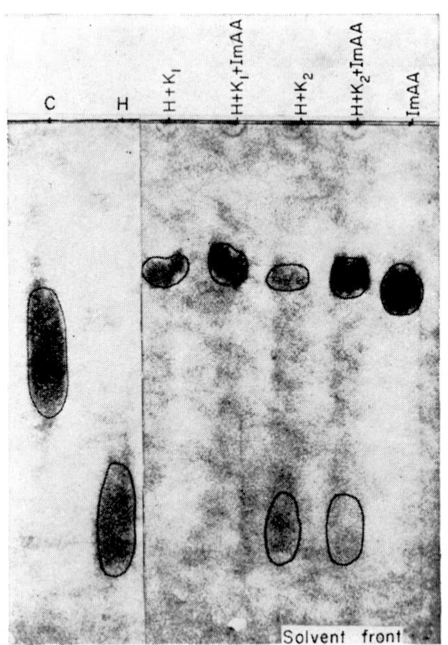


FIG. 7. Paper chromatogram of product obtained from oxidation of the histaminase–histamine metabolite " H " by 0.1 N $KMnO_4$.
C. Control, histaminase–histamine reaction mixture without incubation.
H. The same mixture after incubation.
$K_1$ = 50 $\mu$l 0.1 N $KMnO_4$.
$K_2$ = 20 $\mu$l 0.1 N $KMnO_4$.
ImAA = authentic imidazole acetic acid.

was encountered at any of the purification stages of the present as well as previous work lends no support to Zeller's[3] claim that hog kidney histaminase and DO are a single enzyme.

Two methyl derivatives of histamine, however, with substitution in the imidazole nucleus, the 1-methyl-4-($\beta$-aminoethyl)-imidazole (1,4-methylhistamine) and the 1-methyl-5-($\beta$-aminoethyl)-imidazole (1,5-methylhistamine) proved to be, as can be seen in Table 1, very good substrates of pure histaminase.

Table 1 also shows that in mixtures of histamine with either of these two compounds no additive effect, but competition was obtained, which indicates

TABLE 1. EFFECT OF PURE HISTAMINASE ON HISTAMINE, 1, 4-METHYLHISTAMINE, AND 1, 5-METHYLHISTAMINE, AND ON MIXTURES OF HISTAMINE WITH THESE COMPOUNDS

| Substrate (approx. 2.7 $\mu$moles) | Histaminase activity (units) |
|---|---|
| Histamine | 10.7 |
| 1, 4-Methylhistamine | 7.6 |
| 1, 5-Methylhistamine | 6.5 |
| Histamine + 1, 4-methylhistamine | 8.8 |
| Histamine + 1, 5-methylhistamine | 9.7 |

that a single enzyme was operative during the degradation of these substrate mixtures. Hence, in confirmation of previous findings[6–8] substitution in the imidazole nucleus of histamine does not interfere with histaminase action. Moreover, the fact that pure histaminase is able to degrade not only histamine but also 1,4-methylhistamine, which, according to Schayer[9], is one of the main metabolites of histamine *in vivo*, seems to add to the biological significance of this enzyme.

Contrary to the two N-methyl derivatives of histamine with substitution in the imidazole nucleus, just mentioned, three other histamine derivatives, all with substitution on the side chain-$NH_2$, i.e. N-monomethylhistamine, N-dimethylhistamine and acetylhistamine, are not only not being attacked by histaminase but they are all strong inhibitors of the histaminase action on histamine. Hence, an intact $NH_2$-group in the aminoethyl side chain of histamine seems to be essential for histaminase activity, which confirms previous findings.[6]

*Effect of Various Typical Enzyme Inhibitors on Histaminase*

In agreement with Zeller's[10] work histaminase is inhibited to a varying extent by various carbonyl reagents such as cyanide, bisulphite, hydroxylamine, semicarbazide, isoniazide, aminoguanidine, and phenylhydrazine but is not inhibited by sodium azide, thiourea and $H_2S$, which seems to indicate that heavy metal is not required for histaminase action. Furthermore, histaminase is insensitive towards iodoacetate, *p*-chloromercuribenzoate and similar reagents which seems to point to the absence of SH-groups, essential for its enzymic action.

*Nature of the Prosthetic Group(s) of Histaminase*

Although it has been repeatedly reported and experimental evidence has been presented by some workers that histaminase is a flavoprotein, FAD being involved as a prosthetic group in the oxidative deamination process of histamine by histaminase, no such claim was made by other workers. Moreover, since those histaminase preparations which had been found to contain FAD, had been only partially purified, it could be argued that their content of FAD could have been due to a contamination. Hence, it was decided in this work to re-examine this problem using an electrophoretically pure histaminase preparation. Different solutions of pure histaminase in dilute buffer, pH 6.8, all showing a greenish yellow fluorescence under ultraviolet light, were subjected to a spectrophotometric investigation in the Unicam, SP 500, spectrophotometer. A solution of authentic FAD (L. Light & Co. Ltd.) containing 0.5 $\mu$g FAD/ml of phosphate buffer, pH 6.8, and showing the characteristic absorption maxima at 375 m$\mu$ and 450 m$\mu$ was used as a marker. It was very disappointing to find in many assays that none of the pure histaminase preparations showed the absorption maxima, characteristic of FAD. Since, however, as mentioned above, pure histaminase solutions showed a greenish yellow fluorescence under ultraviolet light, it was decided to investigate those pure histaminase solutions in the Aminco–Bowman spectrofluorometer, which is about 100 times more sensitive than the Unicam, SP 500, spectrophotometer. In this connection a recent report by Theorell[11] should be recalled in which the significance of the great sensitivity of fluorometry as compared to absorption spectrophotometry for the detection of various reactions involving coenzymes is emphasized. It will be seen that also in this work fluorometry has proved to be an essential aid for the detection of the presence in pure histaminase preparations of the prosthetic group, FAD. This is shown in Fig. 8.

In Fig. 8 the activating spectra of pure histaminase, curve A, and of authentic FAD, curve C, obtained at pH 6.8 are shown when the apparatus was set at 530 m$\mu$, the known maximum of fluorescence of FAD. There is a striking similarity between the curves A and C. Curve A shows a small shift of the second activating maximum towards the longer wavelengths (shift from 450 m$\mu$ to 458 m$\mu$). Such shifts of absorption peaks of flavoproteins are well known in the literature. Curve B, showing the activating spectrum, obtained from histaminase on acidification with 0.1 N HCl, seems to suggest that FAD may have been liberated from the enzyme on acidification, since the two absorption peaks, seen in curve B, are located exactly in the same position as those of authentic FAD. That FAD had indeed been liberated follows from the fact that the fluorescence of the enzyme solution increased on acidification so much that the reading in curve B could be only recorded after the sensitivity of the apparatus had been 30-fold reduced.

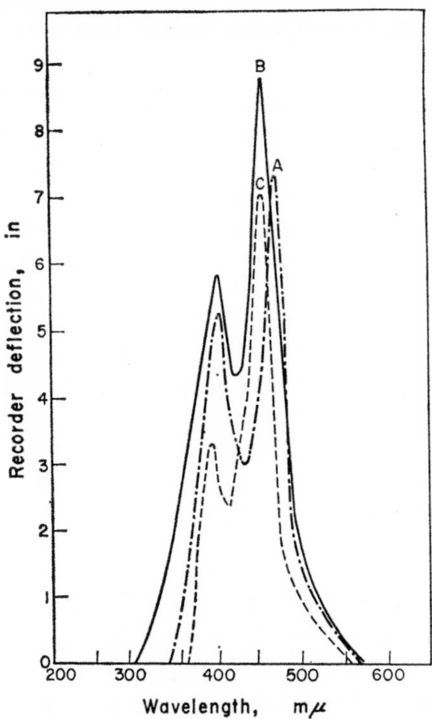


FIG. 8. Activating spectra of pure histaminase before and after acidification with 0.1 N HCl and of authentic FAD at the fluorescence emission maximum at 530 mμ.
A. —·—·— pure histaminase in 0.02 M phosphate buffer, pH 6.8, with 0.44 mg protein/ml.
B. ——— the same enzyme solution after acidification with 0.1 N HCl.
C. – – – – authentic FAD in 0.02 M phosphate buffer, pH 6.8 (0.2 μg FAD/ml).

For further identification of these optical findings, pure histaminase was subjected to a reaction with sodium dithionite and typical results of spectrofluorometric investigations obtained with this conventional test are shown in Fig. 9.

Curve A shows the activating spectrum of pure histaminase before the addition of dithionite, and curve D that of authentic FAD, all activating maxima having been obtained with the apparatus set at the fluorescence maximum of FAD, at 530 mμ. It can be seen from curve B that dithionite considerably affected the spectral behaviour of histaminase, inasmuch as the peak at 375 m$\mu$ appears to have been greatly reduced and that at 458 m$\mu$ almost completely disappeared. Curve C shows the spectrum, obtained when the reduced enzyme solution was rapidly reoxidized by oxygenation for only 60 sec, when both activating maxima were found in the usual position, characteristic of FAD. The behaviour of histaminase towards dithionite with the apparent formation of a leucoflavin derivative and the rapid reoxidation of the latter by molecular oxygen seems to be a further indication

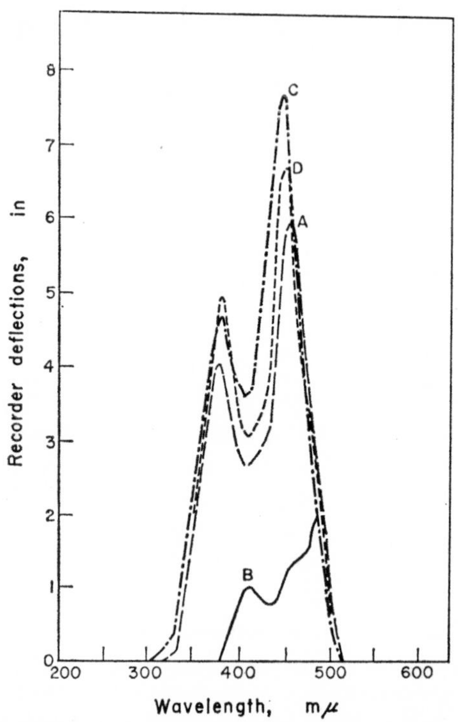


FIG. 9. Activating spectra obtained at the fluorescence emission maximum at 530 m$\mu$ of pure histaminase before and after treatment with dithionite, followed by reoxidation of the reduced enzyme with molecular $O_2$.

A. Histaminase in 0.02 M phosphate buffer, pH 6.8, with 0.44 mg protein/ml.
B. The same enzyme solution after the addition of 0.2 ml of 4 per cent $Na_2S_2O_4$ in phosphate buffer, pH 6.8.
C. B after reoxidation with molecular oxygen.
D. Authentic FAD in 0.02 M phosphate buffer, pH 6.8 (0.2 $\mu$g FAD/ml).

of the involvement of a flavin group in the molecule of this enzyme. According to Singer and Kearney[12] the reoxidation of reduced flavoenzymes by molecular oxygen gives rise to $H_2O_2$ formation, hence the finding of hydrogen peroxide among the reaction products of a biological oxidation reaction is a reliable indication of the presence of a flavoenzyme. It should be pointed out that the formation of one molecule of $H_2O_2$ per molecule of histamine during the action of histaminase was independently claimed by various workers.

Incidentally, results similar to those observed with dithionite were obtained on addition of histamine to a pure histaminase solution, whereby a distinct bleaching of the pale yellow colour of the solution took place. Owing, however, to a rapid reoxidation of the reduced enzyme which could not be adequately controlled, the fluorometric changes on addition of histamine were less dramatic as compared with those seen with dithionite. Morell[13] also found that hypoxanthine decreased the absorption of xanthine oxidase at 450 mμ much more slowly than did sodium dithionite.

It was very interesting to find that although pure preparations of histaminase had failed to show in the spectrophotometer, SP 500, the absorption peaks, typical of FAD, two different absorption maxima, however, a very small one at 330 mμ and a much larger one at 405 mμ were regularly observed in all the spectrophotometric examinations of histaminase. Since various workers such as Werle and Pechmann[14], Sinclair[15], Davison[16], and Goryachenkova[17] had previously claimed that histaminase was a pyridoxal phosphate-(PLP)-dependent enzyme, and because of the well known fact, quoted above, that carbonyl reagents are strong inhibitors of histaminase activity, and, finally, because of the absolute requirement of histaminase for an unsubstituted side chain–$NH_2$-group in the molecule of its substrate, which is also known to be indispensable for the activity of all PLP-dependent enzymes, it was decided to investigate whether the absorption maxima, observed in the spectrophotometer SP 500, could be possibly related to the existence of PLP in the histaminase molecule. It is known that synthetic PLP shows at pH 7.0 two absorption maxima, one at 330 mμ and another one at 388 mμ.

Figure 10 shows typical absorption spectra obtained with pure histaminase at pH 6.8 (□ . . . □), and at pH 6.1 ( ○ . . . ○), and also the absorption spectrum of authentic PLP (Roche Products Ltd.) at pH 6.8 (0.047 μmoles PLP/ml) (—●—●—). It can be seen from this figure that at both pH 6.1 and pH 6.8 the spectral absorption pattern of histaminase greatly resembled that shown by authentic PLP. The intensity of the absorption maxima of histaminase appeared to be greater at pH 6.1 compared with that at pH 6.8. Shukuya and Schwert[18] made similar observations with the PLP-dependent glutamic acid decarboxylase when they found that a change in the absorption maxima greatly depended upon the pH value of the solution. A small shift of the larger absorption peak of histaminase at both pH 6.1 and pH 6.8 occurred towards the longer wavelengths, from 388 mμ to 405 mμ. Spectral changes of this type have been observed with many PLP-dependent enzymes[19–21] and it has been suggested that an absorption band found with such enzymes in the region of 400 mμ to 415 mμ may indicate the intermediate formation of an azomethine bond (Schiff base) between PLP and the enzyme protein.

Finally, it can be seen in Fig. 10 that the addition of histamine (0.45 μmoles) to the histaminase solution, at pH 6.1, caused a significant alteration of the absorption spectrum, with the appearance of only one absorption maximum at 405 mμ the absorption peak at 330 mμ having been completely obliterated.

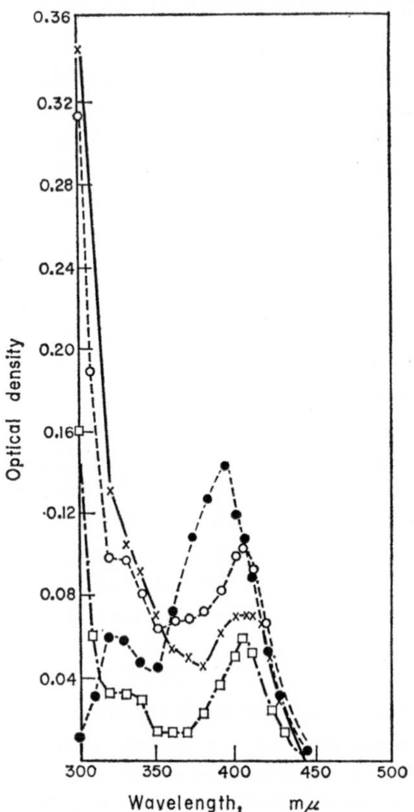


FIG. 10. Absorption atectra of pure histaminase and of authentic PLP.
□- - -□ Histaminase in phosphate buffer, pH 6.8 }
○——○ Histaminase in phosphate buffer, pH 6.1 } Enzyme protein 0.72 mg/ml.
×——× Histaminase after addition of 50 μg histamine as substrate, pH 6.1. }
—●—●—●— Authentic PLP in phosphate buffer, pH 6.8 (10 μg/ml).

Jenkins and Sizer[22] found that PLP showed at pH 7.0 a strong fluorescence at 400 mμ, whereby the activating maximum was located at 322 mμ, and a very weak fluorescence at 495 mμ with an activating maximum at 395 mμ.

Figure 11 shows the activating spectra of a purified histaminase solution (curve A) as well as of authentic PLP (curve B) both in phosphate buffer, pH 6.8, obtained with the spectrofluorometer (Aminco–Bowman) set at the fluorescence maximum of PLP, at 400 mμ. In agreement with references in the literature the activating peak of authentic PLP was found to be at 322 mμ, while the activating peak of the histaminase preparation moved towards the shorter wavelengths.

Some additional evidence that both FAD and PLP are prosthetic groups of histaminase was obtained in many different assays leading to a successful,

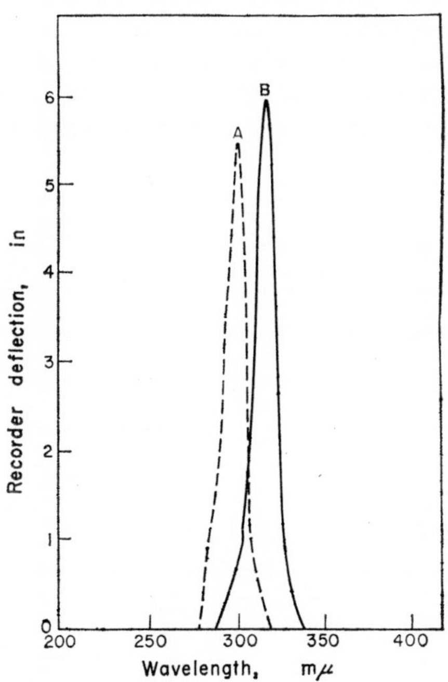


FIG. 11. Activating spectra of pure histaminase and of authentic PLP at the fluorescence emission maximum, at 400 mμ.
A. — — — — Histaminase in 0.02 M phosphate buffer, pH 6.8 (enzyme protein 0.72 mg/ml).
B.———Authentic PLP in 0.02 M phosphate buffer, pH 6.8 (10 μg/ml).

reversible, partial resolution of histaminase, followed by reactivation of the enzyme after preincubation with added synthetic FAD or PLP. Partial resolution of the enzyme was effected either by prolonged dialysis or by mild acidification of pure histaminase solutions to pH 5.2 in the presence of ammonium sulphate at 0.6 saturation. Optimal reactivation results were obtained on preincubation of the partially resolved enzyme solution (about 25 units) with added either 0.029 μmoles FAD or 0.166 μmoles of PLP, 30 min/37°. (Substrate used 5.44 μmoles of histamine dihydrochloride in a final volume of 10 ml.)

*Effects of Prolonged Dialysis on the Activity of Pure Histaminase and Effect of added FAD, or PLP, or a Mixture of FAD and PLP on the Dialysed Enzyme.*

It can be seen from Table 2, which is typical of such experiments that on prolonged dialysis (22 hr) against 0.02 M phosphate buffer, pH 6.8, 15.8 per cent of the original histaminase activity was lost, probably due to the partial removal of one or both of the prosthetic groups. On preincubation of the dialysed enzyme with the added optimal amount of FAD (30 min/37°) there was not only a complete recovery of the enzyme activity, which had been lost on dialysis, but there was even a gain in activity. After incubation of the dialysed enzyme with the optimal amount of added PLP, the enzyme activity lost on dialysis, was to a large extent but not completely regained. Finally, it is seen in this table that on incubation of the dialysed enzyme with an added mixture of optimal amounts of both FAD and PLP only about 50 per cent of the histaminase activity, which had been removed by dialysis was restored. Since no additive effect was obtained these results may indicate that FAD and PLP are involved in the same reaction mechanism.

TABLE 2. EFFECT OF PROLONGED DIALYSIS ON THE ACTIVITY OF HISTAMINASE, AND EFFECTS OF ADDED FLAVIN ADENINE DINUCLEOTIDE (FAD), OR PYRIDOXAL PHOSPHATE (PLP), OR OF A MIXTURE OF BOTH COMPOUNDS ON THE DIALYSED ENZYME

| | |
|---|---|
| Effect of prolonged dialysis on histaminase | Percentage of decrease in enzyme activity |
| | 15.8 |
| Preincubation of dialysed enzyme with added | Percentage of increase in enzyme activity |
| FAD | 26.0 |
| PLP | 11.7 |
| mixture of FAD and PLP | 8.0 |

*Partial Reversible Resolution of Pure Histaminase by Acidification to pH* 5.2 *in the presence of* $(NH_4)_2SO_4$ (0.6 *Saturation*)

Table 3 shows representative results from which one can see that on mild acidification of a histaminase solution to pH 5.2 about 30 per cent of the enzyme activity was lost. Unlike in experiments with prolonged dialysis, however, added FAD did not restore completely the original activity, only about 66 per cent of the lost enzyme activity having been regained. This seems to indicate that, whereas on prolonged dialysis the enzyme may have been reversibly split, on acidification to pH 5.2 a certain proportion of histaminase must have been denatured.

On addition of PLP to the partially reduced enzyme only 56 per cent of the lost activity was restored. Finally, when a mixture of both FAD and PLP was incubated with the enzyme after acidification, barely 46 per cent of the lost activity was regained, which confirms similar observations made in dialysis experiments, quoted above, and adds weight to the hypothesis that FAD and PLP may be involved in the same reaction mechanism.

Inasmuch as the foregoing data seem to present good evidence for accepting that both FAD and PLP are prosthetic groups of histaminase and thus substantiate early relevant suggestions by Werle and Pechmann[14] and more recent ones by Goryachenkova[17], the question why pure histaminase solutions should have allowed one of the prosthetic groups, PLP, to be easily revealed in the not very sensitive spectrophotometer, SP 500, whereas for the detection of the other prosthetic group, FAD, the 100 times more sensitive spectrofluorometer, Aminco–Bowman, had to be used, is, at present, a matter for speculation. It may well be that more molecules of PLP than of FAD

TABLE 3. EFFECT OF ACIDIFICATION TO pH 5.2 ON THE ACTIVITY OF HISTAMINASE AND EFFECTS OF ADDED FAD, OR PLP, OR OF A MIXTURE OF FAD AND PLP ON THE ACTIVITY OF THE PARTIALLY RESOLVED ENZYME

| | |
|---|---|
| Acidification of histaminase to pH 5.2 in the presence of $(NH_4)_2SO_4$ (0.6 sat.) | Percentage of decrease in enzyme activity<br>31.7 |
| Preincubation of the partially resolved enzyme with added | Percentage of increase in enzyme activity |
| FAD | 21.1 |
| PLP | 17.9 |
| Mixtures of FAD and PLP | 14.6 |

are attached to the apoenzyme of histaminase. In this connection it is relevant to mention that Singer and Kearney[12] have stressed the fact that most flavoproteins in very reliable measurements have been found to contain only one molecule of flavin per molecule of protein. On the other hand, considerable attention has been drawn to a report from Cori's Laboratory by Baranowski *et al.*[23] that crystalline phosphorylase contained four molecules of PLP per molecule of enzyme. More work will have to be devoted to further studies concerning the problem of the attachment of FAD and PLP to the apoenzyme of histaminase.

Incidentally, an important feature of the PLP catalysis of the histaminase–histamine reaction, not to be disregarded, became apparent during the study of the effects of added PLP on histaminase preparations which had been subjected to prolonged dialysis. When attempting to determine the optimal amounts of FAD and PLP, to be added to the dialysed enzyme, in order to achieve best reactivation of the enzyme, it was found that, unlike FAD, PLP showed a very distinct concentration optimum which, if largely overstepped, could even cause an inhibition of histaminase action on histamine. At this point it should be also recalled that, as stressed above, a very sharp substrate optimum was found to be essential for best histaminase action on histamine, since, in the presence of superoptimal concentrations, histamine strongly inhibited its own degradation. Hence, it appears that both the specific substrate of histaminase, histamine, as well as one of its two prosthetic groups, PLP, may under not fully controlled experimental conditions act as inhibitors of the very reaction mechanism in which they are fundamentally involved. This phenomenon of an interaction between histaminase and its substrate as well as one of its prosthetic groups may possibly find its explanation, when one considers that, as reported in the literature, histamine belongs to the very small group of compounds which are capable of reacting irreversibly with PLP with the formation of stable, non-dissociable, cyclic condensation products. It may well be that excessive amounts of histamine may cause a strong histaminase inhibition by removing the PLP, thus rendering it unavailable to the apoenzyme. Conversely, superoptimal amounts of PLP may condense with histamine and, hence, may deprive at least partly, histaminase of its substrate. These considerations seem to support the view that optimal experimental conditions should be first established before trying to assess the *in vitro* reaction mechanism of histaminase. The finding that PLP may under certain conditions inhibit histaminase activity seems to raise the interesting question as to the biological significance of the existence of PLP in the histaminase molecule. It may be that the importance of PLP as a prosthetic group of histaminase lies just in its inhibitory faculties, thus enabling it to regulate the action of histaminase on its specific substrate, histamine. It may be of interest to recall her results, mentioned above, obtained on incubation of dialysed pure histaminase with an added minute amount of FAD, when more activity was recovered than had been lost on dialysis. This gain in histaminase activity may be possibly explained by the lack of an interaction on the part of PLP which might have been partially removed by dialysis. Thus PLP may in its function as the well known prosthetic group of histidine decarboxylase as well as one of the two prosthetic groups of histaminase, constitute one of the regulatory factors in the biological histamine formation and destruction.

## REACTION MECHANISMS INVOLVED

Finally, two schemes, Scheme 1 and Scheme 2 may be suggested, either of which may be operative during the action of purified histaminase on histamine.

Scheme 1 is similar to that recently proposed by Braunstein[24] for the action of DO on its substrate, involving in its first step a transamination between histamine and the PLP form of histaminase with the formation of a Schiff base, the enzyme bound pyridoxylidene azomethine. Electronic displacements may result in dissociation of the α-hydrogen atom and shifts of double bonds leading to the tautomeric azomethine. This is hydrolysed to imidazole acetaldehyde and the pyridoxamine phosphate enzyme. In the second step of this mechanism the pyridoxamine phosphate form of the

SCHEME 1

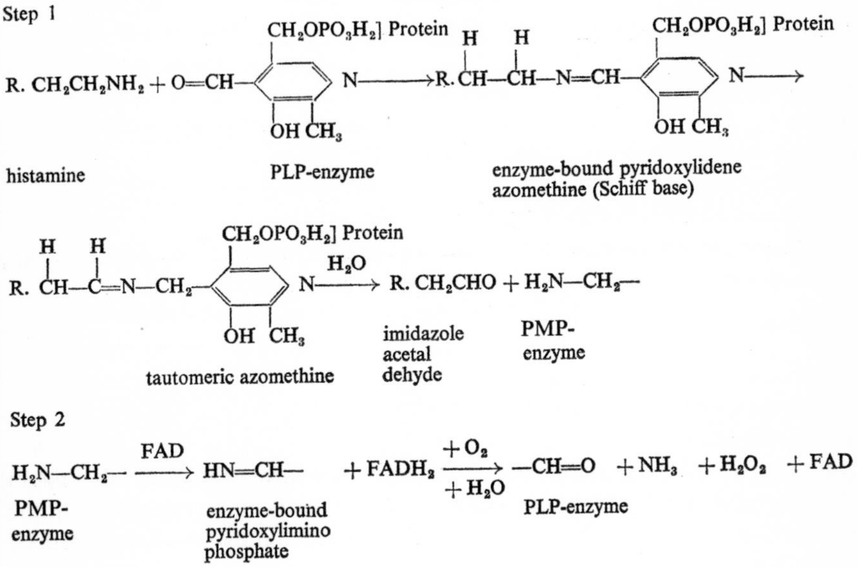

Step 1

R. $CH_2CH_2NH_2$ + O=CH–[ring: $CH_2OPO_3H_2$] Protein, OH, $CH_3$, N] ⟶ R. CH(H)–CH(H)–N=CH–[ring: $CH_2OPO_3H_2$] Protein, OH, $CH_3$, N] ⟶

histamine — PLP-enzyme — enzyme-bound pyridoxylidene azomethine (Schiff base)

R. CH(H)–C(H)=N–$CH_2$–[ring: $CH_2OPO_3H_2$] Protein, OH, $CH_3$, N] $\xrightarrow{H_2O}$ R. $CH_2CHO$ + $H_2N$–$CH_2$–

tautomeric azomethine — imidazole acetal dehyde — PMP-enzyme

Step 2

$H_2N$–$CH_2$– $\xrightarrow{FAD}$ HN=CH– + $FADH_2$ $\xrightarrow[+H_2O]{+O_2}$ –CH=O + $NH_3$ + $H_2O_2$ + FAD

PMP-enzyme — enzyme-bound pyridoxylimino phosphate — PLP-enzyme

R = imidazole.

PLP = pyridoxal-5-phosphoric ester.

PMP- = pyridoxamine-5-phosphoric ester.

FAD = flavin adenine dinucleotide.

enzyme may undergo dehydrogenation by the second prosthetic group of histaminase, FAD, to the pyridoxylimino phosphate, enzyme bound compound, and the reaction mechanism is completed by reoxidation of the leucoflavin by oxygen to FAD, and hydrolysis of the enzyme bound pyridoxylimino phosphate to the PLP form of histaminase with the formation of $NH_3$ and $H_2O_2$.

Scheme 2 shows a reaction mechanism similar to that, proposed in 1949 by Werle and Pechmann[14], for the action of plant DO on its substrates. According to this scheme the enzymic deamination of histamine may first proceed by condensation of histamine with the PLP form of histaminase with the formation of a Schiff base which, however, does not undergo

SCHEME 2

$$\underset{\text{histamine}}{R{-}CH_2.CH_2.NH_2} + \underset{\text{PLP-enzyne}}{O{=}CH{-}} \longrightarrow \underset{\substack{\text{azomethine deriv.}\\\text{(Schiff base)}}}{R{-}\overset{H}{\overset{|}{C}}H{-}\overset{H}{\overset{|}{C}}H{-}N{=}CH{-}} \xrightarrow{+FAD}$$

$$\longrightarrow \underset{\substack{\alpha,\ \beta\text{-unsaturated}\\\text{azomethine deriv.}}}{R{-}CH{=}CH{-}N{=}CH{-}} + FAD.H_2$$

$$FAD.H_2 + O_2 \longrightarrow FAD + H_2O_2$$

$$R{-}CH{=}CH{-}N{=}CH{-} + H_2O \longrightarrow \underset{\substack{\text{free}\\\text{enzyme}}}{O{=}CH{-}} + \underset{\substack{\alpha,\ \beta\text{-dehydro-}\\\text{amine}}}{R{-}CH{=}CH.NH_2} \xrightarrow{+H_2O} \underset{\substack{\text{imidazole-}\\\text{acetaldehyde}}}{R{-}CH_2.CHO} + NH_3$$

R = imidazole.

tautomeric rearrangement, but is directly dehydrogenated by the flavin prosthetic group, FAD, to the $\alpha$–$\beta$-unsaturated azomethine complex with the formation of the leucoflavin, FAD $H_2$. The reaction cycle is completed by reoxidation of the leucoflavin by $O_2$ with the formation of $H_2O_2$, and stepwise hydrolysis of the $\alpha$–$\beta$-unsaturated azomethine complex to the PLP form of histaminase, $NH_3$, and imidazole acetaldehyde, the latter via the imidazole, $\alpha$–$\beta$-dehydroamine.

It should be mentioned here that Goryachenkova[25] failed to achieve net transamination between diamines and added PLP or free pyridoxal in her experiments with purified DO preparations from hog kidney or clover seedlings, which finding may favour Scheme 2. It was, however, pointed out above that *in vitro* enzymic experiments with added PLP and diamines, especially histamine should be assessed only with greatest reserve because of the possible intermediate formation of non-dissociable cyclic condensation products.

Only further studies will help to decide which of the two reaction mechanisms, described, is indeed operating during the action of histaminase on histamine.

## REFERENCES


1. C. H. Best; *J. Physiol.* **67**, 256 (1929).
2. C. H. Best and E. W. McHenry; *J. Physiol.* **70**, 349 (1930).
3. E. A. Zeller; *Helv. Chim. Acta* **21**, 880 (1938).
4. R. Kapeller-Adler; *Biochim. et Biophys. Acta* **22**, 391 (1956).
5. R. Kapeller-Adler and M. Fletcher; *Biochim. et Biophys. Acta* **33**, 1 (1959).
6. R. Kapeller-Adler and B. Iggo; *Biochim. et Biophys. Acta* **25**, 394 (1957).
7. S. E. Lindell and H. Westling; *Acta Physiol. Scand.* **39**, 370 (1957).
8. G. A. Alles, B. B. Wisegarver and M. A. Shull; *J. Pharmacol. Exptl. Therap.* **77**, 54 (1943).
9. R. W. Schayer; *Physiol. Rev.* **39**, 116 (1959).
10. E. A. Zeller; *The Enzymes* (edited by J. B. Sumner and K. Myrbäck), vol. II, pt. 1, p. 536, Academic Press, New York (1951).
11. H. Theorell; *Advances in Enzymol.* **20**, 31 (1958).
12. T. P. Singer and E. B. Kearney; *The Proteins* (edited by H. Neurath and K. Bailey), vol. II, pt. A, p. 123, Academic Press, New York (1954).
13. D. B. Morell; *Biochem. J.* **51**, 658 (1952).
14. E. Werle and E. V. Pechmann; *Ann. Chem. Licbigs.* **562**, 44 (1949).
15. H. M. Sinclair; *Biochem. J.* **51**, X (1952).
16. A. N. Davison; *Biochem. J.* **63**, 25P (1956); **64**, 546 (1956).
17. E. V. Goryachenkova; *Biokhimiya* **21**, 247 (1956).
18. R. Shukuya and G. W. Schwert; *J. Biol. Chem.* **235**, 1653 (1960).
19. Y. Matsuo; *J. Am. Chem. Soc.* **79**, 2011 (1957).
20. D. E. Metzler; *J. Am. Chem. Soc.* **79**, 485 (1957).
21. Yu. M. Torchinskii; *Proc. Vth Int. Cong. Biochem.*, Moscow 1961, Abstr. Communic. Section 5.152.79.
22. W. T. Jenkins and J. W. Sizer; *J. Biol. Chem.* **235**, 620 (1960).
23. T. Baranowski, B. Illingworth, D. H. Brown and C. F. Cori; *Biochim. et Biophys. Acta* **25**, 16 (1957).
24. A. E. Braunstein; *The Enzymes* (edited by P. D. Boyer, H. Lardy and K. Myrbäck), vol. II, pt. A, p. 113, Academic Press, New York (1960).
25. E. V. Goryachenkova; *Biokhimiya* **21**, 322 (1956).


## DISCUSSION

Prof. Siliprandi:

I should like to know something about the intracellular localization or distribution of histaminase. Can you, Dr. Kapeller-Adler, give me some information?

Dr. Kapeller-Adler:

As to the question of the intracellular distribution of histaminase considerable species and organ differences seem to exist. On careful fractionation of hog kidney cortex in sucrose solution the enzyme is predominantly found in the cytoplasm, a very small amount (at the most 10 per cent) being encountered in the mitochondrial fraction (E. A. Zeller; *CIBA Foundation Symposium on Histamine*, p. 339, Churchill, 1956). The mitochondrial histaminase differs from the " cytoplasmic " enzyme in being more sensitive toward octyl alcohol and less sensitive toward high concentrations of histamine in comparison to the soluble cytoplasmic enzyme. It is feasible that in the intact cell a considerable amount of histaminase may be localized in the mitochondria from which the enzyme may be eluted by the conventional methods of enzyme preparation. Contrary to hog kidney cortex, in the rabbit liver histaminase is strongly bound to the mitochondria (G. C. Cotzias and V. P. Dole; *J. Biol. Chem.* **196**, 235, 1952) which particulate components of the liver cell are regarded as a major site of accumulation of this enzyme. Further it is interesting to note that Swanberg (*Acta Physiol. Scand.* **23**, suppl. 79, p. 7, 1950) on account of his studies on the human placenta advanced the theory that the histaminase content of the placenta probably originates from the decidua and that the foetal elements of the placenta are not likely to take part in the production of histaminase.

PROF. SENEZ:

What is the biological meaning of diamine oxidase?

DR. KAPELLER-ADLER:

As far as histaminase is concerned it should be recalled that this enzyme occurs specifically in very much increased amounts in the plasma throughout human pregnancy. Histaminase is produced on the maternal side of the placenta, and the role of this enzyme may be a prophylactic measure to protect the mother from a possible intoxication with histamine which may be formed by an enzymatic decarboxylation of histidine, known to prevail in large amounts during the entire human gestation. The placenta is a barrier for histaminase, and foetal blood does not contain any increased histaminase activity. In this connection it should be mentioned that Kahlson (Lund) advanced the theory that histamine is required by the foetus for its growth.

DR. J. HEDGEGAARD:

I am not quite sure if I just did not catch it or if you did not mention how you measure your enzyme activity. That is, I would like to know how you follow specifically your enzymatic breakdown of the histamine molecule to imidazole acetaldehyde in your system. Therefore, would you mind giving the principle of the reaction and eventually also the assay system? I think this is important since, further down in your report, you refer to units of enzyme which then must have been estimated (and defined) according to a specific assay.

DR. KAPELLER-ADLER:

Histamine is enzymatically degraded by an oxidative deamination according to the equation:

$$RCH_2CH_2NH_2 + O_2 + H_2O \rightarrow RCH_2CHO + NH_3 + H_2O_2$$

R = imidazole.

Histaminase activity was determined by a simple microvolumetric technique (R. Kapeller-Adler and H. MacFarlane; *Biochim. et Biophys. Acta*, in press) involving a coupled oxidation reaction in which indigo disulphonate is oxidized by the $H_2O_2$ formed in the primary reaction, shown above. The assay system consisted of 0.5 ml of a histaminase solution in 0.175 M phosphate buffer, pH 6.8, 0.1 ml of substrate (5 mg histamine 2HCl (B.D.H.)/ml phosphate buffer, pH 6.8), and 1 ml of a solution of sodium indigo disulphonate (200 mg of indigo carmine, " Analar ", B.D.H., in 300 ml glass distilled water). The volume was made up to 10 ml with phosphate buffer, pH 6.8, and one small drop of chloroform was added as a preservative. (The final concentration of the substrate was 2.72 $\mu$moles and that of indigo disulphonate 1.43 $\mu$moles.) Blanks were complete assays without the addition of the substrate.

Blanks and assays were set up in triplicate. Oxygen was then simultaneously passed through the three test tubes of each assay or each blank for 1 min (stop watch), and the test tubes were closed with rubber stoppers. Deionized, glass-distilled water was used throughout all enzyme estimations. After an incubation for 24 hr at 37°, the excess of indigo disulphonate, not oxidized by the $H_2O_2$ formed during the action of histaminase on histamine, was titrated with 0.002 N $KMnO_4$ until the end point of titration was reached (i.e. until the blue colour of the solution had just disappeared). The amount of 0.002 N $KMnO_4$ used for the blank minus that used for the assay indicates the histaminase activity, expressed in units, one unit representing the amount of histaminase which under standard assay conditions, described above, produces the amount of $H_2O_2$ equivalent to 0.1 ml of 0.002 N $KMnO_4$. Since in this stoichiometric reaction one molecule of $H_2O_2$ is formed for each molecule of histamine oxidized (R. Kapeller-Adler; *Biochem. J.* **48**, 99, 1951; *Biochim. et Biophys. Acta* **22**, 391 (1956) this enzymic unit corresponds to the destruction of 0.463 $\mu$g of histamine per hr. To conform with recent recommendations of the Commission on Enzymes of the International Union of Biochemistry this histaminase unit is to be defined as the amount of enzyme which will under standard assay conditions catalyse the degradation of $6.95 \times 10^{-5}$ $\mu$moles of histamine/min. The specific activity of histaminase is defined as the number of enzyme units per mg of protein. Protein was determined by the method of Lowry *et al.* (*J. Biol. Chem.* **193**, 265, 1951).

# STUDIES ON THE COFACTORS AND OPTICAL PROPERTIES OF HOG KIDNEY DIAMINE OXIDASE

by E. V. GORYACHENKOVA and E. A. ERSHOVA

Institute of Radiobiology and Physico-Chemical Biology
Academy of Sciences of the U.S.S.R.
(1. Academichesky Proyezd, 18, Moscow, U.S.S.R.)

SUGGESTIVE evidence indicating the dependence of diamine oxidase (DO) activity on PLP and FAD has been reported by one of the authors in previous papers.[1] It was of interest to investigate the spectral properties of purified DO preparations and to determine their PLP content. For this purpose it was necessary to make available sufficient amounts of stable high-purity preparations of the enzyme.

DO was prepared from hog kidney by a procedure involving dehydration of the aqueous tissue extract with cold acetone, fractionation of the extracted protein with ammonium sulfate and heat denaturation of inactive proteins. Further purification was achieved by ion exchange chromatography on DEAE–cellulose columns in 0.005 M borate buffer (pH 8.0–8.3).

The proteins were eluted stepwise either with the same buffer and increasing concentrations of sodium chloride or by simultaneous alterations of pH and buffer concentration. DO activity was eluted from the column with buffer containing 0.1 M sodium chloride or with 0.1 molar acetate buffer (at pH 5.5). Additional purification of DO was attained by zone electrophoresis in starch blocks[2] or in cellulose powder columns according to Porath[3]. Electrophoresis was conducted in M/30 phosphate buffer (pH 7.4) with a potential gradient of 5–6 V/cm.

DO activity was measured with the aid of several methods (singly or in parallel), namely: measurement of oxygen uptake in Warburg manometers on incubation of DO with histamine or putrescine; estimation of histamine disappearance by the method of Tabor[4], and determination of the oxidation product of putrescine by a modification of the spectrophotometric method of Jakoby and Fredericus[5] with *o*-aminobenzaldehyde.

So as to accumulate preparations of purified DO, we had to abandon the procedure of electrophoresis in starch blocks used in our former experiments, since this step leads to considerable losses of DO activity.

The specific activity of DO preparations obtained after a single chromatographic separation on DEAE–cellulose or after column electrophoresis was increased 300–350-fold over the specific activity of the original kidney extract (the degree of purification of the peak fractions was about 500-fold).

Solutions of DO purified by single or repeated fractionation on DEAE–cellulose columns, with a protein concentration of ~6 mg/ml exhibited a distinct absorption peak at 415 mμ as well as two small peaks at 525 and

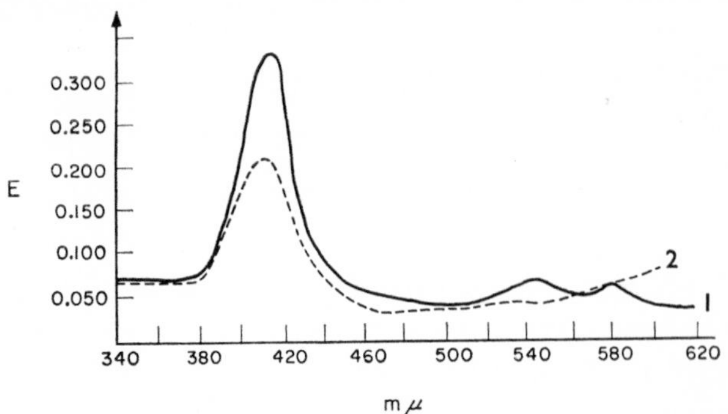


Fig. 1. Interaction of histamine with DO purified on DEAE–cellulose (5.0 mg of protein per 1 ml. [1]Absorption spectrum of DO; [2]spectrum of DO after addition of histamine under anaerobic conditions.

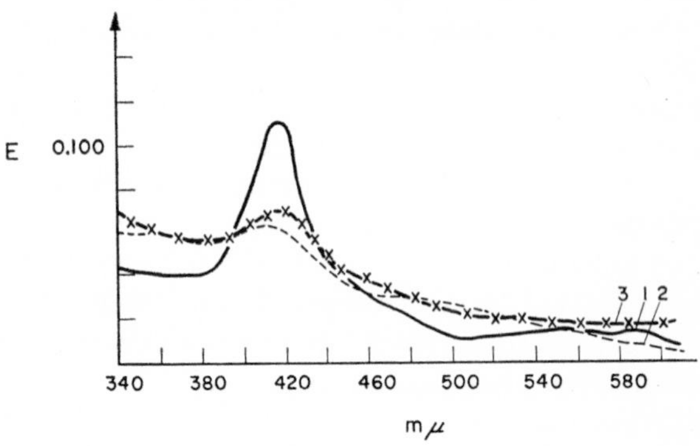


Fig. 2. Interaction of NaOH and Na dithionite with DO purified on DEAE–cellulose. [1]Absorption spectrum of DO; [2]spectrum of DO, 2 hr after the addition of 0.1 N NaOH; [3]spectrum of DO in the presence of Na dithionite (anaerobically).

575 mμ (Fig. 1). The presence of a spectral peak near 415 mμ is a familiar characteristic of some PLP enzymes and may indicate the presence of protein-bound PLP in the DO preparations. On addition of histamine or putrescine to the DO solutions under anaerobic conditions a considerable decrease of the peak at 415 mμ was observed, but the maximum was not restored on aeration of the solution. Similar alterations of the absorption spectrum occurred following addition of carbonyl reagents ($10^{-3}$ M isoniazid or

hydroxylamine), heating of the enzyme solution to 100°, treatment with 0.2 N sodium hydroxide or with Na-dithionite. In the latter case the peaks at 525 and 575 mμ were also bleached (Fig. 2). The various treatments resulting in inactivation of DO and lowering of the maximum at 415 mμ were not associated with the appearance of any new absorption peaks.

In fractions of DO purified on DEAE–cellulose, the height of the 415 mμ peak was roughly dependent on the protein content, with no regular parallel

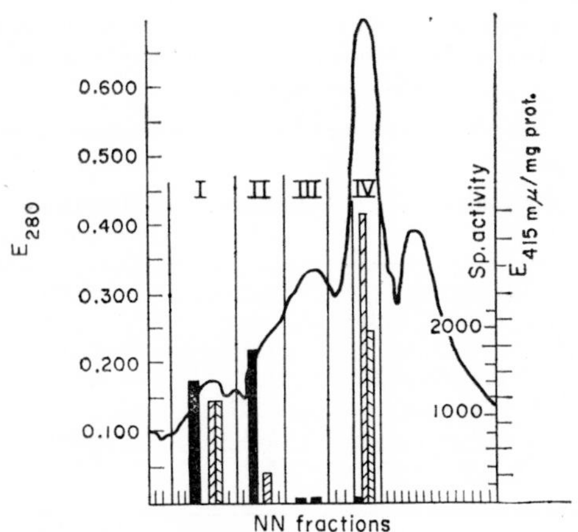


FIG. 3. Distribution of protein, DO activity and $E_{415}$ in a hog kidney DO preparation subjected to column electrophoresis. Full line, $E_{280}$ (protein concentration); black bars, specific activity of DO (μg histamine oxidized per 1 mg protein); hatched bars, $E_{415}$ without substrate and in the presence of histamine under anaerobic conditions.

to the specific enzymatic activity. On replacing this purification step by zone electrophoresis, it was found that the fractions exhibiting maximum DO activity had a very small optical density at 415 mμ (Fig. 3).

Further it could be shown that the peaks at 415, 525 and 575 mμ, formerly observed in solutions of DO, do not belong to the enzyme but result from the presence of two contaminant inactive proteins in the partially purified preparations.

Under the conditions of the electrophoretic experiment one of these proteins has a mobility close to that of DO and travels a little faster to the anode as compared to the enzyme. In solutions of this protein the peak at 415 mμ is not lowered anaerobically in the presence of histamine. The other contaminant has a considerably lower electrophoretic mobility than DO; its absorption maximum exhibits a marked decrease on addition of histamine under anaerobic conditions. Ion-exchange chromatography on DEAE–cellulose fails to separate the enzyme from these colored contaminants.

The purest fractions of DO were tested for their PLP content by means of a modified version of the aspartate apotransaminase method of Holzer[6,7]. With the aid of this highly sensitive method PLP can be determined quantitatively in amounts as low as 0.001–0.005 μg. For instance, samples of pure aspartate–glutamate transaminase containing 0.5–1.0 μg protein are sufficient for the quantitative determination of the PLP content. The method responds specifically to PLP and PMP.

TABLE 1. DETERMINATION OF PLP CONTENT OF PURIFIED PREPARATIONS OF ASPARTATE–GLUTAMATE TRANSAMINASE AND DIAMINE OXIDASE IN THE APOTRANSAMINASE TEST[6,7]

| Samples for analysis | Enzyme (μg) | $E_{453}$ (pyruvate DNP hydrazone) | PLP (mμg) |
|---|---|---|---|
| 1. Yeast apoenzyme (Control) | — | 0.080 | — |
| 2. AS transaminase, treated with 0.2 N NaOH | 1.0 | 0.361 | 4.5 |
| 3. DO, treated with 0.2 N NaOH | 15.0 | 0.080 | 0 |
| 4. DO, treated with 7 per cent $CCl_3COOH$ | 15.0 | 0.030 | 0 |
| 5. DO, heated to 100° for 5 min | 15.0 | 0.060 | 0 |

In order to liberate PLP, the DO preparations were subjected either to 5 min heating to 100° or to treatment in the cold with 7 per cent trichloracetic acid or with 0.2 N sodium hydroxide.

We failed to detect even traces of free PLP in solutions of DO containing up to 15 μg protein per ml after treatment by any one of the procedures mentioned above (Table 1); PLP added to the DO solutions as an internal standard (before protein denaturation) is recovered quantitatively.

These results might be interpreted as indicating the absence of PLP in the DO preparations. However, analysis of autoclaved acid hydrolysates of the same preparations for total vitamin $B_6$ in the microbiological test with *Debaryomyces disporus* revealed the presence of small amounts of vitamin $B_6$—of the order of 0.1–0.2 μg per 1 mg protein.[8]

It seems possible that DO contains firmly bound PLP which either is not liberated by the procedures used in our experiments or is detached from the protein in a form inactive in the apotransaminase test.

A question which is still controversial concerns the identity of DO and histaminase.[9,11] In 1958 we reported[12] that the activities measured with histamine and with putrescine as the substrates were distributed in a strictly parallel manner in protein fractions obtained on fractionation of hog kidney DO by zonal electrophoresis, with coincident activity peaks for both substrates.

On account of these data and of other evidence we concluded that both substrates were oxidized by the same enzyme.

In experiments on purification of DO by electrophoresis followed by ion exchange chromatography on DEAE–cellulose under the conditions indicated by Kapeller-Adler[11] we did not observe any change in distribution of the relative activities of the enzyme towards the two substrates. Thus our current data confirm our previous conclusion concerning the identity of DO and histaminase.

TABLE 2. EFFECTS OF DIETHYLDITHIOCARBAMATE (DEDTC), PLP AND DIVALENT METALS UPON DO ACTIVITY (SUBSTRATE — $8.10^{-3}$ M PUTRESCINE)

| Samples | DO specific activity |
|---|---|
| (Control) | |
| 1. Boiled DO + $Cu^{2+}$ + PLP | 0.00 |
| 2. Boiled DO + $Fe^{2+}$ + PLP | |
| (Exptl.) | |
| 3. DO initial | 1.03 |
| 4. DO, dialyed vs. $10^{-2}$ M DEDTC, 17 hr | 0.78 |
| 5. Same as (4), filtered on Sephadex | 0.92 |
| 6. Same as (5), after dialysis | 0.92 |
| 7. Same as (6) + $Cu^{2+}$ + PLP | 0.92 |

The activity of DO is known to be impaired by metal-chelating reagents. In our experiments concerning the effects of chelating agents on DO from hog kidney, the strongest inhibitory action was observed with diethyldithiocarbamate and with 8-hydroxyquinoline; both agents produced 50–60 per cent inhibition at $10^{-3}$ M.

In reactivation experiments, a slight degree of activity restitution was found to occur upon gel-filtration of solutions of DO inhibited with these agents through a column of Sephadex, followed by dialysis. Addition to the inhibited enzyme solution, treated as indicated above, of divalent metal ions ($Cu^{2+}$, $Fe^{2+}$, $Zn^{2+}$ or $Mn^{2+}$) in low concentrations ($10^{-7}$–$10^{-6}$ M) in the presence of PLP did not result in distinct and reproductible activation (Table 2); at higher concentrations ($10^{-5}$ M) these metals caused further inactivation of the partially inhibited enzyme.

Analysis of 350-fold purified DO preparations by emission spectrometry revealed a Cu content of the order of $\sim$0.03 per cent.

The activity of DO was shown to be impaired in the presence of sulfur-containing reducing agents, viz. dithionite, cysteine, thioglycolic or $\beta$-mercaptopropionic acid. The nature of this inhibition has not been established.

## REFERENCES

1. E. V. Goryachenkova; *Biokhimia* **21**, 247 (1956).
2. V. D. Uspenskaya and E. V. Goryachenkova; *Biokhimia* **23**, 212 (1958).
3. J. Porath; *Arkiv Kemi* **11**, 161 (1957).
4. S. M. Rosenthal and H. Tabor; *J. Pharmacol. Expt. Therap.* **92**, 425 (1948).
5. W. B. Jakoby and J. Fredericus; *J. Biol. Chem.* **234**, 2145 (1959).
6. H. Holzer, V. Gerlach, G. Jakobi and M. Gnoth; *Biochem. Z.* **329**, 529 (1958).
7. E. V. Goryachenkova; *Biokhimia*, in press.
8. E. N. Odintsova; *Microbiological Methods of Determination of Vitamins*, AN SSSR, Moscow (1959).
9. E. A. Zeller; *The Enzymes* (edited by J. B. Sumner and K. Myrbäck), vol. 2, p. 544, Academic Press, New York (1951).
10. R. Kapeller-Adler; *Biochem. J.* **44**, 70 (1949).
11. R. Kapeller-Adler; *Biochem. J.* **82**, 49P (1962).
12. E. V. Goryachenkova; *Doklady Akad. Nauk S.S.S.R.* **123**, 898 (1958).

## DISCUSSION

Dr. Kapeller-Adler:

How do you define a unit and how do you express the specific activity of hog kidney diamine oxidase (DO) using either histamine or putrescine or hexamethylene diamine as substrates? What is the ratio of the enzymatic effect on histamine as compared to that of hexamethylene diamine?

Do the ratios of DO activity upon histamine/putrescine and upon histamine/hexamethylene diamine remain constant throughout all the purification stages?

Have you tested your purest DO preparations on mixtures of histamine and putrescine and of histamine and hexamethylene diamine, and if so, what results have you obtained?

Is there no evidence for the presence of FAD in any of the purest DO fractions which you have obtained by zone electrophoresis? How do you interpret your findings of small amounts of vitamin $B_6$ in autoclaved acid hydrolyzates of purified DO? Does this mean that pyridoxal phosphate is so tightly bound to the apoenzyme of DO that it can be only released by autoclaving the acid hydrolyzates of DO?

Dr. Goryachenkova:

1. We express the specific activity of pig kidney DO by the decrease in $\mu$-moles of histamine or putrescine/mg of protein/min. Histamine and putrescine were tested with specific colorimetric methods. We did not use hexamethylene diamine as substrate for animal DO.

2. The ratios of activities on histamine and putrescine throughout all the purification stages did not remain constant; the activity of DO with histamine in the purest fraction was higher than putrescine.

3. We did not investigate the purest DO fractions on mixtures of histamine and putrescine.

4. We do not have evidence for the presence of FAD in any of the purest DO fractions.

5. We found small amounts of vitamin $B_6$ in autoclaved hydrolyzates of purified DO. We consider that there is an unusual form of pyridoxal phosphate in DO and it releases from apoenzyme only by autoclaving the preparation of DO.

# PLASMA AMINE OXIDASE; A CUPRIC-PYRIDOXAL PHOSPHATE ENZYME*

by KERRY T. YASUNOBU and HIDEAKI YAMADA†

Department of Biochemistry and Biophysics,
University of Hawaii, Honolulu, Hawaii

## INTRODUCTION

ALTHOUGH many pyridoxal enzymes have been studied in detail,[1,2] relatively few enzymes requiring both a metal and pyridoxal phosphate as prosthetic groups have been isolated. Mann[3] was the first to obtain evidence of such an enzyme when he isolated pea seedling diamine oxidase in a highly purified form. At about the same time, research in our laboratories demonstrated that plasma amine oxidase is a cupric-pyridoxal phosphate enzyme.[4,5] Plasma amine oxidase was first discovered by Hirsch[6] and highly purified by Tabor *et al.*[7] and Gorkin[8].

## PHYSICOCHEMICAL PROPERTIES

Beef plasma amine oxidase has been crystallized in our laboratories and shown to be homogeneous by a number of physicochemical criteria. Figure 1 shows a photomicrograph of the crystalline plasma amine oxidase and the details of the purification procedure have already been published.[4] Table 1 summarizes some of the physicochemical properties of the enzyme. The majority of copper proteins have an acid isoelectric point and plasma amine oxidase is no exception to this rule.

The amino acid composition of this enzyme is summarized in Table 2. Noteworthy are the high proline content and the relatively excess amounts of the acidic as compared to the basic amino acids. The low recovery of the residue weight suggests the possible presence of other organic constituents.

### *Copper Requirement*

Since plasma amine oxidase is an oxidative enzyme and since certain chelating agents were reported to inhibit the enzyme,[6,7] our initial efforts were directed toward demonstrating the nature of the metallic prosthetic

*The authors are grateful to the National Institutes of Health, United States Public Health Service (Grant M-2891) and the National Science Foundation (Equipment Grant) for support of this project.

†On leave from the Department of Agricultural Chemistry, University of Kyoto.

TABLE 1. SOME PHYSICOCHEMICAL PROPERTIES OF PLASMA AMINE OXIDASE

| Property | Values |
|---|---|
| 1. Molecular weight | 260,000 |
| 2. $s_{20}^{\circ}, w$ | 9.6 S |
| 3. $v$ | 0.76 |
| 4. $E^{1\%}$ 1 cm, 280 mμ | 9.8 |
| 5. $E_{480}/E_{280}$ and $E_{260}/E_{260}$ mμ | 0.017 and 0.64 |
| 6. Isoelectric point | 4.5 |
| 7. Nitrogen content | 14.98% |
| 8. Specific activity | 500 |
| 9. Turnover no. (moles of substrate/min per mole enzyme) | 40–50 (benzylamine)<br>80–100 (spermine) |
| 10. Copper content | 4 g atom/mole |
| 11. Pyridoxal phosphate content | 2 mole/mole enzyme |

TABLE 2. AMINO ACID COMPOSITION OF PLASMA AMINE OXIDASE

| Amino acid | Protein | | N* | Minimal molecular weight | Nearest integral number of amino acid residues per 260,000 g of protein |
|---|---|---|---|---|---|
| | As amino acid | As amino acid residue | | | |
| Aspartic acid | 8.93 | 7.72 | 6.27 | 1491 | 174 |
| Theonine | 5.14 | 4.45 | 4.03 | 2316 | 112 |
| Serine | 5.70 | 4.72 | 5.07 | 1845 | 141 |
| Glutamic acid | 14.10 | 12.37 | 8.95 | 1044 | 249 |
| Proline | 8.10 | 6.83 | 6.57 | 1422 | 183 |
| Glycine | 5.20 | 3.95 | 6.47 | 1445 | 180 |
| Alanine | 5.42 | 4.32 | 5.68 | 1645 | 158 |
| Valine | 7.31 | 6.19 | 5.84 | 1602 | 162 |
| Methionine | 2.16 | 1.90 | 1.35 | 6974 | 37 |
| Isoleucine | 3.03 | 2.61 | 2.16 | 4336 | 60 |
| Leucine | 9.01 | 7.77 | 6.42 | 1456 | 178 |
| Tyrosine | 4.80 | 4.32 | 2.47 | 3773 | 69 |
| Phenylalanine | 7.65 | 6.82 | 4.33 | 2158 | 121 |
| Lysine | 3.32 | 2.91 | 4.24 | 4405 | 59 |
| Histidine | 3.81 | 3.37 | 6.89 | 4070 | 64 |
| Arginine | 6.80 | 6.10 | 14.60 | 2586 | 101 |
| Amide ammonia | 1.76 | — | 9.68 | — | — |
| Tryptophane | 2.81 | 2.59 | 2.60 | 7197 | 36 |
| Total half-cystine | 1.23 | 0.75 | 0.68 | 13,752 | 19 |
| Total | — | 89.69 | 104.30 | — | — |

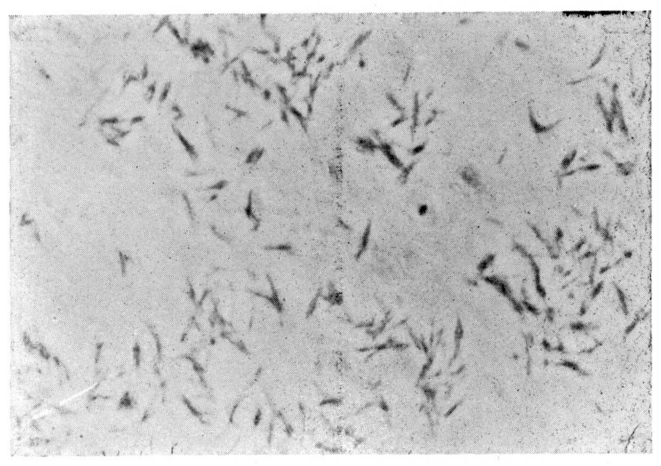

FIG. 1. Photomicrograph of crystalline plasma amine oxidase (magnified 620-fold).

group. Fortunately, copper was one of the first metals investigated and during the purification of the enzyme, a direct proportionality between copper content and specific activity of the enzyme was observed as shown in Fig. 2.

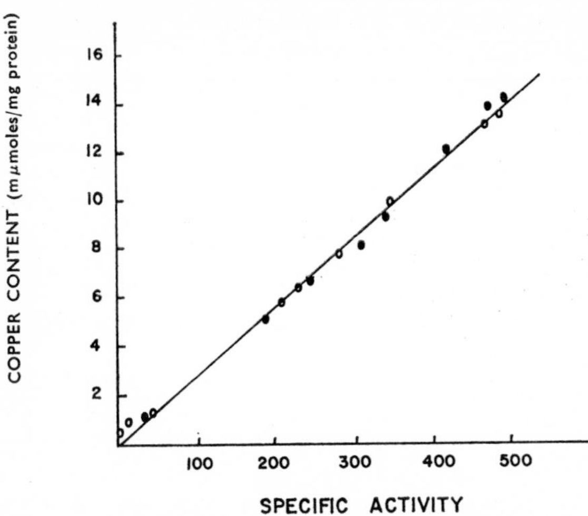


FIG. 2. Proportionality between copper content and specific activity during the purification of plasma amine oxidase.

TABLE 3. METAL CONTENTS OF RECRYSTALLIZED PLASMA AMINE OXIDASE[a]

| Metal | Flame spectrography[b] | Chemical analysis (mμmoles/mg protein) |
|---|---|---|
| Copper | + + + | 13.78 |
| Iron | — | 0.16 |
| Zinc | — | 0.43 |
| Molybdenum | — | 0.00 |
| Manganese | — | 0.03 |

[a]For all these studies, the recrystallized enzyme preparations with a specific activity of 482 were used.

[b]These are qualitative results and a (+) sign indicates detectable and a (—) sign indicates undetectable amounts of the metals. The enzyme solution containing 25 mg of protein per ml was analyzed with flame spectrophotometer.

The crystalline enzyme with a specific activity of 500 contained approximately 4 g atoms of copper per mole of enzyme. Other metals which were present occurred in insignificant amounts are shown in Table 3. Chemical determination of the valence state of copper using the method of Griffiths and Wharton[9] showed that all of the copper was in the cupric state and none in the cuprous state. In a joint research effort with Dr. Howard S. Mason, University of Oregon Medical School, these results were confirmed using EPR techniques.[10] The EPR spectrum of the enzyme is shown in Fig. 3 and a $g$ value of 2.053

TABLE 4. RESOLUTION AND REACTIVATION OF ENZYME BY CUPRIC IONS

| Treatment | Specific activity (units/mg protein) | Copper content (mμmoles/mg protein) |
|---|---|---|
| 1. None | 482 | 13.93 |
| 2. Dialysis against 0.1 M sodium diethyldithiocarbamate | 9 | 0.63 |
| 3. Dialysis of (2) against cupric sulfate | 341 | 12.64 |
| 4. Dialysis of (2) against cuprous sulfate | 172 | 38.71 |

TABLE 5. EFFECT OF CHELATING AGENTS ON PLASMA AMINE OXIDASE

The recrystallized enzyme, 0.5 mg, with a specific activity of 482 was preincubated for 10 min with chelating agents prior to the addition of benzylamine under the standard assay conditions.

| Chelating agents | Concentration ($M \times 10^{-5}$) | Inhibition (%) |
|---|---|---|
| 1. Sodium diethyldithiocarbamate | 3.0 | 9.7 |
| | 6.0 | 13.8 |
| 2. Cuprizone | 3.0 | 67.4 |
| | 6.0 | 97.7 |
| 3. Neocuproine | 6.0 | 0.0 |
| | 12.0 | 0.3 |
| 4. Sodium cyanide | 30.0 | 24.1 |
| | 100.0 | 76.2 |
| 5. 8-Hydroxyquinoline | 3.8 | 20.6 |
| | 7.5 | 27.4 |
| 6. 2, 2′-Bipyridyl | 3.8 | 5.8 |
| | 7.5 | 9.7 |
| 7. *o*-Phenanthroline | 3.8 | 33.6 |
| | 7.5 | 40.8 |
| 8. EDTA | 30.0 | 0.0 |
| | 300.0 | 0.2 |
| 9. Sodium azide | 100.0 | 0.5 |
| 10. Sodium thioglycolate | 100.0 | 13.2 |

and a hyperfine splitting constant of 0.02 was determined. Additional evidence for the cupric copper requirement was obtained with the copper-free enzyme obtained by sodium diethyldithiocarbamate treatment of the enzyme. The results are summarized in Table 4 and cupric copper was found to be much more effective than cuprous copper in reactivating the copper-free enzyme. Whatever activity was observed could easily be attributed to autoxidation of the cuprous copper during the experiments.

Additional evidence for the copper requirement of the enzyme was obtained using copper-chelating agents. The results are summarized in Table 5 and as

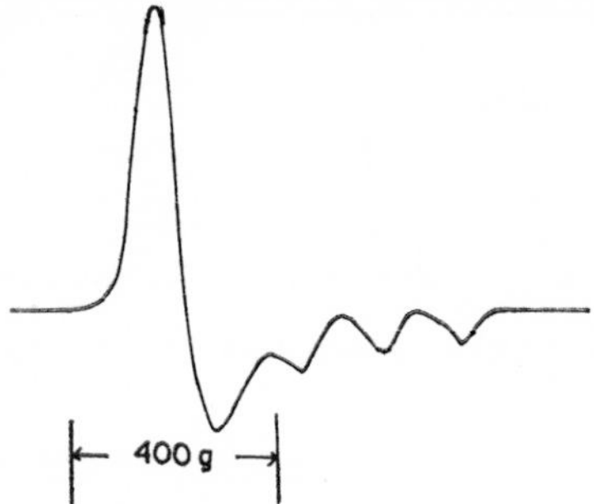


FIG. 3. EPR spectrum of plasma amine oxidase.

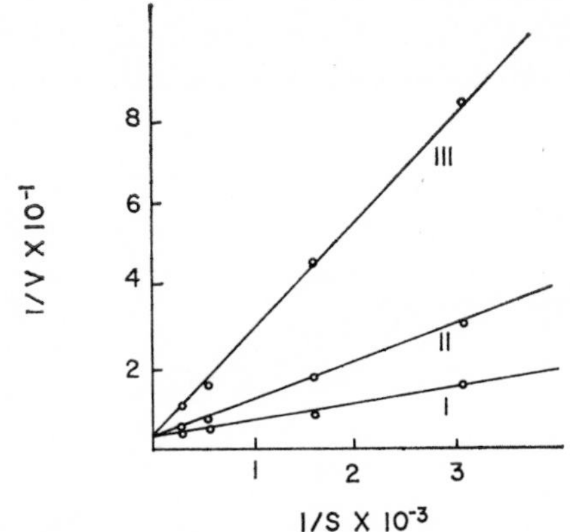


FIG. 4. Inhibition of plasma amine oxidase by cuprizone. I, 0.0; II, 1.5; III, 5.0; $10^{-5}$ M cuprizone.

shown in Fig. 4, cuprizone was found to be a competitive inhibitor of the enzyme and a $K_I$ value of $1.4 \times 10^{-5}$ M was obtained.

*Pyridoxal Phosphate Requirement*

In contrast to certain pyridoxal enzymes, complete resolution of pyridoxal phosphate from the enzyme has not been possible. Many different methods were used but partial resolution of the enzyme was accomplished by alkaline hydroxylamine treatment of the enzyme. Although this treatment resulted in large losses in activity, the pyridoxal phosphate was not removed quantitatively. The enzyme was partially reactivated by pyridoxal phosphate and pyridoxal but not by pyridoxamine phosphate or pyridoxine. The initial reaction velocity was restored to the original value but the velocity decreased initially and remained constant thereafter. The results are summarized in Table 6.

TABLE 6. EFFECT OF PYRIDOXINE DERIVATIVES ON ALKALINE- HYDROXYLAMINE-TREATED PLASMA AMINE OXIDASE

| Addition | | Concentration (M) | Initial reaction |
|---|---|---|---|
| Untreated enzyme | | | 393 |
| Hydroxylamine treated enzyme | pyridoxal phosphate | $3 \times 10^{-5}$ | 83 |
| | pyridoxal | $3 \times 10^{-5}$ | 21 |
| | pyridoxamine phosphate | $3 \times 10^{-5}$ | 0 |
| | pyridoxamine | $3 \times 10^{-5}$ | 0 |

The spectra of the native and copper-free enzyme were determined at several pH values and are shown in Figs. 5 and 6. The native enzyme, possibly the uncomplicated Schiff's base, showed a maximum at 410 mμ at alkaline pH and a maximum at 480 mμ at slightly acidic pH. The copper-free enzyme

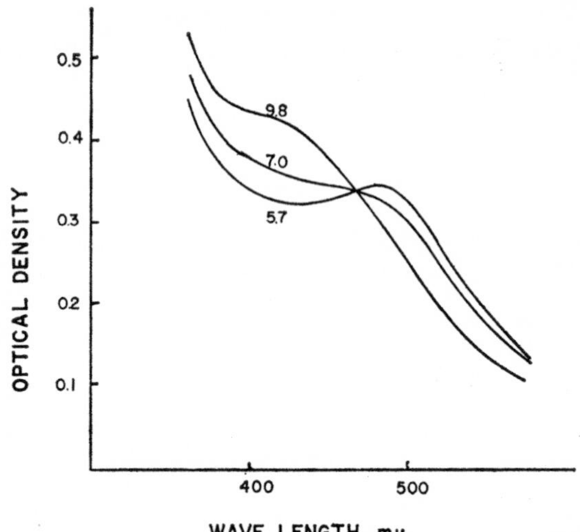


FIG. 5. Absorption spectra of plasma amine oxidase at various pH.

showed maxima at 375–380 mμ at acidic pH and at 330 mμ in basic solutions. The maximum at 380 mμ is very similar to pyridoxal phosphate and the maximum at 330 mμ may be due to the presence of a complicated Schiff's base as reported for phosphorylase.[11]

The use of carbonyl reagents aided greatly in demonstrating the presence of pyridoxal phosphate. The spectra of the oxime and various hydrazide derivatives are shown in Figs. 7 and 8. The maxima are very similar to those

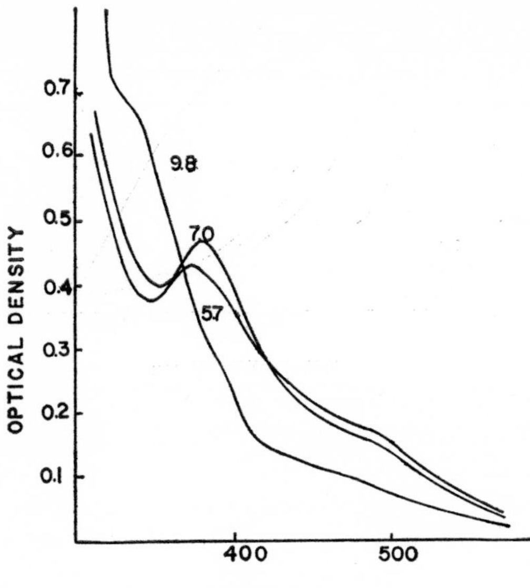


FIG. 6. Absorption spectra of copper-free plasma amine oxidase at various pH.

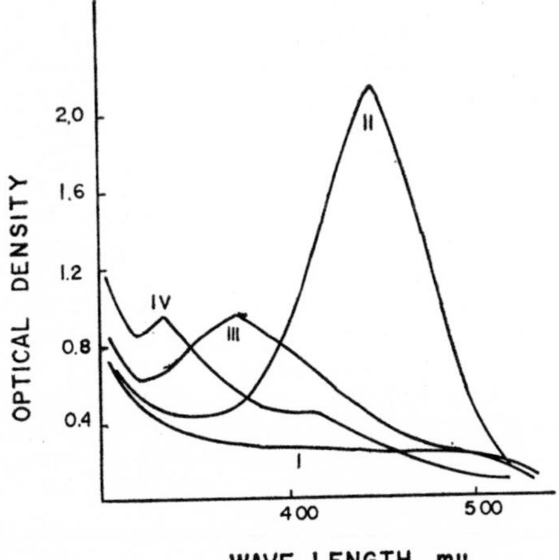


FIG. 7. Absorption spectra of plasma amine oxidase in the presence of carbonyl reagents. I, no addition; II, phenylhydrazine; III, hydroxylamine; IV, hydrazine.

of the oxime and hydrazide derivatives of pyridoxal phosphate.[12,13] Table 7 summarizes the spectral properties of the enzyme. Figure 9 shows the variation of the activity of plasma amine oxidase with varying concentrations

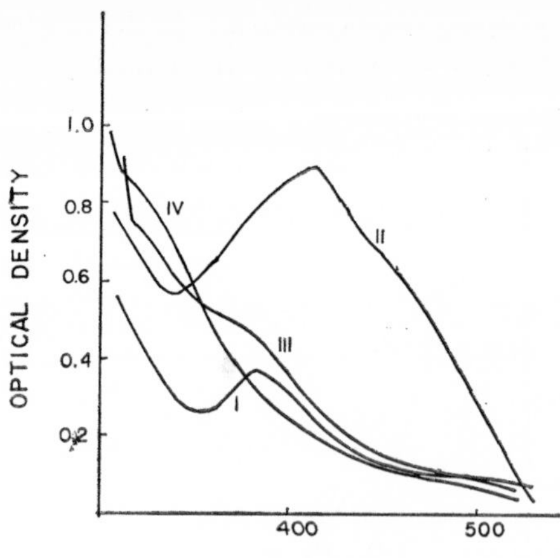


FIG. 8. Absorption spectra of copper-free plasma amine oxidase in the presence of carbonyl reagents. I, no addition; II, phenylhydrazine; III, hydroxylamine; IV, hydrazine.

TABLE 7. SPECTRAL DATA OF PLASMA AMINE OXIDASE

| | pH | $\lambda_{max}$ (m$\mu$) |
|---|---|---|
| Native enzyme | 9.8 | 410 |
| | 5.7 | 480 |
| Copper-free enzyme | 5.7 | 370 |
| | 7.0 | 380 |
| | 9.8 | 330 |
| Native enzyme + $NH_2NH_2$ | 7.0 | 320 and 410 |
| Native enzyme + phenylhydrazine | 7.0 | 447 |
| Native enzyme + $NH_2OH$ | 7.0 | 370 |
| Copper-free enzyme + $NH_2NH_2$ | 7.0 | 320 |
| Copper-free enzyme + phenylhydrazine | 7.0 | 410 |
| Copper-free enzyme + $NH_2OH$ | 7.0 | 330 |
| Peptide fragment | 1.0 | 305 |
| | 7.0 | 400 |
| | 13.0 | 400 |

Fluorescence properties of peptide fragment

| | | |
|---|---|---|
| Peptide isolated from native enzyme | 7.0 | 310 (excitation) |
| | | 410 (emission) |
| Peptide isolated from reduced enzyme | 7.0 | 330 (excitation) |
| | | 400 (emission) |

of a number of carbonyl reagents. Although all the reagents were inhibitors, phenylhydrazine, hydrazine and hydroxylamine were the most potent inhibitors. Hydrazine was shown to be a competitive inhibitor and a $K_I$ value of $8.7 \times 10^{-7}$ M was determined.

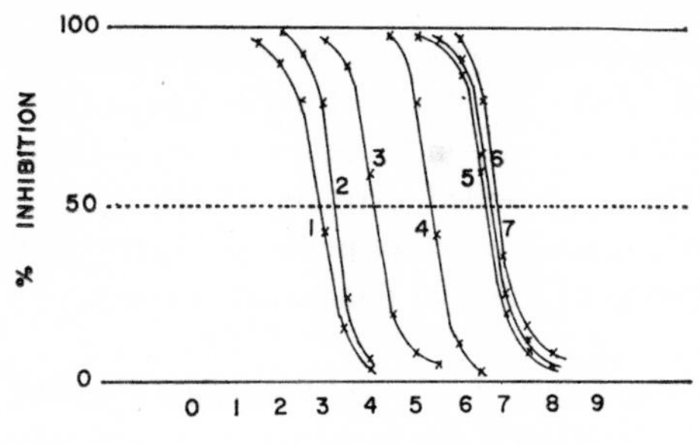


FIG. 9. Inhibition of plasma amine oxidase by various carbonyl reagents. 1, sodium bisulfite; 2, sodium cyanide; 3, isonicotinic acid hydrazide; 4, semicarbazide; 5, hydroxylamine; 6, phenylhydrazine; 7, hydrazine.

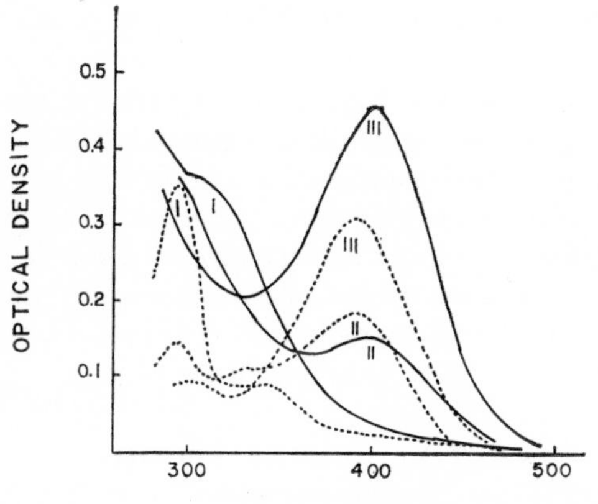


FIG. 10. Absorption spectra of chromophore isolated from plasma amine oxidase (solid line) and pyridoxal phosphate (broken line). I, in 0.1 M HCl; II, in 0.06 M phosphate (pH 7.0); III, in 0.1 M NaOH.

The heat denatured enzyme was hydrolyzed by pronase and a pyridoxal phosphate peptide was obtained. Dowex 50 and Dowex 1 resins were used to purify the peptide. The spectra of the peptide showed a maximum at 401 m$\mu$ (Fig. 10). The peptide showed maximal fluorescence excitation at

310 m$\mu$ and maximal fluorescence emission at 410 m$\mu$. The aldehyde group was incapable of reacting with phenyldrazine.

In order to quantitate the amount of pyridoxal phosphate present, the native enzyme was hydrolyzed with perchloric acid and the amount of inorganic phosphate determined. Approximately 1.8 moles of phosphate per mole of enzyme was obtained. This value agrees with the spectrophotometric determination of the pyridoxal phosphate content assuming a molar absorbancy index of 4900[14] at 380 m$\mu$ for the copper-free enzyme.

No flavins were detected in significant quantities in the enzyme. Trichloroacetic acid or filtrates of boiled extracts of the enzyme did not activate apo-D-amino acid oxidase. Furthermore, no flavopeptides were obtained after pronase digestion of the heat denatured enzyme.

### *Possible Evidence of a Cupric-Pyridoxal Phosphate Chelate*

Previous studies established the fact that 4 g atoms of cupric copper and 2 moles of pyridoxal phosphate were present per mole of enzyme. An interesting question is how these prosthetic groups are linked to the enzyme. All of the copper proteins studied to date show maxima either in the 340 m$\mu$ or in the 600–700 m$\mu$ region. Pyridoxal enzymes show maxima in the 330–415 m$\mu$ wavelength region. Plasma amine oxidase exhibits a maximum at 480 m$\mu$ in slightly acidic solutions. The spectrum is unlike any previously reported copper protein or pyridoxal enzyme with the exception of pea seedling amine oxidase.[3] The copper-free enzyme exhibits a maximum at about 380 m$\mu$ at pH 7.0 and upon the addition of cupric copper, a maximum at 480 m$\mu$ reappears. This suggests that copper and pyridoxal phosphate are reacting together to possibly form a chelate. The hyperfine splitting constant of the enzyme is more in the range of a simple copper chelate.[10] Although further studies are needed, plasma amine oxidase also has an acid isoelectric point which is so characteristic of copper proteins as to suggest that a part of the copper may be bound to the protein.

## ACTIVE CENTER STUDIES

Certain laboratories are currently engaged in isolating pyridoxal phosphate peptides from pyridoxal enzymes.[15] Similar studies are being carried out with the plasma amine oxidase but our results are still incomplete. However, the results are being presented now since they provide further evidence that this enzyme is a pyridoxal enzyme.

The Schiff base involving pyridoxal phosphate and an amino group of the enzyme was found to be reduced by the addition of sodium borohydride at pH 13.0. The enzyme, which showed a maximum around 320 m$\mu$, was heated and digested with pronase. Gradient elution with Dowex 50 columns provided an initial separation of the peptides and the main yellow-colored fraction was further separated on Dowex 1 columns giving rise to a partially purified pyridoxal phosphate peptide in about 40 per cent yield and whose fluorescence property is shown in Fig. 11. An aliquot of the pronase digest was also hydrolyzed with 6N HCl and purified by paper chromatography. The $R_f$ of the derivative was found to be slightly lower than the authentic reduced Schiff base obtained from pyridoxal phosphate and lysine ($\epsilon$-pyridoxyl-lysine). Further studies are in progress to determine the structure of the peptide.

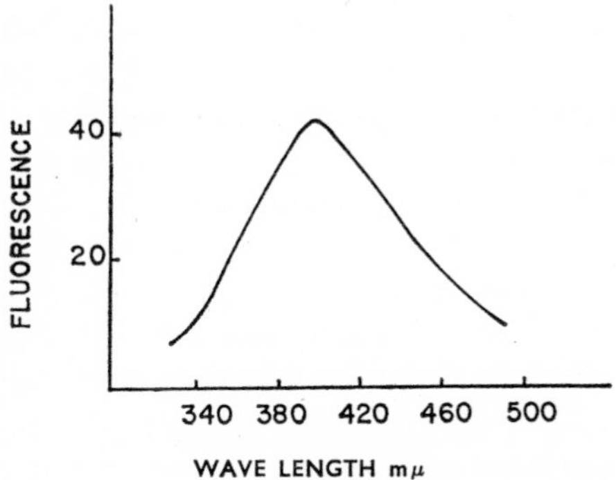


FIG. 11. Fluorescence emission spectra of chromophore isolated from reduced plasma amine oxidase. Excitation at 330 mμ.

## MECHANISM OF ACTION OF PLASMA AMINE OXIDASE

Because of the lack of an adequate theoretical basis at the present time, any interpretation concerning the mechanism of action of this enzyme must be speculative in nature. The reaction catalyzed by the enzyme is :

$$RCH_2NH_2 + O_2 + H_2O = RCHO + NH_3 + H_2O_2$$

The reaction can further be broken down into half cell reactions as follows :

Oxidation

$$RCH_2NH_2 + H_2O = RCHO + NH_3 + 2e + 2H^+$$

Reduction

$$2e + O_2 + 2H^+ = H_2O_2$$

These half cell reactions are written only to emphasize that the overall reaction involves a two-electron oxidation–reduction process. Furthermore, it is probable that oxygen is converted to $H_2O_2$ and that the oxygen incorporated into the aldehyde group probably arises from water.

Braunstein[2] and Blaschko[16] have discussed possible reaction mechanisms for amine oxidases. Since plasma amine oxidase is not a flavoenzyme, Braunstein's mechanisms are no longer applicable. Blaschko's mechanism is an extension of the mechanism proposed by Snell *et al.*[17] for other pyridoxal phosphate dependent enzymes. The mechanism does not take into account the role of copper in the enzymes and is shown below:

$$E + S = ES_I$$

$$ES_I = ES_{II}$$

$$ES_{II} + H_2O = ES_{III} + R\text{—}\overset{\overset{\displaystyle O}{\|}}{C}H$$

$$ES_{III} + O_2 = E + H_2O_2 + NH_3$$

$ES_I$ is the Schiff base intermediates; $ES_{II}$ is a tautometer of $ES_I$ in which the double bond has migrated to the $\alpha$ and $\beta$ C atoms of the amine; and $ES_{III}$ is the pyridoxamine phosphate enzyme derivative.

TABLE 8. VALENCY STATE OF COPPER IN PLASMA AMINE OXIDASE

Valency state of copper in plasma amine oxidase was determined by the method of Griffiths and Wharton[9]. The recrystallized enzyme with a specific activity of 482 was used.

| State of enzyme | Copper reduction (%) |
|---|---|
| 1. Oxidized (bubbled with $O_2$) | 0 |
| 2. " Steady-state " after adding 6 $\mu$moles of benzylamine | 0 |
| 3. Reduced (same as 2, under anaerobic conditions) | 0 |
| 4. Reduced form 3, shaken with $O_2$ | 0 |
| 5. Reduced by adding 6 $\mu$moles of dithionite under anaerobic conditions | 85–95 |
| 6. Reduced by adding 6 $\mu$moles of hydroxylamine under anaerobic conditions | 85–95 |

In our studies, indirect experimental evidence for the formation of a Schiff's base has been obtained. The addition of substrate benzylamine, to the enzyme did not alter the spectrum of the enzyme in the presence of oxygen. However, the anaerobic addition of substrate resulted in a bleaching of the maximum observed at 480 m$\mu$. We are interpreting this result as the formation of $ES_{II}$ or $ES_{III}$. The addition of substrate to the copper-free enzyme did not alter the spectrum of the enzyme suggesting that both cupric copper and pyridoxal phosphate are required for these reactions. Chemical determination of the valency of the copper by the method of Griffiths and Wharton[9] demonstrated that the copper did not undergo a valency change during the anaerobic addition of substrate (Table 8). These results were confirmed by EPR studies.[10] Therefore, the copper in $ES_I$, $ES_{II}$ and possibly $ES_{III}$ is in the cupric state.

Concerning the structures of $ES_{II}$ and $ES_{III}$, the addition of sodium hydrosulfite to the native enzyme at pH 7.0 causes a bleaching of the visible absorption band of the enzyme. Therefore, the structure of $ES_{II}$ or $ES_{III}$ formed during the anaerobic addition of substrate and the compound formed by the addition of sodium hydrosulfite may have some common structural features. Further mechanistic studies are in progress.

## SUMMARY

Plasma amine oxidase is a pyridoxal phosphate–copper enzyme containing 4 g atoms of cupric copper and 2 moles of pyridoxal phosphate. Various physicochemical properties of the crystalline preparations of the enzyme are described. The preliminary studies dealing with the nature of the pyridoxal phosphate peptide obtained by pronase digestion of the heat denatured enzyme as well as mechanism of action of this enzyme are presented and discussed.

## REFERENCES

1. E. E. Snell; *Vitamins and Hormones* **16**, 77 (1958).
2. A. E. Braunstein; *The Enzymes* (edited by P. D. Boyer, H. Lardy and K. Myrbäck), 2nd ed., vol. II, p. 113, Academic Press, New York (1951).
3. P. J. Mann; *Biochem. J.* **79**, 623 (1961).
4. H. Yamada and K. T. Yasunobu; *J. Biol. Chem.* **237**, 1511 (1962).
5. H. Yamada and K. T. Yasunobu; *Biochem. Biophys. Research Comm.* **8**, 387 (1962).
6. J. G. Hirsch; *J. Exptl. Med.* **97**, 345 (1953).
7. C. W. Tabor, H. Tabor and S. M. Rosenthal; *J. Biol. Chem.* **208**, 645 (1954).
8. V. Z. Gorkin; *Biochimiya* **7**, 632 (1961).
9. D. E. Griffiths and D. C. Wharton; *J. Biol. Chem.* **236**, 1857 (1961).
10. H. Yamada, K. T. Yasunobu, T. Yamano and H. S. Mason; Unpublished results.
11. A. B. Kent, E. G. Krebs and E. H. Fischer; *J. Biol. Chem.* **232**, 549 (1958).
12. C. R. Sutton and H. K. King; *Arch. Biochem. Biophys.* **96**, 360 (1962).
13. H. Wada and E. E. Snell; *J. Biol. Chem.* **236**, 2089 (1961).
14. E. A. Peterson and H. A. Sober; *J. Am. Chem. Soc.* **76**, 169 (1954).
15. E. H. Fischer, A. B. Kent, E. R. Snyder and E. G. Krebs; *J. Am. Chem. Soc.* **80**, 2906 (1958).
16. H. Blaschko; *Advances in Comparative Physiology and Biochemistry*, vol. I, p. 68, Academic Press, New York (1962).
17. D. E. Metzler, N. Ikawa and E. E. Snell; *J. Am. Chem. Soc.* **76**, 648 (1954).
18. H. Yamada and K. T. Yasunobu; *J. Biol. Chem.* In press.

## DISCUSSION

DR. KAPELLER-ADLER:

How does your purified plasma amine oxidase compare with spermine oxidase, as described by Tabor, and with Blaschko's pig's serum monoamine oxidase? Is your preparation identical with either of those two enzymes? Does your purified enzyme preparation act on histamine as substrate?

DR. YASUNOBU:

The plasma amine oxidase is identical to the spermine oxidase isolated by Tabor. According to Tabor, the enzyme does not act on histamine to any significant extent.

# AN ADP DEPENDENT THREONINE DEHYDRASE FROM *CLOSTRIDIUM TETANOMORPHUM*

by OSAMU HAYAISHI,* MALCOLM GEFTER and HERBERT WEISSBACH

National Heart Institute, National Institutes of Health,
Bethesda 14, Maryland, U.S.A.

THE enzyme "threonine dehydrase", which catalyzes the conversion of threonine to α-ketobutyrate (Eq. 1), has been studied from both animal and microbial sources.

$$\begin{array}{c} CH_3 \\ | \\ CHOH \\ | \\ CHNH_2 \\ | \\ COOH \end{array} \xrightarrow[\text{threonine dehydrase}]{\text{PLP}} \begin{array}{c} CH_3 \\ | \\ CH_2 \\ | \\ C{=}O \\ | \\ COOH \end{array} + NH_3 \qquad (1)$$

This enzyme has been shown to contain very tightly-bound pyridoxal phosphate as its prosthetic group. However, it has long been known that other substances can stimulate the activity of this enzyme. Lichstein *et al.*[1,2] first reported stimulation of threonine dehydrase activity of aged *E. coli* cells by the addition of either yeast extract, biotin or adenosine-5′-phosphate (AMP). Wood and Gunsalus[3] demonstrated that a cell-free enzyme from *E. coli* requires AMP and glutathione for maximum activity. More recently Sayre and Greenberg[4] reported a stimulation of sheep liver enzyme by AMP but these findings have not been fully explained or confirmed.

In the course of studies on the metabolism of threonine by cell-free extracts of *Clostridium tetanomorphum*, an adenosinediphosphate (ADP) dependent conversion of threonine to α-ketobutyrate was observed. Evidence is presented that ADP influences the binding of low levels of substrate to enzyme.

## ASSAY

Since many of the experiments presented in this paper were carried out with extremely low levels of substrate (20 mμmoles), it was not possible to assay enzyme activity by the conventional methods. Therefore, a rapid and convenient microassay method was developed using L-threonine-$C^{14}$. The

*Visiting Scientist, on leave from Kyoto University, Kyoto, Japan.

standard incubation contained in a total volume of 0.2 ml; enzyme, 10 μmoles of Tris buffer pH 8.7, 50 mμmoles of ADP, 20 mμmoles of $C^{14}$ threonine (500 counts/min per mμmole) and water. Incubations were done at 37° usually for periods up to 20 min. The reactions were stopped by the addition of 0.3 ml of 2 N HCl. The acidified reaction mixture was passed through a Dowex-50 $H^+$ column ($\frac{1}{2} \times 2$ cm) and the resin was washed with 1.0 ml $H_2O$. The effluent and wash were collected in a counting vial and 10 ml of a

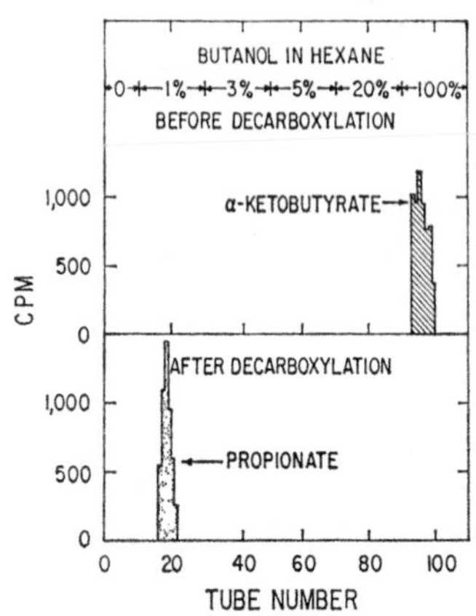


FIG. 1. Celite chromatography of the product before and after decarboxylation by ceric sulfate. Standard assay conditions were used. Contents of two test tubes were combined, passed through a Dowex-50-$H^+$ column as described in the text. The total volume was 3 ml. To a 1.0 ml aliquot containing about 13,580 counts/min were added about 16 μmoles of α-ketobutyrate and the mixture was decarboxylated by ceric sulfate. $C^{14}O_2$ was trapped by a 1 M hyamine solution placed in the centre well of a Warburg flask. Approximately 1,985 counts (70 per cent of theoretical) were trapped. The remaining counts in the main chamber were extracted with ethylacetate, combined and chromatographed. To another aliquot (1.0 ml) 16 μmoles of α-ketobutyrate were added, extracted with ethylacetate, combined and chromatographed. The recovery of α-ketobutyrate and propionate was approximately 50 and 58 per cent, respectively, based on radioactivity. Butanol–hexane mixtures were used to elute the products from the celite column (2 × 12 cm) 8 ml fractions were collected. The various acids tested were eluted as follows: Butyrate, 100 per cent hexane; propionate, 1 per cent butanol in hexane; acetate, 3 per cent butanol in hexane; formate, 20 per cent butanol in hexane; α-ketobutyrate, 100 per cent butanol.

naphthalene-dioxane scintillation counting fluid added.[5] Radioactivity was determined in a Packard Tri-Carb Scintillation Counter. Under these conditions, the substrate threonine was virtually completely adsorbed on the column, while α-ketobutyrate was quantitatively recovered in the effluent.

Since any acidic metabolite would be assayed by this procedure, it was necessary to verify that the product was α-ketobutyrate. When high concentrations of substrate was employed ($5 \times 10^{-2}$ M), the α-ketobutyrate was readily identified and quantitatively determined by its reaction with lactic dehydrogenase as well as its chromatographic behavior. However, when millimicromole levels of substrate were used, where the ADP effect was most pronounced, it was necessary to identify the small amounts of product. This was accomplished by celite chromatography[6] as shown in Fig. 1, the radioactive product through the Dowex-50 column co-chromatographed with α-ketobutyrate. If the product was treated with ceric sulfate, $C^{14}O_2$ was evolved and a new peak appeared on a celite chromatography which behaves identically with propionic acid.

Further evidence for the identity was provided by paper chromatography. $R_f$ of α-ketobutyrate; 0.75 with isoamylalcohol saturated with 4N formic acid,[7] 0.78 with ether, glacial acetic acid and water (13 : 3 : 1).[8] $R_f$ of propionic acid; 0.59 with butanol and 1.5 N $NH_4OH$ (1 : 1).[9]

TABLE 1. PURIFICATION OF THREONINE DEHYDRASE FROM *Clostridium tetanomorphum*

| Fraction | % Total activity | Specific activity |
|---|---|---|
| Charcoal, protamine supernatant | 100 | 20–35 |
| Ammonium sulfate 44–58% | 80–90 | 250 |
| DEAE—Peak 1 | 30 | 570 |
| DEAE—Peak 2 | 45 | 710 |

A unit of activity is defined as mμmoles α-ketobutyrate formed per 10 min. Specific activity is units per mg protein. The charcoal protamine extract contained about 500 units of activity per ml.

The enzyme was prepared by sonication of cells of *Clostridium tetanomorphum* in the presence of charcoal and corundum. The extract was then cleared by centrifugation and subjected to protamine sulfate followed by ammonium sulfate fractionation (43–60 per cent saturation). The enzyme (about 20 mg protein/ml) was then dialyzed against 0.001 M Tris buffer pH 7.4, containing 0.001 M mercaptoethanol. The enzyme activity at this stage was stable for periods of several weeks. Adsorption of the ammonium sulfate fraction on a DEAE column, followed by a gradient elution (between 0.05 and 0.25 M NaCl) showed the presence of two protein fractions with threonine dehydrase activity. It was possible to separate the two fractions rapidly by elution first with 0.14 M NaCl followed by 0.2 M NaCl. The following procedure was used: 2 ml of the dialyzed ammonium sulfate fraction was diluted to 20 ml with 0.001 M Tris pH 7.4 containing 0.01 M mercaptoethanol. The diluted enzyme was passed through a DEAE column

(1 × 11 cm) equilibrated with 0.001 M Tris pH 7.4. The column was washed with 30 ml 0.08 M NaCl containing 0.01 M mercaptoethanol, followed by 40 ml of 0.14 M NaCl containing 0.01 M mercaptoethanol to elute the

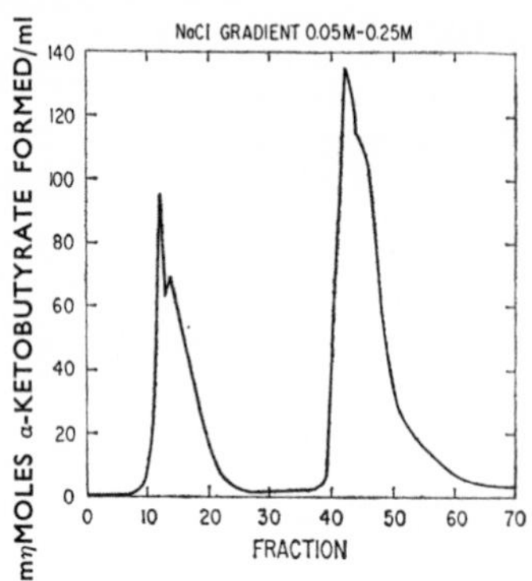


FIG. 2. Elution pattern of enzyme(s) using DEAE–cellulose chromatography.

first enzyme peak. The second peak was then eluted with 0.2 M NaCl containing mercaptoethanol. A summary of the purification procedures and the DEAE elution are shown in Table 1 and Fig. 2.

Enzyme activity is expressed as millimicromoles α-ketobutyrate formed per 10 min. Protein was determined by the method of Sutherland *et al.*[10]

TABLE 2. SPECIFICITY OF NUCLEOTIDE

| Nucleotide | mμmoles α-ketobutyrate per 10 min |
|---|---|
| — | 0.45 |
| ADP | 6.3 |
| GDP | 3.5 |
| IDP | 3.4 |
| AMP | 0.45 |

Nucleotide concentration $2.5 \times 10^{4}$ M. Standard assay system was employed. Other nucleosides mono-, di- and tri-phosphates were all ineffective including deoxy ADP and ATP.

*Effect of ADP*

When low levels of threonine were used the requirement for ADP was almost absolute as shown in Table 2. ATP, AMP and deoxy-ADP could not replace ADP although IDP and GDP gave from 33 to 50 per cent of the activity observed with ADP. All the other nucleotides tested were completely inactive. In the presence of ADP the activity was proportional to enzyme concentration and linear with time. The effect of ADP concentration on the rate of reaction is shown in Fig. 3. Maximal velocity was obtained with $2 \times 10^{-4}$ M ADP and the $K_m$ for ADP was calculated to be $5.8 \times 10^{-5}$ M.

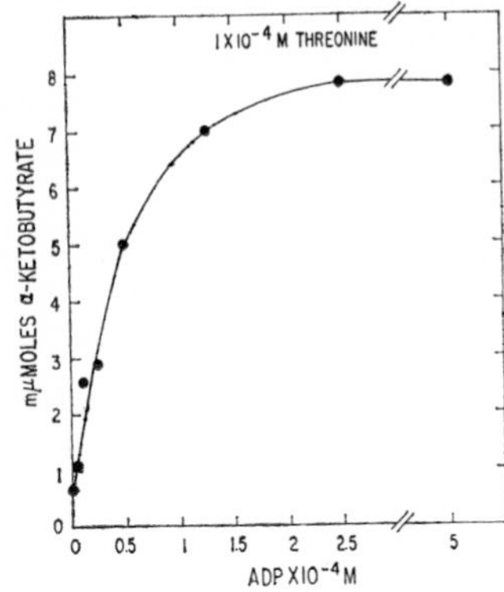


FIG. 3. Effect of ADP concentration on threonine dehydrase activity.

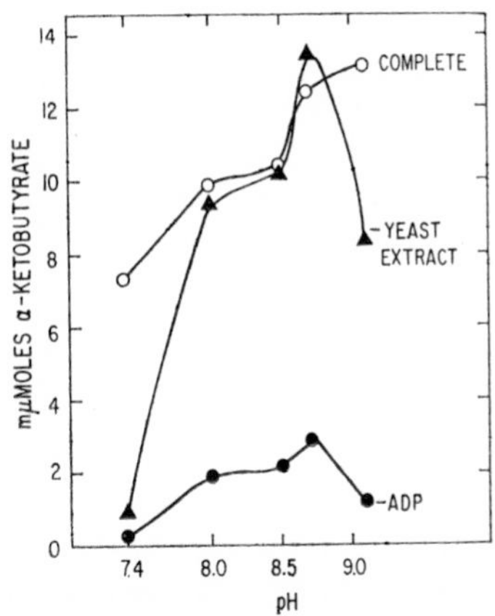


FIG. 4. Effect of pH on ADP and yeast extract requirement. Tris buffer (0.05 M) was used at the various pH values.

The rate of reaction was maximal between pH 8.7–9.3, with a marked drop in activity below pH 8.0 (Fig. 4). The ADP requirement was seen over the entire pH range tested although at pH 7.4 little activity was observed even in the presence of ADP unless yeast extract was also added (Table 3). This effect of yeast extract was not seen above pH 8.0. In fact with some enzyme preparations the yeast extract inhibited at the higher pH values. The factor in yeast extract has been purified although not identified. It is not retained by Dowex-50 Na or Dowex-1-Cl resins from neutral pH, but is retained by a Dowex-50-H column. It can be eluted from the latter with $NH_4OH$ and then adsorbed on a Dowex-2-OH column and subsequently eluted with acid. It was not adsorbed on charcoal. A Difco Casamino extract could replace the yeast extract indicating the requirement of an amino acid, although known amino acids alone or in combination were not effective. The presence of a peptide has not been excluded and appears to be a reasonable possibility considering the known data.

TABLE 3. REQUIREMENTS FOR THREONINE DEHYDRASE

| | mμmoles α-ketobutyrate per 10 min | |
|---|---|---|
| | pH 7.4 | pH 8.7 |
| Complete | 7.9 | 11.2 |
| —ADP | 0.2 | 1.7 |
| —Yeast | 1.0 | 14.4 |

Standard assay conditions were used. Tris buffer was employed at both pH 7.4 and 8.7. 0.03 ml of a Difco yeast extract (25 mg/ml), partially purified by passage through a Dowex-1-Cl column, was used where indicated.

### *Effect of Threonine Concentration*

The one factor that markedly affected the ADP requirement was the concentration of threonine present in the incubation. At high threonine concentrations, where the reaction was proceeding at maximal velocity, ADP was no longer stimulatory. Kinetic studies as shown in Fig. 5 show this most clearly. The marked dependency on ADP at low threonine concentration is barely evident in this figure. The ADP requirement at low threonine concentration is more clearly shown in Fig. 6. The ADP effect was most marked up to a threonine concentration of $2 \times 10^{-3}$ M. Above this threonine level the effect of ADP rapidly diminished. Due to the unique effect of threonine concentration on the reaction velocity in the absence of ADP, it was not possible to obtain a typical Lineweaver–Burk reciprocal plot of velocity vs. substrate concentrations at all threonine concentrations. If the values between $5.0 \times 10^{-3}$ and $7.5 \times 10^{-2}$ M are plotted in this way, using an

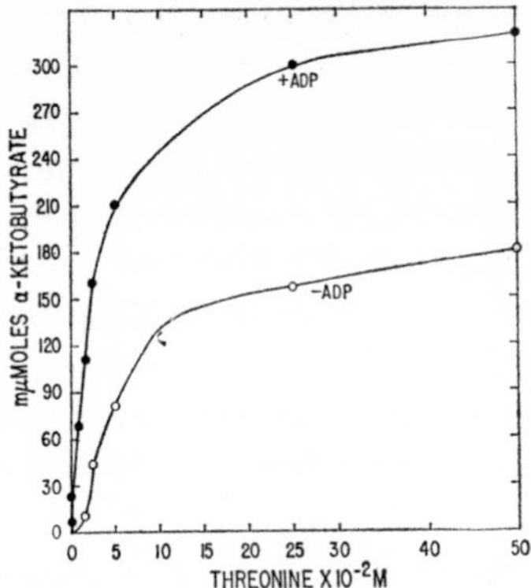


FIG. 5. Effect of threonine concentration on enzyme activity in the complete system and minus ADP.

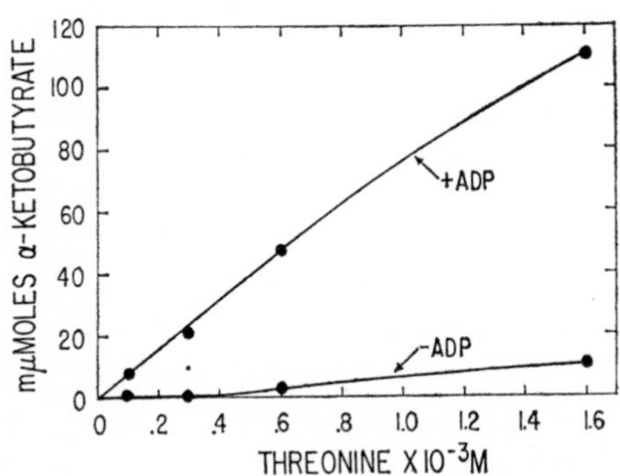


FIG. 6. Effect of ADP on reaction rate at low concentrations of threonine.

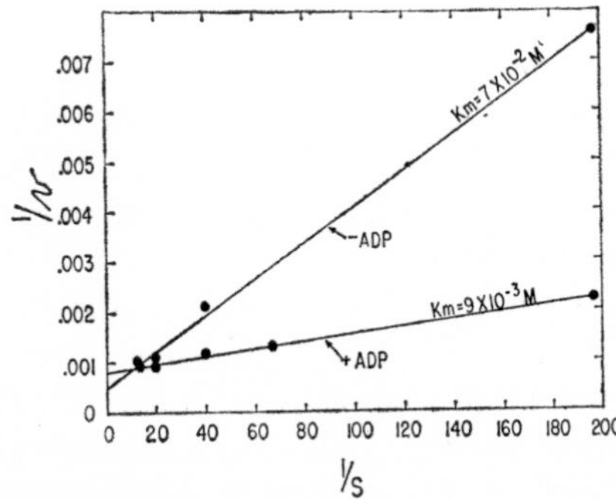


FIG. 7. Reciprocal plot of activity vs. substrate concentration.

ammonium sulfate fraction as shown in Fig. 7, the following $K_m$ values are obtained: complete system $9 \times 10^{-3}$ M, minus ADP $7 \times 10^{-2}$ M. In several experiments with various extracts the $K_m$ in the absence of ADP varied between one-third and one-eighth of the value with ADP present. The $V_{max}$ value was slightly higher (about 50 per cent) in the incubations without ADP.

As described above, two protein fractions with threonine dehydrase activity were obtained by further purification by DEAE fractionation. Preliminary experiments indicate no significant differences between the two active fractions, in $K_m$, relative effect of ADP and $V_{max}$.

*Attempts to Show Participation of ADP in the Reaction*

Under conditions in which threonine was actively converted to α-keto-butyrate, dependent on ADP, there was no exchange of $P^{32}O_4$ or $P^{32}P^{32}$ into ADP. Using $C^{14}$ ADP it was also not possible to show any metabolism of ADP during the reaction using chromatographic techniques to separate the various possible degradation products from ADP.

The exact role of ADP in the action of threonine dehydrase has not been elucidated. The data suggest that the binding of the substrate to enzyme (especially at low substrate concentration) is markedly enhanced by the presence of ADP. The marked specificity of ADP appears to eliminate a non-specific reaction of the nucleotide.

A nucleotide requirement for threonine dehydrase was reported by previous investigators in studies of an enzyme from *E. coli.*[1-3] Several differences are apparent. The *E. coli* enzyme required AMP, not ADP, and the level of AMP needed was relatively high, giving a maximal effect at $6 \times 10^{-3}$ M, as compared to $2 \times 10^{-4}$ for ADP in the *Cl. tetanomorphum* system. The ADP effect in the *Cl. tetanomorphum* system was also only apparent at low threonine levels.

The presence of two threonine dehydrases in our extracts may be related to the studies of Umbarger and Brown.[11] These authors presented evidence for two threonine dehydrases, one synthetic, important in the biosynthesis of isoleucine, the other degradative. The former enzyme was shown to be repressed by isoleucine and not requiring AMP, while the degradative enzyme was unaffected by isoleucine but dependent on AMP.

In the studies reported here both enzymes required ADP, and, *in vitro*, there was no effect of isoleucine.

Although pyridoxal phosphate has been reported to be involved in this reaction, the enzyme preparation used in the present study could not be resolved by conventional procedures. It appears unlikely that ADP is related to the binding of pyridoxal phosphate with the enzyme protein.

The phenomenon described in this paper is very similar to the activation of liver glutamic dehydrogenase by ADP described by Frieden in 1959[12] and further investigated by Mildvan and Greville in 1962[13]. According to Frieden the activation of the enzyme by ADP correlates with association of subunits, and further purification of the ADP dependent threonine dehydrase is now in progress in order to investigate the nature of this activation.

## REFERENCES

1. H. C. LICHSTEIN and W. W. UMBREIT; *J. Biol. Chem.* **170**, 423 (1947).
2. H. C. LICHSTEIN and J. F. CHRISTMAN; *J. Biol. Chem.* **175**, 649 (1948).
3. W. A. WOOD and I. C. GUNSALUS; *J. Biol. Chem.* **181**, 171 (1949).
4. F. W. SAYRE and D. M. GREENBERG; *J. Biol. Chem.* **220**, 787 (1956).
5. G. BRAY; *Anal. Biochem.* **1**, 279 (1960).
6. E. BUEDING, S. P. COLOWICK and N. O. KAPLAN (Ed.), *Methods in Enzymology*, vol. III, p. 367, Academic Press, New York (1957).
7. M. FLAVIN and S. OCHOA; *J. Biol. Chem.* **229**, 965 (1957).
8. F. W. DENISON and E. F. PHARES; *Anal. Chem.* **24**, 1628 (1952).
9. F. BROWN; *Biochem. J.* **47**, 598 (1950).
10. E. W. SUTHERLAND, C. F. CORI, R. HAYNES and N. S. OLSEN; *J. Biol. Chem.* **180**, 825 (1949).
11. H. E. UMBARGER and B. BROWN; *J. Bacteriol.* **73**, 105 (1957).
12. C. FRIEDEN; *J. Biol. Chem.* **234**, 815 (1959).
13. A. S. MILDVAN and G. D. GREVILLE; *Biochem. J.* **82**, 22p (1962).

## DISCUSSION

DR. GUNSALUS:

Is there any evidence of phosphoric acid (i.e. nucleotide) in those dehydrases, for serine and threonine which did not require addition of nucleotides for reactivation?

DR. HAYAISHI:

I am sorry to say that our enzyme preparation has not been purified enough to answer Dr. Gunsalus's question.

DR. JENKINS:

The behavior of the threonine dehydrase is strongly reminiscent of the bacterial carbamyl transferase studied by Gerhart and Pardee (*J. Biol. Chem.* March 1962). They also observed a sigmoid velocity substrate curve which became the expected hyperbolic (Michaelis–Menten) curve in the presence of ADP. They now have good evidence that the effect of ADP is due to the dissociation of a tetrameric form of the enzyme to an active monomer. The tetramer behaves similarly to the combination of oxygen with haemoglobin and it is tempting to assume that the explanation is similar. That is that combination with the first site facilitates combination with the other three sites in the tetramer.

DR. HAYAISHI:

I have overlooked Gerhart and Pardee's paper. However, as I pointed out in my presentation, Mildvan and Greville have recently presented some evidence that the effect of ADP on glutamic dehydrogenase is similarly due to the association of a monomeric form. I quite agree with you that this may be very similar to the combination of oxygen with haemoglobin. This point was raised by B. Davis in a discussion of Changeux's paper on threonine dehydrase in the *Cold Spring Harbour Symposia* XXVI, 318 (1961).

DR. BRAUNSTEIN:

(1) Is there any evidence that ADP is actually bound by the enzyme protein? (2) Is your enzyme inhibited by carbonyl reagent?

DR. HAYAISHI:

(1) We have attempted several experiments to demonstrate the binding of ADP by the enzyme protein without success. Perhaps the enzyme should be purified more extensively in order to show this clearly.

(2) We did not carry out inhibition experiments with this particular enzyme preparation.

DR. HOLZER:

Is ATP antagonistic against ADP? Does metal play any role in the effect of ADP?

DR. HAYAISHI:

As far as we can tell there was no antagonistic effect of ATP against ADP. We have not done exhaustive experiments on the effect of metals but they do not replace ADP.

DR. MEISTER:

Do FAD or DPN replace ADP in your system?

DR. HAYAISHI:

I do not think we have tried FAD or DPN.

DR. MEISTER:

Dr. Hayaishi's finding that ADP is required for threonine dehydrase is very interesting. Work in our laboratory on glutamine synthetase indicates that ADP is a constituent of the catalytic site. The same may be true for the enzyme that catalyzes the synthesis of glutathione and perhaps other enzymes. It is possible that such nucleotide requirements are associated with changes in conformation of the enzyme necessary for the binding of substrate.

# EFFECTS OF THYROID HORMONES ON DIFFERENT TYPES OF PYRIDOXAL PHOSPHATE-DEPENDENT ENZYMES OF RAT LIVER

by FERNANDE CHATAGNER and BERNADETTE JOLLÈS-BERGERET

Laboratoire de Chimie biologique de la Faculté des Sciences,
96 Bld Raspail, Paris 6, France

THE catalytic function of pyridoxal phosphate (PLP) in a large number of enzymic reactions involving amino acids is well established and general mechanisms have been proposed to explain this action.[1,2] However, concerning the problem of physiological control of activities of PLP-dependent enzymes, progress is much more limited and the most striking results so far obtained concern essentially the numerous events occurring in pyridoxine deficient animals. In consideration of the fundamental role of PLP in general metabolism and specially in protein metabolism, investigations of physiological factors controlling activities of these enzymes and eventually an elucidation of the mechanism by which they act are therefore of special interest.

The results presented in this paper are part of those which were obtained in the course of a systematic study of the effects of thyroid hormones on PLP-dependent enzymes and concern the alterations observed on the activities of three enzymes from rat liver : the L-cysteine sulfinic acid (CSA) decarboxylase, the L-cysteine-$\alpha$-ketoglutaric acid transaminase and the L-cysteine desulfurase which we refer to as " soluble " cysteine desulfurase. The choice of these enzymes is due to the fact that each of them is an example of the three principal types of PLP-dependent systems acting on amino acids, that is to say the $\alpha$-decarboxylases, the transaminases and the enzymes of elimination of $\beta$- or $\gamma$-substituents.

The CSA decarboxylase catalyzes the formation of hypotaurine;[3] in rat liver the enzyme is present in the non-particulate fraction.[4] However, the determination of the activity of this enzyme could be done directly on an homogenate since in the particulate fractions there is no enzyme giving rise to an evolution of $CO_2$ from CSA, and the L-cysteine sulfinic acid–$\alpha$-keto-glutaric acid transaminase[5] of the particulate fractions has practically no action if $\alpha$-keto acids are not added and could not, for this reason, cause a significant decrease of substrate concentration. Furthermore, we have determined that the activity of the " direct " cysteine sulfinic desulfinase of rat liver[6] is not high enough to consume a great deal of the substrate.

The L-cysteine-α-ketoglutaric acid transaminase[7] catalyzes the production of β-mercaptopyruvic acid which is split into pyruvic acid and sulfur by the β-mercaptopyruvic acid desulfurase;[8] the sulfur formed could be chemically reduced to $H_2S$, for example, by the excess of cysteine in the medium. The result of the sequence of these reactions is thus a formation of $H_2S$. These two enzymes are present in the particulate fractions of liver, the transaminase requiring PLP for its activity while the β-mercaptopyruvic acid desulfurase is not a PLP-dependent enzyme.[8,9] In addition, we have observed that in our experiments the β-mercaptopyruvic desulfuration is never the limiting step in the reaction so that the determination of $H_2S$ formation in washed particulate fractions is a direct measure of the transaminase activity.

The so-called " soluble " cysteine desulfurase is present only in the non-particulate fraction of rat liver[10] and catalyzes an enzymic formation of $H_2S$ from cysteine which requires PLP but is completely independent of the occurrence of an α-keto acid in the medium.

Some comments seem necessary at this point. It should be mentioned that the demonstration of the occurrence of two enzymic processes for $H_2S$ formation from cysteine in rat liver, which was performed in our labotratory[10] and independently by Goryachenkova[11], provides more accurate knowledge on the function of activators of $H_2S$ production. The requirement of α-keto-glutaric acid[12] is explained by the participation of a transaminase in the reaction sequence and is demonstrated only in the particulate system. As far as PLP is concerned, Braunstein and Azarkh[13] first reported the need of PLP for enzymic desulfuration of cysteine, but in addition it has now been demonstrated that PLP is required in the non-particulate fraction as coenzyme for the " soluble " desulfurase and also in the particulate fractions as coenzyme for the transaminase. It may be pointed out that, although progress has been made in the field of enzymic production of $H_2S$, nothing is definitely known, as yet, of the catalytic mechanism of " soluble " desulfurase. Even concerning the name of the enzyme some discrepancies are observed, the terms of cysteine desulfhydrase and of cysteine desulfurase being used. At various points of this text, mention will be made either of cysteine desulfurase or of desulfuration of cysteine, this always means production of $H_2S$ by a rat liver *homogenate* where the two mechanisms are operating; in all other cases, when experiments are performed with enzymic preparations obtained by differential centrifugation, the terms " soluble " desulfurase or desulfuration by particulate fractions will clearly be emphasized.

The starting point of our research was the demonstration of decrease of activities of some PLP-dependent enzymes, Dopa decarboxylase,[14] cysteine desulfhydrase, serine dehydrase, threonine dehydrase,[15] tyrosine–α-keto-glutaric acid transaminase[16] in the liver of thyrotoxic rats. According to these data, we have attempted to determine whether similar results could be observed on PLP-dependent enzymes that we have studied earlier, for it seems conceivable that such an action of thyroxine is general, and to obtain information on the effects of thyroidectomy on activities of these enzymes. Since our results were consistent with a control of PLP-dependent enzymes activities by thyroid hormones, some experiments were carried out to investigate the mechanism by which these hormones eventually act.

## I. RESPONSES OF ENZYMIC ACTIVITIES TO THYROID HORMONES

### *Effects of Injections of High Doses of* DL-*Thyroxine*[17–19]

The magnitude of the CSA decarboxylase and cysteine desulfurase responses which occur in the liver of rats treated with thyroxine for 15 days are shown by the results given in Fig. 1. As can be seen from these results, the activities

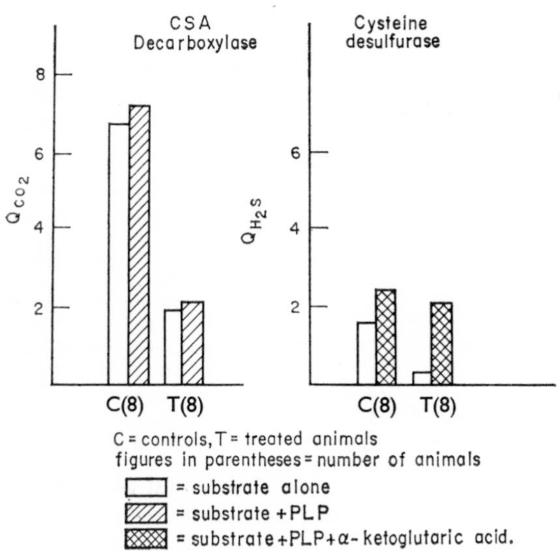


FIG. 1. Effects of daily injection of 500 μg DL-thyroxine for 15 days, on enzymic activities in male rat liver.

of CSA decarboxylase and of cysteine desulfurase, the measures being carried out in homogenates of treated rats without addition of activators (PLP for the decarboxylase and PLP + α-ketoglutaric acid for the cysteine desulfurase), are significantly decreased. However, when these homogenates are fortified by the activators, a striking difference between the two reactions appears: while PLP is ineffective to accelerate decarboxylation, PLP + α-ketoglutaric acid produces a level of desulfuration which is very similar to the level observed, under the same conditions, with normal liver homogenates.

Similar experiments were performed to determine the effects of such a treatment on the two separated enzymic systems of desulfuration, and Table 1 records the results obtained.

From the figures in Table 1, it appears that the enzymic formation of $H_2S$ by particulate fractions (column B) is practically unmodified in thyrotoxic liver when measures are carried out in presence of activators, while the activity of soluble desulfurase (columns C) is strikingly decreased (I) and furthermore could not be re-established (II) by PLP addition.

Thus it should be emphasized that the responses of soluble desulfurase and of CSA decarboxylase to the thyroxine injections are similar, i.e. the two

TABLE 1. EFFECTS OF DAILY INJECTION OF 500 $\mu$g OF DL-THYROXINE FOR 10 DAYS ON THE TWO SEPARATED ENZYMIC SYSTEMS OF DESULFURATION

| | A | B | C | |
|---|---|---|---|---|
| | Homogenate IV | Particulate fractions IV | Supernatant | |
| | | | I | II |
| C (7) | 189 ± 19[a] | 159 ± 21 | 57 ± 3.5 | 127 ± 18 |
| T (7) | 112 ± 12 | 141 ± 11 | 16 ± 2.5 | 38 ± 5 |
| | $P = 0.01$ | $P \gg 0.05$ | $P \ll 0.001$ | $0.001 < P < 0.01$ |

C = controls; T = treated animals; figures in parentheses = number of animals. Activities are expressed as $\mu$g $H_2S$ formed in 30 min by 2 ml of each enzymic preparation. I = experiment with cysteine alone; II = experiment with cysteine + PLP; IV = experiment with cysteine + PLP + $\alpha$-ketoglutaric acid.

[a]Standard deviation of mean; $P$ = probability factor.

enzymic activities are significantly decreased and are not re-established by addition of the coenzyme. Contrasting with these results, desulfurating system of particulate fractions, and especially cysteine–$\alpha$-ketoglutaric acid, exhibit a different behavior. It should be kept in mind that these variations of enzymic activities could be observed only on enzymic preparations from thyrotoxic rat liver, DL-thyroxine added *in vitro* to similar preparations from normal rat liver is ineffective.

### *Effects of Thyroidectomy*[18–20]

These experiments were performed on female rats because we observed that thyroidectomy rapidly induces tremendous alterations of general metabolism (important decrease of weights of the whole animal and of liver) in male, while in female these manifestations are not so acute. Figure 2 records the results obtained by determination of CSA decarboxylation and of cysteine desulfuration with homogenates of livers from rats destroyed

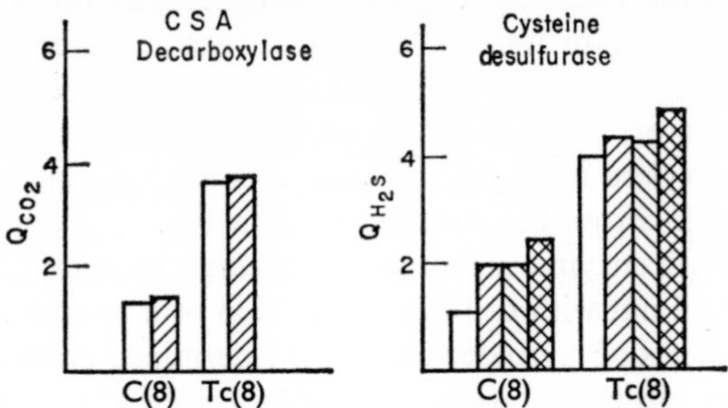


Tc = thyroidectomized rats
[hatched] = substrate + α-ketoglutaric acid
See fig. I for other explanations.

FIG. 2. Effects of thyroidectomy, performed 3 weeks before experimentation, on enzymic activities in female rat liver.

TABLE 2. EFFECTS OF THYROIDECTOMY ON THE TWO SEPARATED ENZYMIC SYSTEMS OF DESULFURATION

**A**
**Homogenate**

| | I | II | III | IV |
|---|---|---|---|---|
| C (7) | 71 ± 7 | 131 ± 7 | 124 ± 5 | 183 ± 5 |
| $T_c$ (7) | 182 ± 14 | 285 ± 19 | 232 ± 14 | 283 ± 22 |

**B**
**Particulate fractions**

| | I | II | III | IV |
|---|---|---|---|---|
| C (7) | 33 ± 3 | 66 ± 8 | 104 ± 11 | 134 ± 4 |
| $T_c$ (7) | 69 ± 5 | 135 ± 9 | 155 ± 8 | 199 ± 6 |

**C**
**Supernatant**

| | I | II | III | IV |
|---|---|---|---|---|
| C (7) | 61 ± 7 | 103 ± 7 | 73 ± 6 | 110 ± 5 |
| $T_c$ (7) | 125 ± 6 | 182 ± 18 | 134 ± 10 | 188 ± 12 |

C = controls; $T_c$ = thyroidectomized rats.
III = experiment with cysteine + α-ketoglutaric acid.
See Table 1 for other explanations.

three weeks after thyroidectomy. Some comment seems necessary. The level of CSA decarboxylase in normal female rat liver is lower than in normal male, as we have previously observed, and this is due to an effect of estradiol[21]. However, we have clearly established[22] that effect of thyroxine on CSA decarboxylase in female rat liver is completely independent of the effect of estradiol. From the data reported in Fig. 2, it appears that after thyroidectomy both enzymic activities are strikingly increased, the determinations being carried out with or without addition of activators.

In addition, effects of thyroidectomy were determined on the two separated enzymic systems of desulfuration, and Table 2 shows the results obtained.

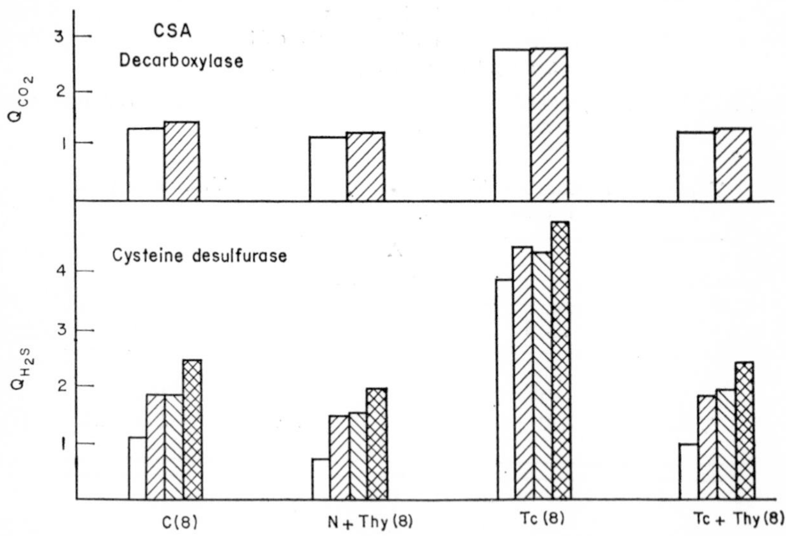


FIG. 3. Effects of daily injection of 10 μg of DL-thyroxine for 15 days on enzymic activities in the liver of normal rats and of thyroidectomized rats.

The rats used in these studies were female. N + Thy = normal injected rats. Tc + Thy = thyroidectomized injected rats. See Fig. 1 and 2 for other explanations.

From the figures in Table 2, it is apparent that both systems of desulfuration are increased in a significant manner, the measures being carried out with or without addition of activators.

In conclusion, thyroidectomy results in an increase in the three enzymic activities.

*Effects of Injections of Physiological Doses of Thyroxine to Normal Rats and to Thyroidectomized Rats*[18]

Considering the above data, one can suggest that there is good evidence for a relation between thyroid status of an animal and levels of enzymic activities, and it seems worthwhile to test the effect of injections of physiological doses of thyroxine to thyroidectomized rats. As shown in Fig. 3, physiological doses of thyroxine are without effect on CSA decarboxylase and on cysteine desulfurase in normal rats; however, when injected to thyroidectomized rats, similar doses of the hormone give rise to a marked decrease of the two enzymic activities which return to normal levels.

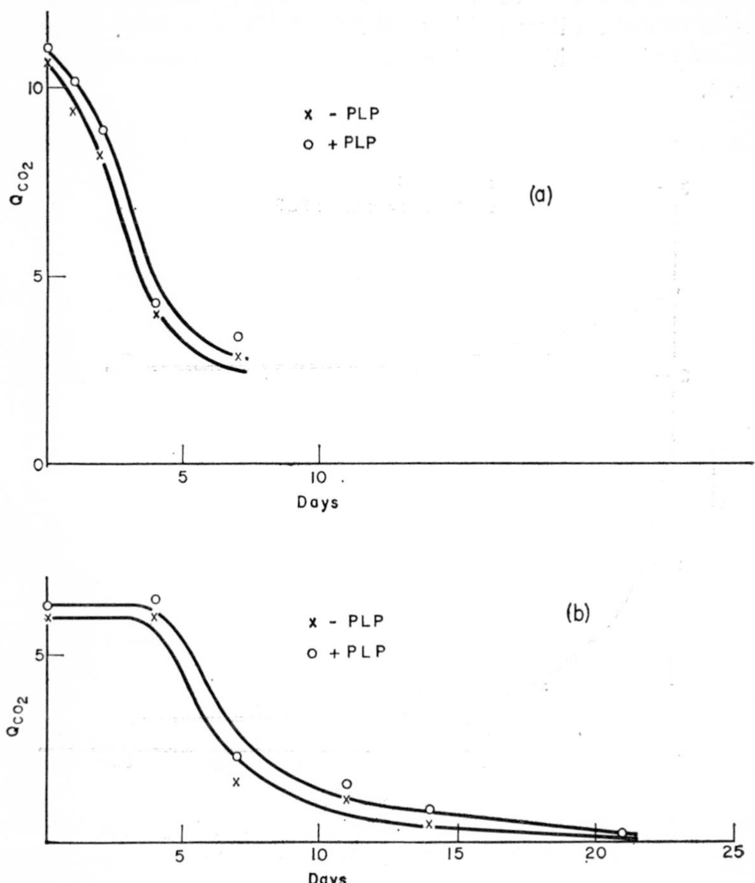


FIG. 4. (a) Time course of the effect of daily injection of 500 $\mu$g DL-thyroxine on CSA decarboxylase of male rat liver. (b) Time course of the effect of a pyridoxine deficiency on CSA decarboxylase of male rat liver.

## II. ATTEMPTS TO ELUCIDATE THE MECHANISMS BY WHICH THYROID HORMONES ACT ON ENZYMIC ACTIVITIES

The reported effects of thyroid hormones on PLP-dependent enzymic activities make some sort of interaction of these enzymes with thyroid hormones likely and support evidence for a physiological control of these enzymes by thyroid hormones. It seems therefore of special interest to investigate mechanisms underlying this action. In consideration of the role of PLP as coenzyme for all enzymes examined here, it seems quite conceivable to suggest a control of enzyme activity by thyroid hormones by means of alteration of PLP levels. Two different experiments have been carried out to substantiate this hypothesis.

We have determined[23] the time course response of CSA decarboxylase in thyroxine treated rat liver and in pyridoxine-deficient rat liver. Comparison of the enzymic activities obtained with both these treatments are shown in Fig. 4.

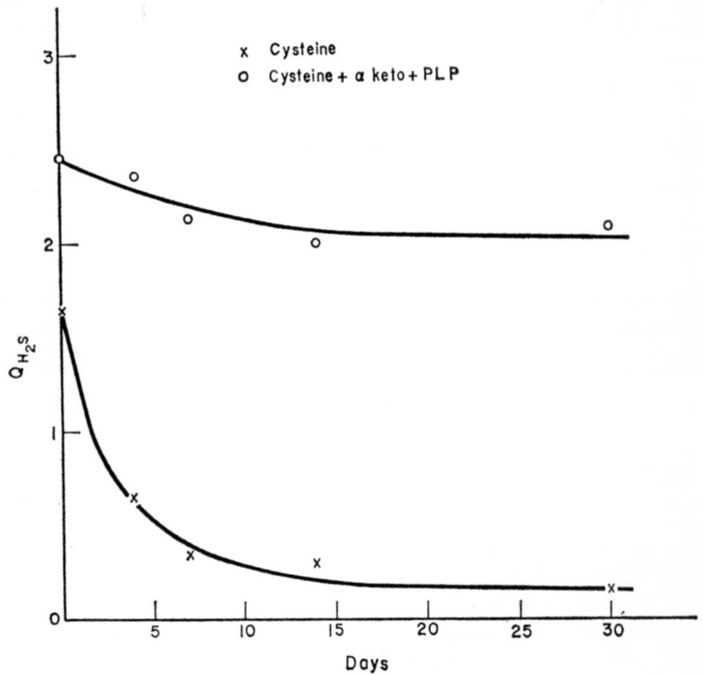


FIG. 5. Time course of the effect of daily injection of 500 μg DL-thyroxine on cysteine desulfurase in male rat liver.

The effects of the two treatments are similar: after thyroxine injections or after pyridoxine-deficient diet administration, enzymic activity disappears and is not re-established by *in vitro* addition of PLP to homogenates. Such a result was earlier observed with pyridoxine-deficient animals.[24]

The results of similar experiments carried out on cysteine desulfurase are reported in Fig. 5. The decrease of enzymic activity produced by thyroxine injections could always be counteracted by addition of activators even after 30 days of treatment. Analogous results have been obtained with pyridoxine-deficient animals: even after administration of a pyridoxine-deficient diet during 30 days, the decrease of enzymic activity is suppressed by *in vitro* addition of cofactors. But, according to the data previously obtained on soluble cysteine desulfurase and on desulfuration by particulate fractions, it seems conceivable that only cysteine transaminase is reactivated by co-factors while soluble desulfurase has disappeared.

In conclusion these results indicate an identical behavior of each of the three enzymes under both treatments; however, as already pointed out, it is of some interest to keep in mind that cysteine transaminase response differs from soluble cysteine desulfurase and CSA decarboxylase responses. It is also of interest to indicate that Horvath[15] has obtained similar findings : while some enzymes, previously quoted, exhibit decreased activities in liver of thyroxine treated rats, glutamic–aspartic transaminase shows little change, under the same conditions.

Determinations of levels of PLP in the liver of normal, thyroxine-treated and thyroidectomized rats, were carried out[25] according to a process analogous to the method described by Umbreit *et al.*[26]. Table 3 records the data obtained.

TABLE 3. CONCENTRATIONS OF PLP IN NORMAL, THYROTOXIC AND THYROIDECTOMIZED RAT LIVERS

Daily injections of 500 μg pf DL-thyroxine were performed for 12 days before experimentation (exp. I). Thyroidectomy was performed three weeks before experimentation (exp. II).

| | Exp. I | | Exp. II | |
|---|---|---|---|---|
| | C (7) | T (7) | C (8) | Tc (8) |
| Weights of livers (g) | 5.50 ± 0.3[a] | 5.20 ± 0.35 | 6.90 ± 0.30 | 3.30 ± 0.20 |
| PLP (mμg/mg wet weight of tissue) | 25.5 ± 2 | 19.0 ± 1.5 | 26.5 ± 2.0 | 36.5 ± 2.5 |
| | $0.01 < P < 0.02$ | | $P = 0.01$ | |

See Table 1 for symbol explanations.

The figures of this table show that the level of PLP is significantly decreased in thyroxine-treated rat liver and significantly increased in thyroidectomized rats. Similar results were previously obtained with thyrotoxic animals by Mascitelli-Coriandoli[27].

According to the above data obtained by the two types of experiments, the hypothesis of an effect of thyroid hormone on PLP-dependent enzyme activities by means of a variation of the coenzyme level was strongly supported. Thus, it seemed necessary to determine if these coenzyme level variations could explain all the alterations observed on enzyme activities. If such was the case, it should be possible in some way to " protect " enzymes against thyroxine action by means of injections of high doses of pyridoxine which were supposed to maintain the level of PLP. In some such experiments where pyridoxine was injected to thyrotoxic rats, the level of CSA decarboxylase is higher than in untreated thyrotoxic rats. In other experiments, however, carried out in a similar manner, injections of pyridoxine were ineffective.[18] In consideration of the well known effects of thyroid hormones on phosphorylation processes, an impairment of pyridoxine phosphorylation in thyrotoxic rats could be anticipated, via alterations of ATP levels or via decrease of pyridoxine phosphorylating enzymes. We have determined[28] the levels of ATP in livers of normal, thyrotoxic and thyroidectomized rats, according to the method of Strehler and Totter[29]. The results of these determinations are given in Table 4.

TABLE 4. CONCENTRATIONS OF ATP IN NORMAL, THYROTOXIC AND THYROIDECTOMIZED RAT LIVERS

Daily injections of 150 μg of DL-thyroxine were performed for 15 days before experimentation (exp. I). Thyroidectomy was performed 3 weeks before experimentation (exp. II).

| | Exp. I (male rats) | | Exp. II (female rats) | |
|---|---|---|---|---|
| | C (15) | T (15) | C (15) | Tc (15) |
| Weights of livers (g) | 6.50 ± 0.29 | 6.45 ± 0.23 | 6.20 ± 0.18 | 3.90 ± 0.12 |
| ATP (μg/g wet weight of tissue) | 686 ± 65 | 207 ± 12 | 995 ± 123 | 884 ± 88 |
| | $P \leqslant 0.001$ | | $0.3 < P < 0.5$ | |
| Quantity of ATP (μg for the whole organ) | 4.450 | 1.335 | 6.150 | 3.450 |

See Table 1 for symbol explanations.

From the figures of Table 4, the level of ATP is tremendously decreased (−70 per cent) in thyrotoxic rat liver whereas it is not modified by thyroidectomy. Incidently, it should be mentioned that the level of ATP is significantly higher (+30 per cent) in female rat liver than in male rat liver.

It could be suggested that the lower concentration of ATP in thyrotoxic rat liver is responsible for the decrease of pyridoxine phosphorylation. However, we have determined[30] that the level of PLP in an homogenate and even in a supernatant of thyrotoxic rat liver is significantly increased when this animal has been injected with high doses of pyridoxine, whereas the CSA decarboxylase activity in the same tissue is not restored to a normal level but remains lowered. The data obtained in such experiments are given in Table 5.

In conclusion, although the ATP concentration in thyrotoxic rat liver is strikingly decreased, phosphorylation of part of the injected pyridoxine could be demonstrated. In the recently published general review on Biochemical Actions of Thyroid Hormones, Hoch[31] suggests (p. 639) that " PLP concentration in the livers and the hearts of thyroxine treated rats is considerably diminished because of defective phosphorylation of pyridoxine rather than a conditioned pyridoxine deficiency ". The results mentioned in Table 5 disagree with this point of view. Furthermore, it clearly appears that there is no absolute correlation between the PLP concentration in rat liver and the activities of some PLP-dependent enzymes; this suggests that the alteration of PLP concentration by thyroid hormones cannot explain the variations observed on enzyme activities and indicates that thyroid hormones affect PLP concentration as well as apoenzymes themselves. This hypothesis thus deserves to be examined.

TABLE 5. ACTIVITY OF CSA DECARBOXYLASE AND CONCENTRATION OF PLP IN AN HOMOGENATE AND IN A SUPERNATANT OF LIVER OF MALE RAT INJECTED DAILY, FOR 14 DAYS, WITH 150$\mu$g DL-THYROXINE AND SIMULTANEOUSLY WITH 5 mg PYRIDOXINE HYDROCHLORIDE

| | C (7) | Injected rats (7) | % of variation in injected rats |
|---|---|---|---|
| Weights of liver (g) | 6.60 ± 0.30 | 6.60 ± 0.30 | |
| *Homogenates* | | | |
| $\mu$l $CO_2$/hr per g wet weight | 1.897 ± 194 | 777 ± 120 $P < 0.001$ | − 59 |
| $\mu$g PLP/g wet weight | 7.20 ± 0.30 | 9.00 ± 0.35 $0.001 < P < 0.01$ | + 25 |
| *Supernatants* | | | |
| $\mu$l $CO_2$/hr per g wet weight | 1.625 ± 159 | 689 ± 103 $P < 0.001$ | − 58 |
| $\mu$g PLP/g wet weight | 3.65 ± 0.20 | 5.10 ± 0.20 $P < 0.001$ | + 40 |

In consideration of the oxydative properties of thyroxine and of the —SH group requirement of a number of PLP enzymes, we injected rats, which were simultaneously treated with thyroxine, separately, with two reducing substances (ascorbic acid and glutathion) which were supposed to counteract effects of thyroxine on —SH groups of apoenzymes. From the experimental data obtained[30] it appears that both substances are completely ineffective: daily injections of from 50 to 100 mg of ascorbic acid or of from 100 to 200 mg of glutathion for 8 days to normal rats treated also daily with from 75 to 150 $\mu$g of DL-thyroxine (minimal doses required for significant alteration of enzymic activities in unthyroidectomized animals) did not prevent the decrease of the activity of CSA decarboxylase.

On the basis of an interaction between thyroid hormones and vitamin $B_{12}$ which has been described in various reports,[32–34] we anticipated as a working hypothesis that a protection of enzymes against effects of thyroxine could be afforded by administration of vitamin $B_{12}$. The results so far obtained[30] in such experiments are not conclusive; they are recorded in Table 6. From these data, under some experimental conditions (injection of a single dose of 500 $\mu$g of DL-thyroxine to rats and of 5 $\mu$g of vitamin $B_{12}$ daily for three days, including the day of thyroxine injection) the activity of CSA decarboxylase remains high (exp. I and II) but in other determinations, when rats were injected daily, for three days, with 150 $\mu$g of DL-thyroxine and, simultaneously, with 5 $\mu$g of vitamin $B_{12}$, the decrease of CSA decarboxylase activity is not suppressed by vitamin $B_{12}$ treatment (exp. III and IV).

TABLE 6. EFFECTS, ON CSA DECARBOXYLASE ACTIVITY, OF INJECTIONS OF VITAMIN $B_{12}$ (5 $\mu$G DAILY FOR 3 DAYS) AND (EXP. I AND II) OF A SINGLE INJECTION OF DL-THYROXINE THE FIRST DAY, OR (EXP. III AND IV) OF DAILY INJECTIONS OF 150 $\mu$G OF DL-THYROXINE

| Exp. | Number of animal in each group | Controls | Vitamin $B_{12}$ | Thyroxine | Thyroxine + vitamin $B_{12}$ |
|---|---|---|---|---|---|
| I | 5 | 7.19 ± 0.45 | — | 5.73 ± 0.30 | 7.57 ± 0.58 $P < 0.001$ |
| II | 7 | 10.11 ± 0.46 | 8.39 ± 0.33 | 5.74 ± 0.28 | 7.93 ± 0.56 $P < 0.001$ |
| III | 4 | 11.24 | 10.26 | 7.56 | 7.08 |
| IV | 8 | 7.93 | 6.94 | 5.02 | 4.96 |

The activities are expressed as $Q_{CO_2}$, the determinations being carried out in presence of PLP. $P$ = probability factor with respect to the thyroxine treated rats.

## CONCLUSIONS

Among the results described in this paper, some are clear-cut and highly consistent with a relationship between the status of thyroid gland of the rat and both the activities of PLP-dependent enzymes in the liver and the PLP concentration in this tissue. Although variations of the enzymic activities and of PLP concentration appear closely correlated, that is to say higher PLP concentrations correspond to higher enzymic activities and inversely lower PLP concentrations are accompanied by lower enzymic activities, the hypothesis of an effect of thyroid hormones on these enzymes by means of effect on PLP concentration alone is not supported. However, the availability of coenzyme is of considerable importance for the activities of these enzymes : independently of the action of thyroid hormones, injections of pyridoxine to a normal rat raise the activity of CSA decarboxylase, and in pyridoxine-deficient animals activities of some PLP-dependent enzymes are strikingly decreased and even disappear.

Another result of special interest is the noticeable difference between PLP enzymes of supernatant fraction (CSA decarboxylase, soluble desulfurase)

and PLP enzymes of particulate fractions (cysteine–α-ketoglutaric acid transaminase). It was observed that, in the first case, apoenzymes themselves disappear when coenzyme availability was decreased, as a result of thyroxine injection or of pyridoxine deficiency, whereas the transaminase could always be restored to full activity and thus apotransaminase is unaffected by one or the other treatment.

Up to now, in this paper, the terms of " activities " of enzyme was systematically used; but it must be clearly indicated that measures are performed in such conditions that the quantity of final product is always proportional to the enzyme concentration, so that the alterations observed reflect variations of enzyme concentrations. Thus, it can be said, from our results, that an increased biosynthesis of the three apoenzymes occurs in thyroidectomized rats, that the biosynthesis of cysteine–α-ketoglutaric acid apotransaminase is not affected by thyroxine injections, and that biosynthesis of the apoenzymes of soluble desulfurase and of CSA decarboxylase appear to be depressed or even abolished by these injections. We have already indicated that the PLP concentration is an important factor for the levels of enzymes, and especially for enzymes of the supernatant which are not saturated in coenzyme. We must add that we have observed a protective effect of PLP against thermal denaturation in the course of purification of soluble desulfurase as well as during ageing of the enzyme.[35] It is perhaps not inconceivable that when availability of PLP is high enough in liver, the degradation of apoenzymes is also decreased. Concerning protein biosynthesis, the results so far described in a general review[31] are in agreement with a stimulation of biosynthesis by low doses of thyroxine and with a decreased biosynthesis by high doses of thyroxine. It should be kept in mind that we used high doses of thyroxine in experiments with normal rats for we observed no variations of enzyme activities by injection of 10 μg of DL-thyroxine, which disagrees with results presented by Horvath[15], such doses were, in our experiments, completely uneffective whereas they act markedly on thyroidectomized animals. Thyroxine effects on protein biosynthesis could reflect an action of this hormone on either nucleic acid metabolism or on other substances required for protein biosynthesis, or could reflect alterations of both. Although numerous data were reported on effects of thyroxine on nucleic acids or ribonucleotides of liver, it appears at present difficult to correlate these results and to give a correct estimation of the various events so far demonstrated. However, it is of special interest to indicate that according to a recent paper of Nathans *et al.*[36] the activation of amino acids and the transfer of sRNA-AA on microsomes requires essentially, in animals, ATP, GTP (guanosine-triphosphate) and glutathion, and to note that thyroid hormones act on these three substances. In rats, the thyrotoxic status produces a decrease of liver concentrations of ATP,[28,37] of GTP[37,38] and of glutathion.[33] However, it is necessary to add that the conceivable decrease of protein biosynthesis in thyrotoxic rats affect, in our experiments, only the apoenzymes of the supernatant fraction of liver. PLP itself is perhaps implicated in biosynthesis or in stability of apoenzymes of the supernatant, while being without effect on apoenzymes of the particulate fraction, but such an effect of PLP was so far never demonstrated. On the other hand, it is not inconceivable that pyridoxine deficiency alters thyroid function, this possibility being suggested by some data[39] on the hypofunctioning of the thyroid gland as a result of excess of vitamin $B_6$. These hypotheses are now under investigation.

## REFERENCES


1. A. E. BRAUNSTEIN and M. M. SHEMYAKIN; *Biokhimya* **18**, 393 (1953); A. E. BRAUNSTEIN; *The Enzymes* (edited by P. D. BOYER, H. LARDY and K. MYRBÄCK), 2nd ed., vol. 2, p. 113, Academic Press, New York (1960).
2. D. E. METZLER, M. IKAWA and E. E. SNELL; *J. Am. Chem. Soc.* **76**, 648 (1954); E. E. SNELL; *Vitamins and Hormones* **16**, 77 (1958).
3. F. CHATAGNER and B. BERGERET; *Compt. rend.* **232**, 448 (1951); B. BERGERET and F. CHATAGNER; *Biochim. et Biophys. Acta* **9**, 141 (1952).
4. A. N. DAVISON; *Biochim. et Biophys. Acta* **19**, 66 (1956).
5. F. CHATAGNER, B. BERGERET, T. SÉJOURNÉ and CL. FROMAGEOT; *Biochim. et Biophys. Acta* **9**, 340 (1952).
6. K. SUMIZU; *Biochim. et Biophys. Acta* **53**, 435 (1961).
7. P. P. COHEN; *J. Biol. Chem.* **133**, XX (1940).
8. A. MEISTER, P. E. FRASER and S. V. TICE; *J. Biol. Chem.* **206**, 561 (1954).
9. E. KUN and D. W. FANSHIER; *Biochim. et Biophys. Acta* **27**, 659 (1958); **32**, 338 (1959).
10. F. CHATAGNER, B. JOLLÈS–BERGERET and J. LABOUESSE; *Compt. rend.* **251**, 3097 (1960).
11. E. V. GORYACHENKOVA; *Biokhimya* **26**, 541 (1961); *C.A.* **55**, 22.428 f.
12. F. CHATAGNER and G. SAURET–IGNAZI; *Bull. Soc. Chim. Biol.* **38**, 415 (1956).
13. A. E. BRAUNSTEIN and R. M. AZARKH; *Doklady Akad. Nauk S.S.S.R.* **71**, 93 (1950); *C.A.* **44**, 7.900 b.
14. P. HOLTZ, K. STOCK and E. WESTERMANN; *Arch. Exptl. Pathol. Pharmakol.* **231**, 311 (1957).
15. A. HORVATH; *Nature* **179**, 968 (1957).
16. G. LITWACK; *J. Biol. Chem.* **228**, 823 (1957).
17. F. CHATAGNER, B. BERGERET and J. LABOUESSE; *Biochim. et Biophys. Acta* **30**, 422 (1958).
18. B. JOLLÈS-BERGERET, J. LABOUESSE and F. CHATAGNER; *Bull. Soc. Chim. Biol.* **42**, 57 (1960).
19. F. CHATAGNER, B. JOLLÈS-BERGERET and O. TRAUTMANN; *Biochim. et Biophys. Acta* **59**, 744 (1962).
20. B. BERGERET, J. LABOUESSE and F. CHATAGNER; *Bull. Soc. Chim. Biol.* **40**, 1923 (1958).
21. F. CHATAGNER and B. BERGERET; *Bull. Soc. Chim. Biol.* **38**, 1159 (1956); *Compt. rend.* **244**, 1322 (1957).
22. F. CHATAGNER, B. BERGERET and J. LABOUESSE; *Biochim. et Biophys. Acta* **35**, 231 (1959).
23. F. CHATAGNER, B. BERGERET and J. LABOUESSE; *Rev. espagn. fisiol.* **16**, suppl. II, 225 (1960).
24. F. CHATAGNER, H. TABECHIAN and B. BERGERET; *Biochim. et Biophys. Acta* **13**, 313 (1954).
25. J. LABOUESSE, F. CHATAGNER and B. JOLLÈS-BERGERET; *Biochim. et. Biophys. Acta* **39**, 372 (1960).
26. W. W. UMBREIT, W. D. BELLAMY and I. C. GUNZALUS; *Arch. Biochem. Biophys.* **7**, 185 (1945).

27. E. MASCITELLI-CORIANDOLI and R. BOLDRINI; *Experientia* **15**, 229 (1959).
28. F. CHATAGNER and D. GAUTHERON; *Biochim. et Biophys. Acta* **41**, 544 (1960).
29. B. L. STREHLER and J. R. TOTTER; *Methods of Biochemical Analysis* (edited by D. GLICK), vol. I, p. 341, Interscience, New York (1954).
30. B. JOLLÈS-BERGERET, J. LABOUESSE and F. CHATAGNER; *Bull. Soc. Chim. Biol.* **44**, 61 (1962).
31. F. L. HOCH; *Physiol. Revs.* **42**, 605 (1962).
32. S. N. GERSHOFF, J. J. VITALE, I. ANTONOWICZ, M. NAKAMURA and E. L. HELLERSTEIN; *J. Biol. Chem.* **231**, 849 (1958).
33. D. K. KASBEKAR, W. V. LAVATE, D. V. REGE and A. SREENIVASAN; *Biochem. J.* **72**, 374 (1959).
34. P. FATTERPAKER, U. MARFATIA and I. SREENIVASAN; *Nature* **176**, 165 (1955).
35. Unpublished experiments.
36. D. NATHANS, G. VON EHRENSTEIN, R. MONRO and F. LIPMANN: *Federation Proc.* **2** No. 1, 127 (1962).
37. E. REID; *Mem. Soc. Endocrinol.* **9**, 130 (1960).
31. P. MANDEL; Personnal communication.
39. G. CAPRETTI and B. MAGNI; *Giorn. clin. med.* (*Parma*) **32**, 417 (1951), quoted by R. W. RAWSON, J. E. RALL and M. SONENBERG, in *The Hormones*, vol. 3, p. 433, Academic Press, New York (1955).

## DISCUSSION

DR. HOLZER:

The decrease of PLP in the cytoplasm reminds me of the decrease of DPN in the cytoplasm which Dr. Roitt and we observed after treatment of tumours with alkylating carcinostatica. In this case the DPN synthesis in the nuclei and the cytoplasm is inhibited. I wonder if in your case also the synthesis of the coenzymes from the vitamin is localized in the cytoplasm and is inhibited.

DR. CHATAGNER:

From the results of Dr. Snell and associates (D. B. McCormick, M. E. Gregory and E. E. Snell; *J. Biol. Chem.* **236**, 2076 (1961), pyridoxal kinase is present in the supernatant fraction of rat liver. We have done no experiments on inhibition of this enzyme in thyrotoxic rat liver, but, if such was the case, it would be rather surprising to observe (and we did) an increase of PLP level after injections of pyridoxine to thyrotoxic animals.

DR. GONNARD:

L'action des hormones thyroïdiennes sur les pyridoxalo-enzymes est peut-être indirecte, s'exerçant sur la pyridoxal-kinase qui parait particulièrement sensible à certains inhibiteurs. Le blocage de la biosynthèse du phosphate de pyridoxal par cette voie entrainerait une diminution de l'activité des pyridoxalo-enzymes (carence en co-facteur) sans qu'ils soient eux-mêmes altérés.

DR. CHATAGNER:

To my knowledge, there is up to now no report of inhibition of pyridoxal kinase by thyroxine. Furthermore, as I just said to Dr. Holzer, the increase of PLP level observed after injections of pyridoxine to thyrotoxic rats is not in agreement with an inhibition of pyridoxal kinase.

DR. CEDRANGOLO: Je voudrais savoir si les valeurs d'activité enzymatique comme les données numériques regardant le phosphate du pyridoxal ont été rapportées à l'azote total ou au poids sec du foie délipidé, parce que, seulement de cette façon, on peut être sûr que les variations trouvées sont significatives.

DR. CHATAGNER:

The results reported in this paper are expressed as m$\mu$g PLP/mg liver (dry weight) but when results are expressed in m$\mu$g PLP/mg protein we have observed the same variations.

DR. CAVALLINI:

Si j'ai bien compris, vous donnez le nom de désulfurase à l'enzyme contenu dans le foie de rat qui produit l'$H_2S$ à partir de la cystine et qui n'est pas la transaminase. Cet enzyme est connu comme cystine désulfhydrase depuis longtemps. Je me demande s'il est nécessaire de donner un second nom à un enzyme qui probablement n'existe pas, parce que comme nous essaierons de démontrer dans notre rapport la cystine dèsulfhydrase et la cystathionase sont le même enzyme.

DR. CHATAGNER:

We observed an enzymic production of $H_2S$ from *cysteine*. The terms *cysteine desulfurase*, *cysteine desulfhydrase*, and *thionase* were used respectively by Cl. Fromageot, Smythe and Binkley for the enzyme responsible for such a reaction and are reported in classical books of biochemistry; the term *cystine desulfurase* is not currently used. Furthermore, there are important discrepancies between the results obtained by each of these authors (and also by several others), especially concerning other products formed from cysteine. We temporarily used the term "*soluble*" cysteine desulfurase to define the PLP-dependent enzyme present only in the non-particulate fraction of rat liver and which produces $H_2S$ from cysteine without participation of a transaminase. This enzyme has been highly purified and we have obtained evidence for the probable identity of "soluble" cysteine desulfurase with cystathionase-homoserine desaminase (F. Chatagner, J. Labouesse, O. Trautmann and B. Jollès-Bergeret; *Compt. rend.* **253**, 742 (1961). Furthermore, this enzyme is an adaptive one and the level of soluble cysteine desulfurase could be increased by injection of homoserine; these results also strongly suggest that soluble cysteine desulfurase is identical with cystathionase (F. Chatagner and O. Trautmann; *Nature* **194**, 1211, (1962), and I agree with you that the correct name is "cystathionase".

# VITAMIN $B_6$ AND TOXOPYRIMIDINE-CONVULSIONS

by KATASHI MAKINO, M. MATSUDA, Y. JOH, M. TSUJI and F. HASEGAWA

Department of Biochemistry, Jikei University School of Medicine,
Shiba, Minatoku, Tokyo

THE pyrimidine moiety of vitamin $B_1$, namely 2-methyl-6-amino-5-hydroxy (or halogeno)-methylpyrimidine which we call toxopyrimidine has been proved in animals[1] and micro-organisms[2] to be one of the vitamin $B_6$-antagonists (Fig. 1). Mice fed on a $B_6$-deficient diet containing toxopyrimidine to 5 per cent lose appetite markedly after 5 days and show a distinct

N—C—$NH_2$
‖ ‖
$H_3C$—C C—$CH_2OH$
| |
N═CH

FIG. 1. Toxopyrimidine

decrease in body weight and loss of vitality. The hairs bristle, and the hind legs swell and redden. A dryness of the skin is apparent. After 10 days loss of hair occurs around nose and mouth, and on the abdominal skin. The symptoms go from bad to worse within 13 days and all animals die within 15 days.

When, besides toxopyrimidine, 6.5 mg of pyridoxine are added to every 100 g of the diet, the above symptoms are prevented.[3] Toxopyrimidine is also noted for its toxicity in causing running fits in mice.[1] This property is connected fairly strictly with the chemical structures of the test compounds : if 5-hydroxymethyl is replaced with a formyl or aminomethyl group the

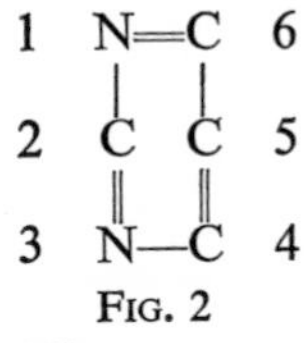


FIG. 2

(1) 2-Amino-6-ethyl pyrimidine
(2) 6-amino-4-ethyl pyrimidine
(3) 4-Methyl-6-amino-5-chloromethyl pyrimidine

} No toxopyrimidine like action

ability to cause running fits is lost. Such pyrimidines as 2-amino-6-ethylpyrimidine, 6-amino-4-ethylpyrimidine, 4-methyl-6-amino-5-chloromethylpyrimidine have no toxopyrimidine-like action[4] (Fig. 2). The compounds which have hitherto been recognized by us to have the ability to cause the same seizures as toxopyrimidine and, like the latter, to be nicely antagonized by vitamin $B_6$ are L-penicillamine and thiosemicarbazide (Fig. 3). The lethal dose of toxopyrimidine is 0.125 mg per g body weight in the $B_6$-deficient mouse. This is counteracted by preliminary treatment with 5 $\mu$g

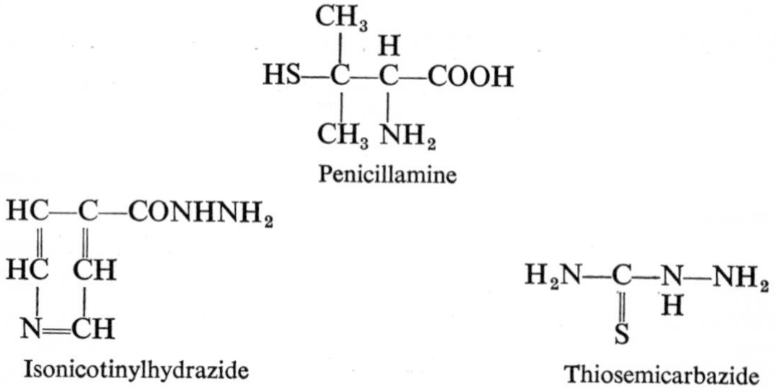

$CH_3$
H
HS—C—C—COOH
$CH_3$ $NH_2$

Penicillamine

HC—C—$CONHNH_2$
HC CH
N═CH

Isonicotinylhydrazide

$H_2N$—C—N—$NH_2$
H
S

Thiosemicarbazide

FIG. 3

of pyridoxine per g body weight, nearly all the test animals being protected from both running fits and death. The same effect is obtained with 7 $\mu$g of pyridoxamine. The action of pyridoxal and its phosphate is stronger than that of other forms of vitamin $B_6$, 0.25 $\mu$g being effective in preventing the test animals from death.

That toxopyrimidine primarily attacks the central nervous system to cause the running fits, seems to be evident from the fact that the convulsive dose

TABLE 1

| Modes of injections | Dose of toxopyrimidine (mg/kg) |
|---|---|
| Internal carotid artery | 50 |
| Vertebral artery | 30 |
| Cisterma magna | 5 |

can be greatly reduced by the cisternal application of toxopyrimidine. According to Mineshita[5], the convulsive doses differ with the modes of injections as in Table 1.

We had at first supposed that the mechanism of the convulsion existed in the antagonism between pyridoxal phosphate and toxopyrimidine phosphate in the brain. Makino and Koike[6] studied the competitive inhibition of pyridoxal phosphate by toxopyrimidine phosphate using partially purified tyrosine decarboxylase prepared from *streptococcus faecalis* R(Fig. 4) (Table 2). The activity of the enzyme activated with 3.29 × $10^{-9}$ M of pyridoxal phosphate is inhibited 100 per cent with $10^{-6}$ M of toxopyrimidine

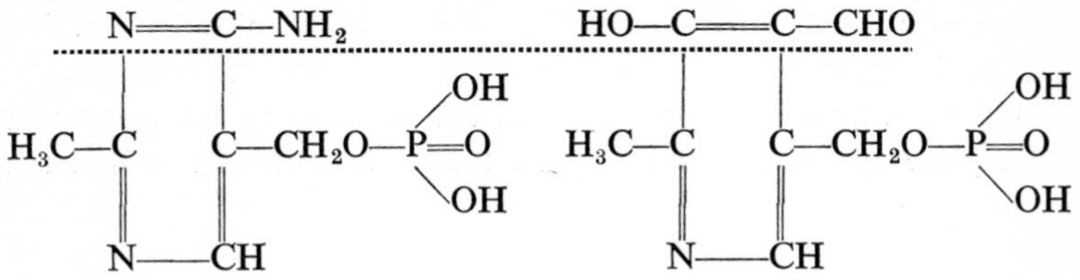

```
   N═══C─NH2                          HO─C═══C─CHO
   |    |                                 |     |
   |    |          OH                     |     |          OH
   |    |         /                       |     |         /
H3C─C   C─CH2O─P═O                 H3C─C   C─CH2O─P═O
   ‖    ‖         \                       ‖     ‖         \
   ‖    ‖          OH                     ‖     ‖          OH
   N────CH                                N────CH
```

Toxopyrimidine phosphate (TXP-P)

Pyridoxal phosphate (PLP)

FIG. 4

phosphate, and 45 per cent with $10^{-7}$ M of the latter, this being thought almost comparable with the competition experiment on mice. However, in the brain homogenate, the glutamic decarboxylase activated with $10^{-6}$ M pyridoxal phosphate is inhibited as much as from 50 to 60 per cent when a

TABLE 2. INHIBITION OF PYRIDOXAL PHOSPHATE ACTION BY TXP PHOSPHATE IN THE TYROSINE DECARBOXYLASE SYSTEM

| Concentration of pyridoxal phosphate (M) | Concentration of TXP phosphate (M) | $Q_{CO_2}$(N) (μl) | Inhibition (%) |
|---|---|---|---|
| 3.29 × $10^{-10}$ | None | 6687 | 0 |
| 3.29 × $10^{-10}$ | 1 × $10^{-7}$ | 1528 | 75 |
| 3.29 × $10^{-10}$ | 1 × $10^{-8}$ | 4012 | 44 |
| 3.29 × $10^{-10}$ | 1 × $10^{-9}$ | 4905 | 27 |
| 3.29 × $10^{-10}$ | 1 × $10^{-10}$ | 6624 | 0 |
| 3.29 × $10^{-9}$ | None | 7197 | 0 |
| 3.29 × $10^{-9}$ | 1 × $10^{-6}$ | 127 | 100 |
| 3.29 × $10^{-9}$ | 1 × $10^{-7}$ | 3949 | 45 |
| 3.29 × $10^{-9}$ | 1 × $10^{-8}$ | 6497 | 10 |
| 3.29 × $10^{-9}$ | 1 × $10^{-9}$ | 7261 | 0 |
| 3.29 × $10^{-9}$ | 1 × $10^{-10}$ | 7133 | 0 |

large amount of toxopyrimidine phosphate such as $10^{-2}$ M is used; moreover, this inhibition is easily reversed with 5 × $10^{-6}$ M pyridoxal phosphate (Fig. 5). The biosynthesis of such a large amount of toxopyrimidine phosphate as $10^{-2}$ M, when mouse brain homogenate is used as a crude kinase source, cannot be attained from toxopyrimidine and ATP.

On the other hand Matsuo[7] and we ourselves[8] found that toxopyrimidine in concentration of from $10^{-3}$ to $5 \times 10^{-3}$ M inhibited the pyridoxal kinase activity as much as from 30 to 60 per cent (Fig. 6). Hence, the decrease in the $B_6$-dependent enzymes such as glutamic decarboxylase and so on may be partly due to this fact.

Is there any connection between the running fits of mice and the decrease in the brain $B_6$-enzymes? In this respect, Roberts[9], Nishizawa[10] and Hayashi[11] have attached importance to the decrease in the brain glutamic decarboxylase activity, considering the metabolic products in this enzymic

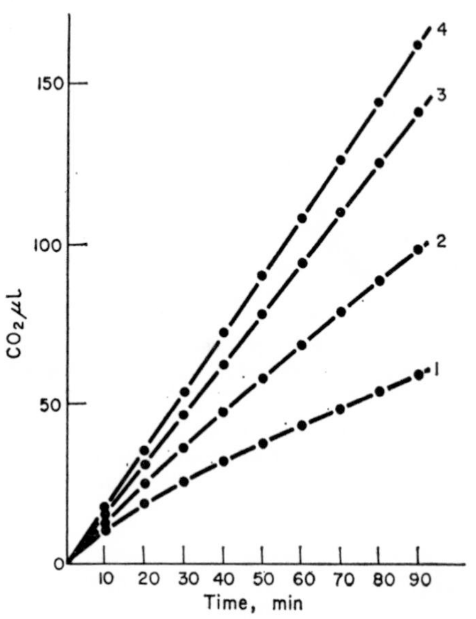


FIG. 5. COMPETITION OF PLP WITH TXP-P

I. No addition (350 mg of mouse brain homogenate in M/15 phosphate buffer, pH 6.5, 15 mg of Na-glutamate in 0.2 ml, total volume, 3.4 ml.
II. TXP–P $10^{-2}$ M + PLP $10^{-6}$ M.
III. TXP–P $10^{-2}$ M + PLP $5 \times 10^{-6}$ M.
IV. TXP–P $10^{-2}$ M + PLP $10^{-5}$ M.

reaction such as $\gamma$-aminobutyric acid and $\gamma$-amino-$\beta$-hydroxybutyric acid to act as nervous depressants (Fig. 7). However, our experiments[12] showed that large amounts of these compounds administered cisternally to dogs exerted hardly any, or only a very weak, antidotal action against toxopyrimidine or isonicotinyl hydrazide administered cisternally in like manner (Table 3), whereas vitamin $B_6$ was evidently active even with one-fortieth the amount of toxopyrimidine (Table 4).

Therefore, we changed the direction of our search for the mechanism of $B_6$-deficiency convulsions. We imagined that vitamin $B_6$-deficiency might elevate the excitation of nerve cells by influencing their active transport of sodium ions. In theory, glutamic acid as one of the acidic amino acids may

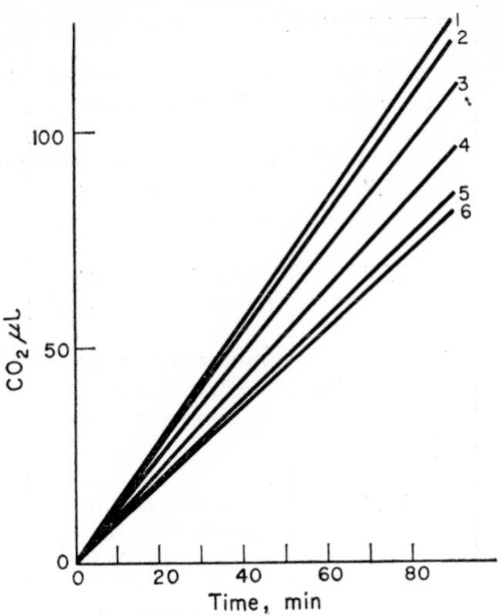


FIG. 6. EFFECT OF TXP ON PL-KINASE OF MOUSE BRAIN

Experimental conditions:
Main compartment of Warburg vessel; 1.2 ml of homogenate in 0.3 M phosphate buffer (pH 6.3) containing 350 mg of mouse brain, 0.5 ml of TXP solution of various concentration, 0.5 ml of 0.06 M NaF solution, 220 μg of PL, 2.5 mg of ATP, filled up to 3.2 ml with water.
Side arm:
15 mg of Na-glutamate in 0.2 ml. Preincubation for 20 min at 35°C.
Curve (1) ATP + PL.
(2) ATP + PL + TXP $10^{-4}$ M (final conc.).
(3) ATP + PL + TXP $10^{-3}$ M (final conc.).
(4) ATP + PL + TXP $5 \times 10^{-3}$ M (final conc.).
(5) ATP + PL + TXP $10^{-2}$ M (final conc.).
(6) Control (substrate and enzyme only).

$NH_2—CH_2—CH_2—CH_2—COOH$

γ-Aminobutyric acid (GABA)

$NH_2—CH_2—CH(OH)—CH_2—COOH$

γ-Amino-β-hydroxybutyric acid (GABOB)

FIG. 7

have a stronger ability to bring about retention of sodium ions than γ-aminobutyric acid. The tractive power of one extra carboxyl directed to a sodium ion may be presumed to be roughly — 3800 cal/mole.[13] Furthermore,

TABLE 3. INHIBITORY EFFECTS OF $\gamma$-AMINO-$\beta$-HYDROXYBUTYRIC ACID (GABOB) OR $\gamma$-AMINOBUTYRIC ACID (GABA) ON THE TOXOPYRIMIDINE CONVULSION OF DOGS (TXP, GABOB and GABA are all administered cisternally)

| | No. of dogs | Dosis of TXP injected (mg/kg) | GABOB or GABA | | | Consequence |
|---|---|---|---|---|---|---|
| | | | Dose for each animal (mg) | Time of injection | Number of convulsions after the injection | |
| Experiments with GABOB | 1 | 6.67 | 35.7 | immediately after the first seizure | none | alive |
| | 2 | 6.67 | 35.7 | immediately after the first seizure | frequent | dead |
| | 3 | 6.67 | The first injection 23.8 the second injection 23.8 | immediately after the first seizure 30 min later | frequent | alive |
| | 4 | 6.67 | 35.7 | injected simultaneously with the injection of TXP | frequent | dead |
| | 5 | 6.67 | 83.3 | Immediately after the first seizure | frequent | dead |
| | 6 | 5.56 | The first injection 35.7 the second injection 23.8 | 1 hr after the first injection of TXP 90 min after the injection of TXP | none | dead |
| | 7 | 6.67 | 71.4 | Immediately after the first seizure | frequent | dead |
| | 8 | 5.56 | The first injection 47.6 the second injection 23.8 | 1 hr after the injection of TXP immediately after the first attack | frequent | dead |
| Experiments with GABA | 1 | 6.67 | 43.9 | Immediately after the first seizure | frequent | dead |
| | 2 | 6.67 | The first injection 67.6 the second injection 21.8 | Immediately after the first attack immediately after the second attack | 4 times | alive |
| | 3 | 6.67 | 87.8 | Immediately after the first attack | none | alive |
| | 4 | 6.67 | 87.8 | Simultaneously with the injection of TXP | frequent | dead |

Christensen *et al.*[14] seemed to presume that α-amino acid could chelate a metal $B^+$ or $\frac{1}{2}B^{2+}$ to produce a complex while γ-amino acid could not do so. If the pathway of glutamic to γ-aminobutymate is inhibited in a nerve cell,

TABLE 4. EFFECT OF PYRIDOXINE (PN) ON THE TOXOPYRIMIDINE (TXP) CONVULSION OF DOGS
(TXP and PN are both administered into cisterna magna)

| No. of dogs | Dose of TXP (mg/kg) | Dose of PN (mg/kg) | Convulsion after the administration of PN | Consequence |
|---|---|---|---|---|
| (1) PN : TXP = 1 : 5 | | | | |
| (1) | 7 | 1.4 | (+) (slight) | alive |
| (2) | 6 | 1.2 | (+) (slight) | alive |
| (3) | 6 | 1.2 | (−) | alive |
| (II) PN : TXP = 1 : 10 | | | | |
| (1) | 7 | 0.7 | (+) (slight) | alive |
| (2) | 6 | 0.6 | (−) | alive |
| (3) | 7 | 0.7 | (−) | alive |
| (III) PN : TXP = 1 : 20 | | | | |
| (1) | 7 | 0.35 | (+) (slight) | alive |
| (2) | 6 | 0.3 | (−) | alive |
| (3) | 6 | 0.3 | (+) | alive |
| (IV) PN : TXP = 1 : 40 | | | | |
| (1) | 7 | 0.185 | (+) | alive |
| (2) | 2 | 0.15 | (+) | alive |
| (3) | 7 | 0.185 | (+) | dead |
| Control | | | | |
| (1) | 7 | 0 | (+) | dead |
| (2) | 7 | 0 | (+) | dead |
| (3) | 5.5 | 0 | (+) | alive |
| (4) | 7 | 0 | (+) | dead |
| (5) | 7 | 0 | (+) | dead |

there may occur a tendency for sodium ions to be retained inside the cell, and accordingly, more energy than usual may be required for driving sodium ions from the cell.

On the other hand, according to Tower *et. al.*[15], oxygen uptake by slices of cerebral cortex from pyridoxine-deficient kittens with seizures, in a system using glucose as substrate, showed a reduction to 33 per cent of normal. This reduction was reversed by the addition of pyridoxal phosphate or $\gamma$-aminobutyrate. Therefore, the oxidation of $\gamma$-aminobutyrate or succinic semialdehyde in the $\gamma$-aminobutyrate shunt pathway seems to have an important physiological significance. As glutamate has a large P/O ratio,[16] the oxidation of succinic semialdehyde may be supposed to produce a large amount of ATP (Fig. 8). This ATP may serve as the substrate of the brain microsomal sodium-stimulated ATPase which has been supposed by Skou[17] and Järnefelt[18] to have an intimate relation with the active transport of sodium ions in nerve tissues. Accordingly, the vitamin $B_6$ deficiency may be expected

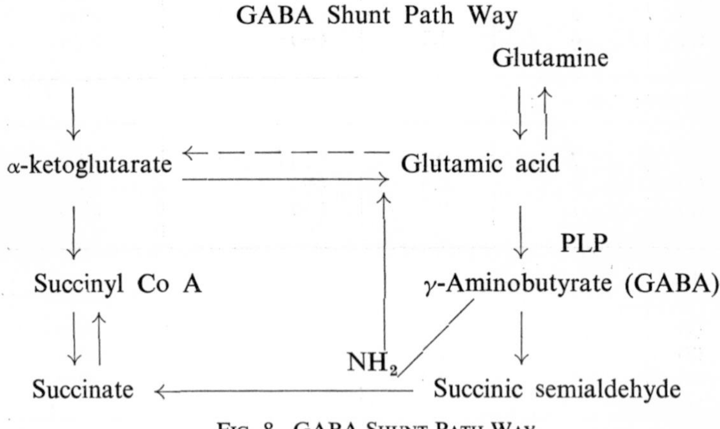


FIG. 8. GABA SHUNT PATH WAY.

to affect the transport of sodium ions in the two ways indicated above. Hence, we imagined that glutamic decarboxylase in co-operation with sodium-stimulated ATPase might regulate the sodium ion transport mechanism. Therefore, we tested the effect of the injection of vitamin $B_6$-antagonists upon the active transport of cations. Contrary to our expectations with both DL-penicillamine or toxopyrimidine injection, no remarkable tendency to retain sodium in the brain was seen. In this connection it seems curious that the subcutaneous injection of ouabain, which is noted for its properties to inhibit the active transport mechanism of sodium ions in the brain slices and known to be taken up into brain tissues when injected, also had no remarkable tendency to influence the output of sodium in the brain *in vivo*, and in this case it produces no convulsions in mice.

On the other hand we have investigated the rise and fall in the mouse brain of the nervous depressants belonging to the biological aromatic

$HO-C_6H_3(NH_2)-CO-CH_2-CH_2-NH_2 \cdot 3\,HCl$

Mausamine hydrochloride

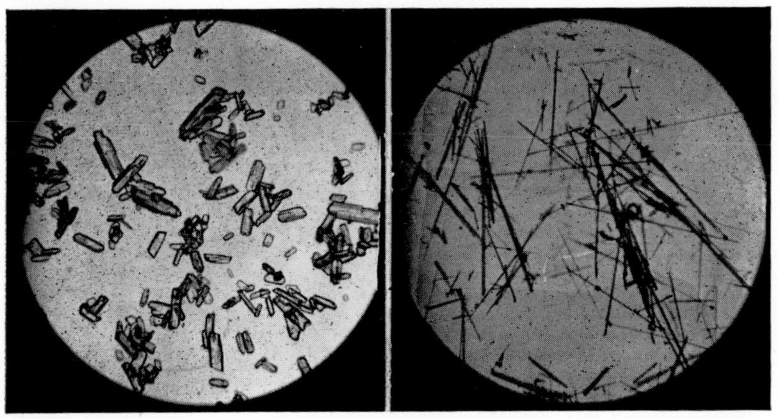

Mausamine hydrochloride — Mausamine picrate

FIG. 9

amines, which are also the metabolic products of another $B_6$-dependent enzymic reaction, namely, aromatic amino acid decarboxylation.

Nowadays such amines as noradrenaline, serotonine and dopamine have been supposed by Marrazzi[19] and others to be nervous depressants.

In our experiments with pyridoxine-deficient mice the dopa decarboxylase activity showed a 20 per cent reduction from normal. In purifying the amine fractions of mouse brain, we[20] found a strongly basic amine which we called mausamine and identified as 5-hydroxykynuramine (Fig. 9) by comparing it with the synthetic sample as follows.

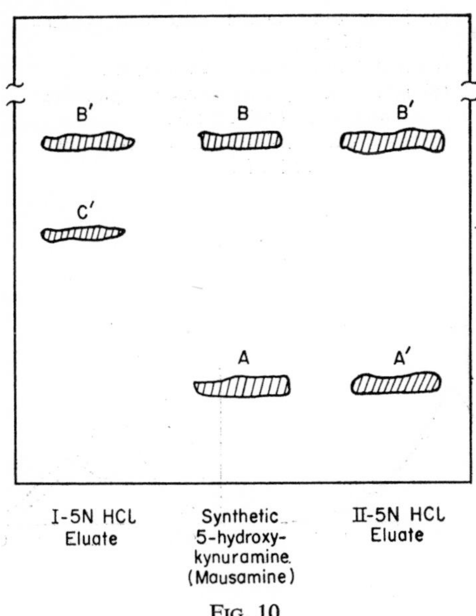


FIG. 10

A hundred and thirty grammes (130 g) of mouse brain were homogenized with diluted hydrochloric acid and centrifuged. The clear supernatant fluid was deproteinized and the filtrate was passed through Dowex 50 and eluted with 5 N HCl. The eluate was concentrated to a syrup *in vacuo* under nitrogen and paper chromatographed in isobutanol, acetic acid and water (4 : 1 : 5). One spot, which gave the same diazo-color reaction as that of the synthetic 5-hydroxykynuramine A, was found at $R_f$ 0.07, and another one showing the same diazo-color reaction and white fluorescence as that of 5-hydroxykynuramine B (auto-oxidation product of A) was detected at $R_f$ 0.31 (Fig. 10). Further identification of these metabolites was achieved by paper chromotography using four different solvent systems (Table 5) and by fluorescence spectrophotography (Fig. 11). Mausamine is easily produced from 5-hydroxykynurenine by the aromatic amino acid decarboxylase of the

TABLE 5. INDENTIFICATION OF BAND B′ FROM MICE BRAIN WITH HK(BAND B)

| Solvent system | $R_f$ Band B | Band B′ |
|---|---|---|
| a | 0.28 | 0.29 |
| b | 0.13 | 0.13 |
| c | 0.23 | 0.23 |
| d | 0.59 | 0.60 |

(a) Isobutanol, acetic acid and water (4 : 1 : 5).
(b) n-Butanol saturated with water.
(c) Isopropanol, concentrated ammonia and water (100 : 8 : 8).
(d) Methanol, n-butanol, benzene and water (2 : 1 : 1 : 1).

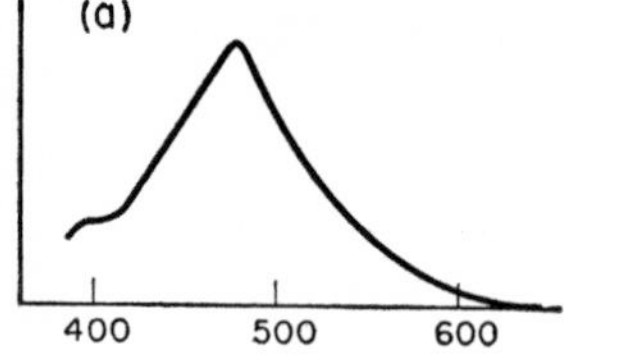


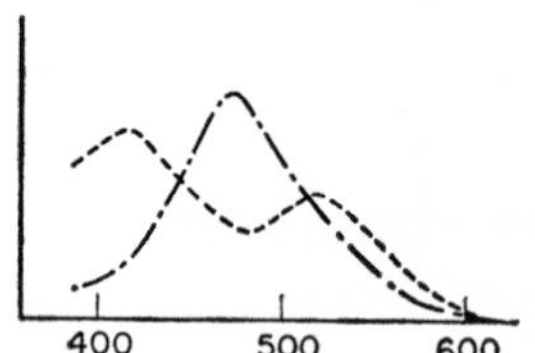


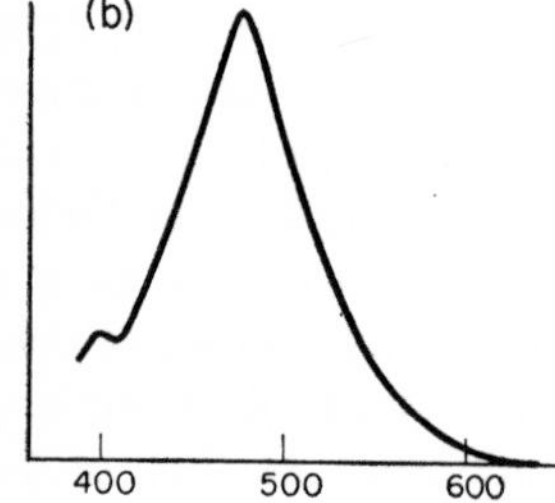


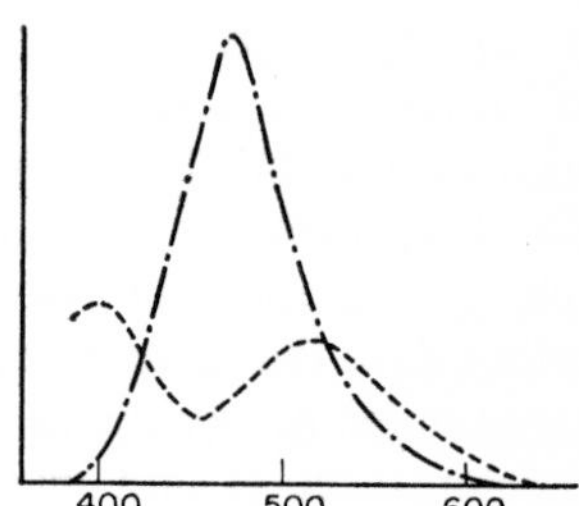


FIG. 11
(a) Natural product (mausamine B). (b) Synthetic 5-hydroxykynuramine (B-band).
Activating wavelength : 345 mμ.
Fluorescence max. 475 mμ. —·—·— pH 11.8.
———— pH 7.4. - - - - - - pH 1.0.

mouse brain like dopamine from dopa (Fig. 12 and 13). Therefore, we compared the rise and fall of mausamine in mouse brain extract from normal mice and from mice with toxopyrimidine convulsions. The 5 N HCl eluate of 300 brains of toxopyrimidine-treated mice was investigated by paper chromatography to detect mausamine. The chromatogram showed scarcely any B-band in spite of the fact that the brain homogenate of these mice still retained a considerable ability to convert hydroxykynurenine* to mausamine. These facts, together with the 20 per cent reduction of dopa decarboxylase in $B_6$-deficient mice brains observed *in vivo* suggest that the amount of

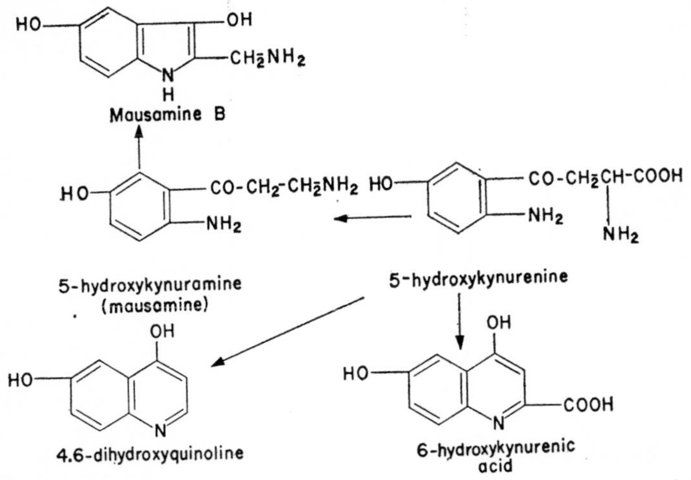

FIG. 12

operative brain aromatic amino acid decarboxylase in the living mice may be relatively small in comparison with the amount of masked enzyme. According to Udenfriend *et al.*[21], nearly all aromatic amino acids are decarboxylated by the same decarboxylase. Therefore, it is supposed that in toxopyrimidine convulsions, various aromatic amines other than mausamine may be decreased (amine crisis).

Though the decrease in glutamic decarboxylase activity in the brain seems as important as ever for the mechanism of convulsions caused by $B_6$-antagonists, conclusive evidence is still lacking. Another $B_6$-enzyme, namely aromatic amino acid decarboxylase, seems to be affected in toxopyrimidine convulsions. The decrease in the amount of mausamine is dramatic in contrast to that amount found in normal mouse brain.

Mausamine is difficulty detectable as such in both rat brain extract and the extract of human urine. Kynurenine metabolism in rats seems somewhat

* 5-hydroxykynurenine has recently been found in the normal human urine in our laboratory.

different from that in mice. Kynurenine is the major fluorescent substance of rat skin visible under ultraviolet light, whereas it is scarcely detectable in the hairs of mice. Some conjugation products of mausamine may be expected in rat brain and in human urine.

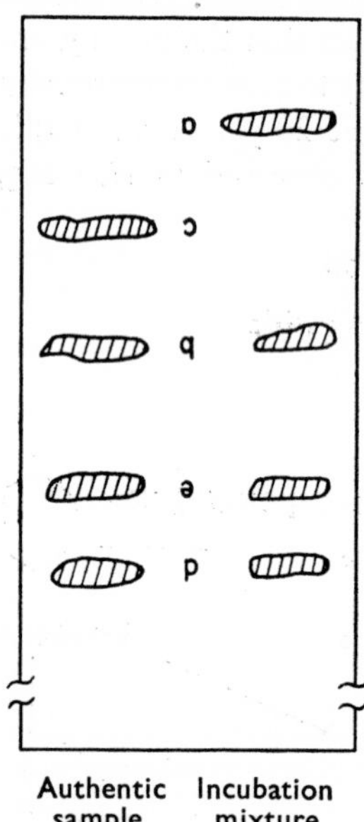


FIG. 13. INCUBATION OF 5-HYDROXYKYNURENINE WITH MICE BRAIN

0.5 g of mice brain was homogenized with 0.5 mg of 5-hydroxykynurenine in 1.5 ml of 0.05 M phosphate buffer (pH 7.4), incubated at 37°C for 1 hr. and an aliquot was taken for paper chromatographic analysis, authentic samples being developed simultaneously.

Solvent system: ispobutanol, acetic acid and water (4 : 1 : 5). Ascending technique. Spots were detected with mineralight.

(d) 4, 6-Dihydroxyquinoline.
(e) 6-Hydroxykynurenic acid.
(b) 5-Hydroxykynuramine (B).
(c) Unchanged DL-5-hydroxykynurenine.
(a) 5-Hydroxykynuramine (A).

## REFERENCES

1. K. MAKINO, T. KINOSHITA, T. SASAKI and T. SHIOI; *Nature* **174**, 34 (1954); K. MAKINO, T. KINOSHITA, Y. ARAMAKI and SHINTANI; *Nature* **174**, 275 (1954).
2. S. OGAWA and HIRAOKA; *Vitamins* (*Kyoto*) **12**, 347 (1957); M. KAWASHIMA; *Vitamins* (*Kyoto*) **12**, 348 (1957).
3. K. TORIGOE; *Vitamins* (*Kyoto*) **9**, 483 (1955).
4. cit. T. SASAKI; *Vitamins* (*Kyoto*) **4**, 45 (1951).
5. T. MINESHITA, R. KIDO, Y. OGAWA, S. TAKAHASHI, A. TANAKA, K. HIRAOKA, K. HIROSE, T. ISHIGAMI, J. KUROZAWA, S. SEKIHARA and K. HORIBE; *Annual Report of Shionogi Laboratory*, No. 7 (2), 575 (1957).
6. K. MAKINO and M. KOIKE; *Nature* **174**, 1056 (1954).

7. H. Matsuo; *Vitamins (Kyoto)* **14**, 77 (1958).
8. K. Makino and M. Tsuji; Unpublished.
9. Roberts; *Chem. Eng. News*, July 4, p. 40 (1960).
10. Y. Nishizawa; *Vitamins (Kyoto)* **13**, 471 (1957).
11. T. Hayashi; *Neurophysiology and Neurochemistry of Convulsion*, p. 191, Dainihon Tosho, Tokyo (1959).
12. H. Koguchi; *J. Vitaminol. Osaka* **8**, 1 (1962).
13. Y. Ooi; Personal communication.
14. T. R. Riggs, L. M. Walker and H. N. Christensen; *J. Biol. Chem.* **233**, 1483 (1958).
15. G. M. McKhann, O. Kickelsen and D. B. Tower; *Am. J. Physiol.* **200**, 34 (1961).
16. H. McIlwain; *Biochemistry and Central Nervous System*, p. 93, Churchill, London (1955).
17. J. Chr. Skou; *Biochim. et Biophys. Acta* **23**, 394 (1957).
18. J. Järnefelt; *Biochim. et Biophys. Acta* **43**, 105 (1961).
19. A. S. Marrazzi; *Brain Mechanism and Drug Action*, p. 45, Charles C. Thomas, Springfield, Illinois (1957).
20. K. Makino, Y. Joh and F. Hasegawa; *Biochim. Biophys. Research Comm.* **6**, 432 (1961/62); K. Makino; *Ibid.* **5**, 481 (1961).
21. W. Lovenverg, H. Weissbach and S. Udenfriend; *J. Biol. Chem.* **237**, 89 (1962).

## DISCUSSION

Dr. Braunstein:

I would like to submit some recent data of my former student Dr. Yu. Boukine, demonstrating that the actual toxic form of toxopyrimidine (TP) is most probably TP-phosphate. If rats are given subarachnoidal injections of 1 mg of isoniazid (IN) or of 100–10 mg of IN-PL-Hydrazone (but not of In-PLP-phosphate) 20 min prior to the injection (subarachnoidal) of TP, the animals are completely protected against twice the absolute lethal dose of TP (2 mg) and do not even exhibit convulsions.

*In vivo* and *in vitro* experiments have been made to demonstrate that the mentioned concentrations of IN-PL-hydrazone totally inhibit the pyridoxal kinase of brain homogenate. Besides the subarachnoidal injection in IN-PL-hydrazone markedly inhibits the glutamate decarboxylase of brain cortex (even with added PLP).

Dr. Makino:

At first we also imagined that the convulsion-causing principle might be toxopyrimidine phosphate* as can be seen in *Nature* **174**, 1056 (1954).

But it has been confirmed by Prof. Nose (*Vitamins* (*Kyoto*) **24**, 55, 1961) that there is no toxopyrimidine kinase in animal organs. According to our experiments toxopyrimidine phosphate has only the same ability to cause convulsions as that of toxopyrimidine itself (convulsive or lethal doses are the same in both cases). Dr. Braunstein's finding that sublethal dose of isonicotinyl hydrazone has a preventing effect upon toxopyrimidine convulsion, is interesting.

Dr. Cedrangolo:

Je voudrais souligner que nos recherches ont également montré que la vit. $B_6$ est incapable de supprimer les convulsions après administration de INH; nous avons en effet demontré que ces convulsions sont dues à l'$NH_3$ qui se forme à partir de l'INH dans les tissus; l'ac. glutamique, au contraire, supprime complètement ces effets toxiques (convulsivants et lataux) de l'INH en éliminant l'$NH_3$ avec formation de glutamine.

Je voudrais souligner aussi que nous sommes arrivés par un chemin différent, à la même conclusion que vous pour ce qui concerne le GABA : c'est à dire, nous pensons aussi que la diminution du GABA dans le cerveau n'est pas à l'origine des convulsions. Je donnerai des details supplémentaires sur cette question dans mon rapport.

---

*Recently we have isolated toxopyrimidine phosphate from the reaction mixture of toxopyrimidine with pyridoxal kinase partially purified from the mouse brain.

# INHIBITION OF LIVER KYNURENINASE IN HYPOPHYSECTOMIZED OR ADRENALECTOMIZED RATS

by F. M. Chiancone, E. Ginoulhiac and L. T. Tenconi

Medical and Clinical Research Department, Lepetit S.p.A., Milan

SUMMARY

The kynureninase activity measured in dialysed homogenates of rat liver at various time intervals after hypophysectomy or adrenalectomy was always decreased. This behaviour reminds one of other PLP-dependent activities.

The administration of extra tryptophan to hypophysectomized or adrenalectomized rats did not alter the liver kynureninase levels. Thus, in these experimental conditions, as in the normal rat, kynureninase could not be induced by tryptophan.

PLP added *in vitro* to liver preparations of hypophysectomized or adrenalectomized rats increases the kynureninase; however, it does not restore this activity to normal. The activity variation was in all cases of the same order in normal and operated rats. Therefore the ability of the enzyme to bind the coenzyme was unaltered in the liver of hypophysectomized or adrenalectomized rats.

In this communication we briefly relate the still unpublished results of some researches on the enzymatic pyridoxal phosphate dependent activities in the liver of hypophysectomized or adrenalectomized rats.

In our previous investigations (1959–1962) we found that the liver kynureninase activity in the rat decreases following hypophysectomy[1] or adrenalectomy[2].

The decrease is more conspicuous in the hypophysectomized animal. It was observed 5 days after the operation and was more evident 30 days after the operation (Table 1).

It was possible to investigate experimentally whether this was due to a decreased concentration of the liver enzyme, or to a decreased concentration of the coenzyme. We have measured the enzymatic activity in the rat liver according to Knox's method[3]; in our system we have added an excess of pyridoxal phosphate (0.1 mM) to the incubation mixture.

The results of this experiment show that the addition of pyridoxal phosphate increases the kynureninase activity.

The ratio of the enzymatic activity with pyridoxal phosphate to that without pyridoxal phosphate ($b/a$) is constant in both the livers of normal rats and of rats hypophysectomized or adrenalectomized 15 days previously.

TABLE 1. LIVER KYNURENINASE ACTIVITY IN THE HYPOPHYSECTOMIZED OR ADRENALECTOMIZED RAT AFTER ADMINISTRATION OF L-TRYPTOPHAN 500 mg/kg I.P.

| Days after operation | Hypophysectomy | Adrenalectomy |
|---|---|---|
| No operation | 100 | 100 |
| 5 | 64 | 74 |
| 15 | — | 65 |
| 30 | 36 | — |

Values of enzymatic activity are expressed in percentage to that in intact rats.

TABLE 2. *In vitro* EFFECT OF PYRIDOXAL PHOSPHATE ON LIVER KYNURENINASE ACTIVITY IN THE INTACT RAT AND IN THE ADRENALECTOMIZED OR HYPOPHYSECTOMIZED RAT 15 DAYS AFTER OPERATION

(Kynurenine μmoles/hr per 100 mg N)

| Experimental conditions | Without PLP *a* | With PLP *b* | Ratio *b/a* |
|---|---|---|---|
| No operation | 5.34 ± 0.47 | 17.38 ± 1.74 | 3.6 |
| Adrenalectomy | 3.87 ± 0.75 | 11.46 ± 0.93 | 3.2 |
| Hypophysectomy | 2.37 ± 0.74 | 7.43 ± 0.99 | 3.1 |

PLP = pyridoxal-5-phosphate.
Mean ± standard error: Six rats each group.

TABLE 3. LIVER KYNURENINASE ACTIVITY IN A SYSTEM CONTAINING PLP

Values obtained from intact rats and from adrenalectomized or hypophysectomized rats 15 days after operation, treated with tryptophan or not (kynurenine μmoles/h per 100 mg N).

| Experimental conditions | Without tryptophan | With tryptophan |
|---|---|---|
| No operation | 17.38 ± 1.74 | 20.02 ± 2.35 |
| Adrenalectomy | 11.46 ± 0.93 | 13.75 ± 0.76 |
| Hypophysectomy | 7.43 ± 0.99 | 7.81 ± 2.11 |

PLP = pyridoxal-5-phosphate.
Mean ± standard error: six rats in each group.

Under the conditions of our experiments, pyridoxal phosphate does not restore the activity of the hypophysectomized or adrenalectomized rat liver to normal levels (Table 2).

We have also studied the effect of a high l-tryptophan dose (500 mg/kg ip.) on the rat liver kynureninase activity 3 hr after administration of the amino

TABLE 4. *In vitro* EFFECT OF PLP ON LIVER KYNURENINE TRANSAMINASE ACTIVITY IN THE INTACT RAT AND IN THE ADRENALECTOMIZED OR HYPOPHYSECTOMIZED RAT 15 DAYS AFTER OPERATION. (Kynurenic acid μmoles/hr per 100 mg N)

| Experimental conditions | Without PLP *a* | With PLP *b* | Ratio (*b*/*a*) |
|---|---|---|---|
| No operation | 26.8 ± 5.5 | 48.5 ± 11.7 | 1.8 |
| Adrenalectomy | 25.1 ± 3.9 | 49.5 ± 3.2 | 1.9 |
| Hypophysectomy | 30.3 ± 6.8 | 53.4 ± 11.5 | 1.8 |

PLP = pyridoxal-5-phosphate.
Mean ± standard error: six rats in each group.

TABLE 5. TRANSAMINASE ACTIVITIES OF RAT LIVER AFTER ADRENALECTOMY (Mean ± standard error)

| Enzymatic activities | Intact rats | Adrenalectomized rats | References |
|---|---|---|---|
| Glutamic–pyruvic transaminase (μmoles glutamate/hr per mg N) | 29.0 ± 1.66 | 16.9 ± 1.27 | 7 |
| Tryptophan–α-ketoglutarate transaminase (μmoles indolpyruvate/hr per g dry liver) | 14.2 ± 4.38 | 10.6 ± 2.60 | 8 |
| Glutamic–oxaloacetic transaminase (μmoles glutamate/hr per mg N) | 52.9 ± 1.78 | 56.1 ± 1.84 | 7 |
| Glutamic–oxaloacetic transaminase ($Q^{10}_{T}$) | 309.4 ± 13.7 | 381.1 ± 24.1 | 6 |

acid. The enzymatic activity was estimated in the system containing pyridoxal phosphate.

High doses of tryptophan do not modify the levels of kynureninase activity in either the intact animal or the hypophysectomized or adrenalectomized rat. Even under these conditions we observed the decrease due to the ablation of the hypophysis or adrenals (Table 3).

This series of experiments shows that kynureninase decreases owing to hypophysectomy or adrenalectomy. However, its capacity to bind itself to the coenzyme is maintained.

We have determined, according to Mason's method[4] applied to the liver,[5] the kynurenine transaminase activity in the liver of these hypophysectomized or adrenalectomized rats; it is known that this enzyme is pyridoxal-phosphate dependent. The results of these experiments (Table 4) show that this enzymatic activity is unchanged. The determination in the system with excess pyridoxal phosphate indicates an activity increase, which proved to be the same under the conditions of our experiments.

It might be of interest to add that even in the kidney of hypophysectomized or adrenalectomized rats, this enzymatic activity exhibits the same behaviour as we observed in the liver.[5]

We have also studied other transaminase activities in adrenalectomized rats; these data are shown in Table 5, together with others from the literature. It is evident that there are some pyridoxal phosphate dependent activities which vary after hypothysectomy or adrenalectomy while others remain unchanged. This proves the influence of hypophysectomy and adrenalectomy on the enzyme and not on the coenzyme.

## REFERENCES


1. E. Ginoulhiac and L. T. Tenconi; *Boll. soc. ital. biol. sper.* **35**, 1801 (1959).
2. L. T. Tenconi and E. Ginoulhiac; *Boll. soc. ital. biol. sper.* In press.
3. W. E. Knox; *Biochem. J.* **53**, 379 (1953).
4. M. Mason; *J. Biol. Chem.* **227**, 61 (1957).
5. L. T. Tenconi; *Acta Vitaminol.* **16**, 241, (1962).
6. G. Rindi; *Arch. Sci. Biol.* **38**, 155 (1954).
7. V. Ferrari and L. T. Tenconi; *Acta Vitaminol.* **13**, 213 (1959).
8. M. Civen and W. E. Knox; *Science* **129**, 1672 (1959).

# TRYPTOPHANASE–TRYPTOPHAN SYNTHETASE RELATIONSHIP

by F. C. HAPPOLD and T. A. SCOTT
Department of Biochemistry, University of Leeds

## INTRODUCTION

TRYPTOPHANASE was the name given to an enzyme system prepared by Hoyle and myself by shaking a heavy suspension of suitable *E. coli* cells with small concentrations of chloroform or of tolene. The enzyme produced indole ammonia and carbon dioxide from tryptophan according to the equation prepared for whole cell suspensions by Woods. Subsequently Baker, Happold and Dawes, and, Dawson and Happold suggested that a $C_3$–$C_\beta$ fission occurred with the intermediate production of alanine alongside the indole. Woods, Gunsalus and Umbreit showed a $C_3$–$C_\beta$ fission but with the concurrent liberation of pyruvic acid and indole. All these developments are described in my review, Happold (1950).[1A] We have also published work on the mechanism, and the structure of the enzyme since that time which I do not intend to discuss here.

We have also improved the purification of the enzyme beyond published descriptions but no real advance has been made in this direction though knowledge of the inactivation and stability of the enzyme has resulted from these studies and forms a backcloth to the present paper.

The induction of tryptophanase by *Escherichia coli* in the classical types of bacteriological media was shown to be dependent upon the availability of free tryptophan and responsive in the intensity of its development to the concentration of the amino acid.[1B] The non-production of indole in such media if glucose was being fermented was shown to be due to the absence of the enzyme in the cells,[2] findings which were substantiated by later immunological results.[3] These cultures from which the enzyme was prepared were not aerated, though the cells were surface grown and this might be significant since cells grown under forced aeration with glucose rarely show absolute inhibition of tryptophanase formation; in simple salt media also this blockage was only complete in the concurrent presence of L-phenylalanine or L-tyrosine with the glucose and tryptophan during culture. This phenomenon was not a simple pH effect since mannose produced acidity in the cultures as rapidly as the glucose but did not prevent the formation of indole and, therefore, it was assumed, of tryptophanase.[4]

When cells grown in glucose-containing media were washed and suspended in a solution of tryptophan in phosphate buffer the enzyme was developed and its rate of induction could be quickened by an increase in $K^+$ or delayed by an increase in $Na^+$.[5] Uzawa[6] had observed some activation of indole formation from L-tryptophan by $NH^+_4$ salts with dead cells of *E. coli* and with cell free enzymes.[7]

When the tryptophan-synthetizing system was discovered by Bonner and Tatum[8] they considered it responsible for indole formation; that this was not the case was demonstrated by Wood *et al.*[9] as well as by ourselves.

The continuing immunological studies showed the presence of tryptophanase in an inactive form in aqueous extracts of cells and this could be activated by the addition of $NH^+_4$, $K^+$, $Rb^+$. Moreover the dialysis of the enzyme resulted in an apparent irreversible deactivation which was more rapid in the presence of $Na^+$ though no simple relationship between $Na^+$ and the rate of deactivation was established.[10,11] Later Wada *et al.*[12] confirmed almost exactly the quantitative data which we had published on the effect of these monovalent metal ions upon the enzyme tryptophanase. One of our significant findings was that when tryptophanase was dialysed against 0.8 M KCl for some days there was no apparent dissociation between the apo- and co-enzyme and yet from an analysis of the effect of $K^+$ or $NH^+_4$ on the Michaelis constants for apoenzyme–coenzyme combination we deduced that there was no absolute proof of any requirement of these cations for tryptophanase action nor were they engaged in anchoring the substrate or coenzyme to an active centre, since if this was so $KM_1 < KM_2$ where $M^+_1$ is more effective than $M^+_2$ in increasing the initial rate of reaction by the enzyme. Since $K_m$ values with or without $K^+$ or $NH^+_4$ were close to $2.4 \times 10^{-5}$ M we concluded that the cation had either to affect the organization of the enzyme molecule or accelerate the rate of breakdown of the enzyme–substrate complex. Such slight variation as there was gave $K_m(K^+) < K_m(NH^+_4)$. This fits the two latter alternatives.

Were there any physiological relationships between these features, for example, was the effect of $K^+$ as opposed to $Na^+$ on enzyme induction a direct effect upon the activity of the enzyme tryptophanase, was it due to an alteration in the cation balance within the cell or was it due to an effect upon the rate of transport of the tryptophan into the cell?

Davies *et al.*[14] considered the relationship between $K^+$ and $Na^+$ transfer into the bacterial or yeast cell and the transfer of lysine and glutamic acids. The organisms were all gram positive. Results with lysine did not appear to have any common pattern but glutamic acid accumulated within the fermenting cells, conditions which, as we know, cause an increase in cellular $K^+$. Christensen and Riggs[15] have suggested that pyridoxal in the external phase causes erythrocytes and ascites tumour cells to lose $K^+$ and $Cl^-$ and that a part of the $K^+$ is replaced by $Na^+$ as glycine enters the cell. They suggested that the amino acid might exist transiently as a derivative of pyridoxal in passing through the boundaries separating the low and the high amino acid levels. If substrate transport is itself an enzymic process and if in the case of the amino acids this is pyridoxal linked, then since certain pyridoxal phosphate enzyme systems are affected by monovalent cations the transport of amino acids might similarly be affected. There is also the specific affect of phenylalanine and tyrosine upon the tryptophanase formation. Is this also a factor in the transport of tryptophan into the cell?

## THE PHENYLALANINE–TYROSINE EFFECT

Three approaches were first made to this problem.[16]

(1) The Michaelis content of tryptophanase was measured in the presence and in the absence of aromatic amino acids plus glucose by using *E. coli* cells with an already developed tryptophanase and cell-free extract containing tryptophanase. Values between the limits of 0.25 and 0.263 mM were obtained and there were no significant differences in the values. This indicates that L-tryptophan has free passage to the active site of the enzyme in whole cells, indole has a free passage out of the cell and the two processes are not influenced by the presence of other aromatic amino acids in the reaction mixture.

(2) The disappearance of tryptophan from a simple salt medium containing radioactive DL-tryptophan (0.05 mM) and glucose but either no other nitrogen source or else 1 mM L-tyrosine or 1 mM DL-phenylalanine into washed cells of *E. coli* at 35°C was determined. There was no significant difference in the rate and amount of tryptophan disappearing in the presence or absence of other aromatic amino acids.

(3) The disappearance of L-tryptophan from growing cultures was measured in the presence and absence of aromatic amino acids with glucose and ammonium sulphate also present. The effect of serine was also studied. All these cultures were grown under forced aeration, conditions which encourage tryptophanase formation. Indole production was also determined.

When *E. coli* is presented with tyrptophan and glucose in a medium for the first time it reacts in an interesting manner. In the lag phase there is a loss of tryptophan and indole from the cells into the medium. During the logarithmic phase of growth there are alternate phases of loss and uptake of these two substances. The amplitude of these changes per cell decreases until the stationary phase is reached, whereupon indole production proceeds exponentially and the tryptophan level decreases slowly.[17]

These patterns immediately suggest that the bacterium is adjusting itself to its new environment—a series of compensatory changes, each less than that before it, until a steady state is reached. The cells, which can synthesize sufficient tryptophan for growth, have been placed in a tryptophan medium. Tryptophan is therefore present in the cell in excess. This appears to give rise to a feedback mechanism which causes the accumulation of indole—an intermediate in tryptophan biosynthesis.

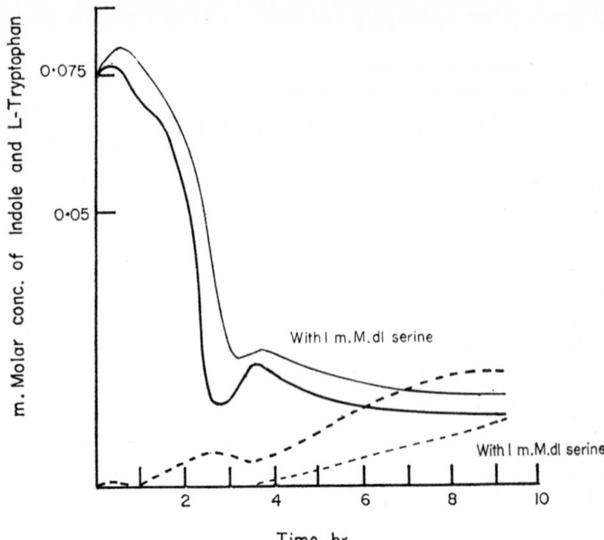


FIG. 1. Disappearance of L-tryptophan upper lines and appearance of indole lower lines in growing cultures of *Escherichia coli* in a simple salt media containing glucose (0.1 per cent).

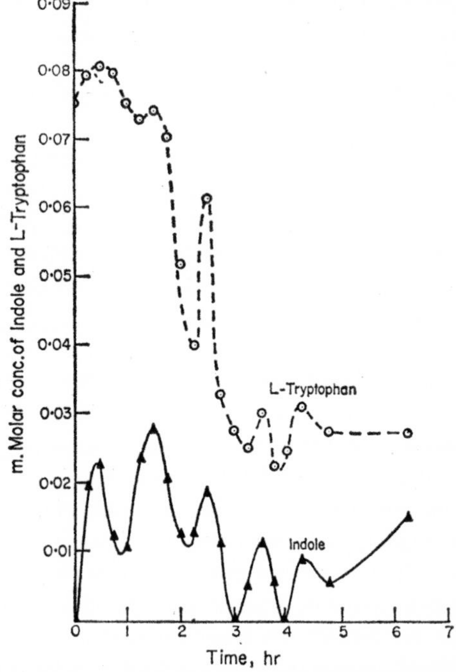


FIG. 2. Disappearance of tryptophan and appearance of indole in simple salt medium containing glucose and L-tyrosine (0.5 mM).

You will observe that an additional variation occurs with the addition of serine. With serine alone (Fig. 1) the onset of indole formation may be delayed and the intracellular tryptophan level is raised throughout the experiment. Where tyrosine alone is present (Fig. 2) the subsidiary levels of indole formation coincide with the levels in the extracellular tryptophan. Where tyrosine and serine are both present (Fig. 3) the peaks alternate

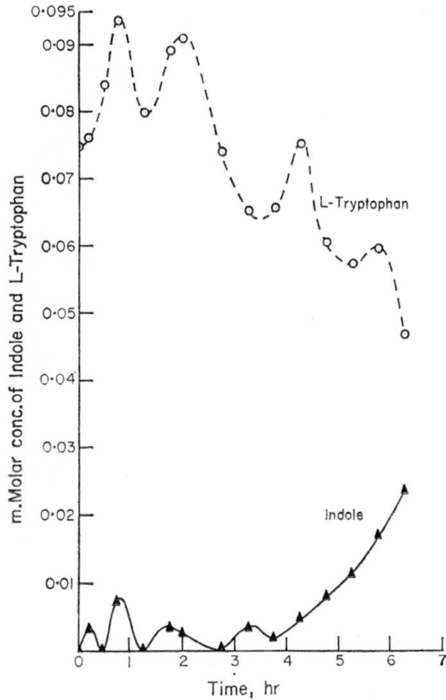


FIG. 3. Medium contains tryptophan, glucose, L-tyrosine and DL-serine (1.0 mM).

and the extracellular levels of tryptophan are much higher than with tryptophan alone.

How is this adjustment achieved enzymically? If we examine the cells at the end of growth we find that tryptophanase has appeared and that the level of tryptophan synthetase has decreased. The higher the starting concentration of tryptophan, the higher the tryptophanase activity and the lower the tryptophan synthetase activity at the end of growth.

This is shown in Fig. 4 and is a good example of enzyme induction and enzyme suppression in response to one metabolite.

Lester and Yanofsky[18] and others have pointed to the principle that the product of a series of biosynthetic reactions exerts a controlling role in its

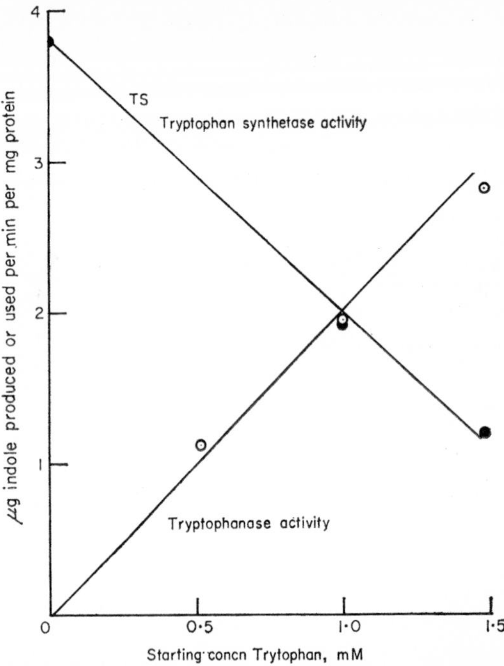


FIG. 4. Reciprocal relationship between tryptophan synthetase activity and tryptophanase activity as influenced by the concentration of tryptophan in the media.

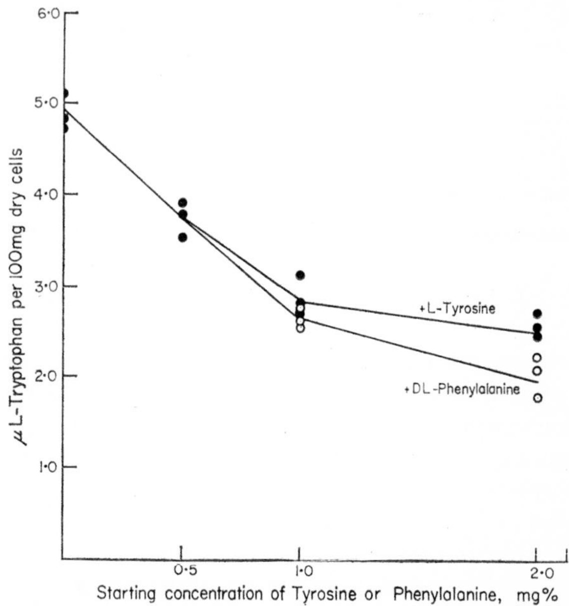


FIG. 5. Effect of phenylalanine and tyrosine upon the internal level of tryptophan.

own formation either by inhibiting the activity or the formation of the enzymes concerned with its synthesis, and that this is largely dependent on the intracellular level of the particular metabolite involved. Thus tryptophan represses its synthetase in *A. aerogenes*[19] in *Neurospora crassa*[20], as well as other enzymes involved in tryptophan synthesis in *E. coli.*[21]

What is the result of this readjustment, and why is tryptophanase not synthesized when tyrosine or phenylalanine is present with glucose in the growth medium?

Possibly the level of free, intercellular tryptophan must remain constant or at least be prevented from rising above a certain value. After growth on the simple-salts glucose medium, the intracellular tryptophan concentration is 5 $\mu$g/100 mg dry weight. Phenylalanine or tyrosine in the growth medium decreases this value to less than half but no further (Fig. 5).

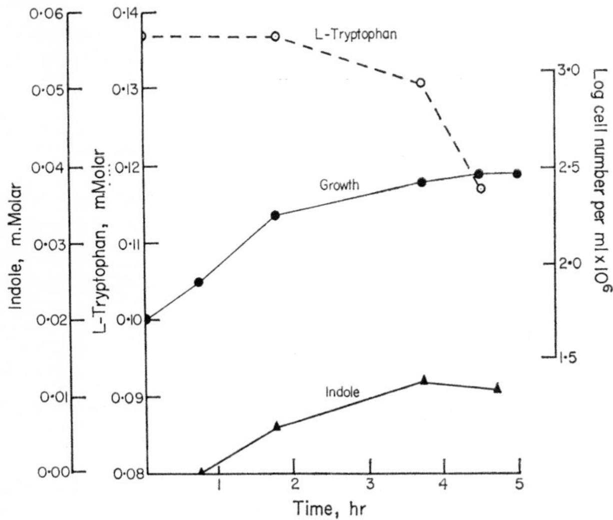


FIG. 6. Growth, indole production and tryptophan disappearance in simple medium and glucose. $Na^+$ as phosphate (0.01 M).

## INFLUENCE OF THE CONCENTRATION OF $Na^+$ AND $K^+$

If there is a relationship between the intracellular level of tryptophan and the appearance of tryptophanase (as a fortunate event for the cell) does the $K^+$, $Na^+$ relationship previously referred to affect the internal level of the free amino acid or are they merely a reflection of the enzyme activations previously discussed?

Cells grown in a potassium-deficient medium containing tryptophan exhibit the lowest indole production but have the highest concentration of intracellular tryptophan at the end of the growth phase (Fig. 6 and Table 1).

In a medium containing equimolar $Na^+$ and $K^+$ the intracellular tryptophan level is lower, indole production at its maximum (Fig. 7 and Table 1). In a K-rich medium the intracellular tryptophan level is at its lowest, the indole production high though lower than where both cations are present in equal concentrations (Fig. 8 and Table 1).

Since these intracellular levels are not measurably influenced by extracellular tryptophan (Table 1) it seems the cells can maintain a constant level of intracellular tryptophan under all three different cation regimes irrespective of the extracellular level of this amino acid. In these series of values the first given was determined by one investigator, the second separately by another.

TABLE 1. THE EFFECT OF $Na^+$ and $K^+$ ON INTERNAL TRYPTOPHAN LEVELS.
*E. coli* grown aerobically in a glucose, ammonium sulphate medium.

| Medium | Internal L-tryptophan ($\mu$g/100 mg dry cell) |
|---|---|
| $NaH_2PO_4$ (0.01 M) | 4.80<br>5.15 |
| $NaH_2PO_4$ (0.005 M)<br>$KH_2PO_4$ (0.005 M) | 3.92<br>4.31 |
| $KH_2PO_4$ (0.01 M) | 2.30<br>2.22 |
| $NaH_2PO_4$ + 0.15 mM tryptophan | 4.91<br>5.0 |
| Na/K + 0.15 mM tryptophan | 3.89<br>4.15 |
| $KH_2PO_4$ + 0.15 mM tryptophan | 2.36<br>2.30 |

I do not propose to comment upon the other values recorded in Figs. 6–8 since further examination is proceeding but growth in the potassium-deficient medium is reduced and there is little tryptophanase activity.

In these experiments washed cells have been introduced to fresh media in which the monovalent cations have been varied. $NH^+_4$ and glucose are both present. In a further series glucose or ammonium sulphate have been removed in turn and the pH of the medium adjusted with NaOH or KOH according to the nature of the ionic mixture it was intended to study. The results are easily summarized. Ammonium salts present but no glucose; the turbidity readings drop, there is no growth, there is no active tryptophanase at zero time but indole production starts after 20–45 min. The onset

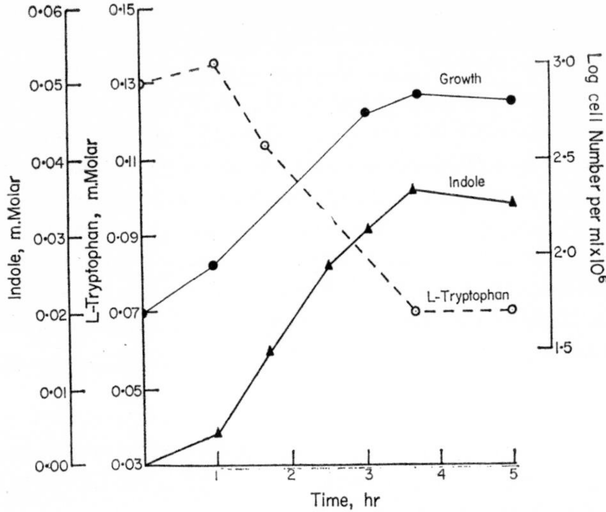


Fig. 7. Same as Fig. 6 but $Na^+$ (0.005 M) and $K^+$ (0.005 M).

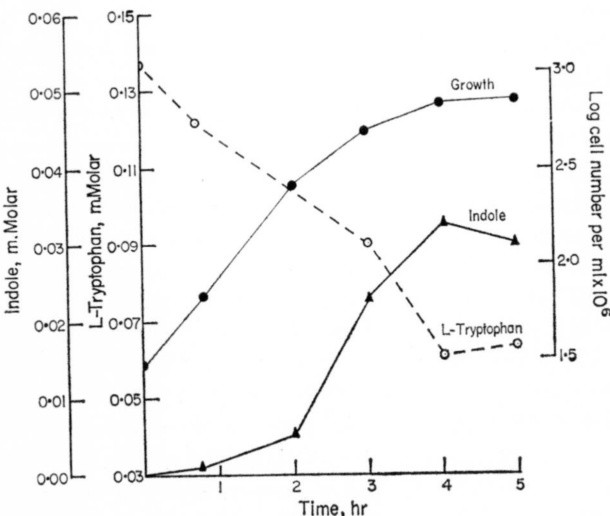


Fig. 8. Same as Fig. 6 but $K^+$ as phosphate (0.01 M).

is delayed in the $Na^+$-rich suspension and the indole production mirrors that in the $K^+$-rich suspension but is retarded by about 1 hr. There is some drop in the level of external tryptophan but the indole production is in excess of this and some must be derived from the cell. Thus some activation of a latent tryptophanase is taking place either by $K^+$ or $NH^+_4$.

With glucose present but no $NH^+_4$ the turbidities double, the external tryptophan entirely disappears but there is no indole formation.

In this phase of the work I have referred to $K^+$-rich and $Na^+$-rich cells although these have been washed cells suspended in media from which one or other of these cations was absent. It is all too easy to disregard the contribution which the inoculum makes to the concentration of the " absent " ion; the deductions we made previously on the results of the $K_m$ values with and without $K^+$ or $NH^+_4$ are open to this objection.

## PHYSIOLOGICAL RELATIONSHIPS

There are a number of observations which one wishes to remember as we continue to reflect upon possible physiological relationships. We have previously considered the effect of the monovalent cations on a number of pyridoxal phosphate enzyme systems : kynureninase, amino acid decarboxylases, transaminases and serine dehydrase. All these enzymes were more stable to dialysis than was tryptophanase; nevertheless, dialysis against $NH_4Cl$ and KCl stabilized the complex, and with kynureninase NaCl was also effective. Some activation of these dialysed enzymes occurred but with a wider range of monovalent cations than with tryptophanase.[13] Those enzymes which are more stable to dialysis within this group are the ones which one might regard as more vital to the cell than tryptophanase. The amino acid decarboxylases are produced by rapidly fermenting cells and the resulting amines have obvious physiological significance. The transaminases are central to the physiology of all living organisms and the kynureninase of the liver is also of continuing importance. I think it may be worth mentioning that the only inhibitor of a pyridoxal phosphate enzyme system I have yet observed present normally in rabbit serum was an antikynureninase.

We have also demonstrated in *E. coli* the likelihood that apotryptophanase can be present but inoperative within the cell because of competition for the coenzyme[22] but one would assume that the presence of free pyridoxal phosphate within the cell is not enough, it has to be complexed with the apoenzyme and energy is required for this to occur. Certainly we have always been conscious of some possible homeostatic competitive relationship between the great number of pyridoxal phosphate enzyme systems associated with amino acid metabolism and in recent years we are all aware that pyridoxal phosphate has a significance in phosphorylation. This increases our problems since it connects us with the field of $K^+$ and $Na^+$ transport as evidenced by the work of Skou[23] and others. When we first demonstrated the

$C_\beta$–$C_3$ fission (first proposed in 1940) for a cell-free enzyme it was in the presence of tryptophan and mepacrine and we obtained the concurrent production of alanine and indole.[24] We knew that there were many enzymes present in our preparation. Wood *et al.*[9] showed with their preparations that the initial products were pyruvic acid, ammonia and indole and that pyridoxal phosphate could cause some reactivation of their enzyme but in our continuing studies we observed a considerable activation of dialysed enzyme preparations which were not activated by pyridoxal phosphate alone but by the addition of riboflavin and diphosphopyridine nucleotides along with the pyridoxal phosphate. A verdoperoxydase and cytochrome *c* had also an activating effect[25] so this could conceivably be associated with the findings of Slater[26] and others on the linkage between hydrogen and electron transfer with phosphorylation.

The action of glutathione upon the stability of tryptophanase has been studied in many laboratories and its effect with us is variable. Gunsalus *et al.*[27] regarded its action as a reversal of a spontaneous deactivation process and I find myself in some agreement with these findings, but I include this reference since I feel it too is a part of the promising morass associated with the potential relationships of the DPN–diaphorase/cytochrome linked phosphorylating mechanism.

## REFERENCES


1A. F. C. Happold; Tryptophanase-tryptophan reaction, *Advances in Enzymology*, IV (1950).
1B. F. C. Happold and L. Hoyle; *Biochem. J.* **29**, 1918 (1935).
2. F. C. Happold and L. Hoyle; *Brit. J. Exptl. Pathol.* **17**, 136 (1936).
3. Doris E. Dolby, D. A. Hall and F. C. Happold; *Brit. J. Exptl. Pathol.* **33**, 304 (1952).
4. W. C. Evans, W. R. C. Handley and F. C. Happold; *Biochem. J.* **35**, 207 (1941).
5. W. C. Evans, W. R. C. Handley and F. C. Happold; *Biochem. J.* **36**, 311 (1942).
6. S. Uzawa; *J. Osaka Med. Assoc.* **41**, 1727 (1942).
7. S. Uzawa; *J. Osaka Med. Assoc.* **42**, 731 (1943).
8. D. M. Bonner and E. L. Tatum; *Proc. Natl. Acad. Sci., U.S.* **30**, 30 (1944).
9. W. A. Wood, W. W. Umbreit and I. C. Gunsalus; *J. Biol. Chem.* **170**, 313 (1947).
10. F. C. Happold and A. Struyvenberg; *Biochem. J.* **58**, 379 (1954).
11. R. B. Beechey and F. C. Happold; *Biochem. J.* **61**, XX (1955).
12. H. Wada, H. Yoshimatsu, T. Koizumi, F. Inque, K. Ito, T. Morisue, H. Nasu, H. Ito, Y. Sakamoto and K. Ichihara; *Proc. Int. Symp. Enzyme Chemistry*, Tokyo and Kyoti, 1957, p. 148, Maruzen, Tokyo (1958).
13. R. B. Beechey and F. C. Happold; *Biochem. Soc. Symposia* **15**, 51 (1958).
14. R. Davies, Joan P. Folkes, E. F. Gale and Lois C. Bigger; *Biochem. J.* **54**, 4 (1953).
15. H. N. Christensen, T. R. Riggs and B. A. Coyne; *J. Biol. Chem.* **209**, 413 (1954).
16. T. A. Scott and F. C. Happold; *Biochem. J.* **82**, 407 (1962).
17. T. A. Scott; Ph.D. thesis, University of Leeds (1960).
18. G. Lester and C. Yanofsky; *J. Bacteriol.* **81**, 81 (1961).
19. J. Monod and G. Cohen-Bazire; *Compt. rend.* **236**, 530 (1953).
20. G. Lester; *J. Bacteriol.* **81**, 964 (1961).
21. C. Yanofsky; *Bacteriol. Rev.* **24**, 221 (1960).
22. A. A. Hakim and F. C. Happold; *Nature* **174**, 358 (1954).

23. J. C. Skou; *Biochim. et Biophys. Acta* **58**, 314 (1962).
24. E. A. Dawes, J. Dawson and F. C. Happold; *Biochem. J.* **41**, 426 (1947).
25. E. A. Dawes and F. C. Happold; *Biochem. J.* **44**, 349 (1948).
26. E. C. Slater; *Proc. Inst. Symp. Enzyme Chemistry*, Tokyo **2**, p. 288, Maruzen, Tokyo (1958).
27. I. C. Gunsalus, C. C. Galeener and J. R. Stamer; *Methods in Enzymology* vol. II p. 238, Academic Press, New York (1955).

## DISCUSSION

Dr. Christensen :

I should like to comment that the the association of $Na^+$ and $K^+$ distribution with amino acid transport, to which Professor Happold has referred, has in the meantime been extended to sugars and to other uncharged organic solutes. In 1958, Riggs (*J. Biol. Chem.* **233**, 1479, 1958) showed that many conditions and agents inhibitory to amino acid transport apparently act by causing depletion of cellular $K^+$, with $Na^+$ replacement. Transport was subsequently restored only to the extent that cellular $Na^+$ was eliminated and $K^+$ repleted. Furthermore the inhibitory action of cardiac steroids on alkaline metal transport extends to a number of organic solutes. From such findings it seems to me likely that when we speak of alkali metal transport we shall also understand amino acid and sugar transport. I think the inverse of this statement may also be correct.

Dr. Happold's comments remind me that in my paper summarizing the relations of vitamin $B_6$ to transport I perhaps neglected the possible participation of the vitamin in alkali metal discrimination. In 1955, I presented evidence for a small degree of chelation of $Na^+$ to pyridoxal in aqueous solution (*Science* **122**, 1087, 1955). The evidence consisted of the production of absorption at about 400 m$\mu$ by $Na^+$ (in comparison with $K^+$), and the shift of the acid–base titration of pyridoxal centred at about pH 8.6, to lower pH values in the presence of $Na^+$. Lithium has the same effects to a slightly greater degree, and calcium and magnesium to even greater degrees. The action of $Na^+$ is, however, strong enough to permit substantial binding of it at physiological levels of $Ca^{2+}$ and $Na^+$.

Sedgwick and his students observed in about 1930 that *o*-hydroxy aromatic aldehydes bind $Li^+$ and $Na^+$ in certain organic solvents : therefore this behaviour is not unique.

I should not want the fact that I have had nothing further to report on this behaviour to reflect unfavourably on the possible significance of the phenomenon. The technical difficulty we have encountered has been to find a suitable cation which we could be sure does not bind to pyridoxal, so that we might determine the binding constant for $K^+$ as we as for $Na^+$. Quaternary ammonium ions have so far not been fully satisfactory. Accordingly it has not yet been possible to evaluate quantitatively the relationship between the strength of $Na^+$ binding and that of $K^+$ binding. From the foregoing you can understand why the finding by Dr. Happold and his associates that a $B_6$-enzyme is distinctly sensitive to the presence of $Na^+$ and $K^+$ interests me very much.

Up to the present time not a single carrier or active site functioning in biological transport has been identified. Our ignorance as to the chemical basis for the differentiation between $Na^+$ and $K^+$ by living cells is a most embarassing deficiency. In this context we need to give attention to all biological structures that are able to differentiate between these two ions.

# ENZYMATISCH-OPTISCHE BESTIMMUNG VON PYRIDOXAL-5-PHOSPHORSÄUREESTER UND PYRIDOXAMIN-5-PHOSPHORSÄUREESTER MIT GLUTAMAT/ASPARTAT-TRANSAMINASE AUS BIERHEFE

by H. Holzer und G. Schreiber

Biochemisches Institut der Universität
Freiburg im Breisgau (Deutschland)

## EINLEITUNG

In einer früheren Arbeit beschrieben wir[1] Anreicherung und Eigenschaften einer Glutamat/Aspartat-Transaminase aus Bierhefe. Das Enzym fällt als Apoenzym an. Da die Reaktionsgeschwindigkeit in einem begrenzten Bereich linear von der Konzentration an Pyridoxal-5-phosphorsäureester abhängt, kann es zur Bestimmung dieser Substanz in einem zusammengesetzten enzymatisch-optischen Test nach folgenden Reaktionsgleichungen benützt werden:*

$$\alpha\text{-Ketoglutarat}^{=} + \text{Aspartat}^{-} \underset{(\text{PLP, PMP})}{\overset{\text{Transaminase}}{\rightleftharpoons}} \text{Glutamat}^{-} + \text{Oxalacetat}^{=}$$

$$\text{Oxalacetat}^{=} + \text{DPNH} + \text{H}^{+} \overset{\text{MDH}}{\rightleftharpoons} \text{Malat}^{=} + \text{DPN}^{+}$$

$$\alpha\text{-Ketoglutarat}^{=} + \text{Aspartat}^{-} + \text{DPNH} + \text{H}^{+} \rightarrow \rightarrow \text{Glutamat}^{-} + \text{Malat}^{=} + \text{DPN}^{+}$$

In der vorliegenden Arbeit studieren wir die Kinetik der Rekombination von Apoenzym und Coenzym. Weiter zeigen wir, daß ebenso wie Pyridoxal-5-phosphorsäureester auch Pyridoxamin-5-phosphorsäureester die Transaminase aktiviert und daher im optischen Test bestimmt werden kann. Mit $KBH_4$ kann Pyridoxal-5-phosphorsäureester zu einer Substanz reduziert werden (wahrscheinlich Pyridoxol-5-phosphorsäureester), die Apotransaminase nicht mehr aktiviert. Da Pyridoxamin-5-phosphorsäureester bei der Behandlung mit $KBH_4$ nicht verändert wird, können durch Messung der

*Abkürzungen: EDTA = Äthylendiamintetraacetat; INH = Isonicotinsäurehydrazid; NS = Nicotinsäure; PL = Pyridoxal; PLP = Pyridoxal-5-phosphorsäureester; PM = Pyridoxamin; PMP = Pyridoxamin-5-phosphorsäureester; PN = Pyridoxol; PNP = Pyridoxol-5-phosphorsäureester.

Transaminase-Aktivität vor und nach Behandlung einer Probe mit $KBH_4$ die Summe Pyridoxal-5-phosphorsäureester + Pyridoxamin-5-phosphorsäureester und Pyridoxamin-5-phosphorsäureester allein bestimmt werden.

## ERGEBNISSE

In unseren früheren Versuchen hatten wir durch partielle Hitzeinaktivierung, Ammoniumsulfatfraktionierung und Behandlung mit Aluminiumhydroxyd-C$\gamma$-Gel eine 5–6fache Anreicherung der Transaminase erreicht.[1] Durch

TABELLE 1. TRANSAMINASE AUS BIERHEFE. AUFARBEITUNGSGANG

Test und Aktivitätseinheiten sowie erste Stufen der Aufarbeitung bis einschliesslich der partiellen Hitzeinaktivierung siehe Holzer *et al.*[1] Der Überstand der Hitzeinaktivierung wurde mit Ammoniumsulfat fraktioniert. Die Fraktion von 47 Prozent bis 58 Prozent Sättigung wurde 11 h gegen fliessendes Aqua dest. (insgesamt etwa 60 l.) bei +4°C dialysiert, mit 1/200 Volumen 1 M Trishydroxymethylaminomethan/HCl-Puffer vom pH 7,3 versetzt und auf eine DEAE–Cellulose-Säule (Abb. 1) gegeben.

| Nr. | Schritt | Gesamtaktivität aus 70 g Trockenhefe | Spezifische Aktivität (Einheiten/mg Protein) | Aktivität ohne PLP in Prozent der Aktivität mit PLP |
|---|---|---|---|---|
| 1 | Macerationssaft | 406 000 | 104 | 29,2 |
| 2 | Überstand der partiellen Hitzeinaktivierung | 359 000 | 159 | 27,1 |
| 3 | Ammonsulfatfraktionierung 47–58 Prozent Sättigung | 336 000 | 380 | 6,4 |
| 4 | 11 h Dialyse | 181 000 | 236 | 2,9 |
| 5 | Chromatographie an DEAE–Cellulose, Elution mit linearem Gradienten von 0,005 M/1 M Trispuffer pH 7,3 (Fraktion 51) | 24 800 | 2 130 | $<1{,}0$ |

Austauschchromatographie an DEAE–Cellulose statt Behandlung mit Aluminiumhydroxyd-Gel kommen wir nun auf etwa 20fache Anreicherung (vgl. Tabelle 1). Der Verlauf der Chromatographie an DEAE–Cellulose ist in Abb. 1 wiedergegeben. Man sieht, daß kurz nach Einsetzen des linearen Gradienten mit zunehmender Konzentration an Trishydroxymethylaminomethan/HCl-Puffer vom pH 7,3 das Enzym von der Säule abgelöst wird. Sättigt man die vereinigten, Transaminase enthaltenden Fraktionen zu 70 Prozent mit Ammoniumsulfat und hält die Suspension bei +4°C, so beträgt der tägliche Aktivitätsverlust etwa 10 Prozent. Wie Tabelle 1 zeigt, wird während der Reinigung das Coenzym so weitgehend abgetrennt, daß im

Test ohne Zusatz von Pyridoxal-5-phosphorsäureester weniger als 1 Prozent der Aktivität bei Sättigung mit Coenzym vorliegt.

Wie Tabelle 2 zeigt, aktivieren weder Pyridoxol-5-phosphorsäureester noch Pyridoxol, Pyridoxal, Pyridoxamin und 4-Pyridoxolsäure die Apotransaminase. Das Enzym kann daher zur spezifischen Bestimmung

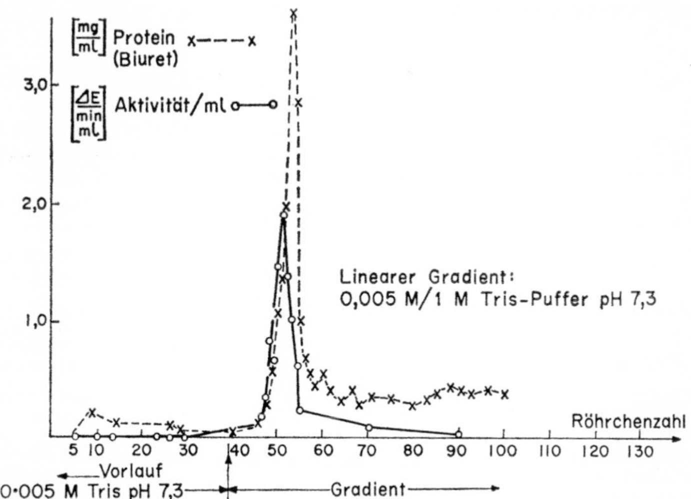


Abb. 1. Transaminase aus Bierhefe. Chromatographie an DEAE-Cellulose. Die dialysierte Enzymlösung (vgl. Tabelle 1) wurde auf eine Säule (27,5 cm × 3,5 cm²) mit DEAE–Cellulose (Serva, Heidelberg) gegeben und nach Waschen mit 0,005 M Trishydroxymethylaminomethan/HCl-Puffer vom pH 7,3 mit demselben Puffer in linear ansteigender Konzentration eluiert (vgl. (2) und (3)). Das Eluat wurde in Portionen von je 12,5 ml aufgefangen. Die höchste spezifische Aktivität fand sich im 12. Röhrchen nach Einsetzen des Gradienten (Röhrchen Nr. 51 der fortlaufenden Zählung). Die Röhrchen mit einer Aktivität von mehr als 600 Einheiten/ml wurden vereinigt und mit Ammoniumsulfat gesättigt. Das nach Zentrifugieren im Sediment enthaltene Enzym wurde in 6 ml $H_2O$ suspendiert und zu 70 Prozent mit Ammoniumsulfat gesättigt. Bei Aufbewahrung bei +4°C verliert es pro Tag etwa 10 Prozent seiner Aktivität.

von Pyridoxal-5-phosphorsäureester und Pyridoxamin-5-phosphorsäureester benützt werden. Die Aktivität der Transaminase mit sättigenden Konzentrationen beider Coenzyme ist innerhalb der Fehlergrenzen unserer Methode gleich.

Abb. 2 gibt die Kinetik der Rekombination von Pyridoxal-5-phosphorsäureester (Kurve 1) und Pyridoxamin-5-phosphorsäureester (Kurve 2) mit dem Apoenzym wieder. In der 2. Minute wurde der Reaktionsablauf durch Zusatz der Coenzyme gestartet. Man sieht, dass unter unseren Bedingungen erst nach etwa 5 min die maximale Reaktionsgeschwindigkeit erreicht ist. Vermutlich ist daher die Rekombination von Apo- und Coenzym ein Vorgang, bei dem Zeit benötigende Strukturänderungen erfolgen. Wir

TABELLE 2. PYRIDOXOLDERIVATE ALS COENZYME FÜR APO-TRANSAMINASE AUS BIERHEFE

Testbedingungen: 2,7–2,9 ml 0,2 M Diäthanolamin/HCl-Puffer pH 9,0; 1,2 mg 83 prozentiges DPNH–$Na_2$; 0,015 mg L-Malatdehydrogenase (C. F. Boehringer und Soehne, spez. Akt. 2000 Einheiten/mg nach Beisenherz *et al.*[4]); 0,06 mg Pyridoxal-5-phosphorsäureester (F. Hoffmann-La Roche, Basel); 0,02 ml 0,05 M $\alpha$-Ketoglutarat; Transaminase–Präparat je nach Aktivität. Nach 2 min Stehen Start mit 0,02 ml 0,5 M Aspartat. $d = 1$ cm, $\lambda = 366$ m$\mu$, $t = 25$°C, Gesamtvolumen 3,0 ml.

| Substanz | Testkonzentration | Aktivität (Prozent) |
|---|---|---|
| Pyridoxal-5-phosphorsäureester | $10^{-5}$ M | 100 ± 5 |
| Pyridoxamin-5-phosphorsäureester | $10^{-5}$ M | 100 ± 5 |
| Pyridoxol-5-phosphorsäureester | $1,5 \times 10^{-4}$ M | <1,0 |
| Pyridoxolhydrochlorid | $1,5 \times 10^{-4}$ M | 2 |
| Pyridoxolphosphat | $1,5 \times 10^{-4}$ M | 2 |
| Pyridoxalhydrochlorid | $1,5 \times 10^{-4}$ M | <1,0 |
| Pyridoxamindihydrochlorid | $1,5 \times 10^{-4}$ M | 1,2 |
| 4-Pyridoxolsäure | $1,5 \times 10^{-6}$ M | <1,0 |

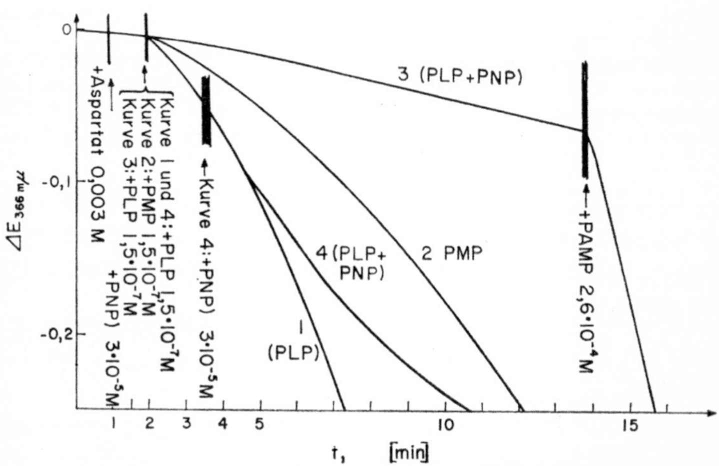


ABB. 2. Rekombination von Apo- und Coenzym. Testbedingungen siehe Legende zu Tabelle 2. Zusatz von PLP, PMP, PNP siehe Abbildung.

haben ähnliches früher bei der Rekombination von Thiaminpyrophosphat mit Pyruvatoxydase aus Schweineherzmuskel[5] und mit Pyruvatdecarboxylase aus Hefe[6] gefunden. Im Gegensatz dazu treten DPN und DPNH mit ihren Apoenzymen so rasch zusammen, dass in weniger als 30 Sekunden die volle Reaktionsgeschwindigkeit erreicht ist. Setzt man vor Zusatz von Pyridoxal-5-phosphorsäureester (Kurve 3) oder kurz nach Start der Reaktion (Kurve 4) Pyridoxal-5-phosphorsäureester zu, so wird die Reaktion gehemmt. Ein Vergleich der Kurven 3 und 4 zeigt, dass auch die Hemmung ein Zeit benötigender Prozess ist. Nachträglicher Zusatz von Pyridoxal-5-phosphorsäureester oder Pyridoxamin-5-phosphorsäureester (vgl. Kurve 3) enthemmt wieder.

TABELLE 3. TRANSAMINASE AUS BIERHEFE. REKOMBINATION VON APO- UND COENZYM
Versuchsbedingungen siehe Legende zu Tabelle 2

| Nr. | $B_6$-Derivat | | $\Delta E/2$ min $\times 10^3$ (3.–5. Minute nach Start) |
|---|---|---|---|
| | Zusatz vor Start | Start mit | |
| 1 | — | PLP | 108 |
| 2 | PM | PLP | 98 |
| 3 | PN | PLP | 90 |
| 4 | PL | PLP | 39 |
| 5 | Orthophosphat | PLP | 27 |
| 6 | PNP | PLP | 8 |
| 7 | — | PLP + PNP | 11 |
| 8 | — | PMP | 45 |
| 9 | PNP | PMP | 7 |

*Konz.*: PLP und PMP $1{,}5 \times 10^{-7}$ M
Orthophosphat 0,2 M
Übrige Substanzen $3 \times 10^{-5}$ M

Wie Tabelle 3 zeigt, hemmen auch die nicht phosphorylierten Vitamin $B_6$-Derivate die Rekombination. Die Wirkung von Pyridoxal ist hierbei deutlich stärker als die von Pyridoxamin und Pyridoxol. Auch Orthophosphat hemmt in höherer Konzentration die Rekombination der phosphorylierten Coenzym mit dem Apoenzyme. Vermutlich handelt es sich bei all diesen Hemmeffekten um Konkurrenz der Hemmstoffe mit dem wirksamen Coenzym um die Stelle des Apoenzyms, an der das Coenzym gebunden wird. Die wesentlich stärkere Wirksamkeit von Pyridoxal gegenüber Pyridoxol spricht dafür, dass die Aldehydgruppe nicht nur am Umsatz der Substrate, sondern auch an der Bindung an das Protein bzw. an der Strukturänderung des Proteins beteiligt ist. Der Pyridinring scheint für die Bindung keine grosse Rolle zu spielen, da Nicotinsäure nicht hemmt (vgl. Tabelle 4).

TABELLE 4. TRANSAMINASE AUS BIERHEFE. REKOMBINATION VON APO- UND COENZYM

Einfluss von $Mg^{2+}$-Ionen, EDTA, NS und INH auf die Rekombination von Apo- und Coenzym. Testbedingungen siehe Legende zu Tabelle 2.

| | $\Delta E/2$ min $\times 10^3$ (4.–6. Minute nach Start mit PLP) |
|---|---|
| Kontrolle | 58 |
| $+10^{-2}$ M EDTA | 54 |
| $+10^{-2}$ M $MgCl_2$ | 41 |
| $+10^{-2}$ M NS | 54 |
| $+10^{-2}$ M INH | −1 |
| $+10^{-4}$ M INH | 12 |

Auch $Mg^{2+}$ dürfte nicht an der Rekombination und am Reaktionsablauf beteiligt sein, da EDTA nicht hemmt und und $Mg^{2+}$ nicht aktiviert, sondern lediglich in hoher Konzentration hemmt. Die bekannte Hemmung von Transaminase durch Isonicotinsäurehydrazid lässt sich im Rekombinationstest besonders deutlich demonstrieren (vgl. die beiden letzten Zeilen von Tabelle 4).

Die Abhängigkeit der Reaktionsgeschwindigkeit von der Konzentration an Pyridoxal-5-phosphorsäureester bzw. Pyridoxamin-5-phosphorsäureester ist in den Abb. 3 und 4 wiedergegeben. Die Michaeliskonstanten beider Coenzyme sind etwa gleich gross; sie betragen nach unseren Messungen 1,8 bzw. 2,1 . $10^{-7}$ Mol/1.

Der im Bereich kleiner Coenzym-Konzentrationen lineare Teil der Sättigungskurven kann zur Bestimmung der Summe von Pyridoxal-5-phosphorsäureester + Pyridoxamin-5-phosphorsäureester ausgenützt werden.[1] Eine selektive Bestimmung beider Coenzyme ist möglich, wenn man eines davon inaktiviert. Wir benützen dazu die Reduktion von Pyridoxal-5-phosphorsäureester mit Kaliumborhydrid. Vermutlich ensteht hierbei Pyridoxol-5-phosphorsäureester. Pyridoxal-5-phosphorsäureester hat im Gegensatz zum entsprechenden Alkohol im neutralen bzw. alkalischen Milieu im langwelligen U.V. eine kräftige Lichtabsorption (vgl. (7)). Man

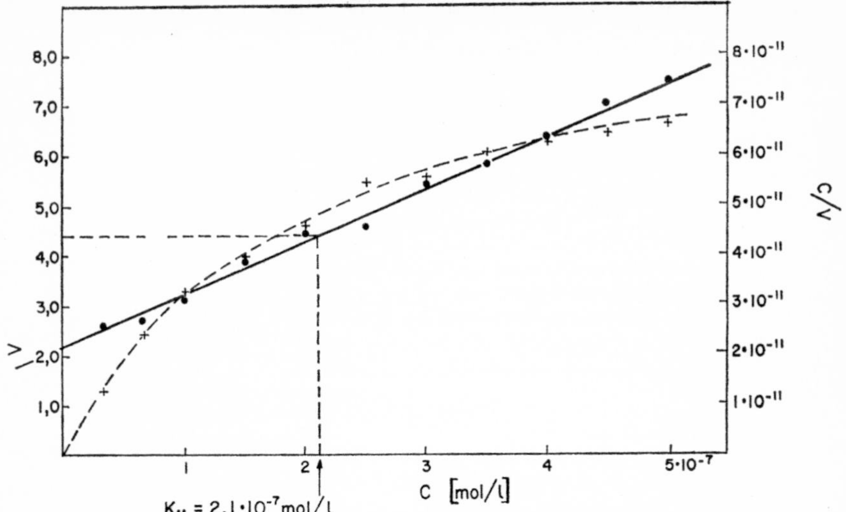


Abb. 3. Sättigungskurve mit Pyridoxamin-5-phosphorsäureester (PMP) für Transaminase aus Bierhefe. Ordinate: (1) Aktivität $V$ in $\Delta E$/ml/min (Testbedingungen wie in Legende zu Tabelle 2). (2) $C/V$. Abscisse: Konzentration von PMP in Mol/1.

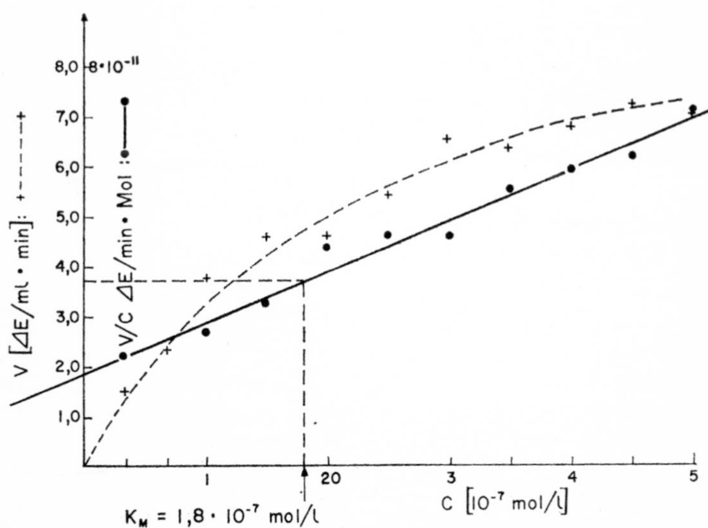


Abb. 4. Sättigungskurve mit Pyridoxal-5-phosphorsäureester (PLP) für Transaminase aus Bierhefe. Abscisse: Konzentration von PLP in $10^{-7}$ Mol/1. Ordinate wie bei Abb. 3.

Tabelle 5. Aktivität von $1{,}3 \times 10^{-2}\gamma$ und $2{,}6 \times 10^{-2}\gamma$ PLP bzw. $1{,}4 \times 10^{-2}\gamma$ und $2{,}8 \times 10^{-2}\gamma$ PMP vor und nach Reduktion mit KBH;

Die Aktivität von $1{,}3 \times 10^{-2}\gamma$ PLP bzw. PMP wurde vor und nach Reduktion mit $KBH_4$ im optischen Test (Testbedingungen vgl. Legende zu Tabelle 2) gemessen. Es wurde die Reaktiongesschwindigkeit in der 10. bis zur 15. min nach Start mit Aspartat ausgewertet. Zur Reduktion wurden 0,5 ml einer $10^{-6}$ M PLP-Lösung, 0,5 ml $10^{-6}$ M PMP-Lösung und ein Gemisch von 0,5 ml $10^{-6}$ M PMP-Lösung + 0,5 ml $10^{-6}$ M PLP-Lösung mit je 0,05 ml 0,1 M Lösung von $KBH_4$ in 0,02 N KOH versetzt und 5 min im Wasserbad bei 37°C gehalten. Dann wurde zur Zerstörung überschüssigen Borhydrids 0,25 ml 0,1 N $H_2SO_4$ hinzugegeben und für 5 min auf 90–100°C erhitzt.

| | vor Reduktion | nach Reduktion |
|---|---|---|
| $1{,}3 \times 10^{-2}\gamma$ PLP | 24,2 | 3,0 |
| $2{,}6 \times 10^{-2}\gamma$ PLP | 45,0 | 6,6 |
| $1{,}4 \times 10^{-2}\gamma$ PMP | 14,2 | 13,6 |
| $2{,}8 \times 10^{-2}\gamma$ PMP | 25,2 | 26,0 |
| $1{,}3 \times 10^{-2}\gamma$ PLP + $1{,}4 \times 10^{-2}\gamma$ PMP | 35,2 | 12,2 |

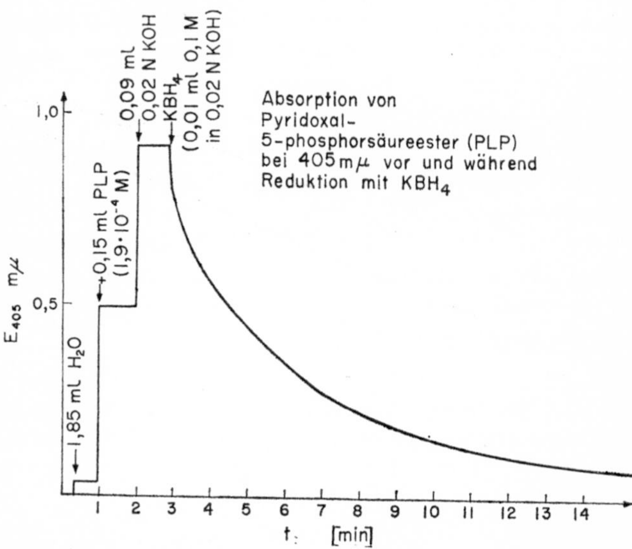


Abb. 5. Kinetik der Reduktion von PLP mit $KBH_4$. Die Lichtabsorption der PLP-Lösung wurde bei 405 mμ gemessen. $d = 1$ cm; $t = 25$°C; pH vor Zugabe der $KBH_4$/KOH-Lösung 5,8.

kann daher die Reduktion von Pyridoxal-5-phosphorsäureester zu Pyridoxol-5-phosphorsäureester im neutralen oder alkalischen Milieu durch Absorptionsmessung bei der Wellenlänge der Quecksilberlinie 405 m$\mu$ verfolgen. Kaliumborhydrid absorbiert bei dieser Wellenlänge nicht. Abb. 5 zeigt, wie die bei der Alkalisierung auftretende Lichtabsorption des Pyridoxal-5-phosphorsäureesters nach Zusatz von Kaliumborhydrid abnimmt. Die beiden oberen Zeilen in Tabelle 5 zeigen, dass die Aktivität von Pyridoxal-5-phosphorsäureester nach Behandlung mit $KBH_4$ weitgehend verschwindet (die Restaktivität beruht vermutlich nicht auf verbliebenem Pyridoxal-5-phosphorsäureester, sondern auf einer Störung unseres Testsystems, der wir zur Zeit nachgehen). Die Coenzym-Aktivität von Pyridoxamin-5-phosphorsäureester wird durch $KBH_4$-Behandlung nicht beeinflust. Wie zu erwarten, findet man bei der Analyse eines Gemisches von Pyridoxal-5-phosphorsäureester und Pyridoxamin-5-phosphorsäureester nach Reduktion mit $KBH_4$ nur noch die Aktivität des darin enthaltenen Pyridoxamin-5-phosphorsäureesters. Wir sind zur Zeit damit beschäftigt, diese Differenzbestimmung der beiden Coenzyme weiter auszubauen und auf biologische Objekte anzuwenden.

## SUMMARY

A glutamate–aspartate transaminase is purified from dried brewer's yeast by partial heat inactivation, ammonium sulfate fractionation and ion exchange chromatography with DEAE–cellulose. More than 99 per cent of the enzyme is in the form of the apoenzyme. The Michaelis constants and some data about the kinetics of the reactivation of the enzyme with pyridoxal phosphate ester and pyridoxamine phosphate ester are presented. The influence of other compounds of the vitamin $B_6$ series on the reactivation has been studied. Determination of pyridoxal phosphate ester and pyridoxamine phosphate ester with apotransaminase in an enzymatic-optical test is described. Pyridoxal phosphate ester in the test sample can be inactivated by reduction with borohydride. Pyridoxamine phosphate ester is not affected by borohydride. The concentrations of pyridoxal phosphate ester and pyridoxamine phosphate ester can be determined from values obtained before and after treating a sample with borohydride.

Wir danken der Deutschen Forschungsgemeinschaft und dem Bundesministerium für Atomkernenergie für Beihilfen, die diese Arbeit ermöglicht haben.

## LITERATUR

1. H. Holzer, U. Gerlach, G. Jacobi und M. Gnoth; *Biochem. Z.* **329**, 529 (1958).
2. S. A. Morell, V. E. Ayers und T. J. Greenwalt; *Anal. Biochem.* **3**, 285 (1962).
3. R. M. Bock und Nan-Sing Ling; *Anal. Chem.* **26**, 1543 (1954).

4. G. Beisenherz, H.-J. Boltze, Th. Bücher, R. Czok, K. H. Garbade, E. Meyer-Arendt und G. Pfleiderer; *Z. Naturforsch.* **8b**, 555 (1953).
5. P. Scriba und H. Holzer; *Biochem. Z.* **334**, 473 (1961).
6. E. Holzer; Unveröffentlichte Versuche.
7. E. A. Peterson und H. A. Sober; *J. Am. Chem. Soc.* **76**, 169 (1954).

## DISCUSSION

Dr. Cedrangolo:

En considérant que la méthode que vous proposez peut présenter plusieurs interférences dans des extraits de tissu, je voudrais savoir si cette méthode a été dèja ou peut être utilisée dans ce cas.

Dr. Holzer:

Experiments for the determination of PLP and PMP in extracts of yeast, liver and *E. coli* are in progress in our laboratory. The determination of the sum PLP + PMP in yeast and liver extracts is described by H. Holzer and U. Gerlach in *Methoden der Enzymatischen Analyse* (edited by H. U. Bergmeyer), Verlag Chemie, Weinheim (Bergstrasse), Germany, 1962.

Dr. E. Goryatchenkova:

Did you investigate the recovery of pyridoxal phosphate after addition of it to yeast extracts?

What methods do you recommend for the releasing of pyridoxal phosphate from tissue.

Dr. Holzer:

Samples were obtained by boiling an aliquot of the yeast suspension, cooling and centrifuging. In control experiments the pyridoxal phosphate added before boiling the yeast suspension was quantitatively recovered in the extract (cf. Holzer *et al.*, *Biochem. Z.* **329**, 540, 1958).

To obtain samples from cell suspensions, we heat an aliquot of the neutral suspension for 5 min to 100°C, cool, centrifuge and determine PLP and PMP in the supernatant. Samples from animal tissues are homogenized for 5 min in boiling water and after cooling centrifuged until clear. Extraction of cells with trichloro-acetic acid is not suitable because much of the pyridoxal phosphate precipitates with the denaturated protein (cf. Holzer in *Methoden der enzymatischen Analyse* (edited by H. U. Bergmeyer), p. 606, Verlag Chemie, Weinheim/Bergstr. (1962).

Dr. Vernon:

I was interested to hear that with your transaminase, combination of PLP and apoenzyme is inhibited by pyridoxal. For the glutamic-aspartic transaminase of heart muscle we did not find this effect even though we would expect to if the kinetically significant step in the binding involves the $\epsilon$-amino group of lysine.

I should like to ask whether you have followed the time course of the recombination with the heart muscle enzyme. Dr. Wootton found that with both forms of the co-factor the time course of the reactions are complex. The initial rates show a simple unit order for each reactant but as recombination proceeds the order (with co-factors in large excess) falls below unity. One interpretation of this is that two co-factor molecules combine with the apoenzyme in such a way that the catalytic activity of one is reinforced by the other.

Dr. Holzer:

Thank you for this interesting comment. We have not worked with a heart muscle enzyme. With our enzyme isolated from brewers yeast we have followed the time course of the recombination of the apo- and the coenzyme without analysing the details of the kinetics.

# THE RELATION OF VITAMIN $B_6$ TO TRANSPORT*

by HALVOR N. CHRISTENSEN

Department of Biological Chemistry, The University of Michigan, Ann Arbor, Michigan

A DECADE ago Dr. Riggs and I[1,2] noted that pyridoxal and pyridoxal phosphate were the only nutritional factors, among a number tested, able to intensify the uphill transport of amino acids into the Ehrlich ascites tumor cell. The observed behavior is shown in Fig. 1. We had been looking for a clue as to the way in which amino acids were grasped to permit their release at a higher chemical potential into another compartment. Since these two aldehydes are able to take hold of the amino acid structure by formation of Schiff bases, as Drs. Metzler, Ikawa, and Snell had shown,[3] we entertained for a time the view that such Schiff bases might be intermediates in amino acid transport. This proposed action is so different from the others that will be discussed at this conference, that I judge you may want me to trace the history of the idea, even though as I shall show you, we soon came to regard the view as somewhat unlikely. At the same time I appreciate the opportunity to speak of relevant aspects of biological transport.

When we studied to see what amino acids are transported into the Ehrlich cell we noted that they tend to be the ones that will react with pyridoxal.[4] Secondary amino acids such as sarcosine and proline, which are transported, do not react as readily with pyridoxal as the ordinary amino acids, but they do react in the presence of metal ions to form chelated products. These are presumably quaternized aldimines or carbinolamines in the case of pyridoxal phosphate, and aminoacetals,[5] in the case of pyridoxal.

In order to familiarize ourselves with the nature of these derivatives, we prepared a number of the chelated Schiff bases.[6] Figures 2 and 3 show the ferric chelate and the nickel chelate, respectively, of pyridoxylidine valine. Whereas the cupric chelate has the structure II of Fig. 4, the structures III and IV appeared to be more correct for the nickel and iron chelates.

Extending the correspondence between transport and the ability to form Schiff bases with pyridoxal or pyridoxal phosphate, dimethylamino acids fail to be transported and fail to react with the aromatic aldehydes. In diamino

*Of the experiments discussed here, those made in the laboratory of the author have been supported in part by a grant (C2645) from the National Cancer Institute, the National Institutes of Health.

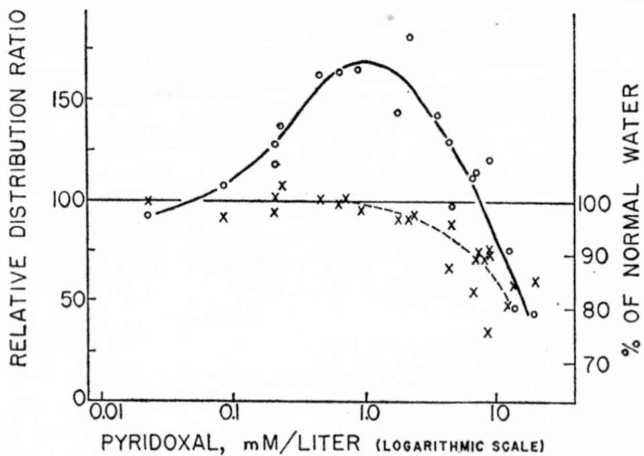


FIG. 1. Action of pyridoxal on the extent of concentrative uptake of glycine. The relative distribution ratio measures the extent to which glycine appears to be concentrated into the cells at a steady state in the presence of the aldehyde, relative to the extent in the absence of added aldehyde. The curve marked X shows the shrinkage of the cells at higher levels. Reproduced from Christensen *et al.*[2], with permission.

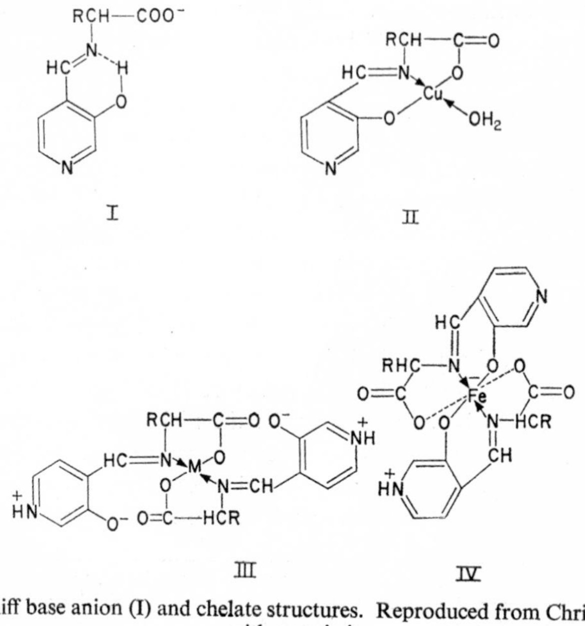

Fig. 4. Schiff base anion (I) and chelate structures. Reproduced from Christensen[6], with permission

FIG. 2. Crystals of ferric (pyridoxylidene-L-valine)$_2$, from water. Magnification 125 ×. The crystals are taken to be completely truncated right-triangular prisms of the orthorhombic hemimorphic class.

FIG. 3. Crystals of nickel (pyridoxylidene-L-valine)$_2$ from water. Magnification 125 ×.

acids the distal amino group can bear two methyl groups; but the α-amino group cannot and yet retains either transport or the characteristic reaction with pyridoxal and a metal ion.[4]

Two circumstances, nevertheless, troubled us from the beginning. First, two interesting analogs of pyridoxal and its phosphate introduced by Metzler *et al.*[3,7], 5-deoxypyridoxal and 4-nitrosalicylaldehyde (Fig. 5), were fully as effective as pyridoxal in stimulating amino acid uptake. Indeed the structural requirements for transport stimulation appeared to be the same ones listed by Metzler *et al.*[3] for the catalysis of non-enzymatic transamination by such aromatic aldehydes.

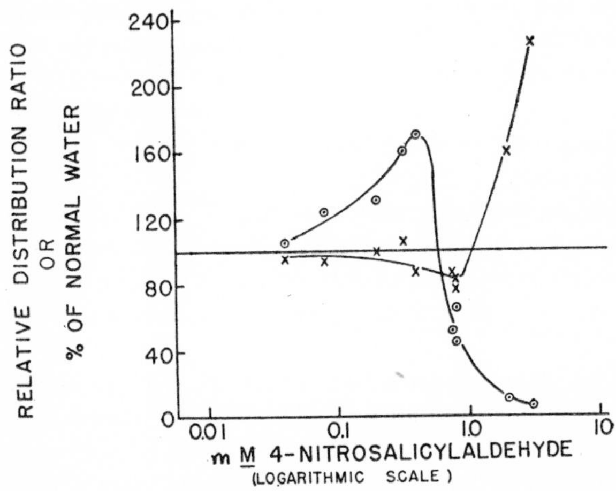


FIG. 5. Action of 4-nitrosalicylaldehyde on the steady state distribution of glycine between ascites tumor cells and the suspending medium. See Fig. 1 for explanatory comments. Reproduced from H. N. Christensen in *Amino Acid Metabolism* (edited by W. D. McElroy and B. Glass), p. 88, Johns Hopkins Press, Baltimore (1955), with permission.

This fact continues to suggest that the action on transport and the catalytic action have a related basis. Nevertheless it would be surprising to have an artificial substitute replace satisfactorily the natural amino acid carrier.

The second difficulty was levels of at least $10^{-4}$ M of pyridoxal or pyridoxal phosphate were needed to secure the action, which was maximal at about $10^{-3}$ M (Fig. 1). Higher levels caused cellular damage and decreased the accumulation of amino acid. Furthermore the effect could be obtained regardless of the state of the $B_6$ nutrition of the mouse bearing the Ehrlich cells, although with high glycine loads a defect of accumulation could be detected in $B_6$-deficient cells.

One further difficulty was that none of the carbonyl reagents tested (semicarbazide, hydroxylamine, isonicotinic hydrazide, and aminoxyacetic acid[8]) were inhibitory to amino acid transport. Accordingly it was difficult to believe that the amino acids react with an accessible carbonyl group in their transport.

The action of added pyridoxal and pyridoxal phosphate on the test cells appeared in many respects not to be part of the normal physiological behavior of the transport system. We reasoned that if either form of vitamin $B_6$ served as the carrier for amino acids, or as an immediate precursor to the carrier, its fluxes between the cells and their environment should be accelerated when amino acid transport is accelerated. To test this possibility, Dr. Prabhat Pal prepared and purified tritiated pyridoxal and pyridoxal phosphate.[9] He found at all levels tested that free pyridoxal enters the Ehrlich cell very quickly to reach an apparent level some 30 or 40 per cent higher than that in the suspending solution. The extra amount probably arises from binding of pyridoxal to macromolecular structures of the cell, since similar excesses are found in cell lysates.

Pyridoxal phosphate, in contrast, is largely excluded from the cell. The small amount taken up may very well represent that fixed on the surface to produce a yellow color, presumably by Schiff-base formation. If the cells are broken, an abundance of new binding sites for pyridoxal phosphate are uncovered.

The fact that these two agents act on transport at the same concentration seems strange considering that one of them is admitted to the cell and the other excluded. Probably the similarity arises from a fortuitous compensation of differences, since we know that pyridoxal phosphate is far more reactive as an aldehyde, whereas a large portion of free pyridoxal is in the hemiacetal form.

Pal found that the presence of ordinary amino acids has only an inhibitory effect on the uptake of both of the aromatic aldehydes (Table 1). As the table shows, several permeating amino acids that are also unusually reactive with pyridoxal (diaminopropionate, $\alpha$, $\gamma$-diaminobutyrate, penicillamine, and cysteine) considerably increase the fixation of free pyridoxal by the cells. Presumably the union between the aldehyde and the amino acid occurs within the cells, and the extra accumulation probably concerns the retention of the products of this union.

In contrast, the presence of these amino acids only depresses the fixation of pyridoxal phosphate, to about the extent that would be expected from their reactivity if both the aldehyde and the product of the reaction were excluded from the cell. This result indicates that pyridoxal phosphate and the amino acids have significant access to each other only in the extracellular fluid.

In neither case does one observe the behavior to be expected of a carrier or a carrier precursor. A carrier precursor might be expected to stimulate the uptake of the solute only during the interval when it is present at a higher level outside than inside the cells. Pyridoxal enters the cells so quickly that one cannot explain the elevated amino acid transport, maintained for several hours, on the basis of a continuing pyridoxal gradient. For pyridoxal phosphate, a concentration gradient does persist, but no gradual entrance of this agent can be detected, either in the presence or absence of added amino acids.

Oxender has studied further the reaction of pyridoxal phosphate with intact Ehrlich cells. He finds that the yellow color produced can be removed

TABLE 1. EFFECT OF AMINO ACIDS ON THE DISTRIBUTION OF PYRIDOXAL AND PYRIDOXAL PHOSPHATE BETWEEN EHRLICH CELLS AND THEIR EXTERNAL ENVIRONMENT.

The distribution ratio in the absence of any added amino acid has been set at 100 per cent. Values in parentheses, and all values for pyridoxal phosphate were obtained under anaerobic conditions. Incubation 25 min. at 37°. From Pal and Christensen[9].

| Amino acid at 10 mM | Relative distribution ratio of aldehyde | | |
|---|---|---|---|
| | Pyridoxal at 2 mM | Pyridoxal at 0.5 mM* | Pyridoxal phosphate at 1 mM |
| Glycine | 83 (99) | 91 | 72 |
| α-Aminoisobutyrate | 96 | 71 | |
| L-Isoleucine | 87 | 55 | |
| L-Arginine | 89 | 65 | |
| L-Lysine | 91 (94) | 108 | 61 |
| L-Ornithine | 88 | 100 | |
| L-α, γ-Diaminobutyrate | 155 (100) | 131 | 53 |
| L-α, β-Diaminopropionate | 225 (181) | 131 | 45 |
| L-Cysteine | 245 | 100 | |
| L-Penicillamine | 144 | 136 | |

*Observed by counting tritium disintegration.

almost instantly by adding in the cold a little sodium borohydride. As a result tritiated pyridoxal phosphate is fixed to the cells. As Fig. 6 shows, this permanent fixation does not interfere with the subsequent uptake of amino acids. But the cells have lost their responsiveness to a new addition of pyridoxal phosphate; no further stimulation of amino acid uptake can be produced.[10]

The position of the fixed phosphopyridoxyl residues on the cell has not yet been established. At the same time that the response to fresh pyridoxal phosphate is lost, the cells become unresponsive to stilbestrol disulfate and estradiol disulfate, two agents that also intensify amino acid uptake at

1-m molar levels. Hence we have indications that these anions and pyridoxal phosphate occupy the same or overlapping sites to influence amino acid transport.

Actually I think the effect of the fixation of pyridoxal phosphate on the cell surface may teach us more about the basis of endocrinological actions, which I believe it is simulating, than about the nature of the mediation *per se* of amino acid transport. This action can be related to that of not only steroid sulfates, but also of free steroids and of auxins on the cell. But this question goes beyond the scope of this present conference.

When the Ehrlich cell is incubated in 1 mM pyridoxal phosphate, the cells frequently clump after an interval of time, and poor transport is observed. Incubation under anaerobic conditions, where acceptable, helps to minimize

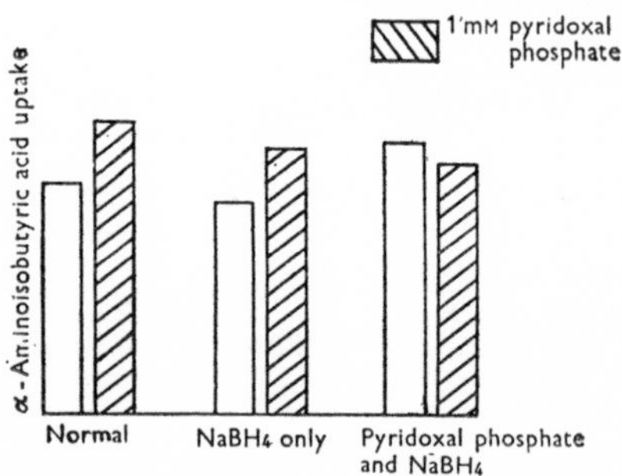


FIG. 6. Effect of borohydride treatment of pyridoxal phosphate-bearing cells on the sensitivity to stimulation of amino acid uptake by pyridoxal phosphate. Borohydride treatment of fresh cells alone has had little influence, but treatment in the presence of pyridoxal phosphate eliminates the response to subsequent addition of the aldehyde. Results of Oxender[10]. Reproduced from Christensen[8], with permission.

this behavior. Oxender has observed that the clumping arises from a somewhat specific release of DNA from the cells, whether in aerobic or anaerobic environments. This clumping could be entirely avoided by including a very small amount of DNAase in the medium. This effect of pyridoxal phosphate is not shared by free pyridoxal.

Oxender has continued the study of the action of pyridoxal phosphate by the differential study of the two amino acid fluxes, inward and outward.[11,12] Such amino acids as valine and leucine show very high fluxes in both directions; the extracellular amino acids engage in a rapid exchange with the amino acids already in the cell. This movement in both directions is *inhibited* by pyridoxal phosphate. The steady-state accumulation of these amino acids is also decreased. The stimulating action on accumulation is seen particularly with the more polar amino acids and those with short side chains, such as glycine and α-aminoisobutyric acid.

Although competition occurs generally among neutral amino acids for transport, it has become apparent that only part of their migrations occur by the same reactive site or carrier; instead two overlapping mediations are involved. Figure 7 shows Oxender's results establishing the separate action of an alanine-preferring and a leucine-prefering mediation. It may be seen as the sensitivity to leucine inhibition decreases (from left to right), that the sensitivity to inhibition by alanine increases. Such a behavior can not be produced by competition for a single site. The operation of two sites appear in this instance to be consistent with the inhibitory actions observed. Each

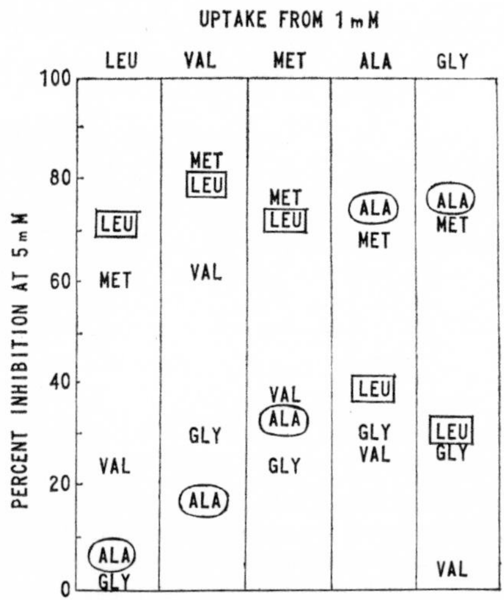


FIG. 7. Demonstration that at least two sites account for the entry of neutral amino acids into Ehrlich cells. The amino acids listed in the body of the table are acting as inhibitors at 5 mM levels to the extent indicated, of the uptake of the amino acids listed at the top of the table at 1 mM levels. Note that leucine tends to become progressively less effective and alanine progressively more effective as an inhibitor, from left to right: from Oxender and Christensen, *Nature*, **197**, 765 (1963), with permission.

of the two sites can be studied in isolation by adding a sufficient level of a suitable competing substrate; for example $\alpha$-aminoisobutyric acid in one case *ter*-leucine in the other.

These are not two similar and parallel transport systems, as is brought out by Oxender's finding that the alanine-preferring one shows very little if any reverse action, i.e. for exodus of amino acids from the cells. Accordingly, those amino acids whose affinity is particularly large for this mediation are accumulated to high degrees, until their escape from the cell by the other, less-preferred mediator finally appears able to compensate for the influx.

Figure 8 is a visualization of the accumulation of glycine. Its entry by a high-affinity carrier, and its escape mainly by the other system, for which its affinity is poor, are pictured in this figure.

The possibility can easily be perceived that if pyridoxal phosphate inhibits this second leucine-preferring mediation, as appears probably to be the case, the steady state accumulation of glycine will be stimulated. The finding by Oxender[10] that the efflux is inhibited to a much greater degree than the initial entry rate is stimulated, supports this supposition. Furthermore the sole action of pyridoxal phosphate on the uptake of leucine and valine is an inhibitory one.

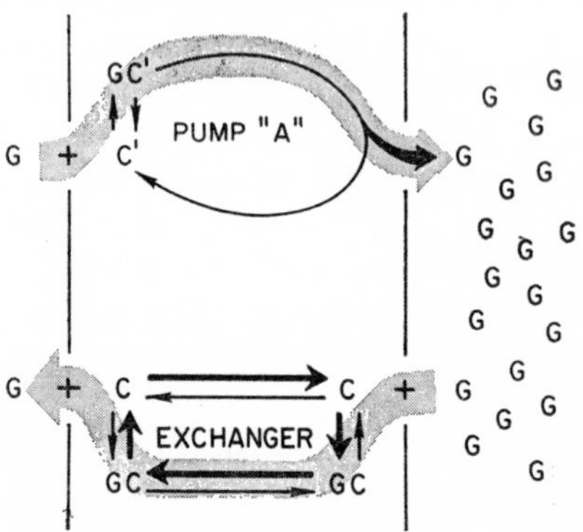


FIG. 8. Scheme to show how such an amino acid as glycine may enter and leave cells. Glycine is visualized to be transported inward by the uphill pump *A*, until it reaches high enough levels in the cells to tend to escape by the other mediator, despite its poor affinity for it.

The binding of pyridoxal and pyridoxal phosphate to the cell surface to cause a yellow staining, in the course of the stimulation of transport, has drawn our attention to the action of these aldehydes on protein structure. Mora and Snell[13] have observed that the naked protoplast of *Lactobacillus arabinosus* is also responsive to pyridoxal in its uptake of amino acids, whereas the organism complete with its cell wall is unresponsive. This finding suggests that only if the aldehydes have access to the plasma membrane can they influence transport, a conclusion that may also support the idea that modification of the macromolecular structures of the membrane may account for the changes. In this connection Dempsey and Christensen[14] observed that the optical rotation of a solution of bovine serum albumin became steadily more positive as the first 3 moles of pyridoxal phosphate bind to the protein. This binding is inhibited by the sulfate esters of estradiol and stilbestrol. The union of pyridoxal phosphate with the apoenzyme of muscle phosphorylase is known to initiate an aggregation of the protein.[15] Mason and

Gullekson[16] have observed that kynurenine apotransaminase becomes more stable when the coenzyme is present; and further, that minute concentrations of the disulfates of estradiol and stilbestrol stabilize the enzyme against the action of chymotrypsin. The estrogen sulfates compete with pyridoxal phosphate in its addition to the apoenzyme. All these findings support the idea that specific combinations with pyridoxal phosphate may modify the tertiary structure of proteins, an action that may underlie its effects, and that of steroids, on the function of the plasma membrane.

We have concluded thus that the action of pyridoxal and pyridoxal phosphate at high levels on the Ehrlich cell is not related to their normal participation in amino acid transport. This conclusion, however, has no effect on the validity of nutritional findings, which still indicate an unidentified relationship. There remains, first of all, the original observation that Ehrlich cells can handle a larger load of glycine when grown in mice receiving normal intakes of vitamin $B_6$. Furthermore, in 1958 Riggs and Walker showed that in vitamin $B_6$ deficient tissues of the rat (excepting the liver) lose much of their ability to accumulate $\alpha$-aminoisobutyrate.[17] Holden and Holman[18] and Holden[19] observed a decrease in the extent but not the initial rate of glutamate accumulation in vitamin $B_6$ deficient cells of *Lactobacillus arabinosus*. Decreases have been found in the intestinal transport of amino acids after rats have been made $B_6$-deficient by administration of 4-deoxy-pyridoxine[20] or of penicillamine.[21] The inhibitory action of 2, 4-dinitrophenol on amino acid transport could be reversed by supplying pyridoxal phosphate either *in vivo* or *in vitro*.[22,23] The suggestion was made that dinitrophenol interferes with the phosphorylation of pyridoxal, and that it is the phosphate derivative that is needed for amino acid transport.

These actions show that the supply of some form of vitamin $B_6$ exerts an important effect on amino acid transport. No direct evidence exists, however, that the carbonyl group of pyridoxal or of its phosphate directly mediates the transport of amino acid. Therefore, the nature of the relationship must be considered undetermined.

## REFERENCES


1. T. R. Riggs, B. A. Coyne and H. N. Christensen; *Biochim. et Biophys. Acta* **11**, 303 (1953).
2. H. N. Christensen, T. R. Riggs and B. A. Coyne; *J. Biol. Chem.* **209**, 413 (1954).
3. D. E. Metzler, M. Ikawa and E. E. Snell; *J. Am. Chem. Soc.* **76**, 648 (1954).
4. H. N. Christensen and T. R. Riggs; *J. Biol. Chem.* **220**, 265 (1956).
5. D. E. Metzler; *J. Am. Chem. Soc.* **79**, 485 (1957).
6. H. N. Christensen; *J. Am. Chem. Soc.* **79**, 4073 (1957).
7. M. Ikawa and E. E. Snell; *J. Am. Chem. Soc.* **76**, 653 (1954).
8. H. N. Christensen; *Advances in Protein Chem.* **15**, 239 (1960).
9. P. R. Pal and H. N. Christensen; *J. Biol. Chem.* **236**, 894 (1961).
10. D. C. Oxender; Unpublished results (1960), cited by H. N. Christensen *Membrane Transport and Metabolism* (edited by Kleinzeller and Kotyk) pp. 472–474, Publishing House of the Czechoslovak Academy of Sciences (1961).
11. D. L. Oxender; *Federation Proc.* **21**, 148 (1962).

12. D. L. Oxender; Unpublished results (1962), cited by H. N. Christensen, *Biological Transport*, pp. 57–59, W. A. Benjamin Co., New York (1962).
13. J. Mora and E. E. Snell; *Biochemistry* **2**, 136 (1963).
14. W. B. Dempsey and H. N. Christensen; *J. Am. Chem. Soc.* **237**, 1113 (1962).
15. C. F. Cori and B. Illingworth; *Proc. Natl. Acad. Sci. U.S.* **43**, 547 (1957).
16. M. Mason and E. H. Gullekson; *J. Biol. Chem.* **235**, 1312 (1960).
17. T. R. Riggs and L. M. Walker; *J. Biol. Chem.* **233**, 132 (1958).
18. J. T. Holden and J. Holman; *J. Biol. Chem.* **234**, 865 (1959).
19. J. T. Holden; *J. Biol. Chem.* **234**, 872 (1959).
20. F. H. Jacobs and R. S. L. Hillman; *J. Biol. Chem.* **232**, 445 (1958).
21. H. Akedo, T. Sugawa, S. Yoshikawa and M. Suda; *J. Biochem.* (*Tokyo*) **47**, 124 (1960).
22. F. A. Jacobs, L. J. Coen and R. S. L. Hillman; *J. Biol. Chem.* **235**, 1372 (1960).
23. K. Ueda, H. Akedo and M. Suda; *J. Biochem.* (*Tokyo*) **48**, 584 (1960).

## DISCUSSION

Dr. Braunstein:

In experiments on intestinal absorption of amino acids in rats, using a modification of Jacob's technique of *in situ* perfusion, Dr. Vilenkina and I have found that the absorption of glycine and lysine, like that of methionine and L-histidine, is vitamin $B_6$-dependent, and can be restored only with PLP after drugging the animal with dinitrophenol. Alanine absorption is slightly dependent on vitamin $B_6$, glutamine absorption (as opposed to glutamate absorption) is markedly dependent, while no dependence was observed with valine and with asparagine.

Dr. Christensen:

I am indebted to Dr. Braunstein for adding this further observation of a close relationship between vitamin $B_6$ and amino acid transport; his comment permits me to re-emphasize that observations on the nature of the stimulating action of pyridoxal on the Ehrlich cell do not controvert the possible normal involvement of vitamin $B_6$ in normal solute transport. Because we observed an action of pyridoxal and of pyridoxal phosphate on transport in Ehrlich cell, it has been our responsibility to describe it and to discover its meaning for transport.

# PYRIDOXAL-5′-PHOSPHATE IN THE STRUCTURE AND FUNCTION OF PHOSPHORYLASE*

by Edmond H. Fischer, Arden W. Forrey, Jerry L. Hedrick, R. Colin Hughes, Alan B. Kent and Edwin G. Krebs

Department of Biochemistry, University of Washington, Seattle, Washington

Phosphorylase,† one of the enzymes playing a key role in the control of glycogen metabolism,[1] has certainly provided the biochemist with a multitude of surprises since its discovery just about 30 years ago. In the late thirties it was considered that muscle phosphorylase was totally inactive in the absence of adenosine-5′-phosphate,‡ and, indeed, this nucleotide was thought to be a coenzyme for the reaction. In 1943, Green and Cori[2] crystallized muscle phosphorylase in a form which did not require added AMP for enzyme activity. It was at first very logically assumed that phosphorylase *a*—a form of the enzyme active in the absence of AMP—contained bound nucleotide,[3] but this hypothesis had to be abandoned for the following reasons: firstly, no AMP was released when active phosphorylase *a* was converted to the original form of the enzyme (now called phosphorylase *b*) by another muscle enzyme called Prosthetic Group Removing (PR) enzyme;[4] and secondly, no AMP could be detected in a total acid hydrolyzate of pure phosphorylase *a*.[5]

In 1950, Sumner *et al.*[6] described the purification of Jack Bean phosphorylase and claimed that this enzyme contained flavin adenine dinucleotide; subsequently this assertion could not be confirmed. The same year Velick and Wicks[5] reported the presence of a vitamin $B_6$ derivative in phosphorylase, but did not consider this compound to be a prosthetic group since it apparently could be partially removed by repeated crystallization of the enzyme without loss of catalytic activity. In a preliminary note, Buell[7] claimed that uridylic acid and a yellow pigment, tentatively identified as 2-methyl-1,4-naphthoquinone could be isolated from the non-protein fraction of seven-times

---

*This work was generously supported by grants from the National Science Foundation (GB-239), and the National Institute of Arthritis and Metabolic Diseases, NIH, USPHS (A-859).

†α-1, 4 glucan: orthophosphateglucosyltransferase; No. 2.4.1.1 IUB Commission on Enzymes.

‡The following abbreviations are used: AMP, adenosine-5′-phosphate; PLP pyridoxal-5′-phosphate; p-CMB, *p*-chloromercuribenzoate.

recrystallized rabbit muscle phosphorylase. This led to a suggestion that uridine nucleotides might be involved in the interconversions of phosphorylase *b* and *a*, as well as in the mechanism of action of these enzymes.[8]

In the late fifties, two different laboratories independently reported the presence of stoichiometric amounts of pyridoxal-5′-phosphate in rabbit muscle phosphorylase.[9–11] However, further investigation of this finding gave two apparently paradoxical results. On the one hand, Cori *et al.*[9,12] demonstrated that the cofactor was indispensable for the enzymatic reaction. Removal of PLP from the enzyme by either acid treatment, or in the case of phosphorylase *b*, by incubation of the protein with cysteine, yielded an enzymatically inactive material that could be almost fully reactivated by restoration of the vitamin $B_6$ derivative. On the other hand, it was demonstrated in this laboratory[13] that treatment of the native enzyme with sodium borohydride, which irreversibly reduces and " fixes " PLP to the protein molecule (see below), resulted in no loss of enzymatic activity. This finding led to the conclusion that, if PLP actually participates in the phosphorylase reaction, it must function in a manner different from that considered to be followed in all other PLP-catalyzed reactions, for which a potential aldehyde group is indispensable.

In recent years PLP has been found in phosphorylase preparations obtained from lobster muscle,[14] cat muscle,[11] human striated[15] and heart muscles,[16] pig liver,[17] and potatoes.[18] The apparent ubiquity of PLP in all of these phosphorylases strongly suggests that the presence of the vitamin derivative must be directly related to catalytic function of phosphorylase itself, rather than to that of some of the enzymes involved in the complex mechanism of activation of phosphorylase[19] known to be operative in many *in vitro* systems, e.g. muscle.

The present article will summarize some of the findings related to the role of PLP in the catalytic activity and molecular conformation of muscle phosphorylase. The structure of the site involved in the binding of PLP to phosphorylase, glutamic–aspartic transaminase and cystathionase will also be described.

## STRUCTURE AND INTERCONVERSIONS OF RABBIT MUSCLE PHOSPHORYLASE

Before entering on a discussion of the role of PLP in the catalytic activity of phosphorylase, it might be relevant to discuss briefly some of the more salient structural features of this rather complex enzyme. Rabbit skeletal muscle phosphorylase exists in two readily interconvertible forms.[19,20] Phosphorylase *b*, of M.W. 242,000, is inactive in the absence of AMP and is found predominantly in resting muscle. At the time of contraction of the muscle or under the influence of the hormone epinephrine, two molecules of phosphorylase *b* will react, not with two, but with four molecules of ATP to give one molecule of phosphorylase *a* of M.W. 495,000; in this reaction, four molecules of phosphate are transferred from ATP to the enzyme, according to the following reaction :[21]

$$\text{2 phosphorylase } b + \text{4 ATP} \xrightarrow[\text{Mg}^{2+}]{\text{active phosphorylase } b \text{ kinase}} \text{phosphorylase } a + \text{4 ADP} \quad (1)$$

In the presence of active rabbit muscle phosphorylase *b* kinase, $Mg^{2+}$ and $P^{32}$-labeled ATP, $P^{32}$-labeled phosphorylase *a* can be synthesized and used as a substrate to study the mechanism of action of " PR-enzyme ". By this means, PR-enzyme was found to hydrolyze the four protein-bound phosphate groups of phosphorylase *a* to produce the original phosphorylase *b* according to reaction (2), and was therefore named phosphorylase phosphatase.[22]

$$\text{phosphorylase } a \xrightarrow[\text{4H}_2\text{O}]{\text{phosphorylase phosphatase}} \text{2 phosphorylase } b + \text{4 Pi} \quad (2)$$

The finding that four phosphate groups were introduced into the phosphorylase *a* molecule was consistent with Madsen and Cori's[23] observation that

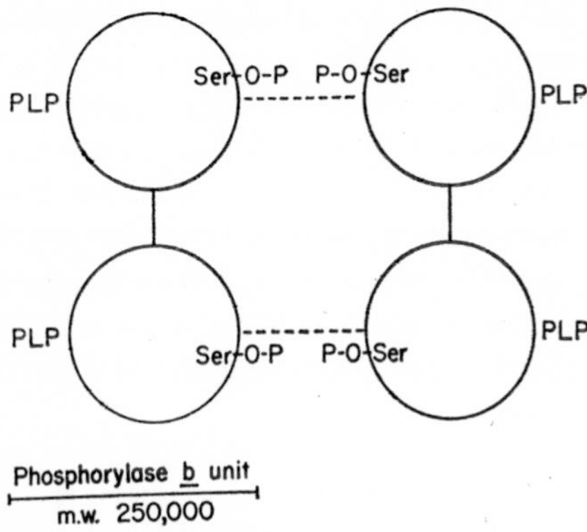


FIG. 1. Schematic representation of phosphorylase *a*.

phosphorylase *b* itself was a dimer that could be dissociated into two sub-units of M.W. 125,000 by the action of sulfhydryl reagents, such as *p*-chloromercuribenzoate, a reaction which was readily reversible on addition of an excess of cysteine. Since phosphorylase *a* can be dissociated by similar means into four sub-units, this form of the enzyme must be visualized as a tetramer containing one molecule of bound phosphate and one molecule of PLP per sub-unit of M.W. 125,000 (Fig. 1).

In Fig. 1 the solid lines between two sets of sub-units depict the bonds in existence in phosphorylase *b*. The dashed lines represent those bonds which are formed between two molecules of phosphorylase *b* following phosphorylation of the protein. Both types of bonds are split by *p*-CMB and their chemical nature is unknown.

The sequence of amino acids around the seryl-phosphate residue has been identified[24] (24, 24a) as:

$$\text{Ser-Asp-GluNH}_2\text{-Glu-Lys-Arg-Lys-GluNH}_2\text{-}\overset{\text{OP}}{\overset{|}{\text{Ileu}}}\text{-Ser-Val-Arg-Gly-Leu}$$

As can be seen, this structure is quite different from any of the peptide sequences that have been reported for any esterase, peptidase, and for phosphoglucomutase. The region of the protein carrying the seryl-phosphate group probably possesses a more random (or less highly organized) structure than the rest of the molecule, or is more " exposed " on the surface of the enzyme, as indicated by the fact that it is attacked by trypsin, chymotrypsin, papain, and other proteases much more readily than the rest of the molecule.

The exact role of AMP in the activation of phosphorylase *b* has not been so far elucidated. The nucleotide is strongly bound to both forms of the enzymes ($K_{\text{dissoc.}}$ approximately $5 \times 10^{-5}$ M for phosphorylase *b*, and $2 \times 10^{-6}$ M for phosphorylase *a*) and has a profound effect on the conformation of both enzymes. This effect is demonstrated by the fact that in the presence of AMP, phosphorylase *a* is completely resistant to the action of phosphorylase phosphatase and the proteolytic enzymes mentioned above which otherwise readily split the phosphorylated site of the enzyme. Similarly, AMP protects to a considerable extent both phosphorylase *a* and *b* from urea denaturation.

Phosphorylase *b* binds two molecules of AMP and, in the presence of divalent metal ions, the enzyme undergoes dimerization and crystallization. It is tempting to postulate that the activation by AMP of phosphorylase *b* is a manifestation of this type of aggregation, but this hypothesis has not been substantiated as yet.

## PROPERTIES OF PHOSPHORYLASE AND $NaBH_4$-REDUCED PHOSPHORYLASE WITH REGARD TO PYRIDOXAL-5′-PHOSPHATE

Neutral solutions of phosphorylase *b* and *a* show, in addition to the classical protein absorption peak at 278 mμ, a second peak at 330 mμ due to the presence of bound pyridoxal-5′-phosphate. When very high concentrations of these enzymes are examined, a third absorption maximum may sometimes be seen at wavelengths above 400 mμ, particularly in aged preparations. It was found that this 415 mμ peak increased considerably at pH's below 4.5 or above 9.5 at which point the solution became intensely yellow with simultaneous disappearance of the 330 mμ absorption[11] (Figs. 2 and 3).

These spectral shifts are characteristic for the various structures displayed by PLP in combination with amines, amino acids, peptides or proteins, and correspond to the formation of carbinolaimnes or amino acetals, Schiff bases and related forms.[25]

In view of these spectral properties and the stability of binding of PLP to phosphorylase, it was proposed[11] that at neutral pH's, PLP is bound to phosphorylase as a substituted aldamine derivative presumably with a free

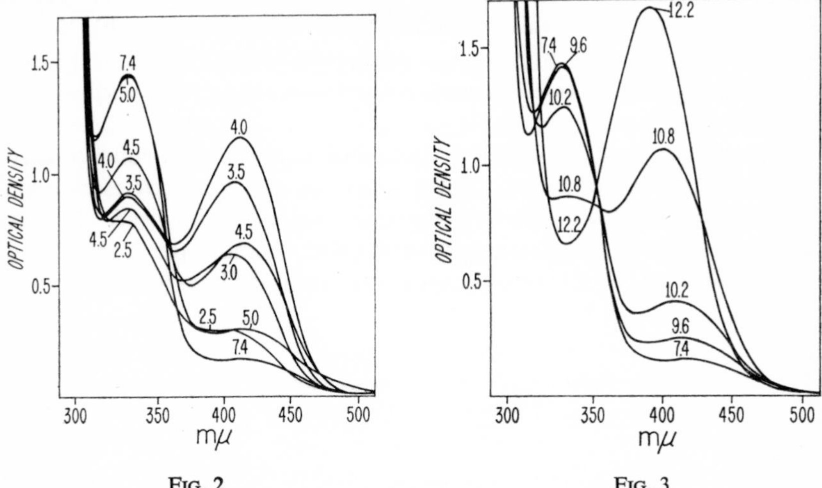


FIG. 2

FIG. 3

amino group of the protein (Structure I, Fig. 4). In acid or base solutions, or under conditions leading to a change in conformation of the protein, e.g. treatment with urea or with detergents, Form (I) is converted to the

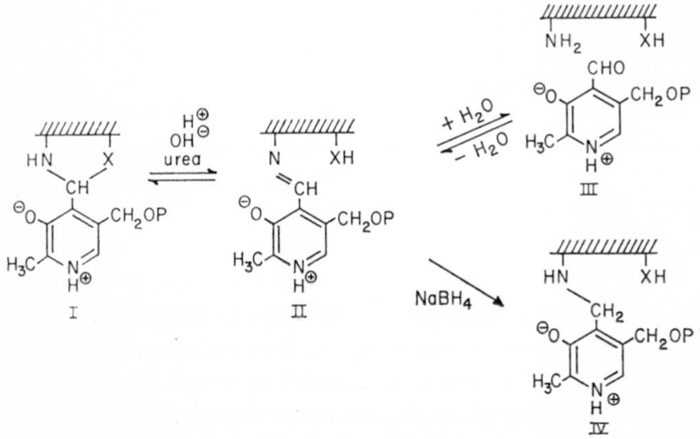

FIG. 4. Na-borohydride reduction of muscle phosphorylase.

yellow Schiff base (II). The formation of the C—N azomethine bond is responsible for the 415 mμ absorption maximum depicted in Fig. 3; this Schiff base is highly polarized and tends to rapidly hydrolyze, giving a mixture of apoenzyme and free PLP (III).

The above assumptions were confirmed[13] by the finding that the Schiff base (II) can be quantitatively converted by sodium borohydride to the colorless pyridoxal derivative (IV) with the complete loss of the absorption maximum at 415 m$\mu$. This derivative has, instead, an absorption peak at 330 m$\mu$ and is stable to acid or base treatment. No reduction with $NaBH_4$ takes place at neutral pH's where phosphorylase displays the spectral properties of Form (I). The reduced enzyme has been purified and crystallized.

The nature of the other group to which PLP is covalently bound in native phosphorylase *b* (denoted as X in Fig. 4) has not yet been established. Thiol, amino, imidazole or hydroxyl groups may all be involved. The fact that urea, or low concentrations of detergents promote the formation of the Schiff base (II) would indicate that group X and the lysyl residue to which

TABLE 1. COMPARATIVE PROPERTIES OF NORMAL AND $NaBH_4$-REDUCED PHOSPHORYLASE *b*

| Properties | Phosphorylase *b* | $NaBH_4$-reduced phosphorylase *b* |
|---|---|---|
| Specific activity (pH 6.8) | 1520 | 1140 |
| Optimum pH | 6.6 | 6.6 |
| $K_M$ glucose-1-P (pH 6.5) | $1.24 \times 10^{-2}$ M | $1.9 \times 10^{-2}$ M |
| $K_M$ AMP | $6.0 \times 10^{-5}$ M | $8.5 \times 10^{-5}$ M |
| Inhibition by phlorizin | | |
| at $2.5 \times 10^{-3}$ M | 82% | 82% |
| at $5 \times 10^{-3}$ M | 97% | 97% |
| Energies of activation between 8 and 16°C | 24.4 kcal/mole | 24.4 kcal/mole |

PLP is bound are not adjacent on the peptide chain; it would also suggest that the spatial conformation of the protein is important in maintaining PLP in the structure characteristic for the native enzyme (I).

Surprisingly, $NaBH_4$-reduced phosphorylases *b* and *a* were found to retain most of their catalytic activities, and to behave normally in the enzymatic interconversions mentioned in the previous section. Native and $NaBH_4$-reduced enzymes have essentially identical optimum pH and pH-dependence activity curves. Their kinetic behavior measured in the direction of glycogen synthesis or during arsenolysis of glycogen, their Michaelis constants for glucose-l-phosphate and AMP, and energies of activation are very similar[26] (see Table 1).

The possibility, although remote, that the pyridoxylamine substituent might be reoxidized to PLP during the assay of enzymatic activity was ruled out, since no vitamin $B_6$ derivative was detected in perchloric acid filtrates of the assay mixture, even when large amounts of enzyme were used. Furthermore, the phosphorylase assay itself could be run in the presence of excess $NaBH_4$ with no appreciable reduction in reaction rate.

Many observations tend to indicate that the binding of PLP to the phosphorylase molecule has profound influence on the conformation of the enzyme. Illingworth *et al.*[12] have shown that phosphorylase *a* free of PLP is partially dissociated to approximately 40 per cent monomer units. Apophosphorylase *b* also shows a more heteorgeneous ultracentrifugal pattern which is restored to normal upon addition of PLP.

PLP also affects the resistance of phosphorylase to denaturating agents,

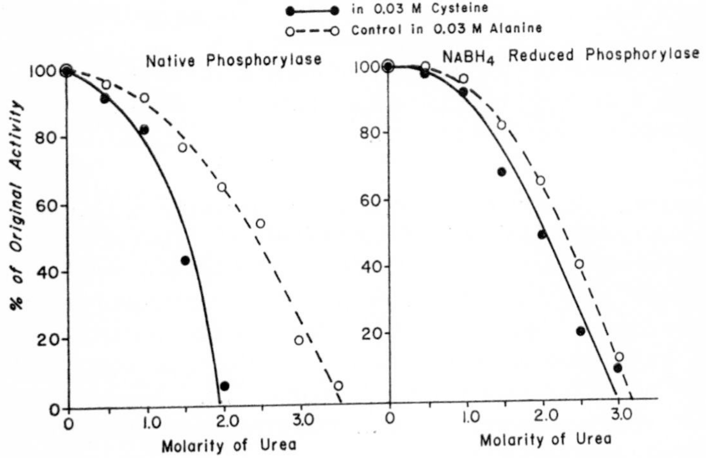


FIG. 5. Effect of cysteine on the inactivation of phosphorlase *b* by urea.

such as urea. Phosphorylase is very sensitive to urea action, being irreversibly denatured at concentrations as low as 3.0 M. Cysteine increases this sensitivity, reducing the urea concentration necessary for complete irreversible inactivation of phosphorylase *b* from 3.0 to 2.0 M. However, $NaBH_4$-reduced phosphorylase is essentially not affected by cysteine,[17] indicating that this amino acid enhances urea denaturation, at least in part, by binding the PLP of the enzyme as a stable thiazolium derivative (Fig. 5). This conclusion is supported by the fact that other sulfhydryl compounds such as thioglycolate, which do not form such stable complexes with PLP, do not affect the extent of urea denaturation. Furthermore, analysis of the protein recovered by ammonium sulfate precipitation at various stages of urea denaturation indicates a clear correlation between the extent of residual activity and the amount of PLP still bound to the enzyme. The overall mechanism of urea denaturation can be depicted by the following set of reactions :[17]

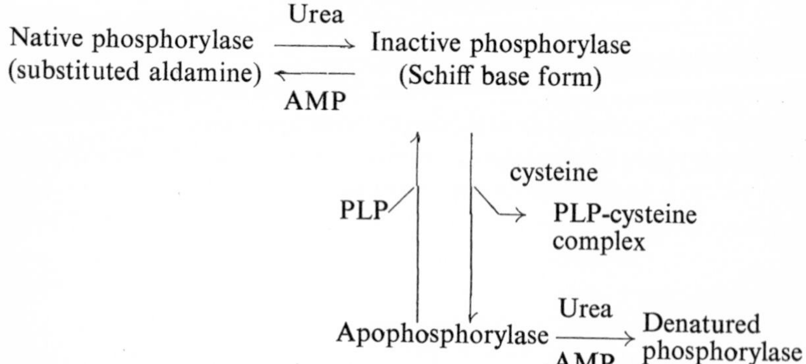


AMP, by stabilizing the tertiary conformation of the protein, opposes the formation of the Schiff base and the ultimate release of PLP, thus protecting the enzyme from urea denaturation.

## SEARCH FOR OTHER ENZYMATIC ACTIVITIES NORMALLY ASSOCIATED WITH PYRIDOXAL ENZYMES

All pyridoxal enzymes thus far well characterized involve an amino acid as a reactant with the exception of the polysaccharide phosphorylases. It was considered a distinct possibility that glycogen phosphorylase might exhibit, in addition to a phosphorolytic activity, an enzymatic activity normally associated with pyridoxal enzymes (i.e. transamination, decarboxylation, elimination reactions, etc.). However, all attempts to demonstrate such activity have failed.

The following amino acids were surveyed for reactivity with phosphorylase *b* in the presence of AMP, glycogen with or without $\alpha$-ketoglutarate at pH 6.8 and pH 8.5 : glutamine, asparagine, aspartic acid, lysine, histidine, arginine, alanine, glycine, isoleucine, leucine, valine, threonine, serine phenylalanine, tryptophan, methionine, and cysteine. The appearance of glutamic acid in the case of a transamination, the corresponding amine in the case of decarboxylation, or decreased amounts of the added amino acid in the case of dehydration reactions, could be detected by high voltage electrophoresis at pH 6.5 in a pyridine–acetic acid buffer. As used, this method would have been capable of detecting a net conversion of 1.5 per cent of $\alpha$-ketoglutarate to glutamic acid if transamination had taken place.

Under these conditions, glycogen phosphorylase does not exhibit any enzymatic activity which is normally associated with pyridoxal enzymes.

## NON-ENZYMATIC CATALYSIS OF INORGANIC PHOSPHATE RELEASE FROM GLUCOSE-1-PHOSPHATE

Model studies involving the reaction of pyridoxal with amino acids have proved very useful in elucidating the mechanism of transamination, decarboxylation, elimination reactions, etc., of amino acids as catalyzed by pyridoxal enzymes.[25,31] With this in mind, we have undertaken the study of model systems involving pyridoxal and its derivatives, glucose-1-phosphate, and glycogen in an effort to reproduce the action of glycogen phosphorylase on its substrates. It was hoped that pyridoxal might non-enzymatically catalyze the release of inorganic phosphate either by a hydrolysis of glucose-1-phosphate to inorganic phosphate and glucose, or by transfer of glucose to glycogen.

The test system consisted of glucose-1-phosphate, glycogen and a pyridoxal derivative (pyridoxal, pyridoxamine, pyridoxine, pyridoxal phosphate, pyridoxamine phosphate, $\epsilon$-N-pyridoxyllysine or poly $\epsilon$-N-pyridoxylpolysine). The incubations were carried out at pH 4.7, 7.0 and 9.6 with heating in a boiling water bath for 60 min. Incubations at pH 4.7 were also carried out in the presence of aluminum ions. The release of inorganic phosphate was followed by the Fiske–Subbarow method, which is sensitive enough to detect with ease a 0.1 per cent net hydrolysis of the glucose-1-phosphate present.

No release of inorganic phosphate could be detected under any of the above conditions, indicating that the model systems used here failed to mimic the action of glycogen phosphorylase.

## THE EFFECT OF LIGHT ON PHOSPHORYLASE *b*

It has been known for some time that pyridoxal and pyridoxal derivatives are sensitive to light.[27,28] In at least two instances PLP enzymes have been indicated as being light sensitive, and in the case of $\beta$-aspartic decarboxylase, the destruction of PLP in the enzyme by photodecomposition has been used as a method of preparing the apoenzyme.[29,30] Consequently, it was considered a distinct possibility that apophosphorylase *b* might also be prepared by irradiation of phosphorylase *b*. The following conditions were used in exploring this possibility.

Phosphorylase *b* solutions were irradiated in a fluorescence spectrometer constructed in this laboratory. The light source was a 300-W xenon arc lamp. The light was dispersed into its component wavelengths by a Bausch and Lomb monochromator. The band pass width used in these experiments was 33 m$\mu$. The solution irradiated was maintained at 5° by a jacketed cell compartment and a constant temperature waterbath.

The rate of destruction of phosphorylase *b* upon irradiation was found to follow first-order kinetics which were used in calculating the half-life of the enzyme. Samples were removed and assayed after irradiation of 0, 5, 10,

15 and 20 min. In the case of apophosphorylase *b*, the enzyme was preincubated before assaying with $3 \times 10^{-5}$ M PLP to reconstitute the enzyme not destroyed. All phosphorylase preparations were free of AMP when irradiated.

Preliminary results obtained are shown in Fig. 6. It can be seen that phosphorylase *b* was sensitive to light of 273 mμ wavelength. This wavelength can only be associated with absorption by the aromatic amino acids present in the protein. There is no destruction by irradiation at 330 or 415 mμ, the two wavelengths corresponding to the absorption bands due to the presence of PLP. Phosphorylase *b* has also been irradiated at pH 10.4 where the Schiff base form (absorbing at 415 mμ) predominates. Even this form was found to be insensitive to irradiation at 415 mμ.

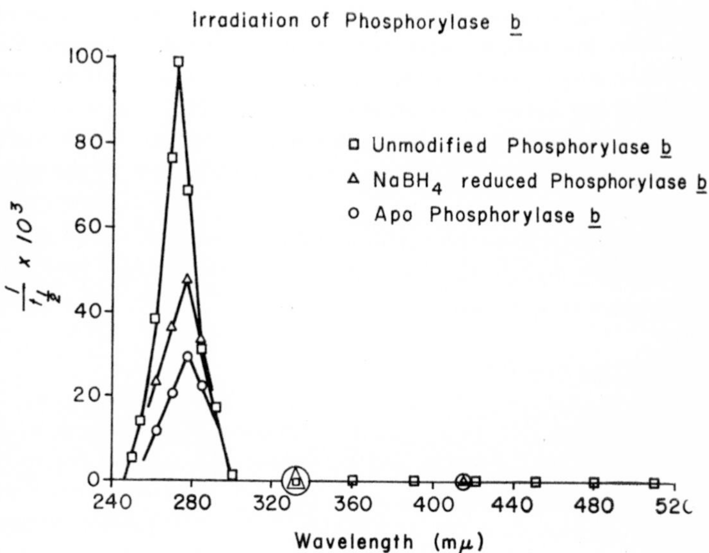


FIG. 6. Irradiation of phosphorylase *b*.

$NaBH_4$-reduced phosphorylase *b* and apophosphorylase *b* show also only one peak of destruction, but the maxima have shifted to slightly higher wavelengths (278 mμ instead of 273 mμ). Furthermore, at these values the proteins appear to be rather more stable to photoinactivation. The reason for the decrease in sensitivity of the modified phosphorylases (which are appreciably less stable under normal conditions) is not known, but it could be related in some way to a modification or disruption of the tertiary conformation of the enzyme. An unfolding of the molecule could in turn interfere with a normal transfer of energy to other groups sensitive to photo-oxidation (histidine, methionine, etc.) within the protein molecule.

In only one instance has destruction been observed at a wavelength other than that associated with absorption of the aromatic amino acids. When NaBH-reduced phosphorylase *b* is irradiated at pH 4.7, it is sensitive to light of 330 m$\mu$. At this pH, the PLP is in a form which absorbs at 330 m$\mu$. Preliminary experiments also indicate that under these conditions, $NaBH_4$-reduced phosphorylase *b* exhibits fluorescence which is associated with PLP. Unmodified or $NaBH_4$-reduced phosphorylase *b* does not exhibit any fluorescence due to PLP at pH 6.8.

The dissimilarities of PLP in phosphorylase *b* and other PLP enzymes cannot be readily explained as yet. It is apparent, however, that whereas the PLP in $\beta$-aspartic decarboxylase is destroyed upon irradiation, it is not specifically destroyed by this means in phosphorylase *b*. The PLP in phosphorylase *b* is also not fluorescent, while glutamic–aspartic transaminase displays some fluorescence associated with PLP. This is suggestive that interactions of the protein moiety of phosphorylase with other groups on the PLP molecule (electrostatic interactions with the phosphate, pyridinium nitrogen and phenolic groups, hydrophobic bonding with the methyl group, etc.) also participate in the binding of the coenzyme.

## BINDING OF PLP TO PHOSPHORYLASE

### A. *Chymotryptic Attack*

When $NaBH_4$-reduced phosphorylase *b* or *a* was degraded with chymotrypsin, a pure, strongly fluorescent pyridoxal-peptide was obtained by conventional techniques from the reaction solutions. The peptide was ninhydrin positive, showed an absorption maximum at 325 m$\mu$, and reacted with dichloroquinone chloroimide[32] and diazotized *p*-amino acetophenone.[33,34] Upon acid hydrolysis lysine, phenylalanine and a basic, fluorescent compound identified as $\alpha$-amino-$\epsilon$-pyridoxylamino-N-caproic acid ($\epsilon$-N-pyridoxyl-lysine) were obtained.[13] End-group analysis using carboxypeptidase A and 2,4-dinitrofluorobenzene indicated the peptide to have the following sequence :*

$\epsilon$-N-Pyrodoxyllysine-Phe

A synthetic $\epsilon$-pyridoxyllysine standard was first prepared from the dipeptide glycyllysine, following the principle used by Heyl *et al.*[35] in the synthesis of many pyridoxal derivatives, i.e. reaction of the amino acid with pyridoxal, reduction of the Schiff base with $NaBH_4$, hydrolysis of other substituents when present and chromatographic separation of the desired product, $\alpha$-Carbobenzoxy-lysine (prepared by the method of Bezas and Zervas[36])

*The establishment of the stoichiometry of PLP-containing peptides is complicated by the breakdown of the bound $\epsilon$-pyridoxyl-phosphate-lysyl residue. Since some lysine appears to be released, the presence of an extra lysyl residue in these peptides was suspected at one time.

served as starting material for the synthesis of ε-pyridoxyllysine; ε-benzoyl or ε-carbobenzoxylysine were used for the synthesis of α-pyridoxyllysine. α,ε-Dipyridoxyllysine was also prepared, but, unexpectedly, two closely related compounds were obtained. Their behavior on paper electrophoresis

TABLE 2. $R_F$'S IN PAPER AND THIN LAYER CHROMATOGRAPHIC SYSTEMS FOR PYRIDOXYL LYSINES
Solvent and Support Systems

| | 1 | 2 | 3 | 4 | 5 |
|---|---|---|---|---|---|
| α-pyridoxyllysine | 0.282 | 0.400 | 0.325 | 0.615 | 0.700 |
| ε-pyridoxyllysine | 0.248 | 0.294 | 0.245 | 0.320 | 0.620 |
| ε-pyridoxyl-phosphate lysine | 0.120 | — | — | — | — |
| di-pyridoxyllysine B | 0.416 | 0.470 | 0.500 | — | 0.800 |
| di-pyridoxyllysine A | — | 0.490 | — | — | — |

(1) n-Butanol, pyridine, acetic acid, $H_2O$, 30 : 20 : 6 : 24, Whatman 3MM PC.*
(2) n-Butanol, pyridine, acetic acid, $H_2O$, 30 : 20 : 6 : 24, MN 300 G TLC.*
(3) n-Butanol, pyridine, acetic acid, $H_2O$, piperidine, 30 : 20 : 0.4 : 24 : 2, Whatman AE 30 PC.
(4) n-Butanol, pyridine, acetic acid, $H_2O$, piperidine, 30 : 20 : 0.4 : 24 : 2, Röhm and Haas SB-2 PC.
(5) 0.35 M pH 5.18 citrate buffer, Röhm and Haas SA-2 PC.
*PC = Paper Chromatography; TLC = Thin Layer Chromatography.

and chromatography, their absorption and fluorescence spectra and response to the 2,6-dichloroquinone chloroimide reagent were found to be slightly different. ε-Pyridoxyl-phosphate-lysine was synthesized in good yield from ε-pyridoxyllysine by the method of Peterson and Sober[37]. The behavior of

TABLE 3. RESPONSE OF PYRIDOXYLLYSINES TO CHEMICAL REAGENTS

| | Molar absorbancy[a] at 325 mμ | 2,6-Dichloro-quinone Chloroimide[b] | p-Amino[b] acetophenone |
|---|---|---|---|
| | Am | % | % |
| α-pyridoxyllysine | 8720 | 86.5 | 80.5 |
| ε-pyridoxyllysine | 9710 | 81.4 | 97.0 |
| dipyridoxyllysine "form B" | 9200 | 72.1 | 72.1 |
| ε-pylP-lysine | 10,150 | 92.0 | 121.0 |

[a]Determined from nitrogen analysis.
[b]Expressed as per cent of concentration determined by optical density at 325 mμ. PM was used as standard.

these derivatives in various chromatographic systems (paper or thin-layer) and on column chromatography has been determined. Table 2 lists $R_F$ values for these derivatives in various chromatographic systems. On the Technicon amino acid analyser, using gradient elution by means of the

" Varigrad ", $\alpha$- and $\epsilon$-pyridoxyllysine emerge from the column in that order as two well-resolved peaks half-way between the peaks of histidine and arginine.

The spectral characteristics of $\alpha$- and $\epsilon$-pyridoxyllysine, $\epsilon$-pyridoxylphosphate-lysine and dipyridoxyllysine (forms A and B, see above) have been studied. Table 3 summarizes some of the spectral and chemical properties of the various pyridoxyllysine derivatives.

### B. *Tryptic Attack*

The isolation and determination of the structure of a larger fragment of the portion of the peptide chain involved in the binding of PLP, e.g. following tryptic attack, has not been successful so far. Here, the main difficulty has been an unexplained disappearance of the fluorescent, spectral and chemical characteristics of the pyridoxal group during purification of the tagged peptides (particularly during Dowex-50 chromatography or butanol–acetic acid chromatography). Pure $\epsilon$-pyridoxyllysine treated under the same conditions (the columns were shielded from light with aluminum foil to avoid photo-oxidations, and chromatography was carried out in the cold room) appears to be perfectly stable; so were $\epsilon$-pyridoxyllysine derivatives substituted on the $\alpha$-amino or carboxyl group. In order to determine the course of this degradative process and detect some of the breakdown products, phosphorylase containing $P^{32}$-labeled PLP has been prepared. After $NaBH_4$-reduction, urea denaturation and tryptic attack, the peptides were fractionated on Sephadex G-25 and Dowex-50. Only a minor amount of a $P^{32}$-labeled material having the expected spectral and chemical characteristics of pyridoxyl-peptides could be recovered. The remainder of the radioactivity was released through the column almost uniformly over 200 fractions; it was identified as inorganic phosphate. Clearly, the PLP derivative had slowly been hydrolyzed during passage through the column, probably following destruction of the pyridoxyl ring. In another single instance involving an investigation of the active site of glutamic–aspartic transaminase by similar procedures (see below), all of the bound phosphate emerged from the Dowex-50 column as a sharp, single fraction in the break-through peak. In this case, the phosphate appeared to be present as organically bound phosphate, but the material had none of the chemical or spectral characteristics of hydroxypyridine derivatives, indicating again that the pyridine ring had been destroyed. Neither the cause nor the nature of this degradative process has yet been elucidated.

## BINDING OF PLP TO OTHER ENZYMES

It is interesting to compare the findings obtained with phosphorylase with the results obtained by similar studies with other enzymes requiring PLP as coenzyme. Probably the two most extensively studied examples of this class of enzymes are pig heart glutamic–aspartic transaminase* and rat liver homoserine deaminase (cystathionase)† which have been investigated respectively by Jenkins *et al.*[38] and by Greenberg and his collaborators.[39] Both of these enzymes are available in relatively large amounts as highly purified proteins and were therefore well suited to a thorough study of the nature of the binding of PLP to the protein moieties.

Jenkins *et al.* have studied the spectral properties of pig heart glutamic–aspartic transaminase. The enzyme is colorless at alkaline pH values with an absorption maximum at 362 m$\mu$, but turns yellow (absorption maximum at 430 m$\mu$) in acid media, pH 4.8. These findings have been interpreted to indicate that PLP is bound to the enzyme in a zwitterionic, non-hydrogen bonded aldimine structure with an amino group on the protein. On the other hand, cystathionase exhibits an absorption maximum at 427 m$\mu$ at all pH values, and it has been postulated that a Schiff base structure exists in this enzyme. In both cases reduction of the enzymes with sodium borohydride results in a complete loss of catalytic activity. Recently we have begun in collaboration with Drs. T. W. Jenkins and D. M. Greenberg a study of the peptide sequences around the prosthetic groups of reduced glutamic–aspartic transaminase and cystathionase, respectively.

Glutamic–aspartic transaminase can be reduced by sodium borohydride at pH 4.8 in acetate buffer; this reduction is accompanied by a shift of absorption maximum from 430 m$\mu$ to 330 m$\mu$ (Fig. 7). The reduced enzyme was denatured in urea and the sulfhydryl groups reacted with iodoacetate.‡ The denatured, reduced enzyme was then subjected to extensive proteolytic attack with chymotrypsin and the release of pyridoxyl-containing material soluble in 5 per cent trichloracetic acid was determined. The reaction was complete after 24 hr when approximately 80 per cent of pyridoxyl material was recovered in the TCA supernatant. The supernatant was then fractionated on a Dowex-50 $\times$ 2 column and a single peak absorbing at 330 m$\mu$ was isolated from the column effluent. The emergence of the peak from the column was also followed by the reaction of pyridoxyl derivatives with dichloroquinone chloroimide and by fluorescence spectra (Fig. 8). The pyridoxyl-peptide was further purified by successive paper chromatography and high voltage electrophoresis and was obtained in approximately 65 per cent yield calculated from the starting material. The structure of the peptide was examined by conventional techniques and a partial structure for the peptide was established as follows :

Ser-Thr-Glu-(Asp, Gly, Ala, Val, Ileu ,$\epsilon$-pylLys, Lys)-Gly-Ser-Asp-Phe

It is interesting to compare this sequence with that of the peptide isolated

---

*L-Aspartate 2-oxoglutarate amino transferase No. 2.6.1.1.

†L-Homoserine Hydro-Lyase (Deaminating); No. 4.2.1.15.

‡Reaction of iodoacetate with the pyridinium nitrogen of $\epsilon$-pyridoxyllysine has been observed with phosphorylase *b*.

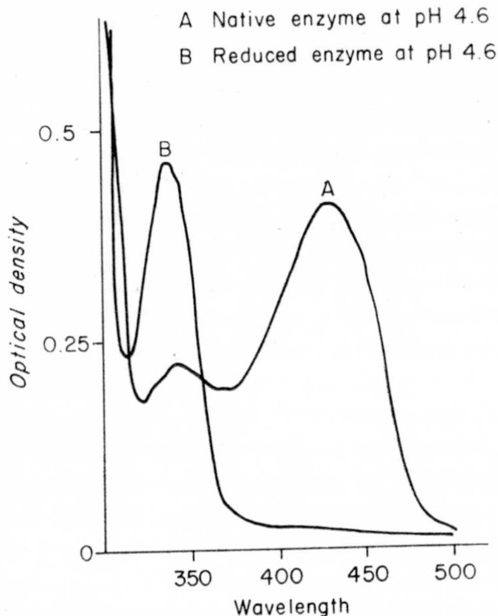


FIG. 7. Spectral properties of native and reduced glutamic–aspartic transaminase.

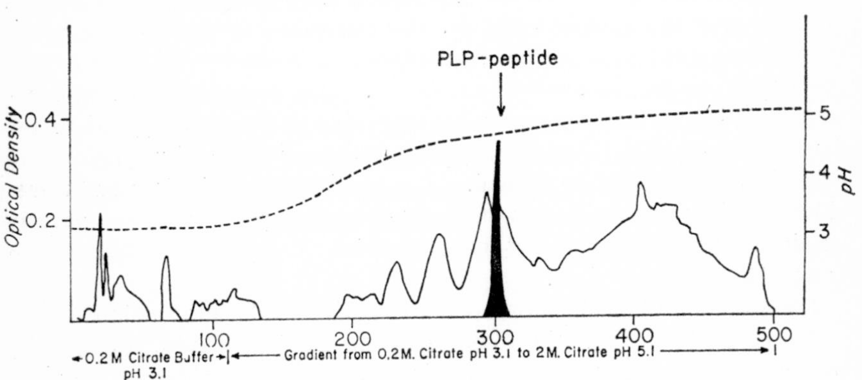


FIG. 8

from reduced phosphorylase *b*. Although the position of ε-pyridoxyllysine residues has not been established in the peptide isolated from glutamic–aspartic transaminase, it is apparent that the same sequence cannot be present since the carboxyl terminal arrangement containing the only phenylalanyl residue of the GAT peptide has been established and does not contain ε-pyridoxyllysine. The possibility that lysine and ε-pyridoxyllysine residues occur in adjacent positions remains to be determined.

Neither peptide contains a cysteinyl residue in the immediate vicinity of the pyridoxal group. This does not eliminate the possibility that a sulfhydryl group is involved in forming the substituted aldamine structure which probably exists to some extent in most of these enzymes. If this is so, however, the cysteinyl residue is either far removed on the same polypeptide chain or even located on separate polypeptide chains. It is, of course, possible that other groups are responsible for forming this structure, for example the ε-amino group of the second lysyl residue probably present in the PLP-peptide isolated from glutamic–aspartic transaminase. It must be noted, however, that in the case of glutamic–alanine transaminase of rat liver, a sulfhydryl group has been directly implicated at the active site of the enzyme and it has been postulated that this group plays a role in the binding of PLP to protein.[40]

A study has also been carried out with homoserine deaminase (cystathionase). Although this work is not yet completed, a pure peptide has been isolated containing ε-pyridoxyllysine after attack of the reduced, denatured enzyme with chymotrypsin and trypsin. However, progress in this work has been delayed again by the apparent destruction of the pyridoxyl containing peptides during the purification procedures, as mentioned above in the case of phosphorylase and glutamic–aspartic transaminase.

The isolation of ε-pyridoxyllysine from total hydrolyzates of various PLP-containing enzymes was the first clear indication of the site of binding of a coenzyme to a protein molecule. It is interesting to note that since then the ε-amino group of lysine has been implicated in the binding of two other coenzymes, namely lipoic acid[41] and biotin.[42] The method of sodium borohydride reduction as used above has also successfully been applied to the fixing of substrate or substrate fragments at the active site of enzymes where Schiff base forms were implicated. Thus, in the case of aldolase and transaldolase, ε-N-lysine derivatives of dihydroxyacetone phosphate were recently obtained,[43] and Westheimer[44] has succeeded in fixing the substrate to acetoacetate decarboxylase.

The studies described in this paper should provide information on the nature of the binding of PLP to enzymes and the roles played, respectively, by the coenzyme and apoenzymes in the catalytic processes. Work is currently being pursued to establish comparative peptide sequences in the near vicinity of the prosthetic groups of a number of PLP-requiring enzymes.

Such sequential studies should prove to be of interest in the correlation of the rather diverse catalytic activities exhibited by this group of enzymes with the structural characteristics of the different proteins. They should also further our understanding of the specific role of the polypeptide chains in enhancing and determining the catalytic properties of vitamin $B_6$-containing enzymes.

## REFERENCES


1. D. STETTEN, JR. and M. R. STETTEN; *Physiol. Revs.* **40**, 505 (1960).
2. A. A. GREEN and G. T. CORI; *J. Biol. Chem.* **151**, 21 (1943).
3. G. T. CORI and A. A. GREEN; *J. Biol. Chem.* **151**, 31 (1943).
4. G. T. CORI and C. F. CORI; *J. Biol. Chem.* **158**, 321 (1945).
5. S. F. VELICK and L. F. WICKS; *J. Biol. Chem.* **190**, 741 (1951).
6. J. B. SUMNER, T. C. CHOU and A. T. BEVER; *Arch. Biochem.* **26**, 1 (1950).
7. M. V. BUELL; *Federation Proc.* **11**, 192 (1952).
8. S. KORKES; *Ann. Rev. Biochem.* **25**, 685 (1956).
9. T. BARANOWSKI, B. ILLINGWORTH, D. H. BROWN and C. F. CORI; *Biochim. et Biophys. Acta* **25**, 16 (1957).
10. C. F. CORI and B. ILLINGWORTH; *Proc. Natl. Acad. Sci. U.S.* **43**, 547 (1957).
11. A. B. KENT, E. G. KREBS and E. H. FISCHER; *J. Biol. Chem.* **232**, 549 (1958).
12. B. ILLINGWORTH, H. S. JANSZ, D. H. BROWN and C. F. CORI; *Proc. Natl. Acad. Sci. U.S.* **44**, 1180 (1958).
13. E. H. FISCHER, A. B. KENT, E. R. SNYDER and E. G. KREBS; *J. Am. Chem. Soc.* **30**, 2906 (1958).
14. R. W. COWGILL; *J. Biol. Chem.* **234**, 3154 (1959).
15. A. A. YUNIS, E. H. FISCHER and E. G. KREBS; *J. Biol. Chem.* **235**, 3163 (1960).
16. A. A. YUNIS, E. H. FISCHER and E. G. KREBS; *J. Biol. Chem.* **237**, 2809 (1962).
17. M. M. APPLEMAN; Thesis, University of Washington (1962).
18. Y. P. LEE; *Biochim. et Biophys. Acta* **43**, 18, 25 (1960).
19. E. G. KREBS and E. H. FISCHER; *Advances in Enzymol.* **24**, 263 (1962).
20. D. H. BROWN and C. F. CORI; *The Enzymes* (edited by P. D. BOYER, H. LARDY and K. MYRBÄCK, vol. V, Academic Press, New York (1961).
21. E. G. KREBS, A. B. KENT and E. H. FISCHER; *J. Biol. Chem.* **231**, 73 (1958).
22. D. J. GRAVES, E. H. FISCHER and E. G. KREBS; *J. Biol. Chem.* **235**, 805 (1960).
23. N. B. MADSEN and C. F. CORI; *J. Biol. Chem.* **223**, 1055 (1956).
24. E. H. FISCHER, D. J. GRAVES, E. R. S. CRITTENDEN and E. G. KREBS; *J. Biol. Chem.* **234**, 1698 (1959).
25. E. E. SNELL; *Vitamins and Hormones* **16**, 77 (1958).
26. Unpublished results from this laboratory.
27. M. HOCKBERG, D. MELNICK and B. L. OSER; *J. Biol. Chem.* **155**, 129 (1944).
28. E. CUNNINGHAM and E. E. SNELL; *J. Biol. Chem.* **158**, 491 (1945).
29. J. S. NISHIMARA, J. M. MANNING and A. MEISTER; *Biochemistry* **1**, 442 (1962).
30. F. SCHLENK, A. FISCHER and E. E. SNELL; *Proc. Soc. Exptl. Biol. and Med.* **61**, 183 (1946).
31. A. E. BRAUNSTEIN; *The Enzymes* (edited by P. D. BOYER, H. LARDY and K. MYRBÄCK), vol. II, p. 113, Academic Press, New York (1960).
32. M. HOCHBERG, D. MELNICK and B. L. OSER; *J. Biol. Chem.* **155**, 109 (1944).
33. E. B. BROWN, A. E. BINA and J. M. THOMAS; *J. Biol. Chem.* **158**, 455 (1945).
34. N. SILIPRANDI, D. SILIPRANDI and H. LIS; *Biochim. et Boiphys. Acta* **14**, 212 (1954).
35. D. HEYL, S. A. HARRIS and K. FOLDERS; *J. Am. Chem. Soc.* **70**, 3429 (1948).
36. B. BEZAS and L. ZERVAS; *J. Am. Chem. Soc.* **83**, 719 (1961).
37. E. A. PETERSON and H. A. SOBER; *J. Am. Chem. Soc.* **76**, 169 (1954).
38. W. T. JENKINS, D. A. YPANTIS and I. W. SIZER; *J. Biol. Chem.* **234**, 51 (1959).
39. Y. MATSUO and D. M. GREENBERG; *J. Biol. Chem.* **234**, 507, 516 (1959).
40. H. L. SEGAL, D. S. BEATTIE and S. HOPPER; *J. Biol. Chem.* **237**, 1914 (1962).

41. H. NAWA, W. T. BRADY, M. KOIKE and L. J. REED; *J. Am. Chem. Soc.* **82**, 896 (1960).
42. D. P. KOSOW and M. D. LANE; *Biochem. Biophys. Research Comm.* **7**, 439 (1962).
43. E. GRAZI, P. T. ROWLEY, T. CHENG, O. TEHOLA and B. L. HORECKER; *Biochem. Biophys. Research Comm.* **9**, 38 (1962).
44. F. WESTHEIMER, personal communication.

## DISCUSSION

DR. JENKINS:

Are the spectral changes of phosphorylase at high pH values due to a proton dissociation, isomerization or cleavage of pyridoxal phosphate from the protein?

DR. FISCHER:

The spectral changes observed in alkaline medium are due first to the formation of the Schiff base (appearance of the 415 mμ absorption peak), then to the formation of free pyridoxal phosphate by hydrolysis of the Schiff base (shift of the absorption maximum from 415 to 388 mμ). These two processes may be superimposed; therefore, one may observe a predominance of one form over the other depending on how rapidly the spectra are determined after adjustment of pH.

DR. METZLER:

Dr. Fischer's picture shows phosphorylase *a* as a tetrameric molecule held together by four " bonds ", two originally present in phosphorylase *b* and two formed following the introduction of the four phosphoryl groups. I wonder whether a tetrahedral arrangement of sub-units is not more likely. If we draw a picture of such an arrangement with the two originally existing bonds shown as solid rods, we can picture the formation of an additional four bonds involving the four phosphoryl groups and producing a symmetrical tetrahedral arrangement of six bonds in all. The four new bonds are shown as arrows in the following picture.

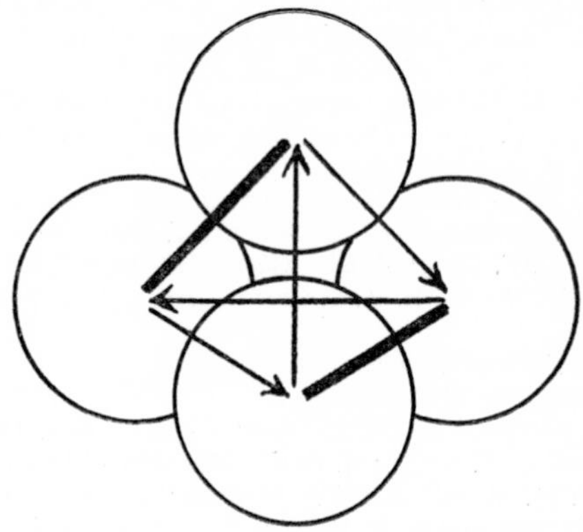

Such an arrangement is reminiscent of that in hemoglobin, and the splitting of phosphorylase into sub-units may be very similar to the interesting cleavages of the hemoglobin molecule being studied by Dr. Rossi-Fanelli and others.

DR. FISCHER:

The figure representing phosphorylase as four circles linked by four bonds was, of course, a completely schematic one. We do not imply that, actually, the sub-units are linked by " one " bond; the nature of the linkage is still completely unknown. Electrostatic, hydrogen, hydrophobic and perhaps even weak covalent bonds could all be involved. The spatial configuration of the tetramer is also unknown. Keller has shown that the enzyme is very asymmetric with an axial ratio of four to eight. However, she found no differences in the axial ratio of phosphorylase *a* and *b*, which is difficult to understand.

DR. METZLER:

Has the pH dependence of the absorption spectrum of phosphorylase been studied in detail? From your published curves (Kent, Krebs and Fischer; *J. Biol. Chem.* **232**, 549, 1958) it appears that the spectrophotometric titration curve may be abnormally steep as in the case of the glutamic acid decarboxylase studied by Shukaya and Schwert (*J. Biol. Chem.* **235**, 1649, 1960). In this latter case the unusual phenomenon of four protons dissociating simultaneously and coupled to a change in the pyridoxal phosphate spectrum is observed.

DR. FISCHER:

Yes, a spectrophotometric titration of phosphorylase has been carried out in some detail (A. B. KENT; Thesis, University of Washington, 1959). Of course, the same problems pointed out in my answer to Dr. Jenkins still hold, namely the superimposed formation of the Schiff base and simultaneous hydrolysis of the latter to apoenzyme and free PLP. These successive reactions take place much more rapidly in alkaline medium than in acid, and therefore, I would not attach too great a significance to the p*K* obtained at high pH values. In the acid range, an apparent p*K* of 4.2 was determined at room temperature (readings made 15–30 sec after adjustment of pH) for the formation of the Schiff base, as measured by 415 mμ absorption. The titration curve indeed appears to be just as steep as that observed by Shukuya and Schwert in the case of glutamic acid decarboxylase.

DR. CHRISTENSEN:

I would like to return to the question of the spontaneous shift of maximal absorption from about 415 mμ to about 330 mμ, either on the reconstitution of holophosphorylase or in an apparently similar model reaction with bovine serum albumin (Dempsey and Christensen; *J. Biol. Chem.* **237**, 1113, 1962). The supposition that a group —X—H— forms a substituted aldimine link certainly needs verification. In fact there may be no group X at all, since superficially similar shifts in absorption occur on the reaction of pyridoxal phosphate with simple compounds such as leucine amide, leucine ethylester or a number of small peptides, without a characteristic decrease in the recoverability of pyridoxal phosphate from the preparations (Christensen; *J. Am. Chem. Soc.* **80**, 99, 1958). Dr. Metzler has also commented privately on the possibility that the absorption change could perhaps arise from a drawing of the aldimine ring out of planarity with the aromatic ring. Whatever the nature of the rearrangement product, its possible formation in other $B_6$ enzymes needs to be taken into account in measuring ketimine formation by determining the absorption at 330 mμ. Whether in studies of kinetics or mechanism of reaction, the possibility that absorption at this wavelength arises without ketimine formation needs to be remembered.

DR. FISCHER:

The principle piece of evidence in support of the hypothesis that the 330 mμ form of the enzyme possesses a substituted aldimine structure comes from the fact that this form is not reduced by sodium borohydride. Even a non-protonated Schiff base should be reduced, as evidenced by the fact that both glutamic aspartic transaminase above pH 7 or phosphorylase at pH 10.5 are readily reduced.

DR. SALVATORE:

Does any evidence exist of the presence of a pyridoxamine form of phosphorylase? Have you tried to add pyridoxamine phosphate to the apophosphorylase and check if there is any catalytic activity?

DR. FISCHER:

No pyridoxamine has ever been isolated after either acid, base, or urea treatment of phosphorylase. Cori has shown that apophosphorylase does not give an active enzyme when reacted with pyridoxamine-5′-phosphate.

DR. FASELLA:

Concerning the information about the nature of coenzyme binding to the protein, which can be obtained by fluorescence studies, we could mention the following observations we made with glutamic–aspartic transaminase. The coenzyme fluorescence of both protonated and non-protonated aldimine enzyme and of the aminic enzyme is strongly quenched in respect to the fluorescence of the free coenzymes. The fluorescence remains quenched also in the presence of concentrated urea (8M). After boron hydride treatment, the fluorescence of the aldimine form of the enzyme is still quenched. With this reduced form of the enzyme, however, fluorescence quenching is removed in the presence of 8 M urea. These data could be interpreted by assuming that the interaction between the chromophore ring and the protein responsible for the quenching of fluorescence occurs at a point of the peptide chain removed, in terms of amino acid sequence, from the lysine residues to which the carbonyl group of pyridoxal phosphate is bound. The changes in the secondary and tertiary structure consequent to treatment with urea would not remove quenching of fluorescence in the native enzyme because, even after loss of the original configuration, the chromophore ring would stick to the peptide site responsible for quenching, breaking loose from the aldimine bond to the protein lysine. After boron hydride treatment, however, the latter bond becomes stronger than the one responsible for quenching so that, upon denaturation, the chromophore would follow the lysine-bearing peptide breaking the bond responsible for fluorescence quenching.

DR. A. ROSSI FANELLI:

The possibility of splitting the phosphorylase molecule into two or four sub-units is very interesting. It is somewhat analogous to what was observed in our laboratory with respiratory proteins. We found in fact that in the presence of saline solutions of high ionic strengths, hemoglobin splits reversibly into two sub-units. I would like to know from Dr. Fischer if the effect of concentrated salt solutions has been tried on phosphorylase.

DR. FISCHER:

Extensive studies of this nature have not been made.

# ENZYMATIC STEPS IN THE DEGRADATION OF VITAMIN $B_6$ BY BACTERIA

by E. E. Snell, R. W. Burg, W. B. Dempsey, E. J. Nyns, T. K. Sundarum and D. Zach

Department of Biochemistry, University of California, Berkeley 4, California

We have described previously[1–4] the isolation and characterization of several degradation products (Figs. 1 and 2) formed from vitamin $B_6$ when certain soil pseudomonads are grown with pyridoxine or pyridoxamine as a sole source of carbon and nitrogen. The sequence in which these products appeared and their oxidation states lead us to suggest that they are probable intermediates in two distinct enzymatic pathways for the stepwise degradation of vitamin $B_6$. These suggested pathways are shown in Figs. 1 and 2.

To test these suggestions and to clarify the nature of the individual enzymatic steps, we have purified several of the enzymes involved. Each of these enzymes has been found only in cells grown with pyridoxine or pyridoxamine as a sole carbon source, i.e. all of them are inducible enzymes. This inducible pathway for degradation of pyridoxine by *Pseudomonas* MA-1 (Fig. 1) certainly represents one of the longest chains of inducible transformations yet studied at the enzymatic level.

In the following discussion we shall present the general characteristics of each of the enzymatic transformations so far studied with only an indication of the procedures followed; experimental details will be presented elsewhere.

## I. DEGRADATION OF PYRIDOXAMINE AND PYRIDOXINE BY ENZYMES OF *PSEUDOMONAS* MA AND MA-1 (SEE FIG. 1)

*Reaction A: Pyridoxamine → Pyridoxal*

Hurwitz[5] reported several years ago that *Acetobacter suboxydans* oxidized pyridoxamine, apparently to pyridoxal, but did not settle the point whether a direct oxidative step or an indirect one (e.g. transamination with keto-glutarate followed by oxidation of the glutamate formed) was involved. All attempts in our laboratory to demonstrate a direct oxidative deamination of pyridoxamine to pyridoxal by *Ps.* MA failed. However, cell-free extracts of this organism in the presence of pyruvate catalyzed the rapid transformation of pyridoxamine to pyridoxal with formation of alanine.[6] By heat denaturation of contaminating proteins, and ammonium sulfate and acetone

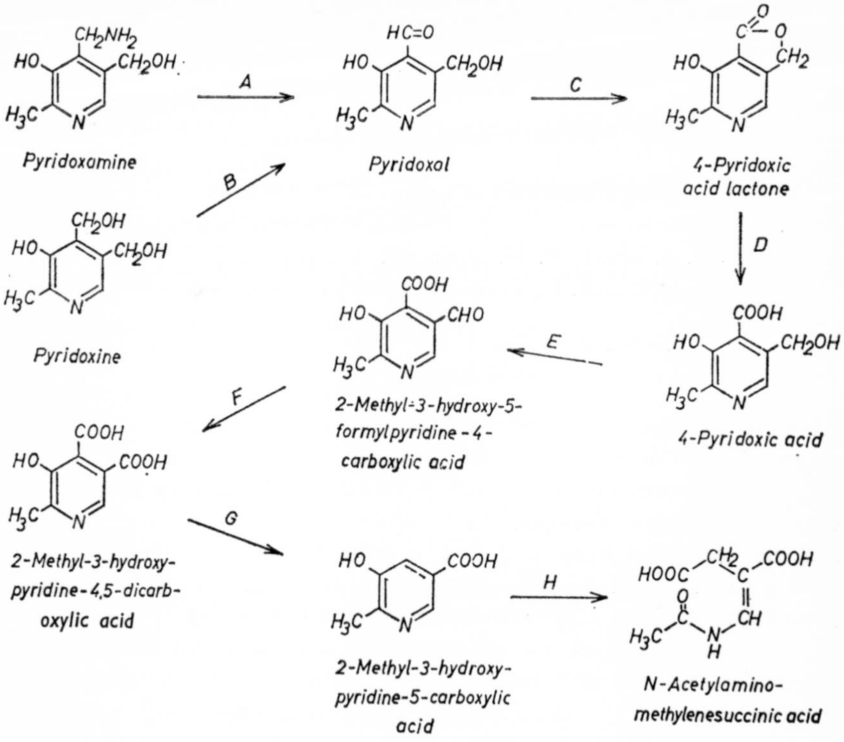

Pyridoxamine

Pyridoxine

Pyridoxal

4-Pyridoxic acid lactone

4-Pyridoxic acid

2-Methyl-3-hydroxy-5-formylpyridine-4-carboxylic acid

2-Methyl-3-hydroxypyridine-4,5-dicarboxylic acid

2-Methyl-3-hydroxypyridine-5-carboxylic acid

N-Acetylaminomethylenesuccinic acid

FIG. 1. Products formed from vitamin $B_6$ during growth of *Pseudomonas* MA-1 and the postulated sequence of their formation.

Pyridoxine

Isopyridoxal

5-Pyridoxic acid lactone

5-Pyridoxic acid

Pyriconic acid

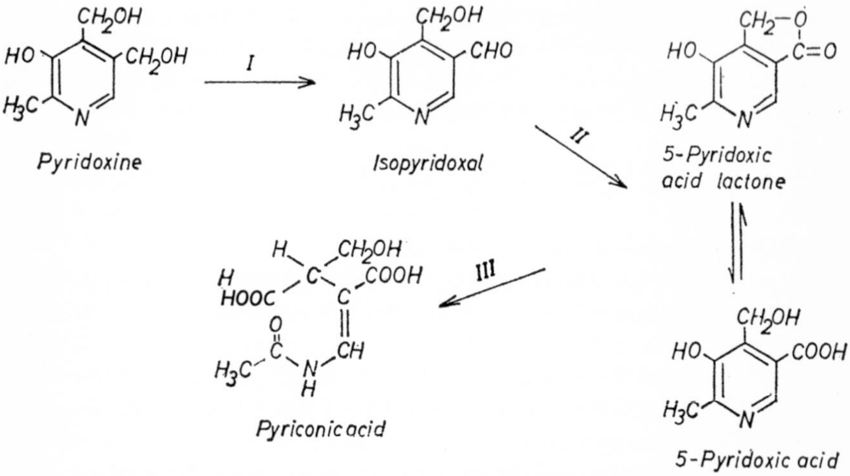

FIG. 2. Products formed from pyridoxine by *Pseudomonas* IA during growth and the postulated sequence of their formation.

fractionations, a highly active transaminase which catalyzes reaction 1 was readily obtained in crystalline form.[6,7] The transaminase is highly specific for each of its substrates,

$$\text{pyridoxamine} + \text{pyruvate} \underset{b}{\overset{a}{\rightleftharpoons}} \text{pyridoxal} + \text{L-alanine} \tag{1}$$

it has a molecular weight and turnover number similar to that of purified preparations of glutamic–aspartic holotransaminase (Table 1), and is unique

TABLE 1. PROPERTIES OF PYRIDOXAMINE–PYRUVATE TRANSAMINASE*

| | |
|---|---|
| Reaction catalyzed | Pyridoxamine + pyruvate $\rightleftharpoons$ pyridoxal + L-alanine |
| pH optimum | 8.8–9.3 |
| Coenzymes | None detected |
| Substrates and $K_M$ values | Pyridoxamine $6 \times 10^{-5}$ M; pyridoxal $1.5 \times 10^{-5}$ M; pyruvate $3 \times 10^{-4}$ M; L-alanine $2 \times 10^{-3}$ M; 5-deoxypridoxamine $3 \times 10^{-5}$ M; $\omega$-methylpyridoxamine $1.7 \times 10^{-3}$ M |
| Inhibitors | Pyridoxine ($K_I = 5.2 \times 10^{-5}$ M); 4-deoxypyridoxine ($K_I = 1.3 \times 10^{-4}$ M); pyridoxyl-L-alanine ($K_I = 1.8 \times 10^{-7}$ M) |
| Molecular weight | 120,000 |
| Binding sites | 2 (for pyridoxal) per 120,000 particle weight |
| Turnover number | (moles substrate/mole enzyme per min) : *ca.* 4500 |

*Wada and Snell[6]; Dempsey and Snell, unpublished.

in that it contains no pyridoxal phosphate as prosthetic group. It binds two moles of pyridoxal per mole of protein with formation of an enzyme–substrate complex with an absorption maximum at 415 m$\mu$, presumably a hydrogen-bonded Schiff base; this color is completely discharged on addition of L-alanine, indicating that the pyridoxal is bound at the active site. In recent experiments we have reduced the pyridoxal–enzyme complex with sodium borohydride (Fig. 3); enzymatic activity is reduced in proportion to the amount of pyridoxal bound (Fig. 4); on hydrolysis of the reduced enzyme, $\epsilon$-pyridoxylidinelysine was isolated in excellent yield.[7] It appears likely from these results and other data[8] that reaction (1) is mechanistically similar to the enzymatic transamination reaction between glutamic and oxaloacetic acids but that the substrates of the former enzyme, pyridoxal and pyridoxamine, react directly with the protein moiety in place of pyridoxal phosphate (or pyridoxamine phosphate) which is an integral part of the more conventional transaminases. In this connection it should be recalled that glutamic–aspartic apotransaminase catalyzes reaction (2), which appears entirely analogous to reaction (1) but proceeds very much more slowly.[8]

$$\text{pyridoxamine} + \begin{matrix}\alpha\text{-ketoglutarate}\\ \text{or}\\ \text{oxaloacetate}\end{matrix} \rightleftharpoons \text{pyridoxal} + \begin{matrix}\text{L-glutamate}\\ \text{or}\\ \text{L-aspartate}\end{matrix} \tag{2}$$

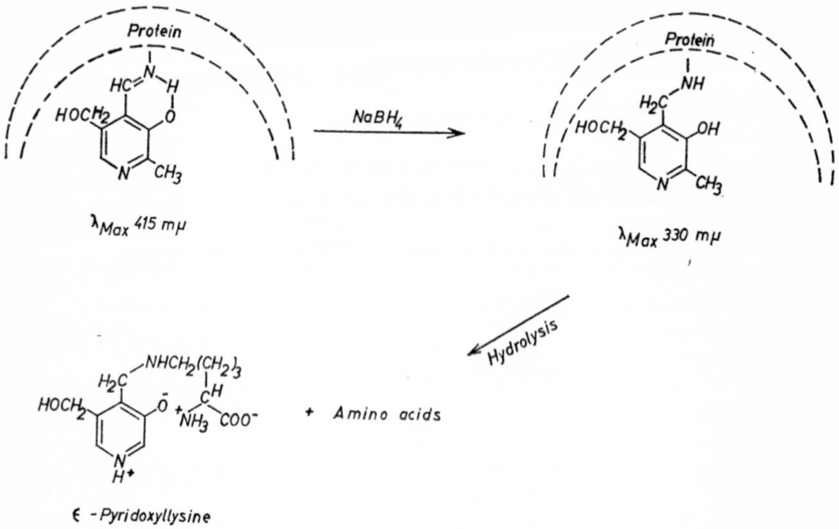

Protein

$NaBH_4$

Protein

$\lambda_{Max}$ 415 mμ

$\lambda_{Max}$ 330 mμ

Hydrolysis

+ Amino acids

ε-Pyridoxyllysine

FIG. 3. The relationship of the pyridoxal–transaminase complex ($\lambda_{max}$ 415 mμ) to the reduced complex ($\lambda_{max}$ 330 mμ) and ε-pyridoxyllysine. (Dempsey and Snell, unpublished.)

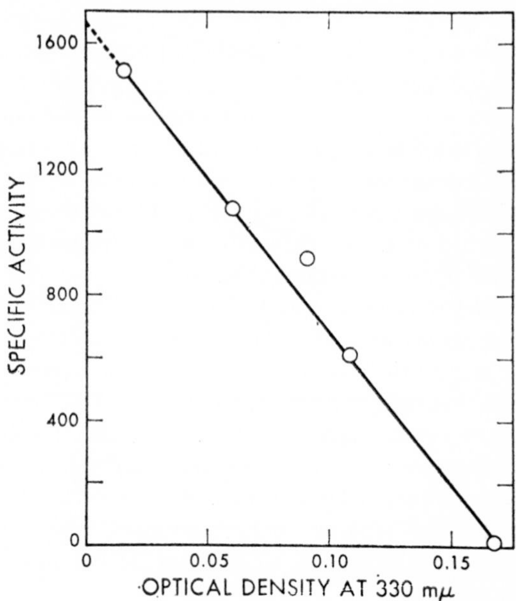


FIG. 4. Relation between activity of pyridoxamine–pyruvate transaminase following reduction with sodium borohydride and the amount of pyridoxal bound to the enzyme (≃ optical density at 330 mμ). (Dempsey and Snell, unpublished.)

Certain other characteristics of the pyridoxamine–pyruvate transaminase are shown in Table 1.

*Reaction B*: *Pyridoxine → Pyridoxal*

Freshly harvested cells of *Ps.* Ma-1 consumed oxygen when incubated

TABLE 2. PROPERTIES OF PYRIDOXINE OXIDASE*

| | |
|---|---|
| Reaction catalyzed | Pyridoxine + $O_2$ → pyridoxal + $H_2O_2$<br>Pyridoxine + dye† → pyridoxal + reduced dye |
| pH optimum | 7.5–8.0 |
| Coenzyme | FAD, $K_M = 2.4 \times 10^{-6}$ M; FMN inactive |
| Substrates | Pyridoxine, $K_M = 4.3 \times 10^{-5}$ M<br>ω-Methylpyridoxine (→ ω-methylpyridoxal) also is a good substrate<br>(PMP, PM, PNP, isopyridoxal, 4-deoxypyridoxine are not attacked) |
| Activators | Reduced glutathione |
| Inhibitors | *p*-Chloromercuribenzoate $10^{-4}$ M (reversed by $CN^-$ or GSH); α,α′-dipyridyl, *o*-, *m*-, and *p*-phenanthroline ($10^{-4}$–$10^{-3}$ M) |

*Sundarum and Snell (unpublished).
†2,6-Dichlorophenolindophenol.

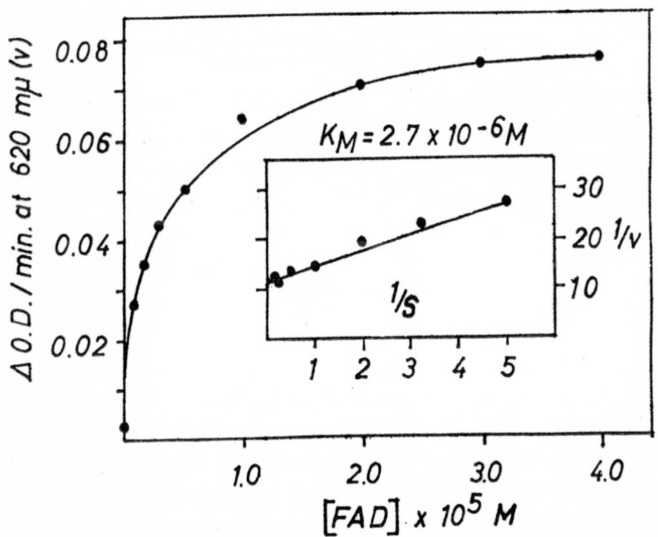


FIG. 5. Effect of added flavin adenine dinucleotide (FAD) on the activity of resolved pyridoxine oxidase. The reaction was followed by measuring the decrease in optical density due to 2,6-dichlorophenolindophenol reduction. (Sundarum and Snell, unpublished.)

aerobically with pyridoxine at pH 8.0, and also decolorized 2,6-dichlorophenolindophenol when incubated anaerobically with pyridoxine. The latter property was used for following purification of the oxidase from disrupted cells. By protamine precipitation of impurities, followed by heat denaturation of impurities at 50°, and fractionation with ammonium sulfate, a 12-fold purification of the enzyme was achieved. During the course of this purification the enzyme became dependent upon added FAD for activity (Fig. 5); FMN was ineffective. It may be recalled in this connection that pyridoxine phosphate oxidase of mammalian livers, which oxidizes PNP and PMP to PLP, is an FMN enzyme and cannot utilize FAD in its stead.[8] Pyridoxal was readily demonstrated by paper chromatography to be the oxidation

TABLE 3. SOME PROPERTIES OF PYRIDOXAL DEHYDROGENASE*

| | |
|---|---|
| Reaction catalyzed | Pyridoxal + $DPN^+ \rightarrow$ 4-pyridoxic acid lactone + DPNH + $H^+$ |
| pH optimum | 9.3 |
| Substrate affinities | Pyridoxal, $K_M = 0.76 \times 10^{-4}$ M (pH dependent)<br>$DPN^+$, $K_M = 2.9 \times 10^{-4}$ M (independent of pH) |
| Specificity | $TPN^+$ does not replace $DPN^+$;<br>5-deoxypyridoxal is not oxidized, but stimulates oxidation of pyridoxal; isopyridoxal is not oxidized |
| Effect of inhibitors | *o*-Phenanthroline, 8-hydroxyquinoline, $\alpha,\alpha'$-dipyridyl inhibit at $10^{-3}$–$10^{-4}$ M; *m*- and *p*-phenanthroline inhibit at $2 \times 10^{-6}$ M; insensitive to $10^{-3}$ M PCMB and $10^{-2}$ M iodoacetamide; inhibited by $10^{-4}$ M $HgCl_2$ |

*Burg and Snell (unpublished).

product formed from pyridoxine by the purified oxidase with either 2,6-dichlorphenolindophenol or oxygen as the hydrogen acceptor. The amount of oxygen consumed per $\mu$mole of pyridoxal formed was decreased by addition of catalase; in the presence of the latter enzyme 1 $\mu$mole of oxygen sufficed for production of 2 $\mu$moles of pyridoxal. The enzyme thus catalyzes reaction (3). Several other properties of the enzyme are given in Table 2.

$$\text{pyridoxine} + O_2 \xrightarrow{\text{pyridoxine oxidase}} \text{pyridoxal} + H_2O_2 \quad (3)$$

*Reaction C: Pyridoxal → 4-Pyridoxic Acid Lactone*

In clarified crude extracts of disrupted cells a DPN-dependent oxidation of pyridoxal could be observed by the increase in absorbancy at 340 m$\mu$, but the product of the reaction was not clear because of the presence of subsequent enzymes of the pathway. Treatment of such extracts with protamine sulfate to remove nucleic acids followed by two ammonium sulfate precipitations gave preparations which, although only from 4- to 5-fold purified, showed excellent stoichiometry for the single-step oxidation shown in reaction (4).

$$\text{Pyridoxal} + DPN^+ \xrightarrow{\text{pyridoxal dehydrogenase}} \text{4-pyridoxic acid lactone} + DPNH + H^+ \quad (4)$$

Some properties of the enzyme are given in Table 3. At pH 9.3 the reaction goes essentially to completion. Attempts to observe reversal of the reaction have failed. Incubation of the dehydrogenase with 4-pyridoxic acid lactone and DPNH at pH 7, 8 or 9 failed to give any measurable decrease in optical density at 340 m$\mu$. Further investigation of this point seems to be required, however, since in crude extracts of the cells (as opposed to these fractionated preparations) incubation with pyridoxal and DPN gives rise to pyridoxine in addition to 4-pyridoxic acid and its lactone.

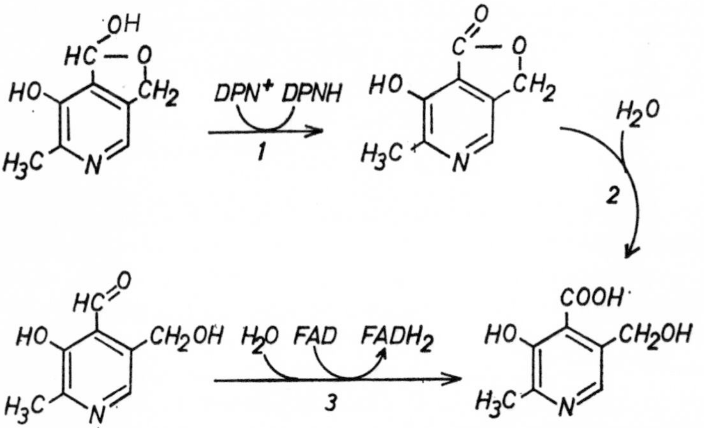

FIG. 6 Comparison of the pathways for oxidation of pyridoxal to 4-pyridoxic acid in *Ps.* MA (reactions 1 and 2) with that found[10] in animals (reaction 3).

The formation of 4-pyridoxic acid lactone in this reaction, and the failure of the enzyme to oxidize the closely related compound, 5-deoxypyridoxal, both point to the fact that the hemiacetal of pyridoxal, rather than the free aldehyde, is the substrate of this dehydrogenase (Fig. 6, reaction 1). The oxidation is analogous, then, to the TPN-specific oxidation of glucose-6-phosphate to 6-phosphoglucono-lactone[9] or the DPN-specific oxidation of L-arabinose to L-arabono-$\gamma$-lactone.[10] In each of the three cases, the lactone is subsequently hydrolyzed by a separate enzyme to the free acid (Fig. 6, reaction 2). Thus, the oxidation of pyridoxal in these bacteria differs fundamentally from that in mammalian tissues, where a flavoprotein, or aldehyde oxidase, acts on the free aldehyde to form 4-pyridoxic acid directly (Fig. 6, reaction 3) without intermediate formation of the lactone.[11]

*Reaction D*: 4-*Pyridoxic Acid Lactone* $\xrightarrow{H_2O}$ 4-*Pyridoxic Acid*

This reaction is readily followed by the decrease in absorbency of the lactone at 340–350 m$\mu$ which accompanies hydrolysis at pH 7.0 The enzyme is rather labile, but fortunately no interfering activities are present to complicate demonstration of its activity in crude extracts. Production of 4-pyridoxic acid is readily demonstrated by chromatography as the lactone disappears. The enzyme is thus a 4-pyridoxic acid lactonase, and catalyzes reaction D, above. Several of its properties are indicated in Table 4.

TABLE 4. PROPERTIES OF 4-PYRIDOXIC ACID LACTONASE FROM PS.MA*

| | |
|---|---|
| Reaction catalyzed | 4-Pyridoxic acid lactone + $H_2O$ → 4-pyridoxic acid |
| pH optimum | 7.3–7.8 |
| Cofactors | None demonstrated |
| Substrate affinities | $K_M$ for 4-pyridoxic acid lactone, $3.1 \times 10^{-6}$ M |
| Effects of inhibitors | *o*-, *m*- and *p*-phenanthroline inhibit at $10^{-3}$–$10^{-4}$ M; substrate inhibits moderately at $10^{-4}$–$10^{-3}$ M |

*Burg and Snell (unpublished).

*Reactions E, F and G*

These reactions have not been studied with cell-free enzymes. However, resting cell preparations of *Ps.* MA were shown earlier[3] to oxidize 4-pyridoxic acid to 2-methyl-3-hydroxy-5-formylpyridine-4-carboxylic acid (reaction E), and this oxidation was used with added bisulfite as a trapping agent to isolate sufficient amounts of the latter pyridinealdehyde to permit its characterization. In the absence of the trapping agent, most of the aldehyde was further oxidized to the corresponding dicarboxylic acid (reaction F) and subsequent degradation products. All of the available evidence thus indicates that these three reactions are discrete and separable enzymatic steps on the main pathway of degradation of pyridoxine in these organisms. It appears unlikely that detailed study of reactions E and F, the oxidation, respectively, of a primary alcohol to an aldehyde and of an aldehyde to an acid, would extend greatly our knowledge of the mechanisms involved in such oxidations. In contrast, it is hoped to study reaction G further since the decarboxylation of aromatic carboxylic acids appears not to have been investigated extensively at the enzymatic level.

*Reaction H: 2-Methyl-3-hydroxypyridine-5-carboxylic Acid → N-Acetylaminomethylene Succinic Acid*

Of the several reactions outlined in Fig. 1, reaction H, in which the aromatic pyridine ring is opened to yield an acylic compound, is certainly the most interesting. The acylic product ($C_7H_9O_5N$) differs from the pyridine monocarboxylic acid ($C_7H_7O_3N$) by two atoms of hydrogen and two of oxygen. One may immediately envisage, therefore, three distinctively different possible mechanisms for the overall reaction involving, respectively, either (1) addition of 2H and 2O without the involvement of water, (2) addition of one water molecule and one atom of oxygen, or (3) addition of two water molecules with removal of 2H, without the immediate involvement of

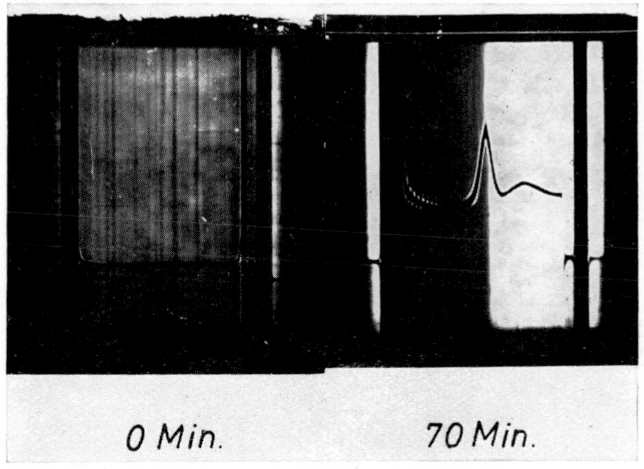


FIG. 7. Sedimentation pattern of purified 5-acid oxygenase in 0.1 M potassium phosphate buffer, pH 8.0, at 59,780 rev/min. The pictures were taken at 0 (left) and 70 min (right) with a yellow filter. The yellow boundary of the flavoprotein coincides with the principal protein peak. (Sundarum, Nyns, Zäch and Snell, unpublished.)

oxygen. The reaction differs from other reactions so far studied in which aromatic rings are opened in that the first open chain product is more reduced than any previously described. Resting cell suspensions of *Ps.* MA readily metabolized 2-methyl-3-hydroxypyridine-5-carboxylic acid (hereafter referred to as " 5-acid ") as evidenced by their rapid oxygen uptake with this compound as substrate; but none of the presumed reaction product, N-acetylaminomethylene succinic acid (hereafter referred to as AAMS) could be detected in the suspending medium, presumably because of its further breakdown. Cell-free extracts of the organism showed no evidence

TABLE 5. REQUIREMENT OF THE RESOLVED 5-ACID OXYGENASE FOR FAD*

| Enzyme and cofactor added† | Activity (Δ O.D./min at 340 mμ) |
|---|---|
| Resolved enzyme | 0.013 (1.0) |
| Resolved enzyme + 0.03 mM FAD | 0.055 (4.2) |
| Resolved enzyme + 0.04 mM FAD | 0.058 (4.4) |
| Resolved enzyme + 0.03 mM FMN | 0.017 (1.3) |

*Sundarum, Nyns, Zäch and Snell (unpublished).
†The reaction mixture contained potassium phosphate buffer, pH 8.0, 50 μmoles; DPNH, 0.02 μmoles; mercaptoethanol, 40 μmoles; 5-acid, 0.2 μmoles; enzyme and cofactors as indicated in 1 ml; optical density measurements were against a matched blank lacking the enzyme.

of metabolizing the 5-acid even on addition of DPN, TPN or 2,6-dichlorophenolindophenol as hydrogen acceptors. However, when DPNH or TPNH was added to such an extract a rapid decrease in absorption at 340 mμ occurred which was dependent upon the presence of the 5-acid as substrate. With this as an assay method, it was possible to purify the active protein some 35-fold by customary procedures of treatment with protamine sulfate, isoelectric precipitation, ammonium sulfate fractionation and adsorption on alumina $C_\gamma$ gel. At this point, the protein shows a bright yellow color, and an absorption spectrum characteristic of flavoproteins. A sedimentation pattern of the protein at this stage of purity, taken with and without a yellow filter (Fig. 7) showed that only the major component was colored. By acid ammonium sulfate precipitation in the presence of stabilizing agents (bovine serum albumin, ethylenediaminetetra-acetic acid and mercaptoethanol) the prosthetic group could be removed; such preparations oxidized DPNH only in the presence of both FAD, the 5-acid and molecular oxygen. In this way it was established that the enzyme which catalyzed the 5-acid-dependent oxidation of DPNH was a flavoprotein, and that molecular oxygen was required.

Despite the fact that a single active flavoprotein constitutes the major portion of this preparation, it was not possible to demonstrate more than traces of AAMS in the reaction products; indeed, added AAMS was destroyed by the preparation. The preparative procedure was therefore recast in the hope of separating the oxidase from the AAMS-destroying enzyme. This was accomplished, the critical step being absorption and elution from a hydroxy-apatite column. The peak tubes from the column contained oxidase purified approximately to the same extent (31-fold) as by the previous procedure, but free of the AAMS-destroying enzyme (Fig. 8).

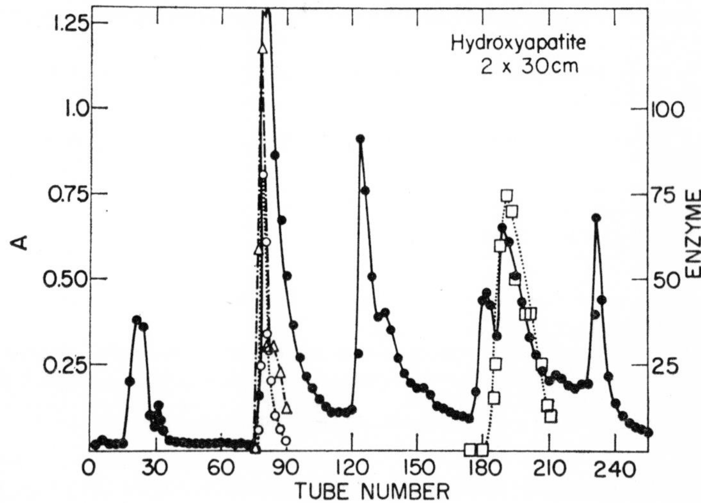


FIG. 8. Chromatography over hydroxyapatite of the protein fraction of *Ps.* MA-1 insoluble in 65 per cent ammonium sulfate. Individual protein peaks were eluted with 0.001, 0.02, 0.04, 0.06 and 0.1 M potassium phosphate buffer, pH 8.0.

— — ● — — ● — — protein
— — ○ — — ○ — — AAMS-hydrolase
— — △ — — △ — — pyridoxamine pyruvate transaminase
— — □ — — □ — — 5-acid oxygenase.

(Sundarum, Nyns, Zäch and Snell, unpublished.)

With preparations of this nature, it was established that utilization of DPNH, 5-acid and $O_2$, and the production of AAMS all were in stoichiometric relationship (Table 6). The latter product was demonstrated to be formed not only by paper chromatography, but by analysis of material isolated in milligram quantities from the reaction mixture. Thus, a highly purified enzyme preparation, consisting principally of a single flavoprotein, has been obtained which catalyzes reaction (5).

$$\text{DPNH} + \text{H}^+ + \text{O}_2 + \text{2-methyl-3-hydroxypyridine-5-carboxylic acid} \rightarrow \text{DPN}^+ + \text{N-acetylaminomethylenesuccinic acid} \qquad (5)$$

We shall tentatively call the enzyme the " 5-acid oxygenase "; the course of the reaction catalyzed excludes the last of the three possible mechanisms discussed earlier for the reaction, but does not distinguish between the first two. Although the complexity of the reaction catalyzed suggests the possibility of a multistep reaction, we have had no indications to date that more than a single enzyme is involved in the reaction. Some properties of the purified enzyme preparation are shown in Table 7. TPNH can substitute for DPNH in the reaction, but the 5-acid cannot be replaced by 5-pyridoxic acid. The lack of sensitivity of the enzyme to a variety of chelating agents indicates that

TABLE 6. STOICHIOMETRY OF THE REACTION CATALYZED BY THE 5-ACID OXYGENASE*

| Oxygen (μmoles) | DPNH (μmoles) | 5-Acid (μmoles) | AAMS (μmoles) |
|---|---|---|---|
| − 0.27 | − 0.35 | − 0.27 | + 0.24 |
| (− 1.0) | (− 1.3) | (− 1.0) | (+ 0.9) |

*Sundarum, Nyns, Zäch and Snell (unpublished).

TABLE 7. SOME PROPERTIES OF THE 5-ACID OXYGENASE*

| | |
|---|---|
| Reaction catalyzed | DPNH + $O_2$ + $H^+$ + 5-Acid → $DPN^+$ + AAMS |
| pH optimum | 7–8 |
| Cofactors | FAD |
| Substrate affinities | DPNH, $K_M = 4.6 \times 10^{-5}$ M |
| | TPNH, $K_M = 6.7 \times 10^{-5}$ M |
| | 5-Acid, $K_M = 2.2 \times 10^{-5}$ M |
| Action of inhibitors | $CN^-$ ($10^{-3}$ M), EDTA ($10^{-2}$ M), α,α′-Dipyridyl ($10^{-3}$ M), $AsO_2^-$ ($10^{-4}$ M), $Cd^{2+}$ ($10^{-4}$ M) all were without effect |
| Stabilizing agents | Mercapethanol, glycerol, serum albumin |

*Sundarum, Nyns, Zäch and Snell (unpublished).

metal ions (specifically Fe), if required, must be firmly bound to the protein. The enzyme is rather labile during fractionation in the absence of stabilizing agents, but can be kept for periods of over two months without loss of activity in the presence of glycerol and other stabilizing agents.

*Reaction J: Hydrolysis of N-Acetylaminomethylenesuccinic Acid*

Reference was made in the preceeding section to an AAMS-destroying enzyme and its separation from 5-acid oxygenase. AAMS shows strong absorption at 260 mμ; disappearance of this peak accompanying hydrolysis provides a convenient assay for the hydrolase. The fraction of the effluent from the hydroxy-apatite column which contained this enzyme was further fractionated over dextran sulfate gel (Sephadex G-75) to yield final preparations with a specific activity 20–23 times that of the initial cell extract. Stoichiometry of the reaction catalyzed by this enzyme corresponded to Eq. (6):

$$\text{N-acetylaminomethylenesuccinic acid} + 2H_2O \rightarrow CH_3COOH + NH_3 + CO_2 + \text{succinic semialdehyde} \quad (6)$$

The same reaction is catalyzed by acid.[3] Some properties of the enzyme are shown in Table 8.

TABLE 8. SOME PROPERTIES OF N-ACETYLAMINOETHYLENE SUCCINIC ACID HYDROLASE*

| | |
|---|---|
| Reaction catalyzed | $HOOC{-}CH_2{-}C(COOH){=}CH{-}NH{-}C({=}O){-}H_3C + 2H_2O \rightarrow CH_3COOH + NH_3 + CO_2 + COOH{-}CH_2{-}CH_2{-}CHO$ |
| pH optimum | Buffer-dependent: pH 6.0 (sodium phosphate); pH 7.0 (pyro-phosphate); pH 6.8–7.5 (Tris). $V_{max}$ in tris buffer is highest. |
| Cofactors and activators | None demonstrated |
| Substrate affinity and specifity | $K_M = 5.3 \times 10^{-5}$; does not hydrolyze and is not inhibited by pyriconic acid |
| Inhibitors | No inhibition by EDTA (0.05 M), by triacetylamine (0.1 M) or by $Zn^{2+}$ ($2 \times 10^{-4}$ M) |

*Nyns, Zäch and Snell (unpublished).

## II. DEGRADATION OF PYRIDOXINE BY ENZYMES OF *PSEUDOMONAS* IA (SEE REACTIONS I–III, FIG. 2).

Relatively little work has been carried out on this pathway. The enzyme catalyzing reaction (I), the oxidation of *pyridoxine* to *isopyridoxal*, has been purified about 3-fold by ammonium sulfate precipitation and absorption and elution from calcium phosphate gel. Some of its properties are summarized in Table 9. Like the enzyme that catalyzes oxidation of pyridoxine to pyridoxal (pyridoxine oxidase), this enzyme, which we shall call *pyridoxine dehydrogenase*, requires FAD. It reacts sluggishly with oxygen as electron acceptor, but much more rapidly with 2,6-dichlorophenolindophenol. Thus it appears that the oxidation *in vivo* is coupled to oxygen only indirectly via an electron transport system. In confirmation of this view, the rate of reduction of dye by the enzyme was increased by cyanide.

Reaction (II), Fig. 2, has not been studied, and it is not yet known whether the immediate oxidation product of isopyridoxal is 5-*pyridoxic acid* or its *lactone*. Reaction (III), the cleavage of the pyridine ring to yield *pyriconic acid*, apparently proceeds in a fashion entirely analogous to that discussed above for reaction H (Fig. 1); the reaction was followed and the enzyme partially purified from cells of *Ps.* IA in an analogous fashion. The enzyme is specific for 5-pyridoxic acid, and also differs from the analogous enzyme from *Ps.* MA in its specific requirement for TPNH.

TABLE 9. SOME PROPERTIES OF PYRIDOXINE DEHYDROGENASE*

| | |
|---|---|
| Reaction catalyzed | Pyridoxine + oxidized dye† → isopyridoxal + reduced dye |
| pH optimum | 5.3 |
| Cofactor | FAD ($K_M = 3 \times 10^{-7}$ M); FMN is inactive |
| Substrate specifity | Pyridoxine ($K_M = 4.8 \times 10^{-4}$ M) is best substrate; pyridoxamine is oxidized at 11 per cent the rate to yield a blue pigment; 4-deoxypyridine at 3 per cent the rate |
| Inhibitors | Insensitive to 4-deoxypyridoxine and to *o*-, *m*- and *p*-phenanthroline ($10^{-3}$ M); inhibited by PCMB ($10^{-3}$ M) |

*Sundarum and Snell (unpublished).
†2,6-Dichlorophenolindophenol.

TABLE 10. SOME PROPERTIES OF THE ENZYME WHICH CLEAVES THE RING OF 5-PYRIDOXIC ACID*

| | |
|---|---|
| Reaction catalyzed | 5-Pyridoxic acid + $O_2$ + TPNH + $H^+$ → $TPN^+$ + pyriconic acid* |
| pH optimum | pH 8.0 |
| Cofactor | FAD |
| Substrates | 5-Pyridoxic acid : (2-methyl-3-hydroxypyridine-5-carboxylic acid is split at < 10 per cent of the rate), TPNH (DPNH is < 10 per cent as effective.) |
| Inhibitors | Not studied |

*Sundarum, Nyns, Zäch and Snell (unpublished).
†The stoichiometry of the reaction was not established since pyriconic acid is further degraded by the same preparation.

## DISCUSSION

The enzymatic studies described herein demonstrate that the compounds previously isolated from the culture medium of *Ps.* MA are intermediates in the degradation of vitamin $B_6$ by that organism. With two exceptions, each compound has been demonstrated to be formed in one enzymatic process and utilized in another. The abbreviated scheme of Fig. 1 may thus be extended, as shown in Fig. 9, to include the enzymatic processes concerned.

The several dehydrogenation processes that occur prior to cleavage of the ring provide several points at which energy can be tapped for use of the organism. Only following cleavage of the first acyclic product of the oxidation, however, do carbon- and nitrogen-fragments become available to permit growth of the organism when pyridoxine is the sole source of carbon and nitrogen. With the formation of $CO_2$, acetate, ammonia and succinic semialdehyde, compounds have become available which, through operation of well-known metabolic pathways common to many organisms, lead to all of the necessary compounds for growth.

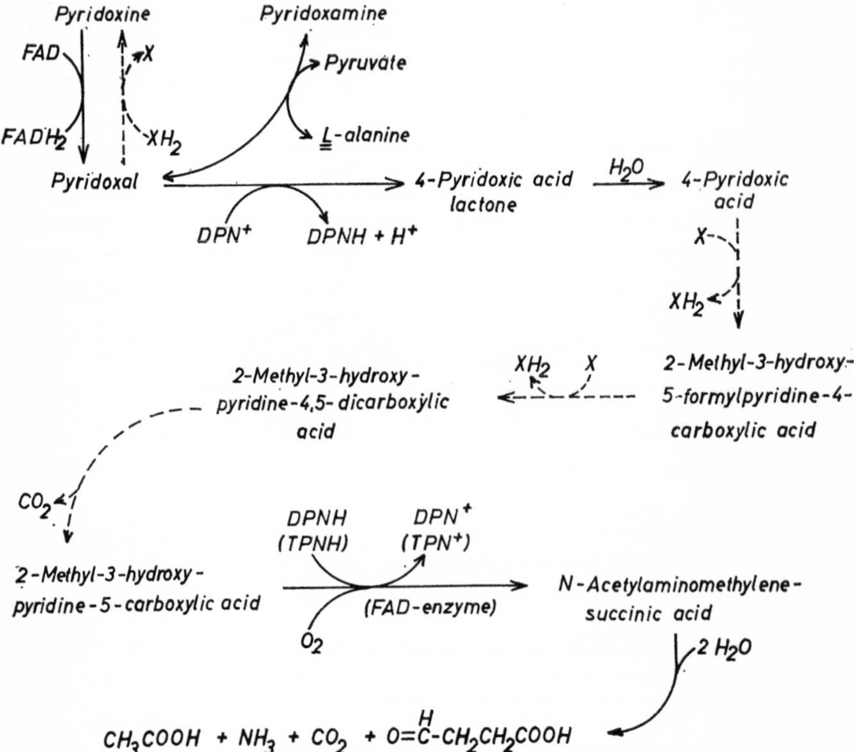


FIG. 9. Enzymatic processes involved in degradation of vitamin $B_6$ by *Pseudomonas* MA-1. Purified enzymes described in the text are indicated by solid arrows; enzymatic transformations known to occur but not yet studied at the enzymatic level are indicated by the dotted arrows.

## SUMMARY

Properties of eight different partially purified enzymes concerned in the overall process by which certain soil pseudomonads utilize vitamin $B_6$ as a sole source of carbon are described. The substrates and products of these enzymes are the compounds previously isolated[1–3] from culture media of organisms growing with pyridoxine or pyridoxamine as a sole carbon source. The enzymes include two different flavoproteins which oxidize pyridoxine to pyridoxal or to isopyridoxal, respectively; a pyridoxal phosphate-independent transaminase which reversibly converts pyridoxamine to pyridoxal; a DPN-specific dehydrogenase which oxidizes pyridoxal to 4-pyridoxic acid lactone; a lactonase which opens the lactone ring; a novel flavoprotein which utilizes oxygen and DPNH to open the pyridine ring of 2-methyl-3-hydroxypyridine-5-carboxylic acid to yield N-acetylaminomethylenesuccinic acid; and a hydrolase which converts the latter compound to the generally useful metabolic intermediates, acetate, ammonia, $CO_2$ and succinic semi-aldehyde. The entire chain of enzymes is induced during growth on pyridoxine, and each is highly specific for its substrates.

## REFERENCES


1. V. W. Rodwell, B. E. Volcani, M. Ikawa and E. E. Snell; *J. Biol. Chem.* **233**' 1548 (1958).
2. M. Ikawa, V. W. Rodwell, and E. E. Snell; *J. Biol. Chem.* **233**, 1555 (1958).
3. R. W. Burg, V. W. Rodwell and E. E. Snell; *J. Biol. Chem.* **235**, 1164 (1960).
4. E. E. Snell; *Proc. Vth Int. Cong. Biochem.*, Moscow, 1961. In press.
5. J. Hurwitz; *National Vitamin Foundation, Nutrition Symposium*, Series Nr. 13, p. 49 (1956).
6. H. Wada and E. E. Snell; *J. Biol. Chem.* **237**, 133 (1962).
7. H. Wada and E. E. Snell; *J. Biol. Chem.* **236**, 2089 (1961).
8. O. Cori and F. Lipmann; *J. Biol. Chem.* **194**, 417 (1952).
9. K. Weimburg and M. Doudoroff; *J. Biol. Chem.* **217**, 607 (1955).
10. J. Hurwitz; *J. Biol. Chem.* **212**, 757 (1955).
11. R. Schwartz and N. O. Kjeldgaard; *Biochem. J.* **48**, 333 (1951).


## DISCUSSION

Dr. Holzer:

Have you looked for a TPN- (or DPN-) dependent enzyme in your organism, which oxidizes reversibly pyridoxine to pyridoxal as we found it in yeast (Holzer and Scheider; *Biochim. et Biophys. Acta*, **48**, 71, 1961)?

Dr Snell:

We have no evidence for such an enzyme, but have not excluded its presence. It should be noted that the $K_M$ value of the flavoprotein studied in our laboratory for pyridoxine is about 0.01 that of the TPN-dependent dehydrogenase of yeast that Dr. Holzer's group studied. One cannot but wonder what the true physiological role of the latter enzyme may be, since it appears unlikely that pyridoxine (or pyridoxal) would accumulate in cells in concentrations sufficient to permit its action.

# CURRENT PROGRESS IN RESEARCH ON BIOLOGICAL PYRIDOXAL CATALYSIS

by A. E. BRAUNSTEIN

Institute of Radiobiology and Physico-Chemical Biology,
Academy of Sciences of the U.S.S.R., Moscow, U.S.S.R.

MAY I begin this talk by giving voice to the sincere gratitude of all participants of our Symposium to its organizers and sponsors, in particular to the International Union of Biochemistry, the Consiglio Nazionale della Ricerche, the Accademia Nazionale dei Lincei, and various national granting agencies, whose very helpful generous support we highly appreciate.

Our warmest thanks are due to our host, Prof. Rossi-Fanelli, Prof. Cavallini, Drs. Mondovì, Fasella, De Marco, Turano and all their colleagues of the Università di Roma, for all their kindness and cordial hospitality and especially for their skill and unfailing patience in managing the scientific and technical organization of this Meeting.

I trust it is our common opinion that the Symposium was a remarkably successful and interesting scientific event and that its social atmosphere was eminently enjoyable. On behalf of the organizers of the Symposium, I also wish to extend our thanks to all participants of the discussions for their scholarly contributions and willing co-operations

The purpose of my lecture is to give a brief survey of recent progress in our knowledge of the catalytic functions and biological role of PLP enzymes, along with a few remarks on topical or controversial issues relating to the problem under discussion.

To my regret, time limitations and the broad scope of the problem do not allow me to present an adequately balanced summary of the discussions.

Some biochemists affirm that it is much easier to make a list of reactions of amino acid metabolism that do not involve PLP than of those which do. This is a jocular statement, but it is not very far from the truth

In several reviews published between 1947 and 1960, I have surveyed various aspects of the crucial significance of PLP-dependent reactions in processes of nitrogen assimilation and dissimilation and in intermediary amino acid metabolism,[1–13] in the biosynthesis and catabolism of sulfur-containing compounds,[2,6,7] and in the integration of respiratory and nitrogen metabolism at the molecular level.[1,4,5,8–10,12]

A rational classification of PLP enzymes was developed,[2,5,6,10] based on a scheme of reaction types made possible by electronic shifts in amino acid molecules interacting with PLP (Fig. 1).

This classification (Table 1) is still valid, although current investigations have shown that there are no hard and fast boundaries between enzymatic reactions of elimination and replacement of polar substituents on $\beta$-C and $\gamma$-C atoms (Table 1, reaction types h, i, l, m), so that their strict subdivision into separate groups may not be justified.

Notable examples of enzymes with overlapping reaction specificities in these groups are phosphohomoserine lyase (threonine synthase)[10,14] and some plurifunctional lyases known under the trivial names cystathionase

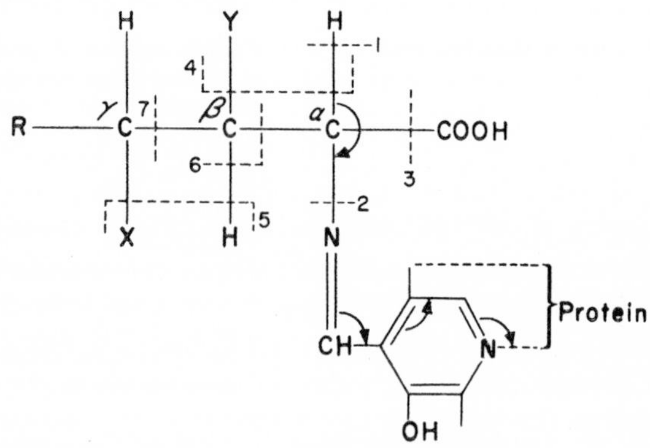


FIG. 1. The activation of chemical bonds in amino acid molecules under the action of PLP enzymes.[6,10]

(homoserine dehydratase, cysteine desulfhydrase, *vide infra*),[15,17] cystathionine synthase I (serine hydratase),[18] and cysteine lyase.[19] Tryptophanase (tryptophan indole-lyase) is also able to catalyse homologous replacement of the $\beta$-substituent in addition to its elimination.[10,13,20]

Within the last years few if any essentially novel biochemical reactions depending on vitamin $B_6$-coenzymes have been definitely established. Among the most interesting ones is the coupled oxidative deamination and decarboxylation of glycine in *Diplococcus glycinophilus*, observed by Sagers and Gunsalus,[36] and the similar process in birds' liver homogenates, investigated by Richert *et al.*[37] In the crude systems reported, these reactions require PLP, $H_4$-folate and NAD.* They result in the conversion of glycine to $CO_2$, $NH_3$ and hydroxymethyl-tetrahydrofolate; the latter compound

*This process has been discussed in the present Symposium by Dr. I. Gunsalus.

TABLE 1. CLASSIFICATION OF PLP-DEPENDENT ENZYME REACTIONS[10]
(Recent additions inserted in **bold-face** type)

| Ruptured bonds | Reaction types | Enzymes (or reactions) |
|---|---|---|
| | 1. *Elimination and Replacement Reactions at α-C atom* | |
| α-C—H | (a) Racemization of α-amino acids | Racemases; **tryptophan racemase**[21] |
| α-C—H | (b) Condensations at α-C of glycine, serine (or **cysteine**) (eventually reversible) | Serine transhydroxymethylase; threonine aldolase; dehydrosphingosine synthase; δ-aminolaevulinate synthase; **aminoacetone synthase** (?);[22] **condensation of cysteine with pimelyl-CoA in *biotin* biosynthesis** (?);[23] **phenylserine aldolase**[24] |
| α-C—N and α-C—H | (c) Transamination | Transaminases;[9] **pyridoxamine transaminase**;[25] **aminomalonate transaminase**;[26] **γ-hydroxyglutamate transaminase**;[27,28] **β-alanine-α-alanine transaminase**[29] a.o. |
| α-C—N and α-C—H | (d) Oxidative deamination | Histaminase (?);[30] **spermine oxidase**[31] |
| α-C—COOH | (e) α-Decarboxylation | Amino acid α-decarboxylases (**aromatic amino acid**,[32] **aminomalonate**,[33] **cysteine-sulfinate**,[34] **leucine**[35] **decarboxylases**) |
| α-C—COOH α-C—H (and α-C—N) | (f) **Coupled decarboxylation and oxidation** | **Glycine: DPN oxidoreductase (decarboxylating, deaminating and $H_4$-folate-hydroxymethylating)**;[36,37] **α-amino acid decarboxy-oxidation** (?)[38] |
| α-C—β-C | (g) α, β-Cleavage of β-hydroxy-amino acids (reversal of type (b) reactions) | Serine and threonine aldolases; **phenylserine aldolase**[24] |
| | 2. *Elimination and Replacement Reactions at β-C atom* | |
| β-C—Y (and α-C—H) | (h) Elimination of substituent on β-C (and of α-H) | Tryptophanase; threonine dehydratase; L-and D-serine dehydratases; alliinase; **glucosaminic acid dehydratase**;[40] **pyrazolylalanine lyase**[41] **Cysteine thioether and disulfide lyases**[15,16,19,42] |
| β-C—Y (and α-C—H) | (i) Replacement of substituent on β-C (and of α-H) | Tryptophan synthase; serine sulfhydrase; **phosphoserine sulfhydrase**;[19] **cysteine thioether and thiosulfonate synthases** (?);[43,44] cystathionine synthase I (serine dehydratase)[18] |

TABLE 1—*continued*

| Ruptured bonds | Reaction types | Enzymes (or reactions) |
|---|---|---|
| $\beta$-C—$\gamma$-C | (j) $\beta$-Decarboxylation (and related reactions) | Aspartate $\beta$-decarboxylase; **cysteine-sulfinate desulfinase**[45] |
| $\beta$-C—$\gamma$-C | (k) Hydrolytic cleavage of $\gamma$-keto-$\alpha$-amino acids | Kynureninase |
| | 3. *Elimination and Replacement Reactions at* $\gamma$-C *atom* | |
| $\gamma$-C—X and $\beta$-C—H | (l) Elimination of substituent on $\gamma$-C (and of $\beta$-H) | Cystathionase (homoserine deaminase, **cystine disulfide lyase**);[15,17] phosphohomoserine lyase (threonine synthase);[14] methionine lyase |
| $\gamma$-C—X and $\beta$-C—H | (m) Replacement of substituent on $\gamma$-C (and of $\beta$-H) | Cystathionine synthase II (?); **canavanine-splitting enzyme** (?)[46] |
| | 4. *Atypical PLP-dependent systems* | |
| | (n) 1,4-Polyglucan phosphorylases (muscle, potato, etc.) | |
| | (o) Intestinal absorption of amino acids[47,48,49] | |
| | (p) **Indoleglycerophosphate indole-lyase**[50] of *Neurospora* | |

may condense with a second molecule of glycine to yield L-serine (this step appears to be catalyzed by the well-known PLP enzyme, serine transhydroxymethylase). The mechanism of coupled dehydrogenation of glycine has been formulated in a scheme[37] based on the conventional interpretation of PLP-catalyzed reactions (Fig. 2). A remotely similar process is the oxidative decarboxylation of methionine and other $\alpha$-amino acids to amides of the next lower carboxylic acids (3-methylthiopropionamide, etc.), observed by Mazelis[38] in a model system with $O_2$, peroxidase, PLP and $Mn^{2+}$ ions. A possible mechanism for this reaction was formulated, as shown in Fig. 3. There is no direct evidence for a biological role in this mechanism; the closely similar oxidation of arginine to 4-guanidinobutyramide in the presence of arginine decarboxy-oxydase, purified from *Streptomyces griseus* extracts by Thoai *et al.*[39] does not appear to be PLP-dependent.

From time to time vitamin $B_6$-coenzymes have been reported to perform unusual and rather perplexing functions in metabolic reactions; to my knowledge most of these claims have not been thoroughly substantiated by the authors or independently confirmed. Thus it has been suggested that pyridoxal phosphate was a cofactor of visual purple formation, of the reductive deamination of glycine in amino acid fermenting *Clostridia* (cf. Ref. 10), of serum lipoprotein lipase, of urocanase,[52] etc. In an interesting series of papers H. Katagiri *et al.*[51] have reported evidence indicating the participation of pyridoxamine phosphate and $Fe^{2+}$ ions in the action of partially purified lactate racemase from *Cl. acetobutylicum*; I am not aware of further developments of this finding.

The only well-established atypical function of PLP is its essential role in polysaccharide phosphorylases of different origin, wherein it apparently acts as a structural unit rather than as a coenzyme.* There is one other

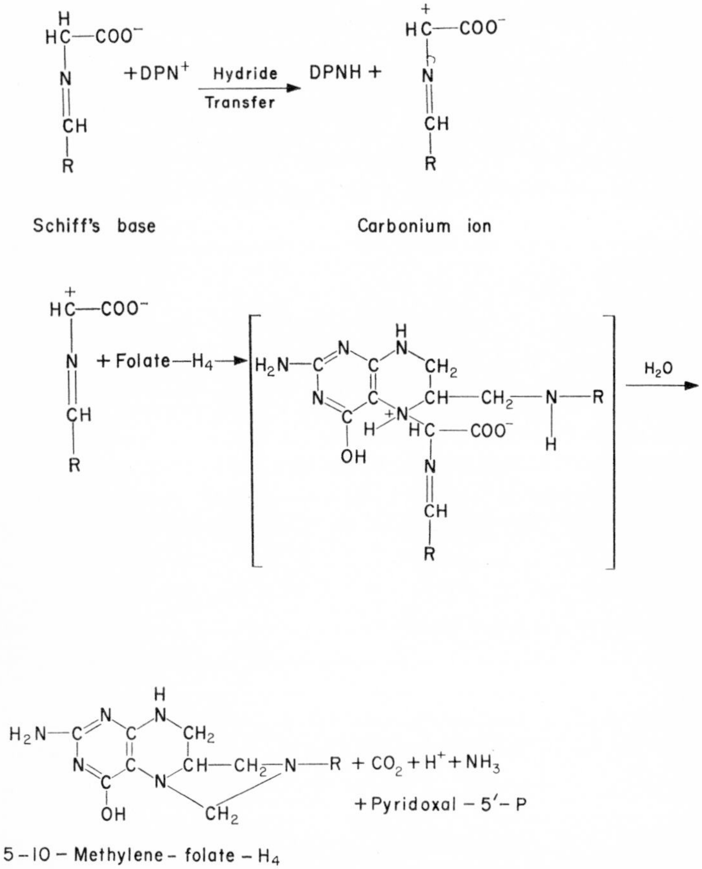
+DPN⁺
Hydride Transfer
DPNH +
Schiff's base
Carbonium ion
+ Folate—H4
H2O
+ CO2 + H⁺ + NH3
+ Pyridoxal – 5′– P
5–10 – Methylene – folate – H4

FIG. 2. Scheme of the postulated reaction mechanism of coupled oxidative decarboxylation and deamination of glycine in chicken liver.[37]

recently demonstrated instance where the binding of PLP to an enzyme protein is required to ensure optimal conformation of a second catalytic centre in the action of which PLP is not directly involved; the case in point is the activation by PLP (and serine) of the interconversion of indole and

*See the paper by E. H. Fischer *et al.*, this volume, pp. 543–62.

indoleglycerophosphate by the bifunctional tryptophan synthase from mutant and wild-type strains of *Neurospora crassa*.[50]

This phenomenon may possibly provide a clue for the explanation of

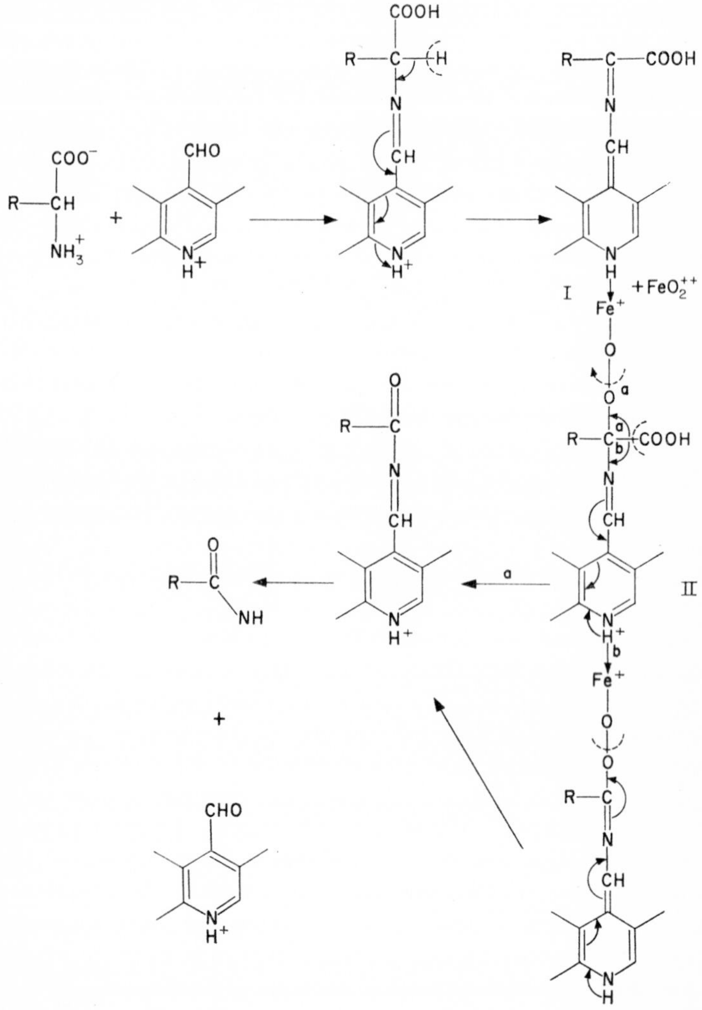

FIG. 3. Possible mechanism for oxidative decarboxylation of an α-amino acid to the corresponding amide, as catalyzed by PLP, metal ions and peroxidase ($Fe^{2+}$).[38]

earlier perplexing observations by Trudinger[53] who found that PLP was required for the formation of free indole from anthranilate in crude extracts from *E. coli.*

The role of PLP in intestinal absorption of some $\alpha$-amino acids has been demonstrated in three laboratories, including my own,[47–49] but the mechanism is obscure; the physiological significance of a similar function of pyridoxal in the active transfer of amino acids into animal cells is questionable (see Ref. 54 and the paper by H. N. Christensen in this volume, pp. 533–42).

A wealth of important information has recently accumulated concerning previously known and newly discovered enzymes which catalyze reactions of the conventional types listed in Table 1; some of these investigations deserve brief mention. New racemases, e.g. tryptophan racemase,[21] have been detected in crude bacterial extracts, but there is no reliable evidence as to their PLP-dependence, and a recent report on the purification of glutamate racemase from *Lactobacillus fermenti* states that this enzyme (in contrast to glutamate racemase from *Lactobacillus arabinosus*) does not appear to require or contain PLP.[55] The aminoacetone forming enzyme found in liver mitochondria by Urata and Granick[22] and observed by several authors in other biological systems may be analogous or identical to the PLP enzyme, $\delta$-aminoleuvulinate synthase. In a report at the Fifth International Biochemical Congress, F. Lynen[23] made the interesting suggestion that a condensation reaction between pimelyl-CoA and the $\alpha$-C atom of cysteine might be an intermediary step in the biosynthesis of biotin; such a reaction would represent a close counterpart of the PLP-dependent synthesis of dehydrosphingosine from palmityl-CoA and serine, discovered by Brady and associates.[56]

Probably the most spectacular progress has been achieved in the study of the structure, kinetics and reaction mechanism of the transaminases. Aspartate–glutamate transaminase from pig heart is now available in quantity in a state of high purity; it currently competes with ribonuclease, chymotrypsin and lysozyme as an especially rewarding object for studies on enzyme structure and catalytic mechanism. Various aspects of the chemistry of aspartate transaminase have been considered in detail in this Symposium. Particularly important advances in the study of this enzyme are: the efficient purification procedures developed in the laboratories of Sizer, Fasella, Vernon and others; the elegant work of Wada and Snell[25] on pyridoxamine transamination catalyzed by aspartate apotransaminases; the elaborate kinetic studies conducted by Velick, Fasella, Vernon and their associates; the researches of Khomutov's group on the peculiar mechanism of inhibition by cycloserine and related compounds;[57] the data of Fischer *et al.* (this volume, pp. 543–62) and Turano *et al.* (this volume, pp. 149–56) on the amino acid composition, N-terminal residues and partial peptide sequences of this enzyme. The great fragility of the closely related alanine–glutamate transaminase has, unfortunately, thus far hindered its preparation in a state of high purity, although a fair degree of purification has been reached by Torchinsky[58] in our laboratory and by Jenkins (this volume, pp. 139–48).

Noteworthy progress has been achieved in the isolation of some other enzymes of this group, e.g. crystalline pyridoxamine transaminase from a strain of *Pseudomonas*,[25] the group-specific tyrosine–glutamate transaminase of rat liver[59] and others.

At present, studies on the specific inhibition and kinetics of transaminases can be conducted in parallel with spectrophotometric and fluorometric observations; reduction with sodium borohydride and other procedures are available for covalent labeling or modification of certain functional groups of the catalytic site, and many isospecific or analogous transaminases from different sources await comparative investigation. [One such study, by Dr. Wada, has been submitted at this Symposium by Dr. Snell (pp. 1–12)]. There is no doubt that rapid progress will be made in the near future in the elucidation of essential features of the structure of aspartate transaminase and other transaminases.

Quite a number of enzymes (including glutamine and asparagine transaminases[60,11]) are currently known which catalyse amino group transfer between pairs of monocarboxylic substrates. However, transaminations involving glutamic acid are still to be considered as the most important among PLP-dependent metabolic reactions.* Current evidence confirms and extends our concept[1,4,8–12] of the crucial significance of these reactions as essential steps in the major pathways of nitrogen assimilation and dissimilation and in the integration of cellular metabolism. It is now evident that in *Bacilli* and other micro-organisms endowed with alanine dehydrogenase, alanine may replace glutamate as the first organic product of amminium assimilation. But even in these organisms the further transfer of amino nitrogen, resulting in synthesis of other amino acids, appears to proceed via glutamic acid;[61,8,9] this probably also applies to green plants, in which the presence of a photosynthetic mechanism for the direct synthesis of alanine has been suggested by Smith *et al.*[62] Alanine dehydrogenase has been claimed, on rather tenuous evidence, to occur in mammalian tissues[63] and in yeast,[64] and several conjectures have been made about other enzymatic mechanisms that might provide for the synthesis of various amino acids in animal tissues by direct amination.[65–67] However, the contribution of direct amination even to the synthesis of alanine in rat liver is probably very small or nil, as shown by the results of our experiments with the use either of cycloserine or of isoniazid and fluorocitrate for the inhibition of the transreamination mechanism.[8,9]

In 1939 I suggested[12] that transamination might represent the initial step in respiratory oxidation of the carbon chains of glutamate or other amino acids without concomittant catabolism of their nitrogen. It has recently been

---

*It is noteworthy that the existence of enzymes specifically catalyzing direct transamination reactions between aspartate and monocarboxylic keto acids has never been unambiguously demonstrated. Such transaminations apparently represent a " prohibited " reaction type, and this is one of the unsolved riddles of biochemical specificity.

shown by Borst and Slater[68], as well as by Krebs and Bellamy[69], that in heart, liver, brain and other respiring tissues the major path of glutamate oxidation is, in fact, its conversion to aspartate by way of transamination associated with the oxidation of α-ketoglutarate to oxaloacetate in the citrate cycle. That the nitrogen of β-, γ- and δ-amino acids, just as α-amino nitrogen, is converted in mammalian liver to urea by way of stepwise transamination, has been demonstrated by Severina[70]. An interesting indirect deamination mechanism, revealed in *E. coli* with the aid of DL- and D-cycloserine by Vyshepan and her associates[71], apparently involves formation of L-alanine via transamination, followed by its racemization and by oxidative deamination of the D-isomer. Incidentally, I would like to mention that the transamination reactions leading to aspartic acid and glycine in the course of biosynthesis of pyrimidines, purines and porphyrins also represent essential steps in the biogenesis of the flavins, pteridines and cobalamins (cf. Refs. 72–74).

Continuing our survey of the metabolic functions of PLP we should next consider the problem, fraught with many difficulties and errors, of the cofactors of diamine oxidase (DO; histaminase) and spermine oxidase. Suggestive indirect evidence for the PLP-dependence of DO was first obtained by my colleague Goryachenkova. But her further studies concerning the role of PLP and those of Mondovì on the mammalian enzyme (see this volume, pp. 447–52 and 415–28), as well as the investigations of Mann[76] and Werle on DO from pea seedlings and the work of Gorkin[75] on spermine oxidase from bovine plood plasma, were for some time led into blind alleys owing to the unorthodox, cryptic properties of the postulated pyridoxal component. The preparation of essentially pure, crystalline spermine oxidase by Yamada and Yasunobu[31] has enabled these authors to come close to solution of the enigma. As reported by Dr. Yasunobu in this Symposium, they have obtained strong evidence for the presence of a copper-chelated and firmly protein-bound, masked PLP derivative in spermine oxidase. On digestion of the enzyme with a fungal proteinase (pronase) the PLP derivative is released in a form that is inactive in test systems with PLP-dependent apoenzymes.[31] A similar prosthetic component may be present in DO (see Ref. 30 and Goryachenkova and Ershova, this volume, pp. 447–52). A number of controversial points still remain to be settled (viz., the nature of the protein-linked pyridoxal derivative; the eventual functions of zinc[75] and possibly of FAD[30]) before we arrive at a consistent picture of the structure and catalytic mechanism of the amine oxidases.

In the field of α-amino acid decarboxylation the most remarkable new investigations are the studies, mentioned above, on PLP-dependent oxidative decarboxylation of glycine and, perhaps, of other amino acids.[36–38] Papers concerning the enzymatic and non-enzymatic PLP-dependent decarboxylation of aminomalonic acid (A. Neuberger, this volume, pp. 243–52) and the inhibition of amino acid α- and β-decarboxylases by aminothiols and by substrate analogs (dicarboxylic acids) (S. Mardashev, this volume, pp. 277–90) have been submitted in the present Symposium.

An interesting contribution to the study of aldolase-type reactions of hydroxyamino acids was the recent demonstration by Wilson and Snell[77] of the synthesis and cleavage of α-methylserine by bacterial PLP enzymes, confirming Snell's opinion that dissociation of the α-H-atom is not an essential step in enzymatic α,β-cleavage of β-hydroxyamino acids.

The number of biological PLP-dependent elimination and replacement reactions of amino acids with a polar substituent on the β-C or γ-C atom is steadily growing. Whenever a new natural amino acid of this type is discovered, the participation of PLP in its biosynthesis and/or catabolism may be suspected.[10] Soon after the isolation of β-(pyrazolyl-N)-alanine from water-melon (Noe and Fowden, 1959) and demonstration of the synthesis of an analogous 3-amino-1,2,4-triazolylalanine in leguminous plants (Massini[78]) it was found in my laboratory by Karpeisky and Severin (unpublished experiments) that pyridoxal ($Al^{3+}$ ions) efficiently catalyzed non-enzymatic condensation of serine with pyrazole to pyrazolylalanine and decomposition of the latter compound by a typical β-elimination mechanism. These studies were discontinued when Hayaishi and his associates[41] reported the discovery of an adaptive bacterial PLP-dependent pyrazolylalanine lyase. Group-specific C—S-lyases that catalyze β-elimination reactions of cysteine thioethers, thiosulphonates or disulfides and their synthesis from serine, phosphoserine or cysteine by β-replacement reactions have been found in animal tissues, plants and bacterial cells.[15,16,19,42–44] Noteworthy examples are the interesting enzymatic conversion of phosphoserine to cysteine in extracts of chicken yolk-sack epithelium (Chapeville and Fromageot, this volume, pp. 395–402), the PLP-dependent synthesis of cysteine-S-sulfonate from serine and thiosulfate, viewed by Nakamura and Sato[43] as a potential intermediary step in the biosynthesis of cysteine in yeast and *Aspergillus*, and the conversion of dimethyldithiocarbamate or related fungicides in plants to C—S derivatives of alanine or of α-aminobutyric acid, presumably by PLP-dependent replacement reactions of serine or homoserine.[44] The paradoxical cysteine β-desulfuration activity of γ-cystathionase is now understandable, owing to the careful studies of Cavallini, De Marco and Mondoví[16] (lately confirmed by Flavin[17]), demonstrating that the substrate undergoing β-cleavage and finally giving rise to pyruvate, $NH_3$ and $H_2S$, was actually cystine and not cysteine. Cystine is an isosteric analogue of cystathionine which, being incapable of γ-elimination, undergoes disulfide β-elimination at the catalytic site of the cystathionase.

An interesting bacterial PLP enzyme described by Merrick and Roseman[40] catalyzes the cleavage of D-glucosaminic acid to $NH_3$ and 2-keto-3-gluconic acid, i.e. a typical β-hydroxy-α-amino acid dehydration reaction.

Aspartate β-decarboxylase has long been known to be activated by α-keto acids. Investigations on the mechanism of this activation, reported in the present Symposium by Dr. J. C. Senez (pp. 217–28) and by Dr. A. Meister (pp. 229–42) resulted in unexpected findings indicating that in this decarboxylase loosely bound PLP may play a supplementary structural or other role which is possibly independent of the coenzymatic function of the firmly bound PLP, and that α-keto acids can under certain conditions replace or potentiate the unknown subsidiary function of the loosely bound PLP. An enzymatic PLP-dependent reaction formally similar to the β-decarboxylation of aspartate is the direct cleavage of cysteine-sulfinate to α-alanine and sulfite in rat liver, reported by Sumizu[45]. Up till now it was generally considered that desulfination proceeded by a two-step mechanism, including transamination of cysteine-sulfinate and spontaneous breakdown of the resulting β-sulfinylpyruvate.[79]

To this certainly incomplete survey of new metabolic functions of PLP enzymes I would like to add some comments on other aspects of the problem discussed in our Symposium.

A valuable contribution to the analytical chemistry of vitamin $B_6$ coenzymes was the development by Holzer *et al.*[80] of a highly sensitive aspartate apo-transaminase test for PLP. Goryachenkova (this volume, pp. 447–52) showed that the test also responded to PMP, which in her experiments was slightly less active than PLP, and applied a modified, even more sensitive version of the test with good success to the estimation of coenzymes in microgram quantities of PLP-enzymes.* The method failed to reveal the presence of PLP in diamine oxidase (Goryachenkova and Ershova, this volume, pp. 447–52); it is possible that this enzyme contains a firmly bound form of PLP inactive in the usual apoenzyme tests, as demonstrated in the similar case of spermine oxidase by Yamada and Yasunobu[31] (*vide supra*).

The main enzymatic steps of the metabolism of vitamin $B_6$ and of its catalytically active forms are now clear, owing to the excellent investigations started in Ichihara's laboratory in Osaka[81] and later continued by H. Wada and others in collaboration with E. Snell (Ref. 82, and this volume, pp. 563–78). One of the most important results of these studies is the discovery that in mammalian tissues phosphorylation of pyridoxol precedes its oxidation to the aldehyde level in the biogenesis of PLP. This route of biosynthesis accounts for the frequently noted fact that pyridoxol is physiologically more efficient than is free pyridoxal in the treatment of vitamin $B_6$-deficiencies in animals. The mechanism is biologically advantageous since it by-passes the formation of free pyridoxal and leads directly to PLP, which is protected from

*In this Symposium Dr. Holzer (see pp. 523–32) reported identical activities for PLP and PMP and described a differential method for estimation of PLP + PMP and for PMP alone (following reduction of PLP with sodium borohydride).

wasteful catabolic destruction owing to its resistance to the action of aldehyde oxidase and to its high affinity for specific apoenzymes.

Our knowledge of the mode of binding of PLP to apoenzymes and of the specific ionic and tautomeric forms of PLP in the active holoenzymes has been greatly promoted by recent comparative spectrophotometric and kinetic investigations of enzymes* and of model systems, including, in particular, the extensive careful studies of Martell and his associates on the structure, optical and chemical properties of the aldimines and other derivatives of PLP (see this volume, pp. 13–28) and the elegant, very important work of Dempsey and Christensen[87] on the specific binding of PLP to bovine serum albumin. Important kinetic studies relating to reactions of amino acids with pyridoxal or its derivatives have been discussed in our Symposium by Drs. Jencks, Bruice, Metzler and other participants of this meeting.

It seems appropriate to re-emphasize the existence of striking differences in the spectral properties of different PLP enzymes (and their substrate or inhibitor complexes), as compared to one another, and to model compounds of presumably analogous structure (e.g. the Schiff bases, oximes, isonicotinylhydrazones of pyridoxal and PLP). When PLP or its complexes are bound at the contacting sites of specific enzymes, configurational constraint and neighbouring group effects can cause marked shifts in the tautomeric or ionization equilibria and in the spectra of the protein-bound coenzyme; at present it is impossible to evaluate correctly these effects. For this reason one should be very cautious in using comparisons with corresponding properties of model complexes as a basis for inferences concerning the exact structure or particular reactions of the coenzyme in PLP-enzymes. Similar caution is necessary in making inferences about the specific role of functional groups of the coenzyme in the catalytic activities of PLP enzymes. The significance of these groups has been studied by Snell and his group in experiments on non-biological pyridoxal catalysis (cf. Ref. 85). By analogy, it is now customary to consider the presence of a hydrogen bond between the phenolic hydroxyl of PLP and the central N atom of the intermediary aldimines (with the H-atom replacing the chelated metal atom of Snell's model systems) as an essential feature of the reactive PLP enzyme–substrate complexes. This view seems questionable since the phenolic hydroxyl is presumably ionized[85] in the alkaline pH range that is optimal for the activity of transaminases and many other PLP enzymes. In the model systems the internal hydrogen or metal chelate bond serves to confer planarity and thereby increased stability on the intermediary aldimines. But in the PLP enzymes sufficient stabilization of the aldimine bond can be ensured by positioning and steric constraint at the active centre—factors that may replace the effect of chelation (or H-bonding). The degree of such stabilization (in the absence

*The spectral properties of enzyme-bound PLP in serine transhydroxymethylase have recently been investigated by Schirch and Mason[86].

of any metal ions) is impressively demonstrated by the unusual stability of the intramolecular ϵ-N-pyridoxylidene-lysine bond of PLP enzymes in aqueous solutions.

Incidentally, a puzzling fact worthy of mention is the complete absence of any evidence indicating the possibility of transamination between the protein-bound PLP and the ϵ-$NH_2$-group of lysine participating in the intramolecular aldimine bond of the PLP enzymes, although ω-amino acids are known to undergo transamination both enzymatically and in non-enzymatic model systems (cf. Siliprandi, this volume, pp. 91–102). I wonder whether a consistent explanation of this puzzle can be proposed.

I shall not dwell on some other debatable points that might be raised. It is time now to close up our extremely saturated scientific program. From the excellent papers and competent discussions presented in this Symposium all of us have derived a wealth of information and stimulating ideas, and leisurely meditation will doubtless suggest new approaches to the experimental verification of such ideas.

The catalytic potentialities of PLP have probably been explored more thoroughly than those of any other coenzyme.[10,84,85] The principal aim for future research is to elucidate the mode of binding of PLP to the protein moieties of individual PLP enzymes, and to obtain insight into the contribution of functional groups of these proteins to the substrate and reaction specificities of their active centers. In comparison to the PLP enzymes, more extensive information has accumulated to date concerning the protein chemistry of some other types of enzymes, e.g. the esterolytic proteinases or ribonuclease. But in the case of PLP enzymes notable advantage is afforded by their conspicuous optical properties, and by the variety of agents available for their selective inhibition and/or covalent labeling. That is why we are justified in considering this group of enzymes as particularly promising objects of investigation, at the molecular level, of the structural and physicochemical aspects of enzyme-catalyzed reactions.

Allow me to conclude with all good wishes to you for efficient progress in your efforts directed to this aim.

## REFERENCES


1. A. E. Braunstein; *Advances in Protein Chem.* **3**, 1 (1947).
2. A. E. Braunstein; *Uspekhi Sovremennoi Biol.* (Russ.) **35**, 25 (1953).
3. A. E. Braunstein; *Ukrain. Biokhim. Zhur.* (Russ.) **27**, 421 (1955).
4. A. E. Braunstein; *Advances in Enzymol.* **19**, 335 (1957).
5. A. E. Braunstein; *The Origin of Life on Earth*, An International Symposium, Moscow, 1957, Pergamon Press (1960).
6. A. E. Braunstein; *Proc. Int. Symp. Enzyme Chemistry*, Tokyo and Kyoto, 1957, p. 135, Maruzen, Tokyo (1958).
7. A. E. Braunstein; *Med. J. Osaka Univ.* **8**, suppl. 1, 105 (1958).
8. A. E. Braunstein; Some Aspects of the Chemical Integration of Nitrogen Metabolism, *Proc. IVth Int. Cong. Biochem.*, Vienna, 1958, vol. XIV, p. 63, Pergamon Press, (1959).

9. A. E. BRAUNSTEIN; *Biochimie Comparée des acides aminés basiques* (Colloque international, Concarneau, 1959), p. 79, Éditions du CNRS, Paris (1960).
10. A. E. BRAUNSTEIN; Pyridoxal Phosphate, *The Enzymes* (edited by P. BOYER, H. LARDY, and K. MYRBÄCK), vol. 2, ch. 6, Academic Press, New York (1960).
11. A. E. BRAUNSTEIN; *Proc. Vth Int. Cong. Biochem.*, Moscow, 1961, Symposium IV, The Molecular Basis of Enzyme Action and Inhibition, Pergamon Press (1962).
12. A. E. BRAUNSTEIN; *Enzymologia* **7**, 25 (1939).
13. A. E. BRAUNSTEIN and M. M. SHEMYAKIN; *Doklady Akad. Nauk S.S.S.R.* **85**, 1115 (1952); *Biokhimiia* **18**, 393 (1953).
14. M. FLAVIN and C. SLAUGHTER; *J. Biol. Chem.* **235**, 1112 (1960).
15. Y. MATSUO and D. M. GREENBERG; *J. Biol. Chem.* **230**, 545 (1958); **234**, 507, 516 (1959).
16. B. MONDOVÌ, C. DE MARCO; *Enzymologia* **23**, 156 (1961); D. CAVALLINI, B. MONDOVÌ, C. DE MARCO, A. SCIOSCIA-SANTORO; *Arch. Biochem. Biophys.* **96**, 456 (1962); This volume, p. **000**.
17. M. FLAVIN; *J. Biol. Chem.* **237**, 768 (1962); This volume, pp. 377–94.
18. A. S. M. SELIM and D. M. GREENBERG; *J. Biol. Chem.* **234**, 1474 (1959); *Biochim. et Biophys. Acta* **42**, 211 (1961).
19. F. CHAPEVILLE and P. FROMAGEOT; *Biochim. et Biophys. Acta* **49**, 328 (1961); This volume, pp. 395–402.
20. E. BEERSTECHER and E. J. EDMONDS; *J. Biol. Chem.* **192**, 497 (1951); *Federation Proc.* **15**, 216 (1956).
21. E. J. BEHRMAN and A. M. CULLEN; *Federation Proc.* **20**, 6 (1961).
22. G. URATA and S. GRANICK; *Biochem. Biophys. Research Comm.* **4**, 96 (1961).
23. F. LYNEN; *Proc. Vth Int. Cong. Biochem.*, Moscow, 1961, vol. IV, Symposium on the Molecular Basis of Enzyme Action and Inhibition, Pergamon (1962).
24. F. H. BRUNS; *Biochem. Z.* **331**, 54 (1958); F. H. BRUNS and L. FIEDLER; *Nature* **181**, 1533 (1958).
25. H. WADA and E. E. SNELL; *J. Biol. Chem.* **237**, 127, 133 (1962); this volume, pp. 1–12.
26. H. NAGAYAMA, M. MURAMATZU and K. SHIMURA; *Nature* **181**, 417 (1958).
27. U. KURATOMI and K. FUKUNADA; *Biochim. et Biophys. Acta* **43**, 562 (1961).
28. U. MAITRA and E. E. DEKKER; *Biochim. et Biophys. Acta* **51**, 416 (1961).
29. Y. NISHIZUKA, M. TAKESHITA, S. KUNO and O. HAYAISHI; *Biochim. et Biophys. Acta* **33**, 591 (1959); O. HAYAISHI *et al.*; *J. Biol. Chem.* **236**, 781 (1961).
30. R. KAPELLER-ADLER and H. MACFARLANE; *Biochim. J.* **82**, 49P (1962); This volume, pp. 429–46.
31. H. YAMADA and K. T. YASUNOBU; *Biochem. Biophys. Research Comm.* **8**, 387 (1962); This volume, pp. 453–66.
32. W. LOVENBERG, H. WEISSBACH and S. UDENFRIEND; *J. Biol. Chem.* **237**, 89 (1962).
33. K. SHIMURA, H. NAGAYAMA and A. KIKUCHI; *Nature* **177**, 935 (1956); A. NEUBERGER; This volume, pp. 243–52.
34. B. SORBO and T. HEYMAN; *Biochim. et Biophys. Acta* **23**, 624 (1957).
35. C. R. SUTTON and H. K. KING; *Arch. Biochem. Biophys.* **96**, 360 (1962); H. K. KING; This volume, pp. 253–66.
36. R. D. SAGERS and I. C. GUNSALUS; *J. Bacteriol.* **81**, 541 (1961); I. C. GUNSALUS; This volume, p. **000**.
37. D. A. RICHERT, R. AMBERG and M. WILSON; *J. Biol. Chem.* **237**, 99 (1962).
38. M. MAZELIS; *J. Biol. Chem.* **237**, 104 (1962); M. MAZELIS and L. L. INGRAHAM; *ibid.* **237**, 109 (1962).
39. N. VAN THOAI and A. OLOMUCKI; *Biochim. et Biophys. Acta* **59**, 533, 545 (1962).
40. J. M. MERRICK and S. ROSEMAN; *J. Biol. Chem.* **235**, 1274 (1960).
41. M. TAKESHITA Y. NISHIZUKA and O. HAYAISHI; *Biochim. et Biophys. Acta* **48**, 409 (1961).
42. S. SCHWIMMER *et al.*; *Acta Chem. Scand.* **14**, 2061 (1960); *Biochim. et Biophys. Acta* **42**, 316 (1960).
43. T. NAKAMURA and R. SATO; *Nature* **185**, 163 (1960); **193**, 481 (1962).
44. J. KASLANDER, A. K. SIJPESTEIJN, and G. J. M. VAN DER KERK; *Biochim. et Biophys. Acta* **60**, 417 (1962); **62**, 587 (1962).

45. K. SUMIZU; *Biochim. et Biophys. Acta* **53**, 435 (1961).
46. G. D. KALYANKAR, M. IKAWA and E. E. SNELL; *J. Biol. Chem.* **233**, 1175 (1958).
47. F. A. JACOBS *et al.*; *J. Biol. Chem.* **232**, 445 (1958); **235**, 1372, 3224 (1960); *Biochim. et Biophys. Acta* **51**, 602 (1961).
48. K. UEDA, H. AKEDO and M. SUDA; *J. Biochem.* (*Tokyo*) **48**, 584 (1960).
49. A. E. BRAUNSTEIN, G. YA. VILENKINA and L. BRUSOVA; *Voprossi Med. Khim.* In press.
50. C. YANOFSKY; *Bacteriol. Rev.* **24**, 221 (1960); J. A. DE MOSS; *Biochim. et Biophys. Acta* **62**, 279 (1962).
51 H. KATAGIRI *et al.*; *Agr. Biol. Chem.* (*Japan*) **25**, 281, 290 (1961).
52. N. K. GUPTA and W. G. ROBINSON; *Federation Proc.* **20**, 4 (1961).
53. P. A. TRUDINGER; *Biochem. J.* **62**, 480 (1956).
54. A. KLEINZELLER and A. KOTYK (Eds.); *Membrane Transport and Metabolism*, Proceedings of a Symposium, Praha, 1960, papers and discussions by H. N. CHRISTENSEN (p. 470), D. H. SMITH (p. 488), H. O. HALVORSON (p. 503), A. E. BRAUNSTEIN (p. 501, 507). Publishing House of Czechoslovak Academy of Sciences, Praha (1961).
55. M. TANAKA, Y. KATO and S. KINOSHITA; *Biochem. Biophys. Research Comm.* **4**, 114 (1961); cf. L. GLASER; *J. Biol. Chem.* **235**, 2095 (1960).
56. R. O. BRADY, J. V. FORMICA and G. J. KOVAL; *J. Biol. Chem.* **233**, 1072 (1958).
57. R. M. KHOMUTOV, M. YA. KARPEISKY and E. S. SEVERIN; *Biokhimiia* **26**, 779 (1961); This volume, pp. 313–22, 323–32.
58. YU. M. TORCHINSKY; *Biokhimiia* **27**, 916 (1962); W. T. JENKINS; *Federation Proc. Proc.* **20**, 978 (1961); This volume, pp. 139–48.
59. F. T. KENNEY; *J. Biol Chem.* **237**, 1605, 1610 (1962); cf. G. A. JACOBY and B. N. LADU; *Biochem. Biophys. Research Comm.* **8**, 352 (1962).
60. A. E. BRAUNSTEIN and T. S. HSU; *Biochim. et Biophys. Acta* **44**, 187 (1960).
61. M. M. HONG, S. C. SHEN and A. E. BRAUNSTEIN; *Biochim. et Biophys. Acta* **36**, 288, 290 (1959); *Biokhimiia* **24**, 929, 957 (1959).
62. D. C. SMITH, J. A. BASSHAM and M. KIRK; *Biochim. et. Biophys. Acta* **48**, 299 (1961).
63. N. N. BEREZOVSKAYA; *Biokhimiia* **23**, 125 (1958); **25**, 106 (1960); **27**, 889 (1962).
64. V. L. KRETOVICH and Z. S. BRONOVITSKAYA; *Doklady Akad. Nauk S.S.S.R.* (1961).
65. H. F. FISHER and L. L. MCGREGOR; *J. Biol. Chem.* **236**, 791 (1961); J. STRUCK and I. W. SIZER; *Arch. Biochem. Biophys.* **86**, 260 (1960).
66. G. M. TOMKINS, K. L. YIELDING and J. CURRAN; *Proc. Natl. Acad. Sci. U.S.A.* **47**, 270 (1961).
67. A. N. RADHAKRISHNAN and A. MEISTER; *J. Biol. Chem.* **233**, 444 (1958).
68. P. BORST and E. C. SLATER; *Biochim. et Biophys. Acta* **41**, 170 (1960).
69. H. A. KREBS and D. BELLAMY; *Biochem. J.* **75**, 523 (1960).
70. I. S. SEVERINA; *Biokhimiia* **26**, 945 (1961).
71. E. D. VYSHEPAN, K. I. IVANOVA and R. K. LEDNEVA; *Biokhimiia* **26**, 758 (1961).
72. W. S. MCNUTT; *J. Biol. Chem.* **210**, 511 (1954); **219**, 365 (1956); *J. Am. Chem. Soc.* **83**, 2303 (1961).
73. A. ALBERT; *Biochem. J.* **65**, 124 (1957).
74. J. W. CORCORAN and D. SHEMIN; *Biochim. et Biophys. Acta* **25**, 661 (1957).
75. V. Z. GORKIN; *Voprossy Med. Khim.* **6**, 632 (1961).
76. P. J. G. MANN; *Biochem. J.* **79**, 623 (1961).
77. E. M. WILSON and E. E. SNELL; *Biochem. J.* **83**, 1P (1962).
78. P. MASSINI; *Biochim. et Biophys. Acta* **36**, 548 (1959).
79. P. FROMAGEOT et U. PATINO-BUN; *Biochim. et Biophys. Acta* **46**, 533 (1961).
80. H. HOLZER *et al.*; *Biochem. Z.* **529** (1958); This volume, pp. 523–32.
81. E. V. GORYACHENKOVA; *Biokhimiia.* In press.
82. K. ICHIHARA *et al.*; *The Metabolism of Cyclic and Sulfur Containing Amino Acids* (collected papers), pp. 308, 314, 324, Sasaki Printing Co., Osaka, Japan (1960).
83. E. E. SNELL; *Proc. Vth Int. Biochem. Cong.*, Moscow, 1961, vol. IV, Symposium on the Molecular Basis of Enzyme Action and Inhibition, Pergamon Press (1962); This volume, pp. 1–12.

84. A. M. Perault, B. Pullman and C. Valdemoro; *Biochim. et Biophys. Acta* **46,** 555 (1961); B. Pullman; This volume, pp. 103–22.
85. E. E. Snell; *Vitamins and Hormones* **16,** 77 (1958).
86. L. V. Schirch and M. Mason; *J. Biol. Chem.* **237**, 2578 (1962).
87. W. B. Dempsey and H. N. Christensen; *J. Biol. Chem.* **237**, 1113 (1962).

# SUBJECT INDEX